1968 · INTEL · 1993 · A QUARTER CENTURY OF INNOVATION

Founded in 1968 to pursue the integration of large numbers of transistors onto tiny silicon chips, Intel's history has been marked by a remarkable number of scientific breakthroughs and innovations. In 1971, Intel introduced the 4004, the first microprocessor. Containing 2300 transistors, this first commercially available computer-on-a-chip is primitive compared with today's million-plus transistor products.

Innovations such as the microprocessor, the erasable programmable read-only memory (EPROM) and the dynamic random access memory (DRAM) revolutionized electronics by making integrated circuits the mainstay of both consumer and business computing products.

Over the last two-and-a-half decades, Intel's business has evolved and today the company's focus is on delivering an extensive line of component, module and system-level building block products to the computer industry. The company's product line covers a broad spectrum, and includes microprocessors, flash memory, microcontrollers, a broad line of PC enhancement and local area network products, multimedia technology products, and massively parallel supercomputers. Intel's 32-bit X86 architecture, represented by the Intel386™ and Intel486™ microprocessor families, is the de facto standard of modern business computing in millions of PCs worldwide.

Intel has over 26,000 employees located in offices and manufacturing facilities around the world. Today, Intel is the largest semiconductor company in the world.

LITERATURE

To order Intel literature or obtain literature pricing information in the U.S. and Canada call or write Intel Literature Sales. In Europe and other international locations, please contact your **local** sales office or distributor.

INTEL LITERATURE SALES
P.O. Box 7641
Mt. Prospect, IL 60056-7641

In the U.S. and Canada
call toll free
(800) 548-4725
This 800 number is for external customers only.

CURRENT HANDBOOKS

Product line handbooks contain data sheets, application notes, article reprints, and other design information. All handbooks can be ordered individually, and most are available in a pre-packaged set in the U.S. and Canada.

Title	Intel Order Number	ISBN
SET OF TWELVE HANDBOOKS (Available in U.S. and Canada)	231003	N/A

CONTENTS LISTED BELOW FOR INDIVIDUAL ORDERING:

Title	Intel Order Number	ISBN
CONNECTIVITY	231658	1-55512-174-8
EMBEDDED APPLICATIONS (1993/94)	270648	1-55512-179-9
EMBEDDED MICROCONTROLLERS & PROCESSORS (2 volume set)	270645	1-55512-176-4
MEMORY PRODUCTS	210830	1-55512-172-1
MICROCOMPUTER PRODUCTS	280407	1-55512-173-X
MICROPROCESSORS (2 volume set)	230843	1-55512-169-1
MOBILE COMPUTER PRODUCTS	241420	1-55512-186-1
i750®, i860™, i960® PROCESSORS AND RELATED PRODUCTS	272084	1-55512-185-3
PACKAGING	240800	1-55512-182-9
PERIPHERAL COMPONENTS	296467	1-55512-181-0
PRODUCT OVERVIEW (A guide to Intel Architectures and Applications)	210846	N/A
PROGRAMMABLE LOGIC	296083	1-55512-180-2

ADDITIONAL LITERATURE:
(Not included in handbook set)

Title	Intel Order Number	ISBN
AUTOMOTIVE	231792	1-55512-125-X
COMPONENTS QUALITY/RELIABILITY	210997	1-55512-132-2
CUSTOMER LITERATURE GUIDE	210620	N/A
INTERNATIONAL LITERATURE GUIDE (Available in Europe only)	E00029	N/A
MILITARY AND SPECIAL PRODUCTS (2 volume set)	210461	1-55512-189-6
SYSTEMS QUALITY/RELIABILITY	231762	1-55512-091-9
HANDBOOK DIRECTORY (Index of all data sheets contained in the handbooks)	241197	N/A

U.S. and CANADA LITERATURE ORDER FORM

NAME: _____

COMPANY: _____

ADDRESS: _____

CITY: _____ STATE: _____ ZIP: _____

COUNTRY: _____

PHONE NO.: _(_____) _____

ORDER NO.	TITLE	QTY.		PRICE		TOTAL
☐☐☐☐☐☐	_____	____	×	____	=	_____
☐☐☐☐☐☐	_____	____	×	____	=	_____
☐☐☐☐☐☐	_____	____	×	____	=	_____
☐☐☐☐☐☐	_____	____	×	____	=	_____
☐☐☐☐☐☐	_____	____	×	____	=	_____
☐☐☐☐☐☐	_____	____	×	____	=	_____
☐☐☐☐☐☐	_____	____	×	____	=	_____
☐☐☐☐☐☐	_____	____	×	____	=	_____
☐☐☐☐☐☐	_____	____	×	____	=	_____
☐☐☐☐☐☐	_____	____	×	____	=	_____

Subtotal _____

Must Add Your
Local Sales Tax _____

Include Postage:
Must add 15% of Subtotal to cover U.S.
and Canada postage. (20% all other.) ⟶ Postage _____

Total _____

Pay by check, money order, or include company purchase order with this form ($200 minimum). We also accept VISA, MasterCard or American Express. Make payment to Intel Literature Sales. Allow 2-3 weeks for delivery.

☐ VISA   ☐ MasterCard   ☐ American Express   Expiration Date _____

Account No. _____

Signature _____

Mail To: Intel Literature Sales
P.O. Box 7641
Mt. Prospect, IL 60056-7641

International Customers outside the U.S. and Canada should use the International order form on the next page or contact their local Sales Office or Distributor.

For phone orders in the U.S. and Canada
Call Toll Free: (800) 548-4725

Prices good until 12/31/93
Source HB

INTERNATIONAL LITERATURE ORDER FORM

NAME: _____

COMPANY: _____

ADDRESS: _____

CITY: _____ STATE: _____ ZIP: _____

COUNTRY: _____

PHONE NO.: _(____)_____

ORDER NO.	TITLE	QTY.		PRICE		TOTAL
☐☐☐☐☐☐	_____	____	×	____	=	____
☐☐☐☐☐☐	_____	____	×	____	=	____
☐☐☐☐☐☐	_____	____	×	____	=	____
☐☐☐☐☐☐	_____	____	×	____	=	____
☐☐☐☐☐☐	_____	____	×	____	=	____
☐☐☐☐☐☐	_____	____	×	____	=	____
☐☐☐☐☐☐	_____	____	×	____	=	____
☐☐☐☐☐☐	_____	____	×	____	=	____
☐☐☐☐☐☐	_____	____	×	____	=	____
☐☐☐☐☐☐	_____	____	×	____	=	____

Subtotal _____

Must Add Your
Local Sales Tax _____

Total _____

PAYMENT

Cheques should be made payable to your *local* Intel Sales Office (see inside back cover).

Other forms of payment may be available in your country. Please contact the Literature Coordinator at your *local* Intel Sales Office for details.

The completed form should be marked to the attention of the LITERATURE COORDINATOR and returned to your *local* Intel Sales Office.

CG/LOF2W/092792

Pentium™ Processor
User's Manual

Volume 3:

Architecture and Programming Manual

1993

TABLE OF CONTENTS

CHAPTER 4
APPLICATION PROGRAMMING   Page

PART II—SYSTEM PROGRAMMING

Page

18.3.2.   PWT Bit...18-6
18.4.   ADDRESS TRANSLATION CACHES...18-6
18.5.   CACHE REPLACEMENT ALGORITHM..18-6
18.6.   EXECUTION PIPELINING AND PAIRING...18-6
18.7.   WRITE BUFFERS...18-7
18.8.   SERIALIZING INSTRUCTIONS..18-7

CHAPTER 19
MULTIPROCESSING
19.1.   LOCKED BUS CYCLES..19-1
19.1.1.   LOCK Prefix and the LOCK# Signal 19-2
19.1.2.   Automatic Locking..19-2
19.2.   MEMORY ACCESS ORDERING 19-3

CHAPTER 20
SYSTEM MANAGEMENT MODE
20.1.   THE SMI INTERRUPT...20-1
20.2.   SMM INITIAL STATE..20-3
20.2.1.   System Management Mode Execution 20-3
20.3.   SMRAM PROCESSOR STATE DUMP FORMAT..20-4
20.3.1.   System Management Mode Revision Identifier (Offset FEFCH)....................20-6
20.3.2.   I/O Trap Restart (Offset FF00H) 20-7
20.3.3.   Halt Auto Restart (Offset FF02H)..20-7
20.3.4.   State Dump Base (Offset FEF8H)..20-7
20.4.   RELOCATING SMRAM 20-8
20.5.   RETURNING FROM SMM 20-8

PART III—COMPATIBILITY

CHAPTER 21
MIXING 16-BIT AND 32-BIT CODE
21.1.   USING 16-BIT AND 32-BIT ENVIRONMENTS...21-1
21.2.   MIXING 16-BIT AND 32-BIT OPERATIONS..21-2
21.3.   SHARING DATA AMONG MIXED-SIZE CODE SEGMENTS.............................21-3
21.4.   TRANSFERRING CONTROL AMONG MIXED-SIZE CODE SEGMENTS 21-3
21.4.1.   Size of Code-Segment Pointer 21-4
21.4.2.   Stack Management for Control Transfer..21-4
21.4.2.1.   CONTROLLING THE OPERAND SIZE FOR A CALL..................................21-6
21.4.2.2.   CHANGING SIZE OF A CALL..21-6
21.4.3.   Interrupt Control Transfers..21-6
21.4.4.   Parameter Translation 21-7
21.4.5.   The Interface Procedure 21-7

CHAPTER 22
VIRTUAL-8086 MODE
22.1.   EXECUTING 8086 CPU CODE 22-1
22.1.1.   Registers and Instructions 22-1
22.1.2.   Address Translation..22-2
22.2.   STRUCTURE OF A VIRTUAL-8086 TASK..22-3
22.2.1.   Paging for Virtual-8086 Tasks...22-4
22.2.2.   Protection within a Virtual-8086 Task 22-5

xi

Page

18.3.2.   PWT Bit...18-6
18.4.   ADDRESS TRANSLATION CACHES...18-6
18.5.   CACHE REPLACEMENT ALGORITHM..18-6
18.6.   EXECUTION PIPELINING AND PAIRING...18-6
18.7.   WRITE BUFFERS...18-7
18.8.   SERIALIZING INSTRUCTIONS..18-7

Figures

Tables

CONTENTS

Table	Title	Page
6-17.	PL/M-386/486 Built-In Procedures	6-35
6-18.	ASM386/486 Storage Allocation Directives	6-36
6-19.	Addressing Method Examples	6-38
7-1.	Arithmetic and Nonarithmetic Instructions	7-2
7-2.	Binary Integer Encodings	7-3
7-3.	Packed Decimal Encodings	7-4
7-4.	Single and Double Real Encodings	7-5
7-5.	Extended Real Encodings	7-6
7-6.	Unsupported Formats	7-7
7-7.	Denormalized Values	7-8
7-8.	Zero Operands and Results	7-10
7-9.	Infinity Operands and Results	7-13
7-10.	Rules for Generating QNaNs	7-17
7-11.	Masked Responses to Invalid Operations	7-22
7-12.	Masked Overflow Results	7-25
7-13.	Transcendental Core Ranges	7-26
9-1.	Exceptions and Interrupts	9-4
11-1.	Application Segment Types	11-14
12-1.	System Segment and Gate Types	12-4
12-2.	Interlevel Return Checks	12-18
12-3.	Valid Descriptor Types for LSL Instruction	12-20
12-4.	Combined Page Directory and Page Table Protection	12-24
13-1.	Checks Made during a Task Switch	13-11
13-2.	Effect of a Task Switch on Busy, NT, and Link Fields	13-12
14-1.	Exception and Interrupt Vectors	14-2
14-2.	Priority Among Simultaneous Exceptions and Interrupts	14-5
14-3.	Interrupt and Exception Classes	14-16
14-4.	Double Fault Conditions	14-16
14-5.	Invalid TSS Conditions	14-17
14-6.	Alignment Requirements by Data Type	14-25
14-7.	Exception Summary	14-26
14-8.	Error Code Summary	14-28
15-1.	I/O Serialization	15-9
16-1.	Processor State Following Reset	16-4
16-2.	FPU State Following FINIT or FNINIT	16-6
16-3.	EM and MP Bits Interpretations	16-7
16-4.	Recommended Values by Processor	16-7
16-5.	Action Taken for Different Combinations of EM, MP, and TS	16-8
16-6.	Software Emulation Settings	16-9
16-7.	The Algorithm and Related Listing Line Numbers	16-16
16-8.	Relationship Between BLD Item and ASM Source File	16-18
17-1.	Breakpointing Examples	17-6
17-2.	Debug Exception Conditions	17-7
18-1.	MESI Cache Line States	18-2
18-2.	Cache Operating Modes	18-4
20-1.	SMM Initial State	20-3
20-2.	State Dump Format	20-5
20-3.	State Disposition	20-6
20-4.	SMM Revision Identifier	20-7
20-5.	Halt Auto Restart	20-7
22-1.	Software Interrupt Operation	22-10
23-1.	Processor State Following Power-Up	23-4
23-2.	FPU and NPX State Following Power-Up	23-5

xxii

Examples

intel®

1

Getting Started

CHAPTER 1
GETTING STARTED

1.1.   HOW TO USE THIS MANUAL

Chapter 1 provides an overview of this manual and the related Pentium™ processor documentation. Also included are some notational conventions regarding reserved bits, instruction operands, number formats, addressing and exceptions found throughout the manual.

Chapter 2 provides an introduction to Intel's Pentium processor family. The remainder of this book presents the architecture of the Pentium processor in five parts:

- Part I—Application and Numeric Programming
- Part II—System Programming
- Part III—Compatibility
- Part IV—Optimization
- Part V—Instruction Set
- Appendices

The first three parts are explanatory, showing the purpose of architectural features, developing terminology and concepts, and describing instructions as they relate to specific purposes or to specific architectural features. The remaining parts are reference material for programmers developing software for the Pentium processor.

The first two parts cover the operating modes and protection mechanism of the Pentium processor. The distinction between application programming and system programming is related to the protection mechanism of the Pentium processor. One purpose of protection is to prevent applications from interfering with the operating system. For this reason, certain registers and instructions are inaccessible to application programs. The features discussed in Part I are those which are accessible to applications; the features in Part II are available only to programs running with special privileges or programs running on systems where the protection mechanism is not used.

The features available to application programs in protected mode and to programs in real-address and virtual-8086 mode are the same. These features are described in Part I of this book. The additional features available to system programs in protected mode are described in Part II. Part III describes virtual-8086 mode, how to mix 16-bit and 32-bit code, and compatibility considerations.

Part IV provides general optimization techniques for programming on Intel x86 architectures. For information on obtaining optimization techniques for the Pentium processor, see Appendix H.

1.1.1. Part I—Application and Numeric Programming

This section presents the features used by most application programmers. It includes features used in numeric applications which are object-code compatible with features provided by the Intel486™ DX processor, and the Intel487™ SX, the Intel387™ DX, and the Intel387 SX math coprocessors used with the Intel486 SX, Intel386™ DX and Intel386 SX processors, respectively.

Chapter 3—Basic Programming Model: This chapter introduces the models of memory organization, defines the data types, presents the register set used by applications, introduces the stack, explains string operations, defines the parts of an instruction, explains address calculations, and introduces interrupts and exceptions as they apply to application programming.

Chapter 4—Application Programming: Chapter 4 surveys the integer instructions commonly used for application programming. Instructions are considered in functionally related groups; for example, string instructions are considered in one section, while control-transfer instructions are considered in another. The concepts behind the instructions are explained. Details of individual instructions are deferred until Part V, the instruction-set reference.

Chapter 5—Feature Determination: This chapter discusses how to determine the CPU type and the presence of a math coprocessor in order to determine what features are available to an application. A program example is provided.

Chapter 6—Numeric Applications: This chapter gives an overview of the floating-point unit and reviews the concepts of numerical computation. The "Architecture of the Floating-Point Unit" section presents the floating-point registers and data types available to both applications and systems programmers. The "Floating-Point Instructions" section of this chapter surveys the instructions commonly used for numeric processing. Details of individual instructions are deferred until Part V, the instruction-set reference. The "Numerics Applications" section describes the Pentium processor's floating-point arithmetic facilities and gives short programming examples in both assembly language and high-level languages.

Chapter 7—Special Computational Situations: This chapter discusses the special values that can be represented in the real formats of the Pentium processor—denormal numbers, zeros, infinities, NaNs (Not a Number)—as well as the numerical exceptions.

Chapter 8—Numeric Programming Examples: Chapter 8 provides detailed examples of assembly-language numeric programming with the Pentium processor, including conditional branching, conversion between floating-point values and their ASCII representations, and use of trigonometric functions.

1.1.2. Part II—System Programming

This section presents the features used by operating systems, device drivers, debuggers, and other software which support application programs.

Chapter 9—Real-Address Mode System Architecture: This chapter explains the real-address mode of the Pentium processor as it relates to the system programmer. In this mode, the Pentium processor appears as a fast real-mode Intel 286 or Intel386 processor or a fast 8086 processor enhanced with additional instructions.

Chapter 10—Protected-Mode System Architecture Overview: Chapter 10 describes the features of the Pentium processor used by system programmers. System-oriented registers and data structures of the Pentium processor which are mentioned briefly in Part I are discussed in detail. The system-oriented instructions are introduced in the context of the registers and data structures they support. References to the chapters in which each register, data structure, and instruction is discussed in more detail.

Chapter 11—Protected Mode Memory Management: This chapter presents details of the data structures, registers, and instructions which support segmentation and paging and explains how system designers can choose between an unsegmented ("flat") model of memory organization and a model with segmentation.

Chapter 12—Protection: This chapter discusses protection as it applies to segments and pages. It explains the implementation of privilege rules, stack switching, pointer validation, user and supervisor modes. The protection aspects of multitasking are deferred until the following chapter.

Chapter 13—Protected-Mode Multitasking: Chapter 13 explains how the hardware of the Pentium processor supports multitasking with context-switching operations and intertask protection.

Chapter 14—Protected-Mode Exceptions and Interrupts: This chapter explains the basic interrupt mechanisms of the Pentium processor, shows how interrupts and exceptions relate to protection, discusses all possible exceptions including floating-point exceptions, listing causes and including information needed to handle and recover from each exception.

Chapter 15—Input/Output: Chapter 15 describes the I/O features of the Pentium processor, including I/O instructions, protection as it relates to I/O, and the I/O permission bit map.

Chapter 16—Initialization and Mode Switching: Chapter 16 defines the condition of the processor and floating-point unit after reset initialization. It explains how to set up registers, flags, and data structures. The steps necessary for switching between real-address and protected modes are also identified.

Chapter 17—Debugging: Chapter 17 discusses how to use the debugging registers and other debug features of the Pentium processor.

Chapter 18—Caching, Pipelining and Buffering: Chapter 18 explains the general concept of caching and the specific mechanisms used by the internal cache on the Pentium processor. It explains how the superscalar pipeline architecture of the Pentium processor and the Translation Lookaside Buffer (TLB) relate to the system programmer.

Chapter 19—Multiprocessing: Chapter 19 explains the instructions and flags which support multiple processors with shared memory.

Chapter 20—System Management Mode: This chapter explains the operation of SMM used to implement power management functions. Some possible customer differentiation features are mentioned.

1.1.3. Part III—Compatibility

This section explains the features of the architecture which support programs written for earlier Intel processors. Three execution modes have support for 16-bit programming: 16-bit operations can be performed in protected mode with or without using the operand-size prefix, programs written for the 8086 processor or the real mode of the Intel 286 processor can run in real mode on one of the 32-bit microprocessors, and a virtual machine monitor can be used to emulate real mode using virtual-8086 mode, even while multitasking with 32-bit programs.

Chapter 21—Mixing 16-Bit and 32-Bit Code: This chapter explains how to mix 16-bit and 32-bit modules within the same program or task. Any particular module can use both 16-bit and 32-bit operands and addresses.

Chapter 22—Virtual-8086 Mode: Chapter 22 describes how to execute one or more 8086, 8088, 80186 or 80188 programs in a Pentium processor protected-mode environment.

Chapter 23—Compatibility: This chapter explains the programming differences between the Intel 286, Intel386, and Intel486 processors. This chapter compares the floating-point unit of the Intel486 and Pentium processors with the arithmetic of the numerics coprocessors used with earlier Intel processors.

1.1.4. Part IV—Optimization

Chapter 24 discusses general optimization techniques for programming in the Intel x86 architecture environment. For obtaining information on Pentium processor-specific optimization techniques, see Appendix H.

1.1.5. Part V—Instruction Set

Parts I, II and III present the general features of the instruction set as they relate to specific aspects of the architecture. Part V, Chapter 25, presents the instructions in alphabetical order, with detail needed by assembly language programmers and programmers of debuggers, compilers, operating systems, etc. Instruction descriptions include an algorithmic description of operations, effect on flag settings, effect of operand- and address-size attributes, and exceptions which may be generated.

1.1.6. Appendices

The appendices present tables of encodings and other details in a format designed for quick reference by programmers.

1.2. RELATED LITERATURE

The following books contain additional material related to Intel processors:

- *Pentium™ Processor Data Book,* Order No. 241428
- *82496 Cache Controller and 82491 Cache SRAM Data Book For Use With the Pentium™ Processor,* Order No. 241429
- *Intel486™ Microprocessor Data Book,* Order Number 240440
- *Intel486™ Processor Hardware Reference Manual,* Order Number 240552
- *Intel486™ DX Processor Programmer's Reference Manual,* Order Number 240486
- *Intel486™ SX CPU/Intel487™ SX Math CoProcessor Data Book,* Order Number 240950
- *Intel486™ DX2 Microprocessor Data Book,* Order Number 241245
- *Intel486™ Microprocessor Product Brief Book,* Order Number 240459
- *Intel386™ Processor Hardware Reference Manual,* Order Number 231732
- *Intel386™ DX Processor Programmer's Reference Manual,* Order Number 230985
- *Intel386™ SX Processor Programmer's Reference Manual,* Order Number 240331
- *Intel386™ Processor System Software Writer's Guide,* Order Number 231499
- *Intel386™ High-Performance 32-Bit CHMOS Microprocessor with Integrated Memory Management,* Order Number 231630
- *376™ Embedded Processor Programmer's Reference Manual,* Order Number 240314
- *80387 DX User's Manual Programmer's Reference,* Order Number 231917
- *376™ High-Performance 32-Bit Embedded Processor,* Order Number 240182
- *Intel386™ SX Microprocessor,* Order Number 240187
- *Microprocessor and Peripheral Handbook* (vol. 1), Order Number 230843

1.3. NOTATIONAL CONVENTIONS

This manual uses special notation for data-structure formats, for symbolic representation of instructions, and for hexadecimal numbers. A review of this notation makes the manual easier to read.

1.3.1. Bit and Byte Order

In illustrations of data structures in memory, smaller addresses appear toward the bottom of the figure; addresses increase toward the top. Bit positions are numbered from right to left. The numerical value of a set bit is equal to two raised to the power of the bit position. The Pentium processor is a "little endian" machine; this means the bytes of a word are numbered starting from the least significant byte. Figure 1-1 illustrates these conventions.

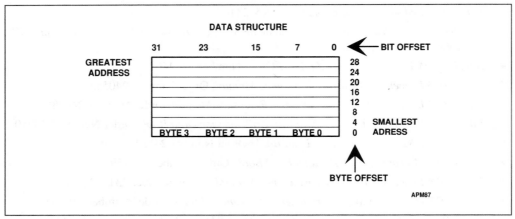

Figure 1-1. Bit and Byte Order

1.3.2. Undefined Bits and Software Compatibility

In many register and memory layout descriptions, certain bits are marked as *reserved*. When bits are marked as undefined or reserved, it is essential for compatibility with future processors that software treat these bits as having a future, though unknown, effect. The behavior of reserved bits should be regarded as not only undefined, but unpredictable. Software should follow these guidelines in dealing with reserved bits:

- Do not depend on the states of any reserved bits when testing the values of registers which contain such bits. Mask out the reserved bits before testing.

- Do not depend on the states of any reserved bits when storing to memory or to a register.

- Do not depend on the ability to retain information written into any reserved bits.

- When loading a register, always load the reserved bits with the values indicated in the documentation, if any, or reload them with values previously read from the same register.

NOTE

Depending upon the values of reserved register bits will make software dependent upon the unspecified manner in which the processor handles these bits. Depending upon reserved values risks incompatibility with future processors. AVOID ANY SOFTWARE DEPENDENCE UPON THE STATE OF RESERVED Pentium PROCESSOR REGISTER BITS.

1.3.3. Instruction Operands

When instructions are represented symbolically, a subset of the assembly language for the Pentium processor is used. In this subset, an instruction has the following format:

label: mnemonic argument1, argument2, argument3

where:

- A *label* is an identifier which is followed by a colon.
- A *mnemonic* is a reserved name for a class of instruction opcodes which have the same function.
- The operands *argument1*, *argument2*, and *argument3* are optional. There may be from zero to three operands, depending on the opcode. When present, they take the form of either literals or identifiers for data items. Operand identifiers are either reserved names of registers or are assumed to be assigned to data items declared in another part of the program (which may not be shown in the example).

When two operands are present in an arithmetic or logical instruction, the right operand is the source and the left operand is the destination.

For example:

```
LOADREG: MOV EAX, SUBTOTAL
```

In this example LOADREG is a label, MOV is the mnemonic identifier of an opcode, EAX is the destination operand, and SUBTOTAL is the source operand. Some assembly languages put the source and destination in reverse order.

1.3.4. Hexadecimal Numbers

Base 16 numbers are represented by a string of hexadecimal digits followed by the character H. A hexadecimal digit is a character from the set (0, 1, 2, 3, 4, 5, 6, 7, 8, 9, A, B, C, D, E, F). A leading zero is added if the number would otherwise begin with one of the digits A-F. For example, 0FH is equivalent to the decimal number 15.

Numbers are usually expressed in decimal notation (base 10). When hexadecimal (base 16) numbers are used, they are indicated by an 'H' suffix. For example 16 = 10H.

1.3.5. Segmented Addressing

The processor uses byte addressing. This means memory is organized and accessed as a sequence of bytes. Whether one or more bytes are being accessed, a byte number is used to address memory. The memory which can be addressed with this number is called an *address space*.

The processor also supports segmented addressing. This is a form of addressing where a program may have many independent address spaces, called *segments*. For example, a program can keep its code (instructions) and stack in separate segments. Code addresses would always refer to the code space, and stack addresses would always refer to the stack space. An example of the notation used to show segmented addresses is shown below.

CS:EIP

This example refers to a byte within the code segment. The byte number is held in the EIP register. CS identifies the code segment.

1.3.6. Exceptions

An exception is an event which typically occurs when an instruction causes an error For example, an attempt to divide by zero generates an exception. However, some exceptions, such as breakpoints, occur under other conditions. Some types of exceptions may provide error codes. An error code reports additional information about the error. Error codes are produced only for some exceptions. An example of the notation used to show an exception and error code is shown below.

#PF(fault code)

This example refers to a page-fault exception under conditions where an error code naming a type of fault is reported. Under some conditions, exceptions which produce error codes may not be able to report an accurate code. In this case, the error code is zero, as shown below.

#GP(0)

See Chapter 14, Protected-Mode Exceptions and Interrupts, for a list of exception mnemonics and their description.

intel.

2

Introduction to the Intel Pentium Processor Family

In 1985, Intel introduced the first in a line of 32-bit microprocessors compatible with the already broad base of existing x86 software. That was the Intel386 microprocessor. The Intel 32-bit architecture has since grown to become the standard for cost-effective, high performance computing with an installed base of over 40 million units. Intel has continued to evolve and improve the basic implementation by incorporating the most advanced computer design and silicon technology. The Intel Pentium family is the most recent product of that effort.

The Intel Pentium processor, like its predecesor the Intel486 microprocessor, is 100% binary software compatible with the installed base of over 100 million compatible Intel x86 systems. In addition, the Intel Pentium processor provides new levels of performance to new and existing software through a reimplementation of the Intel 32-bit instruction set architecture using the latest, most advanced, design techniques. Optimized, dual execution units provide one-clock execution for "core" instructions, while advanced technology, such as superscalar architecture, branch prediction, and execution pipelining, enables multiple instructions to execute in parallel with high efficiency. Separate code and data caches combined with wide 128-bit and 256-bit internal data paths and a 64-bit, burstable, external bus allow these performance levels to be sustained in cost-effective systems. The application of this advanced technology in the Intel Pentium processor brings "state of the art" performance and capability to existing Intel x86 software as well as new and advanced applications.

The Pentium processor has two primary operating modes and a "system management mode". The operating mode determines which instructions and architectural features are accessible. These modes are:

- **Protected Mode**

  This is the native state of the microprocessor. In this mode all instructions and architectural features are available, providing the highest performance and capability. This is the recommended mode that all new applications and operating systems should target.

  Among the capabilities of protected mode is the ability to directly execute "real-address mode" 8086 software in a protected, multi-tasking environment. This feature is known as Virtual-8086 "mode" (or "V86 mode"). Virtual-8086 "mode" however, is not actually a processor "mode", it is in fact an attribute which can be enabled for any task (with appropriate software) while in protected mode.

- **Real-Address Mode (also called "real mode")**

  This mode provides the programming environment of the Intel 8086 processor, with a few extensions (such as the ability to break out of this mode). Reset initialization places the processor in real mode where, with a single instruction, it can switch to protected mode.

- **System Management Mode**

The Pentium microprocessor also provides support for System Management Mode (SMM). SMM is a standard architectural feature unique to all new Intel microprocessors, beginning with the Intel386 SL processor, which provides an operating-system and application independent and transparent mechanism to implement system power management and OEM differentiation features. SMM is entered through activation of an external interrupt pin (SMI#), which switches the CPU to a separate address space while saving the entire context of the CPU. SMM-specific code may then be executed transparently. The operation is reversed upon returning.

Part I

Application and Numeric Processing

intel®

3

Basic Programming Model

CHAPTER 3
BASIC PROGRAMMING MODEL

This chapter describes the application programming environment (except for the floating-point features) as seen by assembly-language programmers. The chapter introduces the architectural features which directly affect the design and implementation of application programs. Floating-point applications are described separately in Chapter 6.

The basic programming model consists of these parts:

- Memory organization
- Data types
- Registers
- Instruction format
- Operand selection
- Interrupts and exceptions

Note that input/output is not included as part of the basic programming model. System designers can choose to make I/O instructions available to applications or can choose to reserve these functions for the operating system. For this reason, the I/O features are discussed in Chapter 9 and Chapter 15.

This chapter contains a section for each feature of the architecture normally visible to applications.

3.1.   MEMORY ORGANIZATION

The memory on the bus of a Pentium processor is called *physical memory*. It is organized as a sequence of 8-bit bytes. Each byte is assigned a unique address, called a *physical address*, which ranges from zero to a maximum of $2^{32}-1$ (4 gigabytes).

Memory management is a hardware mechanism for making reliable and efficient use of memory. When memory management is used, programs do not directly address physical memory. Programs address a memory model, called *virtual memory*.

Memory management consists of segmentation and paging. Segmentation is a mechanism for providing multiple, independent address spaces. Paging is a mechanism to support a model of a large address space in RAM using a small amount of RAM and some disk storage. Either or both of these mechanisms can be used. An address issued by a program is a *logical address*. Segmentation hardware translates a logical address into an address for a continuous, unsegmented address space, called a *linear address*. Paging hardware translates a linear address into a physical address.

Memory can appear as a single, "flat" address space like physical memory. Or, it can appear as one or more independent memory spaces, called *segments*. Segments can be assigned specifically for holding a program's code (instructions), data, or stack. In fact, a single program can have up to 16,383 segments of different sizes and kinds. Segments can be used to increase the reliability of programs and systems. For example, a program's stack can be put into a different segment than its code to prevent the stack from growing into the code space and overwriting instructions with data. Each segment defines a module.

Both the flat and segmented models can provide memory protection. Models intermediate between these extremes also can be chosen. The reasons for choosing a particular memory model and the manner in which system programmers implement a model are discussed in Chapter 11.

Whether or not multiple segments are used, logical addresses are translated into linear addresses by treating the address as an offset into a segment. Each segment has a *segment descriptor*, which holds its base address and size limit. If the offset does not exceed the limit, and no other condition exists which would prevent reading the segment, the offset and base address are added together to form the linear address.

The linear address produced by segmentation is used directly as the physical address if bit 31 of the CR0 register is clear (the CR0 register is discussed in Chapter 10). This register bit controls whether paging is used or not used. If the bit is set, the paging hardware is used to translate the linear address into the physical address.

The paging hardware gives another level of organization to memory. It breaks the linear address space into fixed blocks called *pages*. The logical address space is mapped into the linear address space, which is mapped into some number of pages. A page can be in memory or on disk. When a logical address is issued, it is translated into an address for a page in memory, or an exception is issued. An exception gives the operating system a chance to read the page from disk and update the page mapping. The program which generated the exception then can be restarted without generating an exception.

If multiple segments are used, they are part of the programming environment seen by application programmers. Paging, however, is invisible to the application programmer and is not discussed in this chapter. See Chapter 11 for details on this subject.

3.1.1. Unsegmented or "Flat" Model

The simplest memory model is the flat model. Although there isn't a mode bit or control register which turns off the segmentation mechanism, the same effect can be achieved by mapping all segments to the same linear addresses. This will cause all memory operations to refer to the same memory space.

In a flat model, segments can cover the entire range of physical addresses, or they can cover only those addresses which are mapped to physical memory. The advantage of the smaller address space is it provides a minimum level of hardware protection against software bugs; an exception will occur if any logical address refers to an address for which no memory exists.

3.1.2. Segmented Model

In a segmented model of memory organization, the logical address space consists of as many as 16,383 segments of up to 4 gigabytes each, or a total as large as 2^{46} bytes (64 terabytes). The processor maps this 64 terabyte logical address space onto the physical address space by the address translation mechanism described in Chapter 11. Application programmers can ignore the details of this mapping. The advantage of the segmented model is that offsets within each address space are separately checked and access to each segment can be individually controlled.

A pointer into a segmented address space consists of two parts (see Figure 3-1).

1. A *segment selector*, which is a 16-bit field which identifies a segment.
2. An *offset*, which is a 32-bit byte address within a segment.

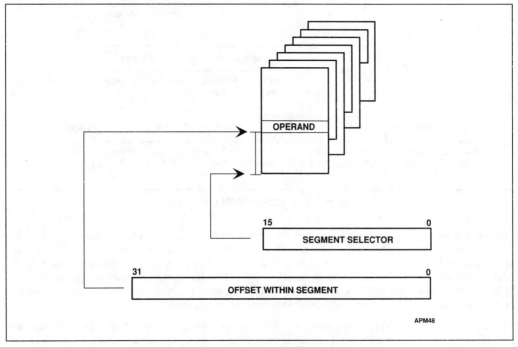

Figure 3-1. Segmented Addressing

The processor uses the segment selector to find the linear address of the beginning of the segment, called the *base address*. Programs access memory using fixed offsets from this base address, so an object-code module can be loaded into memory and run without changing the addresses it uses (dynamic linking). The size of a segment is defined by the programmer, so a segment can be exactly the size of the module it contains.

3.2. DATA TYPES

Bytes, words, doublewords, and quadwords are the principal data types (see Figure 3-2). A byte is eight bits. The bits are numbered 0 through 7, bit 0 being the least significant bit (LSB).

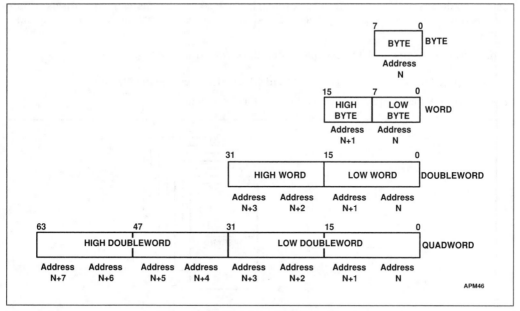

Figure 3-2. Fundamental Data Types

A word is two bytes occupying any two consecutive addresses. A word contains 16 bits. The bits of a word are numbered from 0 through 15, bit 0 again being the least significant bit. The byte containing bits 0-7 of the word is called the *low byte*; the byte containing bits 8-15 is called the *high byte*. The low byte is stored in the byte with the lower address. The address of the low byte also is the address of the word. The address of the high byte is used only when the upper half of the word is being accessed separately from the lower half.

A doubleword is four bytes occupying any four consecutive addresses. A doubleword contains 32 bits. The bits of a doubleword are numbered from 0 through 31, bit 0 again being the least significant bit. The word containing bits 0-15 of the doubleword is called the *low word*; the word containing bits 16-31 is called the *high word*. The low word is stored in the two bytes with the lower addresses. The address of the lowest byte is the address of the doubleword. The higher addresses are used only when the upper word is being accessed separately from the lower word, or when individual bytes are being accessed.

A quadword is eight bytes occupying any eight consecutive addresses. A quadword contains 64 bits. The bits of a quadword are numbered from 0 to 64 with bit 0 being the least significant bit. The doubleword containing bits 0-31 is called the low doubleword and the doubleword containing bits 32-63 is called the high doubleword. The low doubleword is stored in the four bytes with the lower addresses. The higher addresses are used only when the upper doubleword is being accessed separately from the lower doubleword, or when individual bytes are being accessed. Figure 3-3 illustrates the arrangement of bytes within words, doublewords and quadwords.

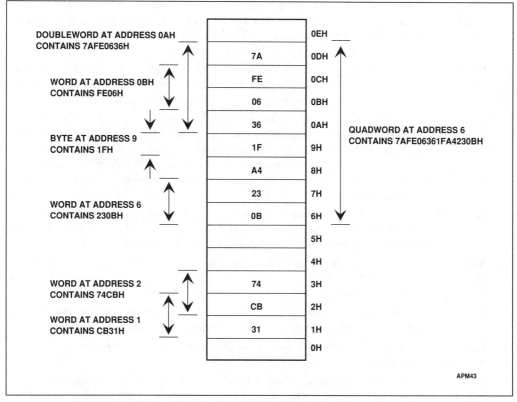

Figure 3-3. Bytes, Words, Doublewords and Quadwords in Memory

Note that words do not need to be aligned at even-numbered addresses, doublewords do not need to be aligned at addresses evenly divisible by four, and quadwords do not need to be aligned at addresses evenly divisible by eight. This allows maximum flexibility in data structures (e.g., records containing mixed byte, word, and doubleword items) and efficiency in memory utilization. Because the Pentium processor has a 64-bit data bus, communication between processor and memory takes place as byte, word, doubleword and quadword transfers. Data can be accessed at any byte boundary, but multiple cycles can be required for unaligned transfers. The Pentium processor considers a 2-byte or 4-byte operand that crosses a 4-byte boundary and an 8-byte operand that crosses an 8-byte boundary to be misaligned. For maximum performance, data structures (especially stacks) should be designed so, whenever possible, word operands are aligned to even addresses, doubleword operands are aligned to addresses evenly divisible by four, and quadwords are aligned to addresses evenly divisible by eight.

Although bytes, words, and doublewords are the fundamental types of operands, the processor also supports additional interpretations of these operands. Specialized instructions recognize the following data types (shown in Figure 3-4):

● *Integer*: A signed binary number held in a 32-bit doubleword, 16-bit word, or 8-bit byte.

All operations assume a two's complement representation. The sign bit is located in bit 7 in a byte, bit 15 in a word, and bit 31 in a doubleword. The sign bit is set for negative integers, clear for positive integers and zero. The value of an 8-bit integer is from -128 to $+127$; a 16-bit integer from $-32,768$ to $+32,767$; a 32-bit integer from -2^{31} to $+2^{31} -1$.

- *Ordinal*: An unsigned binary number contained in a 32-bit doubleword, 16-bit word, or 8-bit byte. The value of an 8-bit ordinal is from 0 to 255; a 16-bit ordinal from 0 to 65,535; a 32-bit ordinal from 0 to $2^{32} - 1$. This is sometimes referred to as an unsigned integer.

- *BCD Integer*: A representation of a binary-coded decimal (BCD) digit in the range 0 through 9. Unpacked decimal numbers are stored as unsigned byte quantities. One digit is stored in each byte. The magnitude of the number is the binary value of the low-order half-byte; values 0 to 9 are valid and are interpreted as the value of a digit. The high-order half-byte must be zero during multiplication and division; it can contain any value during addition and subtraction.

- *Packed BCD Integer* : A representation of binary-coded decimal digits, each in the range 0 to 9. One digit is stored in each half-byte, two digits in each byte. The digit in bits 4 to 7 is more significant than the digit in bits 0 to 3. Values 0 to 9 are valid for a digit.

- *Near Pointer*: A 32-bit effective address. A near pointer is an offset within a segment. Near pointers are used for all pointers in a flat memory model, or for references within a segment in a segmented model.

- *Far Pointer*: A 48-bit logical address consisting of a 16-bit segment selector and a 32-bit offset. Far pointers are used in a segmented memory model to access other segments.

- *Bit field*: A contiguous sequence of bits. A bit field can begin at any bit position of any byte and can contain up to 32 bits.

- *Bit string*: A contiguous sequence of bits. A bit string can begin at any bit position of any byte and can contain up to $2^{32}- 1$ bits.

- *Byte String*: A contiguous sequence of bytes, words, or doublewords. A string can contain from zero to $2^{32} - 1$ bytes (4 gigabytes).

- *Floating-Point Types*: For a discussion of the data types used by floating-point instructions, see Chapter 6.

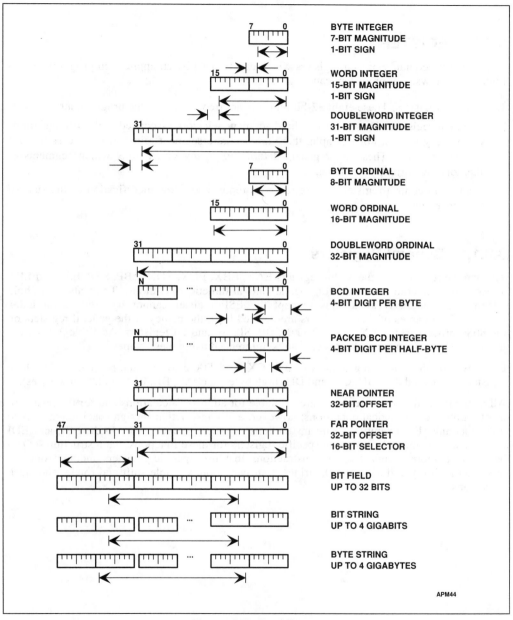

Figure 3-4. Data Types

3.3. REGISTERS

The processor contains sixteen registers which can be used by an application programmer. As Figure 3-5 shows, these registers can be grouped as:

1. General registers. These eight 32-bit registers are free for use by the programmer.

2. Segment registers. These registers hold segment selectors associated with different forms of memory access. For example, there are separate segment registers for access to code and stack space. These six registers determine, at any given time, which segments of memory are currently available.

3. Status and control registers. These registers report and allow modification of the state of the processor.

3.3.1. General Registers

The general registers are the 32-bit registers EAX, EBX, ECX, EDX, EBP, ESP, ESI, and EDI. These registers hold operands for logical and arithmetic operations. They also can hold operands for address calculations (except the ESP register cannot be used as an index operand). The names of these registers are derived from the names of the general registers on the 8086 processor, the AX, BX, CX, DX, BP, SP, SI, and DI registers. As Table 3-1 shows, the low 16 bits of the general registers can be referenced using these names.

Each byte of the 16-bit registers AX, BX, CX, and DX also has another name. The byte registers are named AH, BH, CH, and DH (high bytes) and AL, BL, CL, and DL (low bytes).

All of the general-purpose registers are available for address calculations and for the results of most arithmetic and logical operations; however, a few instructions assign specific registers to hold operands. For example, string instructions use the contents of the ECX, ESI, and EDI registers as operands. By assigning specific registers for these functions, the instruction set can be encoded more compactly. The instructions that use specific registers include: double-precision multiply and divide, I/O, strings, translate, loop, variable shift and rotate, and stack operations.

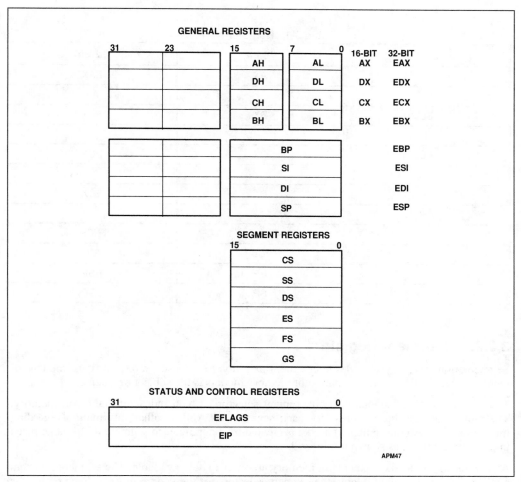

Figure 3-5. Application Register Set

Table 3-1. Register Names

8-Bit	16-Bit	32-Bit
AL	AX	EAX
AH		
BL	BX	EBX
BH		
CL	CX	ECX
CH		
DL	DX	EDX
DH		
	SI	ESI
	DI	EDI
	BP	EBP
	SP	ESP

3.3.2.   Segment Registers

Segmentation gives system designers the flexibility to choose among various models of memory organization. Implementation of memory models is the subject of Chapter 11.

The segment registers contain 16-bit segment selectors, which index into tables in memory. The tables hold the base address for each segment, as well as other information regarding memory access. An unsegmented model is created by mapping each segment to the same place in physical memory, as shown in Figure 3-6.

At any instant, up to six segments of memory are immediately available. The segment registers CS, DS, SS, ES, FS, and GS hold the segment selectors for these six segments. Each register is associated with a particular kind of memory access (code, data, or stack). Each register specifies a segment, from among the segments used by the program (see Figure 3-7). Other segments can be used by loading their segment selectors into the segment registers.

The segment containing the instructions being executed is called the *code segment*. Its segment selector is held in the CS register. The processor fetches instructions from the code segment, using the contents of the EIP register as an offset into the segment. The CS register is loaded as the result of interrupts, exceptions, and instructions which transfer control between segments (e.g., the CALL, RET and JMP instructions).

Before a procedure is called, a region of memory needs to be allocated for a stack. The stack holds the return address, parameters passed by the calling routine, and temporary variables allocated by the procedure. All stack operations use the SS register to find the stack segment. Unlike the CS register, the SS register can be loaded explicitly, which permits application programs to set up stacks.

The DS, ES, FS, and GS registers allow as many as four data segments to be available simultaneously. Four data segments give efficient and secure access to different types of data structures. For example, separate data segments can be created for the data structures of the current module, data exported from a higher-level module, a dynamically-created data structure, and data shared with another program. If a bug causes a program to run wild, the segmentation mechanism can limit the damage to only those segments allocated to the program.

Depending on the structure of data (i.e., the way data is partitioned into segments), a program can require access to more than four data segments. To access additional segments, the DS, ES, FS, and GS registers can be loaded by an application program during execution. The only requirement is to load the appropriate segment register before accessing data in its segment.

A base address is kept for each segment. To address data within a segment, a 32-bit offset is added to the segment's base address. Once a segment is selected (by loading the segment selector into a segment register), an instruction only needs to specify the offset. An operand within a data segment is addressed by specifying its offset either in an instruction or a general register. Simple rules define which segment register is used to form an address when only an offset is specified.

3.3.3. Stack Implementation

Stack operations are supported by three registers:

1. **Stack Segment (SS) Register.** Stacks reside in memory. The number of stacks in a system is limited only by the maximum number of segments. A stack can be up to 4 gigabytes long, the maximum size of a segment. One stack is available at a time—the stack whose segment selector is held in the SS register. This is the current stack, often referred to simply as "the" stack. The SS register is used automatically by the processor for all stack operations.

2. **Stack Pointer (ESP) Register.** The ESP register holds an offset to the top-of-stack (TOS) in the current stack segment. It is used by PUSH and POP operations, subroutine calls and returns, exceptions, and interrupts. When an item is pushed onto the stack (see Figure 3-8), the processor decrements the ESP register, then writes the item at the new TOS. When an item is popped off the stack, the processor copies it from the TOS, then increments the ESP register. In other words, the stack grows *down* in memory toward lesser addresses.

3. **Stack-Frame Base Pointer (EBP) Register.** The EBP register typically is used to access data structures passed on the stack. For example, on entering a subroutine the stack contains the return address and some number of data structures passed to the subroutine. The subroutine adds to the stack whenever it needs to create space for temporary local variables. As a result, the stack pointer gets incremented and decremented as temporary variables are pushed and popped. If the stack pointer is copied into the base pointer before anything is pushed on the stack, the base pointer can be used to reference data structures with fixed offsets. If this is not done, the offset to access a particular data structure would change whenever a temporary variable is allocated or de-allocated.

   When the EBP register is used to address memory, the current stack segment is referenced (i.e., the SS segment). Because the stack segment does not have to be specified, instruction encoding is more compact. The EBP register also can be used to address other segments.

Instructions, such as the ENTER and LEAVE instructions, are provided which automatically set up the EBP register for convenient access to variables.

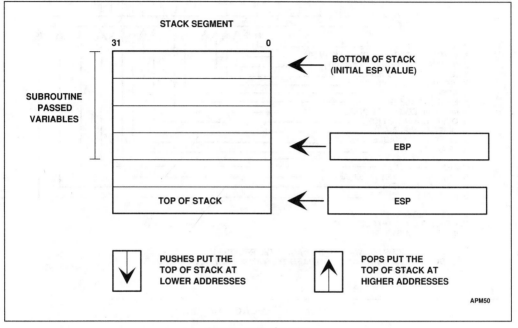

Figure 3-8. Stacks

3.3.4. Flags Register

Condition codes (e.g., carry, sign, overflow) and mode bits are kept in a 32-bit register named EFLAGS. Figure 3-9 defines the bits within this register.

The flags control certain operations and indicate the status of the Pentium processor. Besides status and control flag bits, the flag register also contains system flags. See Chapter 10 for a description of the system and control flags.

3.3.4.1. STATUS FLAGS

The status flags of the EFLAGS register report the kind of result produced from the execution of arithmetic instructions, such as ADD, SUB, MUL, and DIV. The MOV instruction does not affect these flags. Conditional jumps and subroutine calls allow a program to sense the state of the status flags and respond to them. For example, when the counter controlling a loop is decremented to zero, the state of the ZF flag changes, and this change can be used to suppress the conditional jump to the start of the loop. The status flags are shown in Table 3-2.

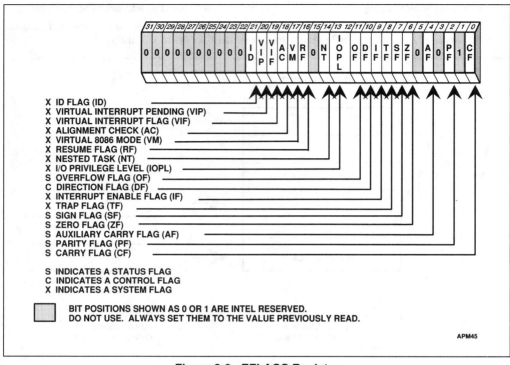

Figure 3-9. EFLAGS Register

Table 3-2. Status Flags

Name	Purpose	Condition Reported
OF	overflow	Result exceeds positive or negative limit of number range
SF	sign	Result is negative (less than zero)
ZF	zero	Result is zero
AF	auxiliary carry	Carry out of bit position 3 (used for BCD)
PF	parity	Low byte of result has even parity (even number of set bits)
CF	carry flag	Carry out of most significant bit of result

3.3.4.2.   CONTROL FLAG

The control flag DF of the EFLAGS register controls string instructions.

DF (Direction Flag, bit 10)

Setting the DF flag causes string instructions to auto-decrement, that is, to process strings from high addresses to low addresses. Clearing the DF flag causes string instructions to auto-increment, or to process strings from low addresses to high addresses.

3.3.5.   Instruction Pointer

The instruction pointer (EIP) register contains the offset in the current code segment for the next instruction to execute. The instruction pointer is not directly available to the programmer; it is controlled implicitly by control-transfer instructions (jumps, returns, etc.), interrupts, and exceptions.

The EIP register is advanced from one instruction boundary to the next. Because of instruction prefetching, it is only an approximate indication of the bus activity which loads instructions into the processor. See Chapter 18 for detailed information on prefetching.

3.3.5.1.   Instruction Format

3.4.   INSTRUCTION FORMAT

The information encoded in an instruction includes a specification of the operation to be performed, the type of the operands to be manipulated, and the location of these operands. If an operand is located in memory, the instruction also must select, explicitly or implicitly, the segment which contains the operand.

An instruction can have various parts and formats. The exact format of instructions is shown in Appendix A; the parts of an instruction are described below. Of these parts, only the opcode is always present. The other parts may or may not be present, depending on the operation involved and the location and type of the operands. The parts of an instruction, in order of occurrence, are listed below:

*   **Prefixes:** one or more bytes preceding an instruction which modify the operation of the instruction. The following prefixes can be used by application programs:
    1. Segment override—explicitly specifies which segment register an instruction should use, instead of the default segment register. The segment override prefixes include:

        2EH   CS segment override prefix

        36H   SS segment override prefix

        26H   ES segment override prefix

        65H   GS segment override prefix
    2. Address size (67H)—switches between 16- and 32-bit addressing. Either size can be the default; this prefix selects the non-default size.

3. Operand size (66H)—switches between 16- and 32-bit data size. Either size can be the default; this prefix selects the non-default size.

4. Repeat—used with a string instruction to cause the instruction to be repeated for each element of the string. The repeat prefixes include:

   F3H   REP prefix (used only with string instructions)

   F3H   REPE/REPZ prefix (used only with string instructions)

   F2h   REPNE/REPNZ prefix (used only with string instructions)

5. Lock (0F0H)—used to ensure exclusive use of shared memory in multiprocessor environments. This prefix can only be used with the following instructions: BTS, BTR, BTC, XCHG, ADD, OR, ADC, SBB, AND, SUB, XOR, NOT, NEG, INC, DEC, CMPXCHG, CMPXCH8B, XADD

Zero or one bytes are reserved for each group of prefixes. The prefixes are grouped as follows:

— Instruction Prefixes: REP, REPE/REPZ, REPNE/REPNZ, LOCK

— Segment Override Prefixes: CS, SS, DS, ES, FS, GS

— Operand Size Override

— Address Size Override

For each instruction, one prefix may be used from each group. The effect of redundant prefixes (more than one prefix from a group) is undefined and may vary from processor to processor.

- **Opcode:** specifies the operation performed by the instruction. Some operations have several different opcodes, each specifying a different form of the operation.

- **Register specifier:** an instruction can specify one or two register operands. Register specifiers occur either in the same byte as the opcode or in the same byte as the addressing-mode specifier.

- **Addressing-mode specifier:** when present, specifies whether an operand is a register or memory location; if in memory, specifies whether a displacement, a base register, an index register, and scaling are to be used.

- **SIB (scale, index, base) byte:** when the addressing-mode specifier indicates the use of an index register to calculate the address of an operand, an SIB byte is included in the instruction to encode the base register, the index register, and a scaling factor.

- **Displacement:** when the addressing-mode specifier indicates a displacement will be used to compute the address of an operand, the displacement is encoded in the instruction. A displacement is a signed integer of 32, 16, or 8 bits. The 8-bit form is used in the common case when the displacement is sufficiently small. The processor extends an 8-bit displacement to 16 or 32 bits, taking into account the sign.

- **Immediate operand:** when present, directly provides the value of an operand. Immediate operands can be bytes, words, or doublewords. In cases where an 8-bit immediate operand is used with a 16- or 32-bit operand, the processor extends the eight-bit operand to an integer of the same sign and magnitude in the larger size. In the same way, a 16-bit operand is extended to 32-bits.

3.5. OPERAND SELECTION

An instruction acts on zero or more operands. An example of a zero-operand instruction is the NOP instruction (no operation). An operand can be held in any of these places:

- In the instruction itself (an immediate operand).

- In a register (in the case of 32-bit operands, EAX, EBX, ECX, EDX, ESI, EDI, ESP, or EBP; in the case of 16-bit operands AX, BX, CX, DX, SI, DI, SP, or BP; in the case of 8-bit operands AH, AL, BH, BL, CH, CL, DH, or DL; the segment registers; or the EFLAGS register for flag operations). Use of 16-bit register operands requires use of the 16-bit operand size prefix if the current default operand size is 32 bits. (See Chapter 11 for information on setting the D-bit in the code segment descriptor to control default operand size.)

- In memory.

- At an I/O port. See Chapter 15 for information on I/O.

Register and immediate operands are available on-chip—the latter because they are prefetched as part of interpreting the instruction. Memory operands residing in the on-chip cache can be accessed just as fast for most instructions.

Of the instructions which have operands, some specify operands implicitly; others specify operands explicitly; still others use a combination of both. For example:

Implicit operand: AAM

By definition, AAM (ASCII adjust for multiplication) operates on the contents of the AX register.

Explicit operand: XCHG EAX, EBX

The operands to be exchanged are encoded in the instruction with the opcode.

Implicit and explicit operands: PUSH COUNTER

The memory variable COUNTER (the explicit operand) is copied to the top of the stack (the implicit operand).

Note that most instructions have implicit operands. All arithmetic instructions, for example, update the EFLAGS register.

An instruction can *explicitly* reference one or two operands. Two-operand instructions, such as MOV, ADD, and XOR, generally overwrite one of the two participating operands with the result. This is one difference between the *source operand* (the one unaffected by the operation) and the *destination operand* (the one overwritten by the result).

For most instructions, one of the two explicitly specified operands—either the source or the destination—can be either in a register or in memory. The other operand must be in a register or it must be an immediate source operand. This puts the explicit two-operand instructions into the following groups:

- Register to register

- Register to memory
- Memory to register
- Immediate to register
- Immediate to memory

Certain string instructions and stack manipulation instructions, however, transfer data from memory to memory. Both operands of some string instructions are in memory and are specified implicitly. Push and pop stack operations allow transfer between memory operands and the memory-based stack.

Several three-operand instructions are provided, such as the IMUL, SHRD, and SHLD instructions. Two of the three operands are specified explicitly, as for the two-operand instructions, while a third is taken from the CL register or supplied as an immediate. Other three-operand instructions, such as the string instructions when used with a repeat prefix, take all their operands from registers.

3.5.1. Immediate Operands

Certain instructions use data from the instruction itself as one (and sometimes two) of the operands. Such an operand is called an *immediate* operand. It can be a byte, word, or doubleword. For example:

```
SHR PATTERN, 2
```

One byte of the instruction holds the value 2, the number of bits by which to shift the variable PATTERN.

```
TEST PATTERN, 0FFFF00FFH
```

A doubleword of the instruction holds the mask which is used to test the variable PATTERN.

```
IMUL CX, MEMWORD, 3
```

A word in memory is multiplied by an immediate 3 and stored into the CX register.

All arithmetic instructions (except divide) allow the source operand to be an immediate value. When the destination is the EAX or AL register, the instruction encoding is one byte shorter than with the other general registers.

3.5.2. Register Operands

Operands can be located in one of the 32-bit general registers (EAX, EBX, ECX, EDX, ESI, EDI, ESP, or EBP), in one of the 16-bit general registers (AX, BX, CX, DX, SI, DI, SP, or BP), or in one of the 8-bit general registers (AH, BH, CH, DH, AL, BL, CL, or DL). Sixty-four bit operands are also used in 32-bit register pairs for operations such as DIV and MUL. Register pairs are represented with a colon separating them. For example, in the register pair EDX:EAX, EDX contains the high order bits and EAX contains the low order bits of the 64-bit operand.

The Pentium processor has instructions for referencing the segment registers (CS, DS, ES, SS, FS, and GS). These instructions are used by application programs only if system designers have chosen a segmented memory model.

The Pentium processor also has instructions for changing the state of individual flags in the EFLAGS register. Instructions have been provided for setting and clearing flags which often need to be accessed. The other flags, which are not accessed so often, can be changed by pushing the contents of the EFLAGS register on the stack, making changes to it while it's on the stack, and popping it back into the register.

3.5.3.   Memory Operands

Instructions with explicit operands in memory must reference the segment containing the operand and the offset from the beginning of the segment to the operand. Segments are specified using a segment-override prefix, which is a byte placed at the beginning of an instruction. If no segment is specified, simple rules assign the segment by default. The offset is specified in one of the following ways:

1. Most instructions which access memory contain a byte for specifying the addressing method of the operand. The byte, called the *modR/M* byte, comes after the opcode and specifies whether the operand is in a register or in memory. If the operand is in memory, the address is calculated from a segment register and any of the following values: a base register, an index register, a scaling factor, and a displacement. When an index register is used, the modR/M byte also is followed by another byte to specify the index register and scaling factor. This form of addressing is the most flexible.

2. A few instructions use implied address modes:

    A MOV instruction with the AL, AX, or EAX register as either source or destination can address memory with a doubleword encoded in the instruction. This special form of the MOV instruction allows no base register, index register, or scaling factor to be used. This form is one byte shorter than the general-purpose form.

    String operations address memory in the DS segment using the ESI register, (the MOVS, CMPS, OUTS, and LODS instructions) or using the ES segment and EDI register (the MOVS, CMPS, INS, SCAS, and STOS instructions).

    Stack operations address memory in the SS segment using the ESP register (the PUSH, POP, PUSHA, PUSHAD, POPA, POPAD, PUSHF, PUSHFD, POPF, POPFD, CALL, LEAVE, ENTER, INT, RET, IRET, and IRETD instructions, exceptions, and interrupts).

3.5.3.1.   SEGMENT SELECTION

Explicit specification of a segment is optional. If a segment is not specified using a segment-override prefix, the processor automatically chooses a segment according to the rules of Table 3-3.

Table 3-3. Default Segment Selection Rules

Type of Reference	Segment Used Register Used	Default Selection Rule
Instructions	Code Segment CS register	Automatic with instruction fetch.
Stack	Stack Segment SS register	All stack pushes and pops. Any memory reference which uses ESP or EBP as a base register.
Local Data	Data Segment DS register	All data references except when relative to stack or string destination.
Destination Strings	E-Space Segment ES register	Destination of string instructions.

Different kinds of memory access have different default segments. Data operands usually use the main data segment (the DS segment). However, the ESP and EBP registers are used for addressing the stack, so when either register is used, the stack segment (the SS segment) is selected.

Segment-override prefixes are provided for each of the segment registers. Only the following special cases have a default segment selection which is not affected by a segment-override prefix:

- Destination strings in string instructions use the ES segment

- Destination of a push or source of a pop uses the SS segment

- Instruction fetches use the CS segment

3.5.3.2. EFFECTIVE-ADDRESS COMPUTATION

The modR/M byte provides the most flexible form of addressing. Instructions which have a modR/M byte after the opcode are the most common in the instruction set. For memory operands specified by a modR/M byte, the offset within the selected segment is the sum of four components:

- A displacement

- A base register

- An index register

- A scaling factor (the index register can be multiplied by a factor of 2, 4, or 8)

The offset which results from adding these components is called an *effective address*. Each of these components can have either a positive or negative value, with the exception of the scaling factor. Figure 3-10 illustrates the full set of possibilities for modR/M addressing.

The displacement component, because it is encoded in the instruction, is useful for relative addressing by fixed amounts, such as:

- Location of simple scalar operands.

- Beginning of a statically allocated array.

- Offset to a field within a record.

The base and index components have similar functions. Both use the same set of general registers. Both can be used for addressing which changes during program execution, such as:

- Location of procedure parameters and local variables on the stack.
- The beginning of one record among several occurrences of the same record type or in an array of records.
- The beginning of one dimension of multiple dimension array.
- The beginning of a dynamically allocated array.

The uses of general registers as base or index components differ in the following respects:

- The ESP register cannot be used as an index register.
- When the ESP or EBP register is used as the base, the SS segment is the default selection. In all other cases, the DS segment is the default selection.

SEGMENT + BASE + (INDEX * SCALE) + DISPLACEMENT

| CS SS DS ES FS GS | + | EAX ECX EDX EBX ESP EBP ESI EDI | + | EAX ECX EDX EBX EBP ESI EDI | * | 1 2 4 8 | + | NO DISPLACEMENT 8-BIT DISPLACEMENT 32-BIT DISPLACEMENT |

APM42

Figure 3-10. Effective Address Computation

The scaling factor permits efficient indexing into an array when the array elements are 2, 4, or 8 bytes. The scaling of the index register is done in hardware at the time the address is evaluated. This eliminates an extra shift or multiply instruction.

The base, index, and displacement components can be used in any combination; any of these components can be null. A scale factor can be used only when an index also is used. Each possible combination is useful for data structures commonly used by programmers in high-level languages and assembly language. Suggested uses for some combinations of address components are described below.

DISPLACEMENT

The displacement alone indicates the offset of the operand. This form of addressing is used to access a statically allocated scalar operand. A byte, word, or doubleword displacement can be used.

BASE

The offset to the operand is specified indirectly in one of the general registers, as for ''based'' variables.

BASE + DISPLACEMENT

A register and a displacement can be used together for two distinct purposes:

1. Index into an array when the element size is not 2, 4, or 8 bytes. The displacement component encodes the offset of the beginning of the array. The register holds the results of a calculation to determine the offset to a specific element within the array.
2. Access a field of a record. The base register holds the address of the beginning of the record, while the displacement is an offset to the field.

An important special case of this combination is access to parameters in a procedure activation record. A procedure activation record is the stack frame created when a subroutine is entered. In this case, the EBP register is the best choice for the base register, because it automatically selects the stack segment. This is a compact encoding for this common function.

(INDEX * SCALE) + DISPLACEMENT

This combination is an efficient way to index into a static array when the element size is 2, 4, or 8 bytes. The displacement addresses the beginning of the array, the index register holds the subscript of the desired array element, and the processor automatically converts the subscript into an index by applying the scaling factor.

BASE + INDEX + DISPLACEMENT

Two registers used together support either a two-dimensional array (the displacement holds the address of the beginning of the array) or one of several instances of an array of records (the displacement is an offset to a field within the record).

BASE + (INDEX * SCALE) + DISPLACEMENT

This combination provides efficient indexing of a two-dimensional array when the elements of the array are 2, 4, or 8 bytes in size.

3.6.   INTERRUPTS AND EXCEPTIONS

The processor has two mechanisms for interrupting program execution:

1. *Exceptions* are synchronous events which are responses of the processor to certain conditions detected during the execution of an instruction.
2. *Interrupts* are asynchronous events typically triggered by external devices needing attention.

Interrupts and exceptions are alike in that both cause the processor to temporarily suspend the program being run in order to run a program of higher priority. The major distinction between these two kinds of interrupts is their origin. An exception is always reproducible by re-executing the program which caused the exception, while an interrupt can have a complex, timing-dependent relationship with programs.

Application programmers normally are not concerned with handling exceptions or interrupts. The operating system, monitor, or device driver handles them. More information on interrupts for system programmers can be found in Chapter 12. Certain kinds of exceptions, however, are relevant to application programming, and many operating systems give application programs the opportunity to service these exceptions. However, the operating system defines the interface between the application program and the exception mechanism of the processor. Table 3-4 lists the interrupts and exceptions.

- A divide-error exception results when the DIV or IDIV instruction is executed with a zero denominator or when the quotient is too large for the destination operand. (See Chapter 3 for more information on the DIV and IDIV instructions.)

- A debug exception can be sent back to an application program if it results from the TF (trap) flag.

- A breakpoint exception results when an INT3 instruction is executed. This instruction is used by some debuggers to stop program execution at specific points.

- An overflow exception results when the INTO instruction is executed and the OF (overflow) flag is set. See Chapter 3 for a discussion of the INTO instruction.

- A bounds-check exception results when the BOUND instruction is executed with an array index which falls outside the bounds of the array. See Chapter 3 for a discussion of the BOUND instruction.

- The device-not-available exception occurs whenever the processor encounters an escape instruction and either the TS (task switched) or the EM (emulate coprocessor) bit of the CR0 control register is set.

- An alignment-check exception is generated for unaligned memory operations in user mode (privilege level 3), provided both AM and AC are set. Memory operations at supervisor mode (privilege levels 0, 1, and 2), or memory operations which default to supervisor mode, do not generate this exception.

The INT instruction generates an interrupt whenever it is executed; the processor treats this interrupt as an exception. Its effects (and the effects of all other exceptions) are determined by exception handler routines in the application program or the operating system. The INT instruction itself is discussed in Chapter 25. See Chapter 14 for a more complete description of exceptions.

Table 3-4. Exceptions and Interrupts

Vector Number	Description
0	Divide Error
1	Debugger Call
2	NMI Interrupt
3	Breakpoint
4	INTO-detected Overflow
5	BOUND Range Exceeded
6	Invalid Opcode
7	Device Not Available
8	Double Fault
9	(Intel reserved. Do not use. Not used by Pentium™ processor.)
10	Invalid Task State Segment
11	Segment Not Present
12	Stack Exception
13	General Protection
14	Page Fault
15	(Intel reserved. Do not use.)
16	Floating-Point Error
17	Alignment Check
18	Machine Check Exception
19-31	(Intel reserved. Do not use.)
32-255	Maskable Interrupts

intel®

4

Application Programming

CHAPTER 4
APPLICATION PROGRAMMING

This chapter is an overview of the integer instructions which programmers can use to write application software for the Pentium processor. The instructions are grouped by categories of related functions. Additional application instructions for operating on floating-point operands are described in Chapter 6.

The instructions not discussed in this chapter or Chapter 6 normally are used only by operating-system programmers. System-level instructions are discussed in Part II.

The instruction set descriptions in Chapter 25 contain more detailed information on all instructions, including encoding, operation, timing, effect on flags, and exceptions which may be generated.

For information on the introduction of new instructions which may not be supported on earlier versions of x86 microprocessors, see Chapter 23.

4.1. DATA MOVEMENT INSTRUCTIONS

These instructions provide convenient methods for moving bytes, words, doublewords, or quadwords between memory and the processor registers. They come in three types:

1. General-purpose data movement instructions.
2. Stack manipulation instructions.
3. Type-conversion instructions.

4.1.1. General-Purpose Data Movement Instructions

MOV (Move) transfers a byte, word, or doubleword from the source operand to the destination operand. The MOV instruction is useful for transferring data along any of these paths:

- To a register from memory.
- To memory from a register.
- Between general registers.
- Immediate data to a register.
- Immediate data to memory.

The MOV instruction cannot move from memory to memory or from a segment register to a segment register. Memory-to-memory moves can be performed, however, by the string move instruction MOVS. A special form of the MOV instruction is provided for transferring data between the AL, AX, or EAX registers and a location in memory specified by a 32-bit offset encoded in the instruction. This form of the instruction does not allow a segment override, index register, or scaling factor to be used. The encoding of this form is one byte shorter than the encoding of the general-purpose MOV instruction. A similar encoding is provided for moving an 8-, 16-, or 32-bit immediate into any of the general registers.

XCHG (Exchange) swaps the contents of two operands. This instruction takes the place of three MOV instructions. It does not require a temporary location to save the contents of one operand while the other is being loaded. The XCHG instruction is especially useful for implementing semaphores or similar data structures for process synchronization.

The XCHG instruction can swap two byte operands, two word operands, or two doubleword operands. The operands for the XCHG instruction may be two register operands, or a register operand and a memory operand. When used with a memory operand, XCHG automatically activates the LOCK signal. (See Chapter 16 for more information on bus locking.)

4.1.2. Stack Manipulation Instructions

PUSH (Push) decrements the stack pointer (ESP register), then copies the source operand to the top of stack (see Figure 4-1). The PUSH instruction often is used to place parameters on the stack before calling a procedure. Inside a procedure, it can be used to reserve space on the stack for temporary variables. The PUSH instruction operates on memory operands, immediate operands, and register operands (including segment registers). A special form of the PUSH instruction is available for pushing a 32-bit general register on the stack. This form has an encoding which is one byte shorter than the general-purpose form.

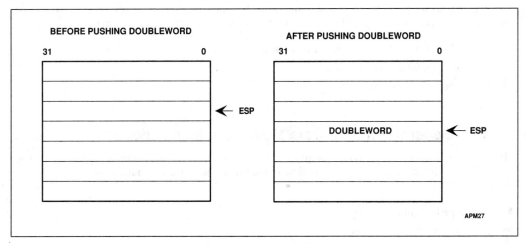

Figure 4-1. PUSH Instruction

PUSHA (Push All Registers) saves the contents of the eight general registers on the stack (see Figure 4-2). This instruction simplifies procedure calls by reducing the number of instructions required to save the contents of the general registers. The processor pushes the general registers on the stack in the following order: EAX, ECX, EDX, EBX, the initial value of ESP before EAX was pushed, EBP, ESI, and EDI. The effect of the PUSHA instruction is reversed using the POPA instruction.

POP (Pop) transfers the word or doubleword at the current top of stack (indicated by the ESP register) to the destination operand, and then increments the ESP register to point to the new top of stack. See Figure 4-3. POP moves information from the stack to a general register, segment register, or to memory. A special form of the POP instruction is available for popping a doubleword from the stack to a general register. This form has an encoding which is one byte shorter than the general-purpose form.

POPA (Pop All Registers) pops the data saved on the stack by PUSHA into the general registers, except for the ESP register. The ESP register is restored by the action of reading the stack (popping). See Figure 4-4.

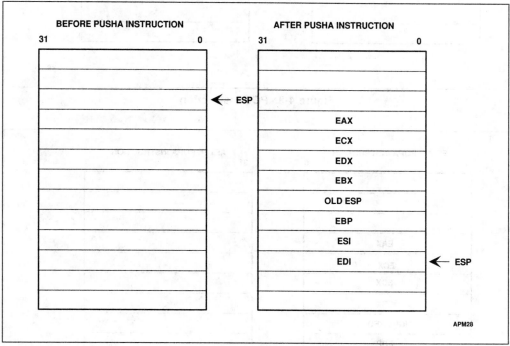

Figure 4-2. PUSHA Instruction

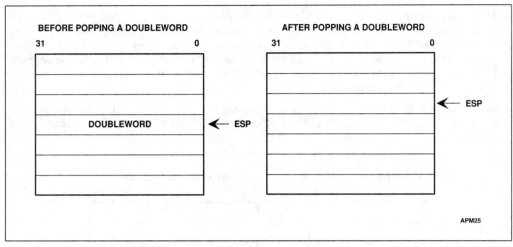

Figure 4-3. POP Instruction

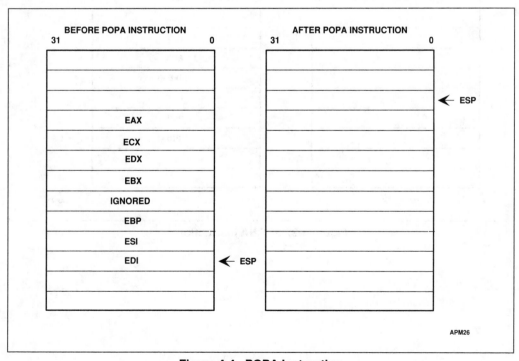

Figure 4-4. POPA Instruction

4.1.3. Type Conversion Instructions

The type conversion instructions convert bytes into words, words into doublewords, and doublewords into 64-bit quantities (called quadwords). These instructions are especially useful for converting signed integers, because they automatically fill the extra bits of the larger item with the value of the sign bit of the smaller item. This results in an integer of the same sign and magnitude, but a larger format. This kind of conversion, shown in Figure 4-5, is called sign extension.

There are two kinds of type conversion instructions:

- The CWD, CDQ, CBW, and CWDE instructions which only operate on data in the EAX register.

- The MOVSX and MOVZX instructions, which permit one operand to be in a general register while letting the other operand be in memory or a register.

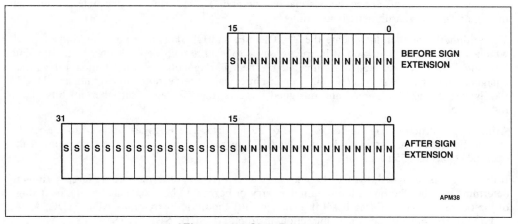

Figure 4-5. Sign Extension

CWD (Convert Word to Doubleword) and **CDQ (Convert Doubleword to Quad-Word)** double the size of the source operand. The CWD instruction copies the sign (bit 15) of the word in the AX register into every bit position in the DX register. The CDQ instruction copies the sign (bit 31) of the doubleword in the EAX register into every bit position in the EDX register. The CWD instruction can be used to produce a doubleword dividend from a word before a word division, and the CDQ instruction can be used to produce a quadword dividend from a doubleword before doubleword division. The CWD and CDQ instructions are different mnemonics for the same opcode. Which one gets executed is determined by whether it is in a 16- or 32-bit segment and the presence of any operand-size override prefixes. See Chapter 25 for a detailed description of these instructions.

CBW (Convert Byte to Word) copies the sign (bit 7) of the byte in the AL register into every bit position of the upper byte of the AX register.

CWDE (Convert Word to Doubleword Extended) copies the sign (bit 15) of the word in the

AX register into every bit position of the high word of the EAX register.

MOVSX (Move with Sign Extension) extends an 8-bit value to a 16-bit value or an 8- or 16-bit value to 32-bit value by using the value of the sign to fill empty positions.

MOVZX (Move with Zero Extension) extends an 8-bit value to a 16-bit value or an 8- or 16-bit value to 32-bit value by clearing the empty bit positions.

4.2. BINARY ARITHMETIC INSTRUCTIONS

The arithmetic instructions operate on numeric data encoded in binary. Operations include the add, subtract, multiply, and divide as well as increment, decrement, compare, and change sign (negate). Both signed and unsigned binary integers are supported. The binary arithmetic instructions may also be used as steps in arithmetic on decimal integers. Source operands can be immediate values, general registers, or memory. Destination operands can be general registers or memory (except when the source operand is in memory). The basic arithmetic instructions have special forms for using an immediate value as the source operand and the AL, AX, or EAX registers as the destination operand. These forms are one byte shorter than the general-purpose arithmetic instructions.

The arithmetic instructions update the ZF, CF, SF, and OF flags to report the kind of result which was produced. The kind of instruction used to test the flags depends on whether the data is being interpreted as signed or unsigned. The CF flag contains information relevant to unsigned integers; the SF and OF flags contain information relevant to signed integers. The ZF flag is relevant to both signed and unsigned integers; the ZF flag is set when all bits of the result are clear.

Arithmetic instructions operate on 8-, 16-, or 32-bit data. The flags are updated to reflect the size of the operation. For example, an 8-bit ADD instruction sets the CF flag if the sum of the operands exceeds 255 (decimal).

If the integer is unsigned, the CF flag may be tested after one of these arithmetic operations to determine whether the operation required a carry or borrow to be propagated to the next stage of the operation. The CF flag is set if a carry occurs (addition instructions ADD, ADC, AAA, and DAA) or borrow occurs (subtraction instructions SUB, SBB, AAS, DAS, CMP, and NEG).

The INC and DEC instructions do not change the state of the CF flag. This allows the instructions to be used to update counters used for loop control without changing the reported state of arithmetic results. To test the arithmetic state of the counter, the ZF flag can be tested to detect loop termination, or the ADD and SUB instructions can be used to update the value held by the counter.

The SF and OF flags support signed integer arithmetic. The SF flag has the value of the sign bit of the result. The most significant bit (MSB) of the magnitude of a signed integer is the bit next to the sign—bit 6 of a byte, bit 14 of a word, or bit 30 of a doubleword. The OF flag is set in either of these cases:

- A carry was generated from the MSB into the sign bit but no carry was generated out of the sign bit (addition instructions ADD, ADC, INC, AAA, and DAA). In other words, the result was greater than the greatest positive number which could be represented in two's complement form.

- A carry was generated from the sign bit into the MSB but no carry was generated into the sign bit (subtraction instructions SUB, SBB, DEC, AAS, DAS, CMP, and NEG). In other words, the result was smaller than the smallest negative number which could be represented in two's complement form.

These status flags are tested by either kind of conditional instruction: Jcc (jump on condition cc) or SETcc (byte set on condition).

4.2.1. Addition and Subtraction Instructions

ADD (Add Integers) replaces the destination operand with the sum of the source and destination operands. The OF, SF, ZF, AF, PF, and CF flags are affected.

ADC (Add Integers with Carry) replaces the destination operand with the sum of the source and destination operands, plus 1 if the CF flag is set. If the CF flag is clear, the ADC instruction performs the same operation as the ADD instruction. An ADC instruction is used to propagate carry when adding numbers in stages, for example when using 32-bit ADD instructions to sum quadword operands. The OF, SF, ZF, AF, PF, and CF flags are affected.

INC (Increment) adds 1 to the destination operand. The INC instruction preserves the state of the CF flag. This allows the use of INC instructions to update counters in loops without disturbing the status flags resulting from an arithmetic operation used for loop control. The ZF flag can be used to detect when carry would have occurred. Use an ADD instruction with an immediate value of 1 to perform an increment which updates the CF flag. A one-byte form of this instruction is available when the operand is a general register. The OF, SF, ZF, AF, and PF flags are affected.

SUB (Subtract Integers) subtracts the source operand from the destination operand and replaces the destination operand with the result. If a borrow is required, the CF flag is set. The operands may be signed or unsigned bytes, words, or doublewords. The OF, SF, ZF, AF, PF, and CF flags are affected.

SBB (Subtract Integers with Borrow) subtracts the source operand from the destination operand and replaces the destination operand with the result, minus 1 if the CF flag is set. If the CF flag is clear, the SBB instruction performs the same operation as the SUB instruction. An SBB instruction is used to propagate borrow when subtracting numbers in stages, for example when using 32-bit SUB instructions to subtract one quadword operand from another. The OF, SF, ZF, AF, PF, and CF flags are affected.

DEC (Decrement) subtracts 1 from the destination operand. The DEC instruction preserves the state of the CF flag. This allows the use of the DEC instruction to update counters in loops without disturbing the status flags resulting from an arithmetic operation used for loop control. Use a SUB instruction with an immediate value of 1 to perform a decrement which updates the CF flag. A one-byte form of this instruction is available when the operand is a general register. The OF, SF, ZF, AF, and PF flags are affected.

4.2.2. Comparison and Sign Change Instruction

CMP (Compare) subtracts the source operand from the destination operand. It updates the OF, SF, ZF, AF, PF, and CF flags, but does not modify the source or destination operands. A subsequent J*cc* or SET*cc* instruction can test the flags.

NEG (Negate) subtracts a signed integer operand from zero. The effect of the NEG instruction is to change the sign of a two's complement operand while keeping its magnitude. The OF, SF, ZF, AF, PF, and CF flags are affected.

4.2.3. Multiplication Instructions

The processor has separate multiply instructions for unsigned and signed operands. The MUL instruction operates on unsigned integers, while the IMUL instruction operates on signed integers as well as unsigned.

MUL (Unsigned Integer Multiply) performs an unsigned multiplication of the source operand and the AL, AX, or EAX register. If the source is a byte, the processor multiplies it by the value held in the AL register and returns the double-length result in the AH and AL registers. If the source operand is a word, the processor multiplies it by the value held in the AX register and returns the double-length result in the DX and AX registers. If the source operand is a doubleword, the processor multiplies it by the value held in the EAX register and returns the quadword result in the EDX and EAX registers. The MUL instruction sets the CF and OF flags when the upper half of the result is non-zero; otherwise, the flags are cleared. The state of the SF, ZF, AF, and PF flags is undefined.

IMUL (Signed Integer Multiply) performs a signed multiplication operation. The IMUL instruction has three forms:

1. A one-operand form. The operand may be a byte, word, or doubleword located in memory or in a general register. This instruction uses the EAX and EDX (or AX and DX) registers as implicit operands in the same way as the MUL instruction.

2. A two-operand form. One of the source operands is in a general register while the other may be in a general register or memory. The result replaces the general-register operand.

3. A three-operand form; two are source operands and one is the destination. One of the source operands is an immediate value supplied by the instruction; the second may be in memory or in a general register. The result is stored in a general register. The immediate operand is a two's complement signed integer. If the immediate operand is a byte, the processor automatically sign-extends it to the size of the second operand before performing the multiplication.

The three forms are similar in most respects:

- The length of the product is calculated to twice the length of the operands.

- The CF and OF flags are set when significant bits are carried into the upper half of the result. The CF and OF flags are cleared when the upper half of the result is the sign-extension of the lower half. The state of the SF, ZF, AF, and PF flags is undefined.

However, forms 2 and 3 differ from 1 because the product is truncated to the length of the operands before it is stored in the destination register. Because of this truncation, the OF flag should be tested to ensure that no significant bits are lost. (For ways to test the OF flag, see the JO, INTO, and PUSHF instructions.)

Forms 2 and 3 of IMUL also may be used with unsigned operands because, whether the operands are signed or unsigned, the lower half of the product is the same. The CF and OF flags, however, cannot be used to determine if the upper half of the result is non-zero.

4.2.4. Division Instructions

The Pentium processor has separate division instructions for unsigned and signed operands. The DIV instruction operates on unsigned integers, while the IDIV instruction operates on both signed and unsigned integers. In either case, a divide-error exception is generated if the divisor is zero or if the quotient is too large for the AL, AX, or EAX register.

DIV (Unsigned Integer Divide) performs an unsigned division of the AL, AX, or EAX register by the source operand. The dividend (the accumulator) is twice the size of the divisor (the source operand); the quotient and remainder have the same size as the divisor, as shown in Table 4-1.

Non-integral results are truncated toward 0. The remainder is always smaller than the divisor. For unsigned byte division, the largest quotient is 255. For unsigned word division, the largest quotient is 65,535. For unsigned doubleword division the largest quotient is $2^{32}-1$. The state of the OF, SF, ZF, AF, PF, and CF flags is undefined.

IDIV (Signed Integer Divide) performs a signed division of the accumulator by the source operand. The IDIV instruction uses the same registers as the DIV instruction.

For signed byte division, the maximum positive quotient is +127, and the minimum negative quotient is −128. For signed word division, the maximum positive quotient is +32,767, and the minimum negative quotient is −32,768. For signed doubleword division the maximum positive quotient is $2^{31}-1$, the minimum negative quotient is -2^{31}. Non-integral results are truncated towards 0. The remainder always has the same sign as the dividend and is less than the divisor in magnitude. The state of the OF, SF, ZF, AF, PF, and CF flags is undefined.

Table 4-1. Operands for Division

Operand Size (Divisor)	Dividend	Quotient	Remainder
Byte	AX register	AL register	AH register
Word	DX and AX	AX register	DX register
Doubleword	EDX and EAX	EAX register	EDX register

4.3. DECIMAL ARITHMETIC INSTRUCTIONS

Decimal arithmetic is performed by combining the binary arithmetic instructions (already discussed in the prior section) with the decimal arithmetic instructions. The decimal arithmetic instructions are used in one of the following ways:

- To adjust the results of a previous binary arithmetic operation to produce a valid packed or unpacked decimal result.

- To adjust the inputs to a subsequent binary arithmetic operation so that the operation will produce a valid packed or unpacked decimal result.

These instructions operate only on the AL or AH registers. Most use the AF flag.

4.3.1.   Packed BCD Adjustment Instructions

DAA (Decimal Adjust after Addition) adjusts the result of adding two valid packed decimal operands in the AL register. A DAA instruction must follow the addition of two pairs of packed decimal numbers (one digit in each half-byte) to obtain a pair of valid packed decimal digits as results. The CF flag is set if a carry occurs. The SF, ZF, AF, PF, and CF flags are affected. The state of the OF flag is undefined.

DAS (Decimal Adjust after Subtraction) adjusts the result of subtracting two valid packed decimal operands in the AL register. A DAS instruction must always follow the subtraction of one pair of packed decimal numbers (one digit in each half-byte) from another to obtain a pair of valid packed decimal digits as results. The CF flag is set if a borrow is needed. The SF, ZF, AF, PF, and CF flags are affected. The state of the OF flag is undefined.

4.3.2.   Unpacked BCD Adjustment Instructions

AAA (ASCII Adjust after Addition) changes the contents of the AL register to a valid unpacked decimal number, and clears the upper 4 bits. An AAA instruction must follow the addition of two unpacked decimal operands in the AL register. The CF flag is set and the contents of the AH register are incremented if a carry occurs. The AF and CF flags are affected. The state of the OF, SF, ZF, and PF flags is undefined.

AAS (ASCII Adjust after Subtraction) changes the contents of the AL register to a valid unpacked decimal number, and clears the upper 4 bits. An AAS instruction must follow the subtraction of one unpacked decimal operand from another in the AL register. The CF flag is set and the contents of the AH register are decremented if a borrow is needed. The AF and CF flags are affected. The state of the OF, SF, ZF, and PF flags is undefined.

AAM (ASCII Adjust after Multiplication) corrects the result of a multiplication of two valid unpacked decimal numbers. An AAM instruction must follow the multiplication of two decimal numbers to produce a valid decimal result. The upper digit is left in the AH register, the lower digit in the AL register. The SF, ZF, and PF flags are affected. The state of the AF, OF, and CF flags is undefined.

AAD (ASCII Adjust before Division) modifies the numerator in the AH and AL registers to prepare for the division of two valid unpacked decimal operands, so that the quotient produced by the division will be a valid unpacked decimal number. The AH register should contain the upper digit and the AL register should contain the lower digit. This instruction adjusts the value and places the result in the AL register. The AH register will be clear. The SF, ZF, and PF flags are affected. The state of the AF, OF, and CF flags is undefined.

4.4.   LOGICAL INSTRUCTIONS

The logical instructions have two operands. Source operands can be immediate values, general registers, or memory. Destination operands can be general registers or memory (except when the source operand is in memory). The logical instructions modify the state of the flags. Short forms of the instructions are available when an immediate source operand is applied to a destination operand in the AL, AX, or EAX registers. The group of logical instructions includes:

- Boolean operation instructions.
- Bit test and modify instructions.
- Bit scan instructions.
- Rotate and shift instructions.
- Byte set on condition.

4.4.1. Boolean Operation Instructions

The logical operations are performed by the AND, OR, XOR, and NOT instructions.

NOT (Not) inverts the bits in the specified operand to form a one's complement of the operand. The NOT instruction is a unary operation which uses a single operand in a register or memory. NOT has no effect on the flags.

The AND, OR, and XOR instructions perform the standard logical operations "and", "or", and "exclusive or". These instructions can use the following combinations of operands:

- Two register operands.
- A general register operand with a memory operand.
- An immediate operand with either a general register operand or a memory operand.

The AND, OR, and XOR instructions clear the OF and CF flags, leave the AF flag undefined, and update the SF, ZF, and PF flags.

4.4.2. Bit Test and Modify Instructions

This group of instructions operates on a single bit which can be in memory or in a general register. The location of the bit is specified as an offset from the low end of the operand. The value of the offset either may be given by an immediate byte in the instruction or may be contained in a general register.

These instructions first assign the value of the selected bit to the CF flag. Then a new value is assigned to the selected bit, as determined by the operation. The state of the OF, SF, ZF, AF, and PF flags is undefined. Table 4-2 defines these instructions.

Table 4-2. Bit Test and Modify Instructions

Instruction	Effect on CF Flag	Effect on Selected Bit
BT (Bit Test)	CF flag ← Selected Bit	no effect
BTS (Bit Test and Set)	CF flag ← Selected Bit	Selected Bit ← 1
BTR (Bit Test and Reset)	CF flag ← Selected Bit	Selected Bit ← 0
BTC (Bit Test and Complement)	CF flag ← Selected Bit	Selected Bit ← − (Selected Bit)

4.4.3. Bit Scan Instructions

These instructions scan a word or doubleword for a set bit and store the bit index (an integer representing the bit position) of the first set bit into a register. The bit string being scanned may be in a register or in memory. The ZF flag is set if the entire word is clear, otherwise the ZF flag is cleared. In the former case, the value of the destination register is left undefined. The state of the OF, SF, AF, PF, and CF flags is undefined.

BSF (Bit Scan Forward) scans low-to-high (from bit 0 toward the upper bit positions).

BSR (Bit Scan Reverse) scans high-to-low (from the uppermost bit toward bit 0).

4.4.4. Shift and Rotate Instructions

The shift and rotate instructions rearrange the bits within an operand.

These instructions fall into the following classes:

- Shift instructions.
- Double shift instructions.
- Rotate instructions.

4.4.4.1. SHIFT INSTRUCTIONS

Shift instructions apply an arithmetic or logical shift to bytes, words, and doublewords. An arithmetic shift right copies the sign bit into empty bit positions on the upper end of the operand, while a logical shift right fills high order empty bit positions with zeros. An arithmetic shift is a fast way to perform a simple calculation. For example, an arithmetic shift right by one bit position divides an integer by two. A logical shift right divides an unsigned integer or a positive integer, but a signed negative integer loses its sign bit.

The arithmetic and logical shift right instructions, SAR and SHR, differ only in their treatment of the bit positions emptied by shifting the contents of the operand. Note that there is no difference between an arithmetic shift left and a logical shift left. Two names, SAL and SHL, are supported for this instruction in the assembler.

A count specifies the number of bit positions to shift an operand. Bits can be shifted up to 31 places. A shift instruction can give the count in any of three ways. One form of shift instruction always shifts by one bit position. The second form gives the count as an immediate operand. The third form gives the count as the value contained in the CL register. This last form allows the count to be a result from a calculation. Only the low five bits of the CL register are used.

When the number of bit positions to shift is zero, no flags are affected. Otherwise, the CF flag is left with the value of the last bit shifted out of the operand. In a single-bit shift, the OF flag is set if the value of the uppermost bit (sign bit) was changed by the operation. Otherwise, the OF flag is cleared. After a shift of more than one bit position, the state of the OF flag is undefined. On a shift of one or more bit positions, the SF, ZF, PF, and CF flags are affected. On a shift of one or more bit positions the state of the AF flag is undefined. If the count length is greater than or equal to the size of the operand, the value of the CF flag is undefined.

SAL (Shift Arithmetic Left) shifts the destination byte, word, or doubleword operand left by one bit position or by the number of bits specified in the count operand (an immediate value or a value contained in the CL register). Empty bit positions are cleared. See Figure 4-6.

SHL (Shift Logical Left) is another name for the SAL instruction. It is supported in the assembler.

SHR (Shift Logical Right) shifts the destination byte, word, or doubleword operand right by one bit position or by the number of bits specified in the count operand (an immediate value or a value contained in the CL register). Empty bit positions are cleared. See Figure 4-7.

SAR (Shift Arithmetic Right) shifts the destination byte, word, or doubleword operand to the right by one bit position or by the number of bits specified in the count operand (an immediate value or a value contained in the CL register). The sign of the operand is preserved by clearing empty bit positions if the operand is positive, or setting the empty bits if the operand is negative. See Figure 4-8.

Even though this instruction can be used to divide integers by an integer power of two, **the type of division is not the same as that produced by the IDIV instruction**. The quotient from the IDIV instruction is rounded toward zero, whereas the "quotient" of the SAR instruction is rounded toward negative infinity. This difference is apparent only for negative numbers. For example, when the IDIV instruction is used to divide –9 by 4, the result is –2 with a remainder of –1. If the SAR instruction is used to shift –9 right by two bits, the result is –3. The "remainder" of this kind of division is +3; however, the SAR instruction stores only the high-order bit of the remainder (in the CF flag).

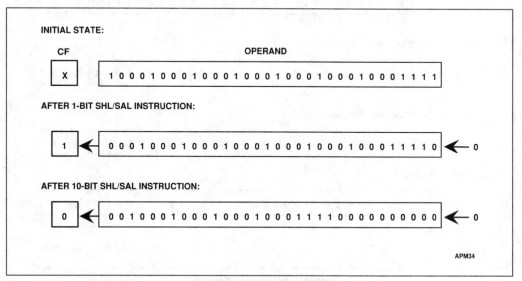

Figure 4-6. SHL/SAL Instruction

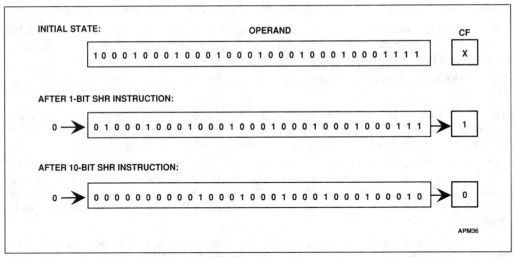

Figure 4-7. SHR Instruction

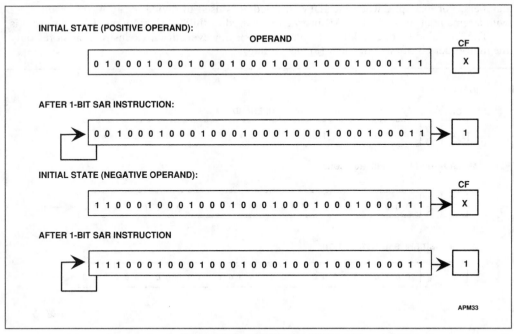

Figure 4-8. SAR Instruction

4.4.4.2.   DOUBLE-SHIFT INSTRUCTIONS

These instructions provide the basic operations needed to implement operations on long unaligned bit strings. The double shifts operate either on word or doubleword operands, as follows:

- Take two word operands and produce a one-word result (32-bit shift).
- Take two doubleword operands and produce a doubleword result (64-bit shift).

Of the two operands, the source operand must be in a register while the destination operand may be in a register or in memory. The number of bits to be shifted is specified either in the CL register or in an immediate byte in the instruction. Bits shifted out of the source operand fill empty bit positions in the destination operand, which also is shifted. Only the destination operand is stored.

When the number of bit positions to shift is zero, no flags are affected. Otherwise, the CF flag is set to the value of the last bit shifted out of the destination operand, and the SF, ZF, and PF flags are affected. On a shift of one bit position, the OF flag is set if the sign of the operand changed, otherwise it is cleared. For shifts of more than one bit position, the state of the OF flag is undefined. For shifts of one or more bit positions, the state of AF flag is undefined.

SHLD (Shift Left Double) shifts bits of the destination operand to the left, while filling empty bit positions with bits shifted out of the source operand (see Figure 4-9). The result is stored back into the destination operand. The source operand is not modified.

SHRD (Shift Right Double) shifts bits of the destination operand to the right, while filling empty bit positions with bits shifted out of the source operand (see Figure 4-10). The result is stored back into the destination operand. The source operand is not modified.

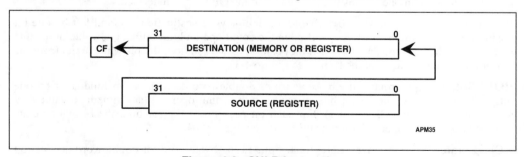

Figure 4-9. SHLD Instruction

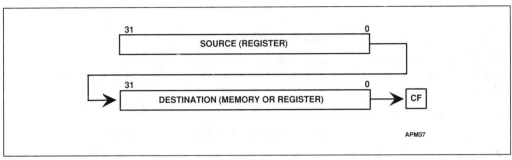

APM37

Figure 4-10. SHRD Instruction

4.4.4.3. ROTATE INSTRUCTIONS

Rotate instructions apply a circular permutation to bytes, words, and doublewords. Bits rotated out of one end of an operand enter through the other end. Unlike a shift, no bits are emptied during a rotation.

Rotate instructions use only the CF and OF flags. The CF flag may act as an extension of the operand in two of the rotate instructions, allowing a bit to be isolated and then tested by a conditional jump instruction (JC or JNC). The CF flag always contains the value of the last bit rotated out of the operand, even if the instruction does not use the CF flag as an extension of the operand. The state of the SF, ZF, AF, and PF flags is not affected.

In a single-bit rotation, the OF flag is set if the operation changes the uppermost bit (sign bit) of the destination operand. If the sign bit retains its original value, the OF flag is cleared. After a rotate of more than one bit position, the value of the OF flag is undefined.

ROL (Rotate Left) rotates the byte, word, or doubleword destination operand left by one bit position or by the number of bits specified in the count operand (an immediate value or a value contained in the CL register). For each bit position of the rotation, the bit which exits from the left of the operand returns at the right. See Figure 4-11.

ROR (Rotate Right) rotates the byte, word, or doubleword destination operand right by one bit position or by the number of bits specified in the count operand (an immediate value or a value contained in the CL register). For each bit position of the rotation, the bit which exits from the right of the operand returns at the left. See Figure 4-12.

RCL (Rotate Through Carry Left) rotates bits in the byte, word, or doubleword destination operand left by one bit position or by the number of bits specified in the count operand (an immediate value or a value contained in the CL register).

This instruction differs from ROL in that it treats the CF flag as a one-bit extension on the upper end of the destination operand. Each bit which exits from the left side of the operand moves into the CF flag. At the same time, the bit in the CF flag enters the right side. See Figure 4-13.

RCR (Rotate Through Carry Right) rotates bits in the byte, word, or doubleword destination operand right by one bit position or by the number of bits specified in the count operand (an immediate value or a value contained in the CL register).

This instruction differs from ROR in that it treats CF as a one-bit extension on the lower end of the destination operand. Each bit which exits from the right side of the operand moves into the CF flag. At the same time, the bit in the CF flag enters the left side. See Figure 4-14.

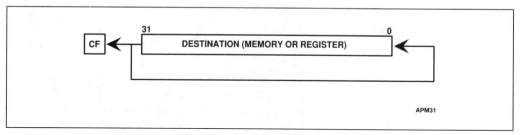

Figure 4-11. ROL Instruction

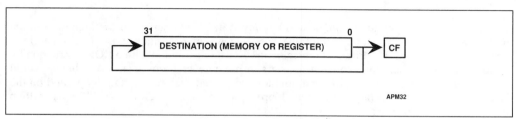

Figure 4-12. ROR Instruction

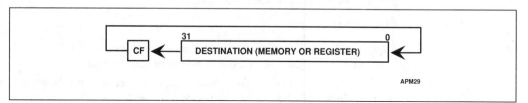

Figure 4-13. RCL Instruction

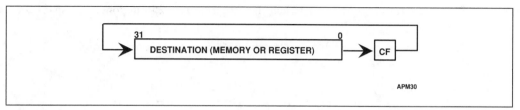

Figure 4-14. RCR Instruction

4.4.4.4.   FAST "bit blt" USING DOUBLE-SHIFT INSTRUCTIONS

One purpose of the double shift instructions is to implement a bit string move, with arbitrary misalignment of the bit strings. This is called a "bit blt" (BIT BLock Transfer). A simple example is to move a bit string from an arbitrary offset into a doubleword-aligned byte string. A left-to-right string is moved 32 bits at a time if a double shift is used inside the move loop.

```
        MOV     ESI,ScrAddr
        MOV     EDI,DestAddr
        MOV     EBX,DWordCnt
        MOV     CL,RelOffset    ; relative offset Dest-Src
        MOV     EDX,[ESI]       ; load first dword of source
        ADD     ESI,4           ; bump source address
BltLoop:
        LODSD                   ; new low order part in EAX
        SHLD    EDX,EAX,CL      ; EDX overwritten with aligned stuff
        XCHG    EDX,EAX         ; Swap high and low dwords
        STOSD                   ; Write out next aligned chunk
        DEC     EBX             ; Decrement loop count
        JNZ     BltLoop
```

This loop is simple, yet allows the data to be moved in 32-bit chunks for the highest possible performance. Without a double shift, the best which can be achieved is 16 bits per loop iteration by using a 32-bit shift, and replacing the XCHG instruction with a ROR instruction by 16 to swap the high and low words of registers. A more general loop than shown above would require some extra masking on the first doubleword moved (before the main loop), and on the last doubleword moved (after the main loop), but would have the same 32-bits per loop iteration as the code above.

4.4.4.5.   FAST BIT STRING INSERT AND EXTRACT

The double shift instructions also make possible:

- Fast insertion of a bit string from a register into an arbitrary bit location in a larger bit string in memory, without disturbing the bits on either side of the inserted bits

- Fast extraction of a bit string into a register from an arbitrary bit location in a larger bit string in memory, without disturbing the bits on either side of the extracted bits

The following coded examples illustrate bit insertion and extraction under various conditions:

1. Bit String Insertion into Memory (when the bit string is 1-25 bits long, i.e., spans four bytes or less):

```
; Insert a right-justified bit string from a register into
; a bit string in memory.
;
; Assumptions:
; 1. The base of the string array is doubleword aligned.
; 2. The length of the bit string is an immediate value
;     and the bit offset is held in a register.
;
; The ESI register holds the right-justified bit string
; to be inserted.
; The EDI register holds the bit offset of the start of the
```

```
; substring.
; The EAX register and ECX are also used.
;
MOV    ECX,EDI              ; save original offset
SHR    EDI,3               ; divide offset by 8 (byte addr)
AND    CL,7H               ; get low three bits of offset
MOV    EAX, [EDI]strg_base  ; move string dword into EAX
ROR    EAX,CL              ; right justify old bit field
SHRD   EAX,ESI,length      ; bring in new bits
ROL    EAX,length          ; right justify new bit field
ROL    EAX,CL              ; bring to final position
MOV    [EDI]strg_base,EAX   ; replace doubleword in memory
```

2. Bit String Insertion into Memory (when the bit string is 1-31 bits long, i.e., spans five bytes or less):

```
; Insert a right-justified bit string from a register into
; a bit string in memory.
;
; Assumptions:
; 1. The base of the string array is doubleword aligned.
; 2. The length of the bit string is an immediate value
;    and the bit offset is held in a register.
;
; The ESI register holds the right-justified bit string
; to be inserted.
; The EDI register holds the bit offset of the start of the
; substring.
; The EAX, EBX, ECX, and EDI registers also are used.
;
MOV    ECX,EDI               ; temp storage for offset
SHR    EDI,5                 ; divide offset by 32 (dwords)
SHL    EDI,2                 ; multiply by 4 (byte address)
AND    CL,1FH                ; get low five bits of offset
MOV    EAX,[EDI]strg_base    ; move low string dword into EAX
MOV    EDX,[EDI]strg_base+4  ; other string dword into EDX
MOV    EBX,EAX               ; temp storage for part of string
SHRD   EAX,EDX,CL            ; shift by offset within dword
SHRD   EAX,EBX,CL            ; shift by offset within dword
SHRD   EAX,ESI,length        ; bring in new bits
ROL    EAX,length            ; right justify new bit field
MOV    EBX,EAX               ; temp storage for string
SHLD   EAX,EDX,CL            ; shift by offset within dword
SHLD   EDX,EBX,CL            ; shift by offset within dword
MOV    [EDI]strg_base,EAX    ; replace dword in memory
MOV    [EDI]strg_base+4,EDX  ; replace dword in memory
```

3. Bit String Insertion into Memory (when the bit string is exactly 32 bits long, i.e., spans four or five bytes):

```
; Insert right-justified bit string from a register into
```

```
; a bit string in memory.
;
; Assumptions:
; 1. The base of the string array is doubleword aligned.
; 2. The length of the bit string is 32 bits
;      and the bit offset is held in a register.
;
; The ESI register holds the 32-bit string to be inserted.
; The EDI register holds the bit offset to the start of the
; substring.
; The EAX, EBX, ECX, and EDI registers also are used.
;
MOV    EDX,EDI                 ; save original offset
SHR    EDI,5                   ; divide offset by 32 (dwords)
SHL    EDI,2                   ; multiply by 4 (byte address)
AND    CL,1FH                  ; isolate low five bits of offset
MOV    EAX,[EDI]strg_base      ; move low string dword into EAX
MOV    EDX,[EDI]strg_base+4    ; other string dword into EDX
MOV    EBX,EAX                 ; temp storage for part of string
SHRD   EAX,EDX                 ; shift by offset within dword
SHRD   EDX,EBX                 ; shift by offset within dword
MOV    EAX,ESI                 ; move 32-bit field into position
MOV    EBX,EAX                 ; temp storage for part of string
SHLD   EAX,EDX                 ; shift by offset within dword
SHLD   EDX,EBX                 ; shift by offset within dword
MOV    [EDI]strg_base,EAX      ; replace dword in memory
MOV    [EDI]strg_base,+4,EDX   ; replace dword in memory
```

4. Bit string Extraction from Memory (when the bit string is 1-25 bits long, i.e., spans four bytes or less):

```
; Extract a right-justified bit string into a register from
; a bit string in memory.
;
; Assumptions:
; 1) The base of the string array is doubleword aligned.
; 2) The length of the bit string is an immediate value
;      and the bit offset is held in a register.
;
; The EAX register hold the right-justified, zero-padded
; bit string that was extracted.
; The EDI register holds the bit offset of the start of the
; substring.
; The EDI, and ECX registers also are used.
;
MOV    ECX,EDI             ; temp storage for offset
SHR    EDI,3               ; divide offset by 8 (byte addr)
AND    CL,7H               ; get low three bits of offset
MOV    EAX,[EDI]strg_base  ; move string dword into EAX
SHR    EAX,CL              ; shift by offset within dword
AND    EAX,mask            ; extracted bit field in EAX
```

5. Bit string Extraction from Memory (when bit string is 1-32 bits long, i.e., spans five bytes or less):

```
; Extract a right-justified bit string into a register from
; bit string in memory.
;
; Assumptions:
; 1) The base of the string array is doubleword aligned.
; 2) The length of the bit string is an immediate
;    value and the bit offset is held in a register.
;
; The EAX register holds the right-justified, zero-padded
; bit string that was extracted.
; The EDI register holds the bit offset of the start of the
; substring.
; The EAX, EBX, and ECX registers also are used.
;
MOV     ECX,EDI                  ; temp storage for offset
SHR     EDI,5                    ; divide offset by 32 (dwords)
SHL     EDI,2                    ; multiply by 4 (byte address)
AND     CL,1FH                   ; get low five bits of offset in
MOV     EAX,[EDI]strg_base       ; move low string dword into EAX
MOV     EDX,[EDI]strg_base +4    ; other string dword into EDX
SHRD    EAX,EDX,CL               ; shift right by offset in dword
AND     EAX,mask                 ; extracted bit field in EAX
```

4.4.5.   Byte-Set-On-Condition Instructions

This group of instructions sets a byte to the value of zero or one, depending on any of the 16 conditions defined by the status flags. The byte may be in a register or in memory. These instructions are especially useful for implementing Boolean expressions in high-level languages such as Pascal.

Some languages represent a logical one as an integer with all bits set. This can be done by using the SETcc instruction with the mutually exclusive condition, then decrementing the result.

SETcc (Set Byte on Condition cc) loads the value 1 into a byte if condition cc is true; clears the byte otherwise. See Appendix D for a definition of the possible conditions.

4.4.6.   Test Instruction

TEST (Test) performs the logical ''and'' of the two operands, clears the OF and CF flags, leaves the AF flag undefined, and updates the SF, ZF, and PF flags. The flags can be tested by conditional control transfer instructions or the byte-set-on-condition instructions. The operands may be bytes, words, or doublewords.

The difference between the TEST and AND instructions is that the TEST instruction does not alter the destination operand. The difference between the TEST and BT instructions is that the

TEST instruction can test the value of multiple bits in one operation, while the BT instruction tests a single bit.

4.5. CONTROL TRANSFER INSTRUCTIONS

The processor provides both conditional and unconditional control transfer instructions to direct the flow of execution. Conditional transfers are taken only for certain combinations of the state of the flags. Unconditional control transfers are always executed.

4.5.1. Unconditional Transfer Instructions

The JMP, CALL, RET, INT, and IRET instructions transfer execution to a destination in a code segment. The destination can be within the same code segment (near transfer) or in a different code segment (far transfer). The forms of these instructions which transfer execution to other segments are discussed in a later section of this chapter. If the model of memory organization used in a particular application does not make segments visible to application programmers, far transfers are not used.

4.5.1.1. JUMP INSTRUCTION

JMP (Jump) unconditionally transfers execution to the destination. The JMP instruction is a one-way transfer of execution; it does not save a return address on the stack.

The JMP instruction transfers execution from the current routine to a different routine. The address of the routine is specified in the instruction, in a register, or in memory. The location of the address determines whether it is interpreted as a relative address or an absolute address.

Relative Address. A relative jump uses a displacement (immediate mode constant used for address calculation) held in the instruction. The displacement is signed and variable-length (byte or doubleword). The destination address is formed by adding the displacement to the address held in the EIP register. The EIP register then contains the address of the next instruction to be executed.

Absolute Address. An absolute jump is used with a 32-bit segment offset in either of the following ways:

1. The program can jump to an address in a general register. This 32-bit value is copied into the EIP register and execution continues.

2. The destination address can be a memory operand specified using the standard addressing modes. The operand is copied into the EIP register and execution continues.

4.5.1.2. CALL INSTRUCTIONS

CALL (Call Procedure) transfers execution and saves the address of the instruction following the CALL instruction for later use by a RET (Return) instruction. CALL pushes the current contents of the EIP register on the stack. The RET instruction in the called procedure uses this address to transfer execution back to the calling program.

CALL instructions, like JMP instructions, have relative and absolute forms.

Indirect CALL instructions specify an absolute address in one of the following ways:

1. The program can jump to an address in a general register. This 32-bit value is copied into the EIP register, the return address is pushed on the stack, and execution continues.
2. The destination address can be a memory operand specified using the standard addressing modes. The operand is copied into the EIP register, the return address is pushed on the stack, and execution continues.

4.5.1.3. RETURN AND RETURN-FROM-INTERRUPT INSTRUCTIONS

RET (Return From Procedure) terminates a procedure and transfers execution to the instruction following the CALL instruction which originally invoked the procedure. The RET instruction restores the contents of the EIP register which were pushed on the stack when the procedure was called.

The RET instructions have an optional immediate operand. When present, this constant is added to the contents of the ESP register, which has the effect of removing any parameters pushed on the stack before the procedure call.

IRET (Return From Interrupt) returns control to an interrupted procedure. The IRET instruction differs from the RET instruction in that it restores the EFLAGS register from the stack. The contents of the EFLAGS register are stored on the stack when an interrupt occurs.

4.5.2. Conditional Transfer Instructions

The conditional transfer instructions are jumps which transfer execution if the states in the EFLAGS register match conditions specified in the instruction.

4.5.2.1. CONDITIONAL JUMP INSTRUCTIONS

Table 4-3 shows the mnemonics for the jump instructions. The instructions listed as pairs are alternate names for the same instruction. The assembler provides these names for greater clarity in program listings.

A form of conditional jump instruction is available which uses a displacement added to the contents of the EIP register if the specified condition is true. The displacement may be a byte or doubleword. The displacement is signed; it can be used to jump forward or backward.

Table 4-3. Conditional Jump Instructions

Mnemonic	Flag States	Description
Unsigned Conditional Jumps		
JA/JNBE	(CF or ZF)=0	above/not below nor equal
JAE/JNB	CF=0	above or equal/not below
JB/JNAE	CF=1	below/not above nor equal
JBE/JNA	(CF o•r ZF)=1	below or equal/not above
JC•	CF=1	carry
JE/JZ	ZF=1	equal/zero
JNC	CF=0	not carry
JNE/JNZ	ZF=0	not equal/not zero
JNP/JPO	PF=0	not parity/parity odd
JP/JPE	PF=1	parity/parity even
Signed Conditional Jumps		
JG/JNLE	((SF xor OF) or ZF) =0	greater/not less nor equal
JGE/JNL	(SF xor OF)=0	greater or equal/not less
JL/JNGE	(SF xor OF)=1	less/not greater nor equal
JLE/JNG	((SF xor OF) or ZF)=1	less or equal/not greater
JNO	OF=0	not overflow
JNS	SF=0	not sign (non-negative)
JO	OF=1	overflow
JS	SF=1	sign (negative)

4.5.2.2. LOOP INSTRUCTIONS

The loop instructions are conditional jumps which use the value of the ECX register as a count for the number of times to run a loop. All loop instructions decrement the contents of the ECX register on each reposition and terminate when zero is reached. Four of the five loop instructions accept the ZF flag as a condition for terminating the loop before the count reaches zero.

LOOP (Loop While ECX Not Zero) is a conditional jump instruction which decrements the contents of the ECX register before testing for the loop-terminating condition. If the contents of the ECX register are non-zero, the program jumps to the destination specified in the instruction. The LOOP instruction causes the execution of a block of code to be repeated until the count reaches zero. When zero is reached, execution is transferred to the instruction immediately following the LOOP instruction. If the value in the ECX register is zero when the instruction is first called, the count is pre-decremented to 0FFFFFFFFH and the LOOP runs 2^{32} times.

LOOPE (Loop While Equal) and **LOOPZ (Loop While Zero)** are synonyms for the same instruction. These instructions are conditional jumps which decrement the contents of the ECX register before testing for the loop-terminating condition. If the contents of the ECX register are non-zero and the ZF flag is set, the program jumps to the destination specified in the instruction. When zero is reached or the ZF flag is clear, execution is transferred to the instruction immediately following the LOOPE/LOOPZ instruction.

LOOPNE (Loop While Not Equal) and **LOOPNZ (Loop While Not Zero)** are synonyms for the same instruction. These instructions are conditional jumps which decrement the contents of the ECX register before testing for the loop-terminating condition. If the contents of the ECX register are non-zero and the ZF flag is clear, the program jumps to the destination specified in the instruction. When zero is reached or the ZF flag is set, execution is transferred to the instruction immediately following the LOOPE/LOOPZ instruction.

4.5.2.3.   EXECUTING A LOOP OR REPEAT ZERO TIMES

JECXZ (Jump if ECX Zero) jumps to the destination specified in the instruction if the ECX register holds a value of zero. The JECXZ instruction is used in combination with the LOOP instruction and with the string scan and compare instructions. Because these instructions decrement the contents of the ECX register before testing for zero, a loop will run 2^{32} times if the loop is entered with a zero value in the ECX register. The JECXZ instruction is used to create loops which fall through without executing when the initial value is zero. A JECXZ instruction at the beginning of a loop can be used to jump out of the loop if the count is zero. When used with repeated string scan and compare instructions, the JECXZ instruction can determine whether the loop terminated due to the count or due to satisfaction of the scan or compare conditions.

4.5.3.   Software Interrupts

The INT, INTO, and BOUND instructions allow the programmer to specify a transfer of execution to an exception or interrupt handler.

INT*n* (Software Interrupt) calls the handler specified by an interrupt vector encoded in the instruction. The INT instruction may specify any interrupt type. This instruction is used to support multiple types of software interrupts or to test the operation of interrupt service routines. The interrupt service routine terminates with an IRET instruction, which returns execution to the instruction following the INT instruction.

INTO (Interrupt on Overflow) calls the handler for the overflow exception, if the OF flag is set. If the flag is clear, execution continues without calling the handler. The OF flag is set by arithmetic, logical, and string instructions. This instruction causes a software interrupt for handling error conditions, such as arithmetic overflow.

BOUND (Detect Value Out of Range) compares the signed value held in a general register against an upper and lower limit. The handler for the bounds-check exception is called if the value held in the register is less than the lower bound or greater than the upper bound. This instruction causes a software interrupt for bounds checking, such as checking an array index to make sure it falls within the range defined for the array.

The BOUND instruction has two operands. The first operand specifies the general register being tested. The second operand is the base address of two words or doublewords at adjacent locations in memory. The lower limit is the word or doubleword with the lower address; the upper limit has the higher address. The BOUND instruction assumes that the upper limit and lower limit are in adjacent memory locations. These limit values cannot be register operands; if they are, an invalid-opcode exception occurs.

The upper and lower limits of an array can reside just before the array itself. This puts the array bounds at a constant offset from the beginning of the array. Because the address of the array already will be present in a register, this practice avoids extra bus cycles to obtain the effective address of the array bounds.

4.6. STRING OPERATIONS

String operations manipulate large data structures in memory, such as alphanumeric character strings. See also the section on I/O for information about the string I/O instructions (also known as block I/O instructions).

The string operations are made by putting string instructions (which execute only one iteration of an operation) together with other features of the instruction set, such as repeat prefixes. The string instructions include:

- MOVS—Move String
- CMPS—Compare string
- SCAS—Scan string
- LODS—Load string
- STOS—Store string

After a string instruction executes, the string source and destination registers point to the next elements in their strings. The string instructions automatically increment or decrement the contents of these registers by the number of bytes occupied by each string element. A string element can be a byte, word, or doubleword. The string registers include:

- ESI—Source index register
- EDI—Destination index register

String operations can begin at higher addresses and work toward lower ones, or they can begin at lower addresses and work toward higher ones. The direction is controlled by:

- DF—Direction flag

If the DF flag is clear, the registers are incremented. If the flag is set, the registers are decremented. These instructions set and clear the flag:

- STD—Set direction flag
- CLD—Clear direction flag

To operate on more than one element of a string, a repeat prefix must be used, such as:

- REP—Repeat while the ECX register not zero
- REPE/REPZ—Repeat while the ECX register not zero and the ZF flag is set
- REPNE/REPNZ—Repeat while the ECX register not zero and the ZF flag is clear

Exceptions or interrupts that occur during a string instruction leave the registers in a state which allows the string instruction to be restarted. The source and destination registers point to the next string elements, the EIP register points to the string instruction, and the ECX register has the value it held following the last successful iteration. All that is necessary to restart the operation is to service the interrupt or fix the source of the exception, then execute an IRET instruction.

4.6.1. Repeat Prefixes

The repeat prefixes **REP (Repeat While ECX Not Zero)**, **REPE/REPZ (Repeat While Equal/Zero)**, and **REPNE/REPNZ (Repeat While Not Equal/Not Zero)** specify repeated operation of a string instruction.

When a string instruction has a repeat prefix, the operation executes until one of the termination conditions specified by the prefix is satisfied.

For each repetition of the instruction, the string operation may be suspended by an exception or interrupt. After the exception or interrupt has been serviced, the string operation can restart where it left off. This mechanism allows long string operations to proceed without affecting the interrupt response time of the system.

All three prefixes shown in Table 4-4 cause the instruction to repeat until the ECX register is decremented to zero, if no other termination condition is satisfied. The repeat prefixes differ in their other termination condition. The REP prefix has no other termination condition. The REPE/REPZ and REPNE/REPNZ prefixes are used exclusively with the SCAS (Scan String) and CMPS (Compare String) instructions. The REPE/REPZ prefix terminates if the ZF flag is clear. The REPNE/REPNZ prefix terminates if the ZF flag is set. The ZF flag does not require initialization before execution of a repeated string instruction, because both the SCAS and CMPS instructions affect the ZF flag according to the results of the comparisons they make.

Table 4-4. Repeat Instructions

Repeat Prefix	Termination Condition 1	Termination Condition 2
REP	ECX=0	none
REPE/REPZ	ECX=0	ZF=0
REPNE/REPNZ	ECX=0	ZF=1

4.6.2. Indexing and Direction Flag Control

Although the general registers are completely interchangeable under most conditions, the string instructions require the use of two specific registers. The source and destination strings are in memory addressed by the ESI and EDI registers. The ESI register points to source operands. By default, the ESI register is used with the DS segment register. A segment-override prefix allows the ESI register to be used with the CS, SS, ES, FS, or GS segment registers. The EDI register points to destination operands. It uses the segment indicated by the ES segment register; no segment override is allowed. The use of two different segment registers in one instruction permits operations between strings in different segments.

When ESI and EDI are used in string instructions, they automatically are incremented or decremented after each iteration. String operations can begin at higher addresses and work toward lower ones, or they can begin at lower addresses and work toward higher ones. The direction is controlled by the DF flag. If the flag is clear, the registers are incremented. If the flag is set, the registers are decremented. The STD and CLD instructions set and clear this flag. Programmers should always put a known value in the DF flag before using a string instruction.

4.6.3. String Instructions

MOVS (Move String) moves the string element addressed by the ESI register to the location addressed by the EDI register. The MOVSB instruction moves bytes, the MOVSW instruction moves words, and the MOVSD instruction moves doublewords. The MOVS instruction, when accompanied by the REP prefix, operates as a memory-to-memory block transfer. To set up this operation, the program must initialize the ECX, ESI, and EDI registers. The ECX register specifies the number of elements in the block.

CMPS (Compare Strings) subtracts the destination string element from the source string element and updates the AF, SF, PF, CF and OF flags. Neither string element is written back to memory. If the string elements are equal, the ZF flag is set; otherwise, it is cleared. CMPSB compares bytes, CMPSW compares words, and CMPSD compares doublewords.

SCAS (Scan String) subtracts the destination string element from the EAX, AX, or AL register (depending on operand length) and updates the AF, SF, ZF, PF, CF and OF flags. The string and the register are not modified. If the values are equal, the ZF flag is set; otherwise, it is cleared. The SCASB instruction scans bytes; the SCASW instruction scans words; the SCASD instruction scans doublewords.

When the REPE/REPZ or REPNE/REPNZ prefix modifies either the SCAS or CMPS instructions, the loop which is formed is terminated by the loop counter or the effect the SCAS or CMPS instruction has on the ZF flag.

LODS (Load String) places the source string element addressed by the ESI register into the EAX register for doubleword strings, into the AX register for word strings, or into the AL register for byte strings. This instruction usually is used in a loop, where other instructions process each element of the string as they appear in the register.

STOS (Store String) places the source string element from the EAX, AX, or AL register into the string addressed by the EDI register. This instruction usually is used in a loop, where it writes to memory the result of processing a string element read from memory with the LODS instruction. A REP STOS instruction is the fastest way to initialize a large block of memory.

4.7. INSTRUCTIONS FOR BLOCK-STRUCTURED LANGUAGES

These instructions provide machine-language support for implementing block-structured languages, such as C and Pascal. They include ENTER and LEAVE, which simplify procedure entry and exit in compiler-generated code. They support a structure of pointers and local variables on the stack called a stack frame.

ENTER (Enter Procedure) creates a stack frame compatible with the scope rules of block-structured languages. In these languages, a procedure has access to its own variables and some number of other variables defined elsewhere in the program. The scope of a procedure is the set of variables to which it has access. The rules for scope vary among languages; they may be based on the nesting of procedures, the division of the program into separately-compiled files, or some other modularization scheme.

The ENTER instruction has two operands. The first specifies the number of bytes to be reserved on the stack for dynamic storage in the procedure being entered. Dynamic storage is the memory allocated for variables created when the procedure is called, also known as automatic variables. The second parameter is the lexical nesting level (from 0 to 31) of the procedure. The nesting level is the depth of a procedure in the hierarchy of a block-structured program. The lexical level has no particular relationship to either the protection privilege level or to the I/O privilege level.

The lexical nesting level determines the number of stack frame pointers to copy into the new stack frame from the preceding frame. A stack frame pointer is a doubleword used to access the variables of a procedure. The set of stack frame pointers used by a procedure to access the variables of other procedures is called the display. The first doubleword in the display is a pointer to the previous stack frame. This pointer is used by a LEAVE instruction to undo the effect of an ENTER instruction by discarding the current stack frame.

Example: ENTER 2048,3

Allocates 2K bytes of dynamic storage on the stack and sets up pointers to two previous stack frames in the stack frame for this procedure.

After the ENTER instruction creates the display for a procedure, it allocates the dynamic (automatic) local variables for the procedure by decrementing the contents of the ESP register by the number of bytes specified in the first parameter. This new value in the ESP register serves as the initial top-of-stack for all PUSH and POP operations within the procedure.

To allow a procedure to address its display, the ENTER instruction leaves the EBP register pointing to the first doubleword in the display. Because stacks grow down, this is actually the doubleword with the highest address in the display. Data manipulation instructions which specify the EBP register as a base register automatically address locations within the stack segment instead of the data segment.

The ENTER instruction can be used in two ways: nested and non-nested. If the lexical level is 0, the non-nested form is used. The non-nested form pushes the contents of the EBP register on the stack, copies the contents of the ESP register into the EBP register, and subtracts the first operand from the contents of the ESP register to allocate dynamic storage. The non-nested form differs from the nested form in that no stack frame pointers are copied. The nested form of the ENTER instruction occurs when the second parameter (lexical level) is not zero.

The psuedo code in Example 4-1 shows the formal definition of the ENTER instruction. STORAGE is the number of bytes of dynamic storage to allocate for local variables, and LEVEL is the lexical nesting level.

Example 4-1. ENTER Definition

```
Push EBP
Set a temporary value FRAME_PTR := ESP
If LEVEL > 0 then
    Repeat LEVEL-1 times
        EBP := EBP-4
        Push the doubleword pointed to by EBP
    End Repeat
    Push FRAME_PTR
End if
EBP := FRAME_PTR
ESP := ESP-STORAGE
```

The main procedure (in which all other procedures are nested) operates at the highest lexical level, level 1. The first procedure it calls operates at the next deeper lexical level, level 2. A level 2 procedure can access the variables of the main program, which are at fixed locations specified by the compiler. In the case of level 1, the ENTER instruction allocates only the requested dynamic storage on the stack because there is no previous display to copy.

A procedure which calls another procedure at a lower lexical level gives the called procedure access to the variables of the caller. The ENTER instruction provides this access by placing a pointer to the calling procedure's stack frame in the display.

A procedure which calls another procedure at the same lexical level should not give access to its variables. In this case, the ENTER instruction copies only that part of the display from the calling procedure which refers to previously nested procedures operating at higher lexical levels. The new stack frame does not include the pointer for addressing the calling procedure's stack frame.

The ENTER instruction treats a re-entrant procedure as a call to a procedure at the same lexical level. In this case, each succeeding iteration of the re-entrant procedure can address only its own variables and the variables of the procedures within which it is nested. A re-entrant procedure always can address its own variables; it does not require pointers to the stack frames of previous iterations.

By copying only the stack frame pointers of procedures at higher lexical levels, the ENTER instruction makes certain that procedures access only those variables of higher lexical levels, not those at parallel lexical levels (see Figure 4-15).

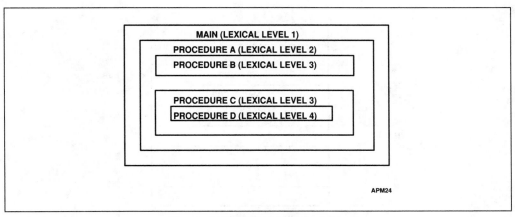

Figure 4-15. Nested Procedures

Block-structured languages can use the lexical levels defined by ENTER to control access to the variables of nested procedures. In the figure, for example, if PROCEDURE A calls PROCEDURE B which, in turn, calls PROCEDURE C, then PROCEDURE C will have access to the variables of MAIN and PROCEDURE A, but not those of PROCEDURE B because they are at the same lexical level. The following definition describes the access to variables for the nested procedures in Figure 4-15.

1. MAIN has variables at fixed locations.

2. PROCEDURE A can access only the variables of MAIN.

3. PROCEDURE B can access only the variables of PROCEDURE A and MAIN. PROCEDURE B cannot access the variables of PROCEDURE C or PROCEDURE D.

4. PROCEDURE C can access only the variables of PROCEDURE A and MAIN. PROCEDURE C cannot access the variables of PROCEDURE B or PROCEDURE D.

5. PROCEDURE D can access the variables of PROCEDURE C, PROCEDURE A, and MAIN. PROCEDURE D cannot access the variables of PROCEDURE B.

In Figure 4-16, an ENTER instruction at the beginning of the MAIN program creates three doublewords of dynamic storage for MAIN, but copies no pointers from other stack frames. The first doubleword in the display holds a copy of the last value in the EBP register before the ENTER instruction was executed. The second doubleword (which, because stacks grow down, is stored at a lower address) holds a copy of the contents of the EBP register following the ENTER instruction. After the instruction is executed, the EBP register points to the first doubleword pushed on the stack, and the ESP register points to the last doubleword in the stack frame.

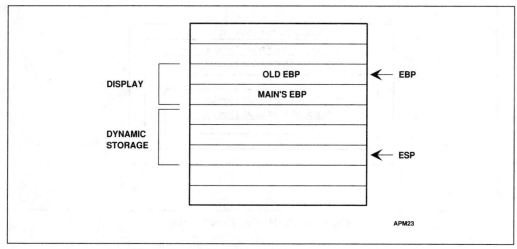

Figure 4-16. Stack Frame After Entering MAIN

When MAIN calls PROCEDURE A, the ENTER instruction creates a new display (see Figure 4-17). The first doubleword is the last value held in MAIN's EBP register. The second doubleword is a pointer to MAIN's stack frame which is copied from the second doubleword in MAIN's display. This happens to be another copy of the last value held in MAIN's EBP register. PROCEDURE A can access variables in MAIN because MAIN is at level 1. Therefore the base address for the dynamic storage used in MAIN is the current address in the EBP register, plus four bytes to account for the saved contents of MAIN's EBP register. All dynamic variables for MAIN are at fixed, positive offsets from this value.

When PROCEDURE A calls PROCEDURE B, the ENTER instruction creates a new display. (See Figure 4-18). The first doubleword holds a copy of the last value in PROCEDURE A's EBP register. The second and third doublewords are copies of the two stack frame pointers in PROCEDURE A's display. PROCEDURE B can access variables in PROCEDURE A and MAIN by using the stack frame pointers in its display.

When PROCEDURE B calls PROCEDURE C, the ENTER instruction creates a new display for PROCEDURE C. (See Figure 4-19). The first doubleword holds a copy of the last value in PROCEDURE B's EBP register. This is used by the LEAVE instruction to restore PROCEDURE B's stack frame. The second and third doublewords are copies of the two stack frame pointers in PROCEDURE A's display. If PROCEDURE C were at the next deeper lexical level from PROCEDURE B, a fourth doubleword would be copied, which would be the stack frame pointer to PROCEDURE B's local variables.

Note that PROCEDURE B and PROCEDURE C are at the same level, so PROCEDURE C is not intended to access PROCEDURE B's variables. This does not mean that PROCEDURE C is completely isolated from PROCEDURE B; PROCEDURE C is called by PROCEDURE B, so the pointer to the returning stack frame is a pointer to PROCEDURE B's stack frame. In addition, PROCEDURE B can pass parameters to PROCEDURE C either on the stack or through variables global to both procedures (i.e., variables in the scope of both procedures).

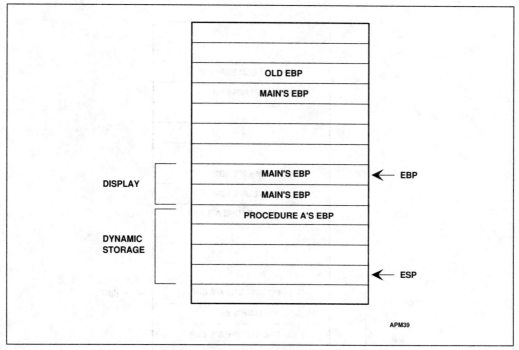

Figure 4-17. Stack Frame After Entering PROCEDURE A

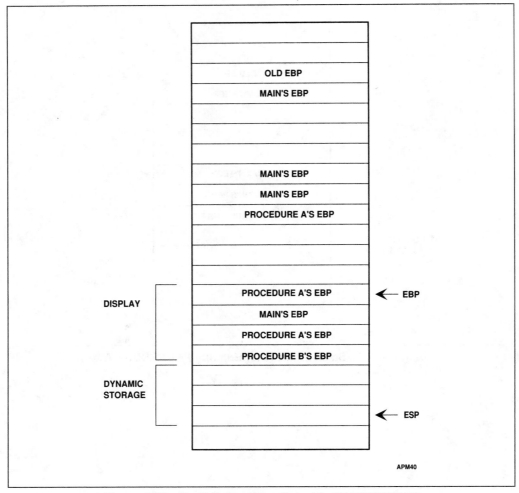

Figure 4-18. Stack Frame After Entering PROCEDURE B

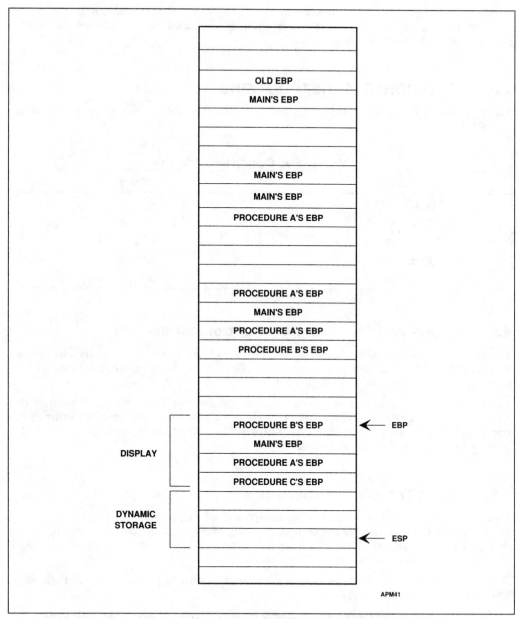

Figure 4-19. Stack Frame After Entering PROCEDURE C

LEAVE (Leave Procedure) reverses the action of the previous ENTER instruction. The LEAVE instruction does not have any operands. The LEAVE instruction copies the contents of the EBP register into the ESP register to release all stack space allocated to the procedure. Then the LEAVE instruction restores the old value of the EBP register from the stack. This simultaneously restores the ESP register to its original value. A subsequent RET instruction then can remove any arguments and the return address pushed on the stack by the calling program for use by the procedure.

4.8. FLAG CONTROL INSTRUCTIONS

The flag control instructions change the state of bits in the EFLAGS register, as shown in Table 4-5.

Table 4-5. Flag Control Instructions

Instruction	Effect
STC (Set Carry Flag)	CF ← 1
CLC (Clear Carry Flag)	CF ← 0
CMC (Complement Carry Flag)	CF ← – CF
CLD (Clear Direction Flag)	DF ← 0
STD (Set Direction Flag)	DF ← 1

4.8.1. Carry and Direction Flag Control Instructions

The carry flag instructions are useful with instructions like the rotate-with-carry instructions RCL and RCR. They can initialize the carry flag, CF, to a known state before execution of an instruction which copies the flag into an operand.

The direction flag control instructions set or clear the direction flag, DF, which controls the direction of string processing. If the DF flag is clear, the processor increments the string index registers, ESI and EDI, after each iteration of a string instruction. If the DF flag is set, the processor decrements these index registers.

4.8.2. Flag Transfer Instructions

Though specific instructions exist to alter the CF and DF flags, there is no direct method of altering the other application-oriented flags. The flag transfer instructions allow a program to change the state of the other flag bits using the bit manipulation instructions once these flags have been moved to the stack or the AH register.

The LAHF and SAHF instructions deal with five of the status flags, which are used primarily by the arithmetic and logical instructions.

LAHF (Load AH from Flags) copies the SF, ZF, AF, PF, and CF flags to the AH register bits 7, 6, 4, 2, and 0, respectively (see Figure 4-20). The contents of the remaining bits 5, 3, and 1 are left undefined. The contents of the EFLAGS register remain unchanged.

SAHF (Store AH into Flags) copies bits 7, 6, 4, 2, and 0 from the AH register into the SF, ZF, AF, PF, and CF flags, respectively (see Figure 4-20).

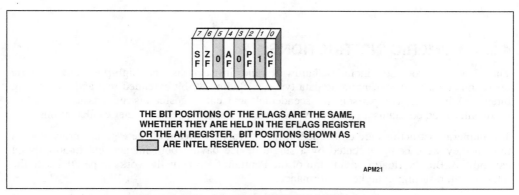

THE BIT POSITIONS OF THE FLAGS ARE THE SAME,
WHETHER THEY ARE HELD IN THE EFLAGS REGISTER
OR THE AH REGISTER. BIT POSITIONS SHOWN AS
■ ARE INTEL RESERVED. DO NOT USE.

APM21

Figure 4-20. Low Byte of EFLAGS Register

The PUSHF and POPF instructions are not only useful for storing the flags in memory where they can be examined and modified, but also are useful for preserving the state of the EFLAGS register while executing a subroutine.

PUSHF (Push Flags) pushes the lower word of the EFLAGS register onto the stack (see Figure 4-21). The PUSHFD instruction pushes the entire EFLAGS register onto the stack (the RF and VM flags read as clear, however).

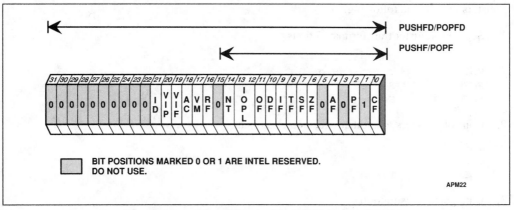

BIT POSITIONS MARKED 0 OR 1 ARE INTEL RESERVED.
DO NOT USE.

APM22

Figure 4-21. Flags Used with PUSHF and POPF

POPF (Pop Flags) pops a word from the stack into the EFLAGS register. Only bits 11, 10, 8, 7, 6, 4, 2, and 0 are affected with all uses of this instruction. If the privilege level of the current code segment is 0 (most privileged), the IOPL bits (bits 13 and 12) also are affected. If the I/O privilege level (IOPL) is 0, the IF flag (bit 9) also is affected. The POPFD instruction pops a doubleword into the EFLAGS register, and it can change the state of the AC bit (bit 18) and the ID bit (bit 21), as well as the bits affected by a POPF instruction.

4.9. NUMERIC INSTRUCTIONS

The Pentium processor includes hardware and instructions for high-precision numeric operations on a variety of numeric data types, including 80-bit extended real and 64-bit long integer. Arithmetic, comparison, transcendental, and data transfer instructions are available. Frequently-used constants are also provided, to enhance the speed of numeric calculations.

The numeric instructions are embedded in the instruction stream of the Pentium processor, as though they were being executed by a single device having both integer and floating-point capabilities. But the floating-point unit of the Pentium CPU actually works in parallel with the integer unit, resulting in higher performance.

Refer to Chapter 5 to confirm the presence of a Pentium processor floating point unit.

Chapter 6 describes the numeric instructions in more detail.

4.10. SEGMENT REGISTER INSTRUCTIONS

There are several distinct types of instructions which use segment registers. They are grouped together here because, if system designers choose an unsegmented model of memory organization, none of these instructions are used. The instructions which deal with segment registers include the following:

1. Segment-register transfer instructions.

    ```
    MOV        SegReg, ...
    MOV        ..., SegReg
    PUSH       SegReg
    POP        SegReg
    ```

2. Control transfers to another executable segment.

    ```
    JMP        far
    CALL       far
    RET        far
    ```

3. Data pointer instructions.

    ```
    LDS    reg, 48-bit memory operand
    LES    reg, 48-bit memory operand
    LFS    reg, 48-bit memory operand
    LGS    reg, 48-bit memory operand
    LSS    reg, 48-bit memory operand
    ```

4. Note that the following interrupt-related instructions also are used in unsegmented systems. Although they can transfer execution between segments when segmentation is used, this is transparent to the application programmer.

```
INT n
INTO
BOUND
IRET
```

4.10.1. Segment-Register Transfer Instructions

Forms of the MOV, POP, and PUSH instructions also are used to load and store segment registers. These forms operate like the general-register forms, except that one operand is a segment register. The MOV instruction cannot copy the contents of a segment register into another segment register.

The POP and MOV instructions cannot place a value in the CS register (code segment); only the far control-transfer instructions affect the CS register. When the destination is the SS register (stack segment), interrupts are disabled until after the next instruction.

No 16-bit operand size prefix is needed when transferring data between a segment register and a 32-bit general register.

4.10.2. Far Control Transfer Instructions

The far control-transfer instructions transfer execution to a destination in another segment by replacing the contents of the CS register. The destination is specified by a far pointer, which is a 16-bit segment selector and a 32-bit offset into the segment. The far pointer can be an immediate operand or an operand in memory.

Far CALL. An intersegment CALL instruction places the values held in the EIP and CS registers on the stack.

Far RET. An intersegment RET instruction restores the values of the CS and EIP registers from the stack.

4.10.3. Data Pointer Instructions

The data pointer instructions load a far pointer into the processor registers. A far pointer consists of a 16-bit segment selector, which is loaded into a segment register, and a 32-bit offset into the segment, which is loaded into a general register.

LDS (Load Pointer Using DS) copies a far pointer from the source operand into the DS register and a general register. The source operand must be a memory operand, and the destination operand must be a general register.

Example: LDS ESI, STRING_X

Loads the DS register with the segment selector for the segment addressed by STRING_X, and loads the offset within the segment to STRING_X into the ESI register. Specifying the ESI register as the destination operand is a convenient way to prepare for a string operation, when the source string is not in the current data segment.

LES (Load Pointer Using ES) has the same effect as the LDS instruction, except the segment selector is loaded into the ES register rather than the DS register.

Example: `LES EDI, DESTINATION_X`

Loads the ES register with the segment selector for the segment addressed by DESTINATION_X, and loads the offset within the segment to DESTINATION_X into the EDI register. This instruction is a convenient way to select a destination for string operation if the desired location is not in the current E-data segment.

LFS (Load Pointer Using FS) has the same effect as the LDS instruction, except the FS register receives the segment selector rather than the DS register.

LGS (Load Pointer Using GS) has the same effect as the LDS instruction, except the GS register receives the segment selector rather than the DS register.

LSS (Load Pointer Using SS) has the same effect as the LDS instruction, except the SS register receives the segment selector rather than the DS register. This instruction is especially important, because it allows the two registers which identify the stack (the SS and ESP registers) to be changed in one uninterruptible operation. Unlike the other instructions which can load the SS register, interrupts are not inhibited at the end of the LSS instruction. The other instructions, such as POP SS, turn off interrupts to permit the following instruction to load the ESP register without an intervening interrupt. Since both the SS and ESP registers can be loaded by the LSS instruction, there is no need to disable or re-enable interrupts.

4.11. MISCELLANEOUS INSTRUCTIONS

The following instructions do not fit in any of the previous categories, but are no less important.

The CMPXCHG8B and CPUID instructions are new instructions on the Pentium processor and bring improved functionality by providing a single instruction to accomplish what previously took multiple instructions on earlier microprocessors.

The BSWAP, XADD, and CMPXCHG instructions are not available on Intel386 DX or SX microprocessors. An Intel386 CPU can perform the same operations in multiple instructions. To use these instructions, always include functionally-equivalent code for Intel386 CPUs.

To determine whether these new instructions can be used, the type of processor in a system needs to be determined. See Chapter 5 for code examples and information on determining the type of the different processors.

4.11.1. Address Calculation Instruction

LEA (Load Effective Address) puts the 32-bit offset to a source operand in memory (rather than its contents) into the destination operand. The source operand must be in memory, and the destination operand must be a general register. This instruction is especially useful for initializing the ESI or EDI registers before the execution of string instructions or initializing the EBX register before an XLAT instruction. The LEA instruction can perform any indexing or scaling which may be needed.

Example: LEA EBX, EBCDIC_TABLE

Causes the processor to place the address of the starting location of the table labeled EBCDIC_TABLE into EBX.

4.11.2. No-Operation Instruction

NOP (No Operation) occupies a byte of code space. When executed, it increments the EIP register to point at the next instruction, but affects nothing else.

4.11.3. Translate Instruction

XLATB (Translate) replaces the contents of the AL register with a byte read from a translation table in memory. The contents of the AL register are interpreted as an unsigned index into this table, with the contents of the EBX register used as the base address. The XLAT instruction does the same operation and loads its result into the same register, but it gets the byte operand from memory. This function is used to convert character codes from one alphabet into another. For example, an ASCII code could be used to look up its EBCDIC equivalent.

4.11.4. Byte Swap Instruction

BSWAP (Byte Swap) reverses the byte order in a 32-bit register operand. Bit positions 7..0 are exchanged with 31..24, and bit positions 15..8 are exchanged with 23..16. This instruction is useful for converting between "big-endian" and "little-endian" data formats. Executing this instruction twice in a row leaves the register in the same value as before. This instruction also speeds execution of decimal arithmetic by operating on four digits at a time as shown in Example 1.

Example 4-2. ASCII Arithmetic Using BSWAP

```
$title('ASCII Add/Subtract with BSWAP')

      name ASCII_arith

code segment    er public use32
;
;     Add a string of 4 ASCII decimal digits together.
;     The upper nibble MUST be 3.
;     DS:[ESI] points at operand 1
;     DS:[EBX] points at operand 2
;     DS:[EDI] points at the destination
;

add10 proc near
;
;     Perform ASCII add using BSWAP instruction
```

```
;
        mov    eax, [esi]      ; Get low four digits of first operand
        bswap eax              ; Put into big-endian form
        add    eax, 96969696H  ; Adjust for addition so carries work
        mov    ecx, [ebx]      ; Get low four digits of second operand
        bswap ecx              ; Put into big-endian form
        add    eax, ecx        ; Do the add with inter-digit carry
        rcr    ch,1            ; Save the carr flag
        mov    edx,eax         ; Save the value
        and    eax, 0F0F0F0F0H ; Extract the uppernibble
        sub    eax, eax        ; Zero out uppernibble of each byte
        shr    eax, 4          ; Prepare for fixup
        and    eax, 0A0A0A0AH  ; If non-zero upper nibble then form
                               ; as adjustment value to lower nibble
        add    eax, edx        ; Form adjusted lower nibble value
                               ; Upper nibbles may be 1 from adjustment
        or     eax, 30303030H  ; Convert back to ASCII
        bswap eax              ; Back to little-endien
        mov    [edi], eax      ; Set destination
        rcl    ch, 1           ; Restore carry
        ret

add10      endp

;      Subtract a string of 4 ASCII decimal digits together.
;      The upper nibble must be 3.
;      DS:[ESI] points at operand 1
;      DS:[EBX] points at operand 2
;      DS:[EDI] points at the destination
;
sub10 proc near
;
;      Perform ASCII subtract using BSWAP instruction.

        mov    eax, [esi]      ; Get low four digits of first operand
        bswap      eax         ; Put into big-endian form
        mov    ecx, [ebx]      ; get low four digits of second operand
        bswap      ecx         ; Put into big-endian form
        sub    eax,ecx         ; Do the subtraction with inter-digit borrow
        rcr    ch, 1           ; Save the carry flag
        mov    edx, eax        ; Save the value
        and    eax, 0F0F0F0F0H ; Extract upper nibble, F if borrow happened
        sub    edx, eax        ; Zero out upper nibble of each byte
        shr    eax, 4          ; Prepare for fixup
        and    eax,0A0A0A0AH   ; If non-zero upper nibble then form
                               ; 10 as adjustment value to lower nibble
        add    eax, edx        ; Form adjusted lower nibble value
                               ; upper nibbles may be 1 from adjustment
        or     eax, 30303030H  ; Convert back to ASCII
```

```
        bswap eax                ; Convert to little-endian
        mov   [edi], eax         ; Set to destination
        rcl   ch, 1              ; Restore borrow
        ret

sub10 endp

code ends
      end
```

4.11.5. Exchange-and-Add Instruction

XADD (Exchange and Add) takes two operands: a source operand in a register and a destination operand in a register or memory. The source operand is replaced with the destination operand, and the destination operand is replaced with the sum of the source and destination operands. The flags reflect the result of the addition. This instruction can be combined with LOCK in a multiprocessing system to allow multiple processors to execute one do loop.

4.11.6. Compare-and-Exchange Instructions

CMPXCHG (Compare and Exchange) takes three operands: a source operand in a register, a destination operand in a register or memory, and the accumulator (i.e., the AL, AX, or EAX register, depending on operand size). If the values in the destination operand and the accumulator are equal, the destination operand is replaced with the source operand. Otherwise, the original value of the destination operand is loaded into the accumulator. The flags reflect the result which would have been obtained by subtracting the destination operand from the accumulator. The ZF flag is set if the values in the destination operand and the accumulator were equal, otherwise it is cleared.

The CMPXCHG instruction is useful for testing and modifying semaphores. It performs a check to see if a semaphore is free. If the semaphore is free it is marked allocated, otherwise it gets the ID of the current owner. This is all done in one uninterruptible operation. In a single processor system, it eliminates the need to switch to level 0 to disable interrupts to execute multiple instructions. For multiple processor systems, CMPXCHG can be combined with LOCK to perform all bus cycles atomically.

CMPXCHG8B (Compare and Exchange 8 Bytes) takes three operands: a destination operand in memory, a 64-bit value in EDX:EAX and a 64-bit value in ECX:EBX. CMPXCHG8B compares the 64-bit value in EDX:EAX with the destination. If they are equal, the 64-bit value in ECX:EBX is stored in the destination. If EDX:EAX and the destination are not equal, the destination is loaded into EDX:EAX. The ZF flag is set if the values in the destination and EDX:EAX are equal, otherwise it is cleared. The CF, PF, AF, SF, and OF flags are unaffected. CMPXCHG8B can be combined with LOCK to perform all bus cycles in one uninterruptible operation.

4.11.7. CPUID Instruction

CPUID provides information to software about the the vendor and model of microprocessor on which it is executing. By loading a zero into EAX and then executing the CPUD instruction, the ECX, EDX, and EBX registers will contain a vendor identification string. The EAX register will contain the highest input value understood by the CPUID instruction. Software can then obtain additional information regarding which features are present by moving a one (or up to the highest value returned in EAX previously) into EAX and executing the CPUID instruction again.

When a one is loaded into the EAX register before executing the CPUID instruction, the EAX register contains information regarding the family, model and stepping of the processor as shown in Figure 4-22. Bits 8-11 of the EAX register indicate what family the processor belongs to and will be 5 for the Pentium microprocessor. Bits 4-7 of the EAX register indicate the model and will be 0 to indicate the first model in the Pentium family. Bits 0-3 of the EAX register indicate the Stepping ID which is a unique identifier for each revision level.

The EBX and ECX registers are reserved following execution of this instruction with an input value of one, and the EDX register will contain information on which features are present on a particular processor. For more information on the feature bits of EDX, see Appendix H.

The ability to set and clear the ID flag in the EFLAGS register indicates whether the processor supports the CPUID instruction. The CPUID instruction can be executed at any privilege level to serialize instruction execution. Serializing instruction execution guarantees that any modifications to flags, registers, and memory for previous instructions are completed before the next instruction is fetched and executed. For more information on serializing operations, see Chapter 18.

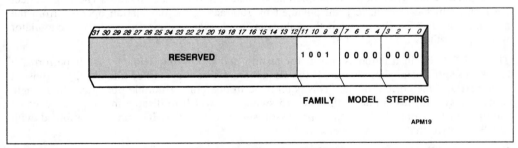

Figure 4-22. EAX Following the CPUID Instruction

intel®

5

Feature
Determination

CHAPTER 5
FEATURE DETERMINATION

Identifying the type of processor present in a system may be necessary in order to determine which features are available to an application. Chapter 23 contains a complete list of which features are available for the different Intel architectures. The absence of an integrated floating-point unit (FPU) or numeric processor extension (NPX) may also need to be determined if software needs to emulate the floating-point instructions.

This chapter discusses processor identification, as well as on-chip FPU and NPX presence detection and identification. Sample code is provided in Example 5-1.

5.1. CPU IDENTIFICATION

The setting of the flags stored by the PUSHF instruction, by interrupts, and by exceptions is different on the 32 bit processors than that stored by the 8086 and Intel 286 processors in bits 12 and 13 (IOPL), 14 (NT), and 15 (reserved). These differences can be used to distinguish what type of processor is present in a system while an application is running.

- 8086 processor — bits 12 through 15 are always set.

- Intel 286 processor — bits 12 through 15 are always clear in real-address mode.

- 32-bit processors — in real-address mode, bit 15 is always clear and bits 14 through 12 have the last value loaded into them. In protected mode, bit 14 has the last value loaded into it, bit 15 is always clear, and IOPL depends on the CPL (if CPL ≠ 0, the IOPL is unchanged, otherwise it is updated).

Other EFLAG register bits that can be used to differentiate between the 32 bit processors include:

- Bit 18 (AC), implemented on the Intel486 and Pentium processors, can be used to distinguish an Intel386 processor from the Intel486 and Pentium processors as it will always be clear on an Intel386 processor.

- Bit 21 (ID) can be used to determine if an application can execute the CPUID instruction. This instruction supplies information to applications at runtime that identifies the vendor, family, model, stepping, and what features are implemented on the processor in the system an application is running on. The ability to set and clear this bit indicates that the CPUID instruction is supported by the processor. See Chapter 25 for details on this instruction.

5.2. FPU DETECTION

To determine whether an FPU or NPX is present in a system, applications can write to the status and control word registers using the FNINIT instruction and then verify the correct values are read back. Once an FPU or NPX is determined to be present, its type can then be determined. In most cases, the processor type will determine the type of FPU or NPX, however, an Intel386 microprocessor may work with either an Intel287 or Intel387 math coprocessor. To determine which of these is present, the infinity of the coprocessor must be checked. On the Intel287 math coprocessor, positive infinity is equal to negative infinity. On the Intel387 math coprocessor, however, positive infinity is not equal to negative infinity.

5.3. SAMPLE CPUID IDENTIFICATION/FPU DETECTION CODE

Example 5-1 is the Intel recommended method of determing the processor type as well as the presence and type of NPX or integrated FPU. This code has been modified from previous versions of Intel's recommended CPU identification code by modularizing the printing functions so that applications not running in a DOS environment can remove or change the print function to conform to the appropriate environment. Note that this code (and previous versions) is supported on the Intel 286 in real-address mode only. This example was created using Microsoft's assembler directives.

Example 5-1. CPU Identification and FPU Detection

```
;       Filename: cpuid32.msm
;
;       This program has been developed by Intel Corporation. You have
;       Intel's permission to incorporate this source code into your
;       product royalty free.
;
;       Intel specifically disclaims all warranties, express or implied,
;       and all liability, including consequential and other indirect
;       damages, for the use of this code, including liability for
;       infringement of any proprietary rights. Intel does not assume
;       any responsibility for any errors which may appear in this code
;       nor any responsibility to update it.
;
;       This program determines the type of processor present in the
;       system it is running on. It also determines the presence of a
;       floating-point unit or numeric processor extension on the
;       system.
;
;       This program is modularized and contains two parts:
;       Part 1: Identifies CPU type in cpu_type:
;           0=8086 processor
;           2=Intel 286 processor
;           3=Intel386(TM) processor
;           4=Intel486(TM) processor
;           5=Pentium(TM) processor
;           The presence of a floating-point unit is
;           indicated in fp_flag (1=present).
;
;           The variable infinity is used to determine if
;           an Intel287(TM) NPX (2) is being used with an Intel386 cpu
```

```
;           or an Intel387(TM) NPX (3) is being used.
;
;     Part 2: Prints out the appropriate message.  This part can
;           be removed or modified if this program is not used in a
;           DOS-based system. Portions affected are at the end of the
;           data segment and the print procedure in the code
;           segment.
;
;     This program uses 32-bit instructions and operands.
;     For use on 16-bit assemblers, replace 32-bit instructions
;     with 16-bit versions and use the override prefix 66H, for
;     example:
;
;           Instead of:     POPFD EAX
;                           MOV ECX, EAX
;
;           Use:      DB 66H
;                     POPF AX
;                     DB 66H
;                     MOV CX, AX


      TITLE CPUID
      DOSSEG
      .model small
      .stack      100h
      .486

CPUID MACRO
      db    0Fh   ; Hardcoded opcode for CPUID instruction on Pentium
                  CPU
      db    0a2h
ENDM

      .data
fp_status       dw    ?
saved_cpuid     dd    ?
vendor_id       db    12 dup (?)
cpu_type        db    ?
model           db    ?
stepping        db    ?
id_flag         db    0
fpu_present     db    0
intel_proc      db    0
infinity        db    0
;
;remove the remaining data declarations if not using print procedure
;
id_msg    db    "This system has a$"
fp_8087   db    " and an 8087 math coprocessor$"
```

```
fp_80287    db    " and an Intel287(TM) math coprocessor$"
fp_80387    db    " and an Intel387(TM) math coprocessor$"
c8086       db    "n 8086/8088 microprocessor$"
c286        db    "n Intel 286 microprocessor$"
c386        db    "n Intel386(TM) microprocessor$"
c486        db    "n Intel486(TM) DX microprocessor or Intel487(TM) SX
                  math coprocessor$"
c486nfp     db    "n Intel486 SX microprocessor$"
Pentium     db    " Pentium(TM) microprocessor",13,10,"$"
intel       db    " This system contains a Genuine Intel
                      processor",13,10,"$"
modelmsg        db    "Model:          $"
steppingmsg     db    "Stepping:       $"
familymsg       db    "Processor Family: $"
period          db    ".",13,10,"$"
dataCR          db    ?,13,10,"$"
intel_id        db    "GenuineIntel"


;
;      The purpose of this code is to allow the user the
;      ability to identify the processor and coprocessor
;      that is currently in the system.  The algorithm of
;      the program is to first determine the processor
;      id.  When that is accomplished, the program continues
;      to then identify whether a coprocessor exists
;      in the system.  If a coprocessor or integrated
;      coprocessor exists, the program will identify
;      the coprocessor id.
;
            .code
start:      mov  ax,@data
        mov  ds, ax          ; set segment register
        mov  es, ax          ; set segment register
        mov  ebx, esp        ; save current stack pointer to align
        and  esp, not 3      ; align stack to avoid AC fault
        pushfd               ; save for restoration at end
        call get_cpuid
        call check_fpu
        call print
        popfd
        mov  esp,ebx         ; restore original stack pointer
        mov  ax,4c00h        ; terminate program
        int  21h


get_cpuid proc


;
;      8086 CPU check
```

```
;     Bits 12-15 are always set on the 8086 processor.
;
check_8086:
      push ebx
      push ecx
      pushf                 ; save EFLAGS
      pop  bx               ; store EFLAGS in BX
      mov  ax,0fffh         ; clear bits 12-15
      and  ax,bx            ;    in EFLAGS
      push ax               ; store new EFLAGS value on stack
      popf                  ; replace current EFLAGS value
      pushf                 ; set new EFLAGS
      pop  ax               ; store new EFLAGS in AX
      and  ax,0f000h        ; if bits 12-15 are set, then CPU
      cmp  ax,0f000h        ; is an 8086/8088
      mov  cpu_type, 0      ; turn on 8086/8088 flag
      je   end_get_cpuid    ; if CPU is 8086/8088, check for 8087


;
;     Intel 286 CPU check
;     Bits 12-15 are always clear on the Intel 286 processor.
;
check_80286:
      or   bx,0f000h        ; try to set bits 12-15
      push bx
      popf
      pushf
      pop  ax
      and  ax,0f000h        ; if bits 12-15 are cleared, CPU=Intel 286
      mov  cpu_type, 2      ; turn on Intel 286 CPU flag
      jz   end_get_cpuid    ; if CPU is Intel 286,
                            ; check for Intel287 math coprocessor

;     Intel386 CPU check
;     The AC bit, bit #18, is a new bit introduced in the EFLAGS
;     register on the Intel486 DX CPU to generate alignment faults.
;     This bit can not be set on the Intel386 CPU.
;
check_Intel386:
      pushfd
      pop  eax              ; get original EFLAGS
      mov  ecx,eax          ; save original EFLAGS
      xor  eax,40000h       ; flip AC bit in EFLAGS
      push eax              ; save for EFLAGS
      popfd                 ; copy to EFLAGS
      pushfd               ; push EFLAGS
      pop  eax              ; get new EFLAGS value
      xor  eax,ecx          ; can't toggle AC bit, CPU=Intel386
      mov  cpu_type, 3      ; turn on Intel386 CPU flag
```

```
        je    end_get_cpuid   ; if CPU is Intel386, now check
                              ; for an Intel287 or Intel387 MCP

;     Intel486 DX CPU, Intel487 SX MCP, and Intel486 SX CPU checking
;
;
;     Checking for ability to set/clear ID flag (Bit 21) in EFLAGS
;     which differentiates between a Pentium CPU or other
;     processor with the ability to use the CPUID instruction. If this
;     bit cannot be set, CPU=Intel486.
;
check_Intel486:
        mov   cpu_type, 4     ; turn on Intel486 CPU flag
        pushfd               ; push original EFLAGS
        pop   eax            ; get original EFLAGS in eax
        mov   ecx,eax        ; save original EFLAGS in ecx
        xor   eax,200000h    ; flip ID bit in EFLAGS
        push eax             ; save for EFLAGS
        popfd                ; copy to EFLAGS
        pushfd               ; push EFLAGS
        pop   eax            ; get new EFLAGS value
        xor   eax, ecx
        je    end_get_cpuid   ; if ID bit cannot be changed, CPU=Intel486
                              ; without CPUID instruction functionality

;     Otherwise, execute CPUID instruction to determine vendor,
;     family,model and stepping.

check_vendor:
        mov   id_flag, 1      ; set flag indicating use of CPUID inst.
        mov   eax, 0          ; set up for CPUID instruction
        CPUID                ; macro for CPUID instruction
        mov   dword ptr vendor_id, ebx   ; Test for "GenuineIntel"
                                         ;vendor id
        mov   dword ptr vendor_id[+4], edx
        mov   dword ptr vendor_id[+8], ecx
        mov   esi, offset vendor_id
        mov   edi, offset intel_id
        mov   ecx, length intel_id
compare:
        repe cmpsb
        cmp   ecx, 0                ; must be GenuineIntel if ecx = 0
        jne   cpuid_data

intel_processor:
        mov   intel_proc, 1

cpuid_data:
        mov   eax, 1
        CPUID
```

```
        mov   saved_cpuid, eax      ; save for future use
        and   eax, 0F00H            ; mask everything but family
        shr   eax, 8
        mov   cpu_type, al          ; set cpu_type with family

        mov   eax, saved_cpuid      ; restore data
        mov   stepping, al
        and   stepping, 0FH         ; isolate stepping info

        mov   eax, saved_cpuid
        mov   model, al
        and   model, 0F0H           ; isolate model info
        shr   model, 4

end_get_cpuid:
        pop   ecx
        pop   ebx
        ret
get_cpuid endp

check_fpu proc

;
;     Co-processor checking begins here for the
;     8086, Intel 286, and Intel386 CPUs.  The algorithm is to
;     determine whether or not the floating-point
;     status and control words can be  written to.
;     If they are not, no coprocessor exists.  If
;     the status and control words can be written
;     to, the correct coprocessor is then determined
;     depending on the processor id.  Coprocessor
;     checks are first performed for an 8086, Intel 286
;     and an Intel486 DX CPU.  If the coprocessor id is still
;     undetermined, the system must contain an Intel386 CPU.
;     The Intel386 CPU may work with either an Intel287 or
;     an Intel387 math coprocessor.  The infinity of the
;     coprocessor must be checked to determine the correct
;     coprocessor id.
;
        push eax
                            ; check for 8087, Intel287, or
                            ; Intel387 math coprocessor
        fninit              ; reset FP status word
        mov  fp_status,5a5ah ; initialize temp word to
                            ; non-zero value
        fnstsw fp_status    ; save FP status word
        mov  ax,fp_status   ; check FP status word
        cmp  al,0           ; see if correct status with
                            ; written
        je   check_control_word
```

```
        mov    fpu_present, 0  ; no fpu present
        jmp    end_check_fpu

check_control_word:
        fnstcw fp_status        ; save FP control word
        mov    ax,fp_status     ; check FP control word
        and    ax,103fh         ; see if selected parts
                                ; looks OK
        cmp    ax,3fh           ; check that 1's & 0's
                                ; correctly read
        je     set_fpu_present
        mov    fpu_present, 0
        jmp    end_check_fpu
 set_fpu_present:
        mov    fpu_present, 1


;
;    Intel287 and Intel387 math coprocessor check for the Intel386 CPU
;
check_infinity:
        cmp    cpu_type, 3
        jne    end_check_fpu
        fld1                    ; must use default control from FNINIT
        fldz                    ; form infinity
        fdiv                    ; 8087 and Intel287 MCP says +inf = -inf
        fld    st               ; form negative infinity
        fchs                    ; Intel387 MCP says +inf <> -inf
        fcompp                  ; see if they are the same and remove them
        fstsw fp_status ; look at status from FCOMPP
        mov    ax,fp_status
        mov    infinity, 2      ; store Intel287 MCP for fpu infinity
        sahf                    ; see if infinities matched
        jz     end_check_fpu    ; jump if 8087 or Intel287 MCP is present
        mov    infinity, 3      ; store Intel387 MCP for fpu infinity
end_check_fpu:
        pop eax
        ret
check_fpu endp


;
;    This procedure prints the appropriate cpuid string and
;    numeric processor presence status.  If the CPUID instruction
;    was supported, prints out cpuid info.

print proc
        push eax
        push ebx
        push ecx
        push edx
        cmp    id_flag, 1               ;if set to 1, cpu supported CPUID
```

```
                                        ;instruction
                                        ;print detailed CPUID information
        je    print_cpuid_data

        mov   dx, offset id_msg       ;print initial message
        mov   ah, 9h
        int   21h

print_86:
        cmp   cpu_type, 0
        jne   print_286
        mov   dx, offset c8086
        mov   ah, 9h
        int   21h
        cmp   fpu_present, 0
        je    end_print
        mov   dx, offset fp_8087
        mov   ah, 9h
        int   21h
        jmp   end_print

print_286:
        cmp   cpu_type, 2
        jne   print_386
        mov   dx, offset c286
        mov   ah, 9h
        int   21h
        cmp   fpu_present, 0
        je    end_print
        mov   dx, offset fp_80287
        mov   ah, 9h
        int   21h
        jmp   end_print

print_386:
        cmp   cpu_type, 3
        jne   print_486
        mov   dx, offset c386
        mov   ah, 9h
        int   21h
        cmp   fpu_present, 0
        je    end_print
        cmp   infinity, 2
        jne   print_387
        mov   dx, offset fp_80287
        mov   ah, 9h
        int   21h
        jmp   end_print

print_387:
```

```
        mov    dx, offset fp_80387
        mov    ah, 9h
        int    21h
        jmp    end_print

print_486:
        cmp    fpu_present, 0
        je     print_Intel486sx
        mov    dx, offset c486
        mov    ah,9h
        int    21h
        jmp    end_print

print_Intel486sx:
        mov    dx, offset c486nfp
        mov    ah,9h
        int    21h
        jmp    end_print

print_cpuid_data:
        mov    edx, offset familymsg        ; print family msg
        mov    ah, 9h
        int    21h
        mov    al, cpu_type
        mov    byte ptr dataCR, al
        add    byte ptr dataCR, 30H         ; convert to ASCII
        mov    edx, offset dataCR           ; print family info
        mov    ah, 9h
        int    21h

        mov    edx, offset steppingmsg      ; print stepping msg
        mov    ah, 9h
        int    21h
        mov    al, stepping
        mov    byte ptr dataCR, al
        add    byte ptr dataCR, 30H         ; convert to ASCII
        mov    edx, offset dataCR           ; print stepping info
        mov    ah, 9h
        int    21h

        mov    edx, offset modelmsg         ; print model msg
        mov    ah, 9h
        int    21h
        mov    al, model
        mov    byte ptr dataCR, al
        add    byte ptr dataCR, 30H         ; convert to ASCII
        mov    edx, offset dataCR           ; print model info
        mov    ah, 9h
        int    21h
```

```
end_print:
      pop   edx
      pop   ecx
      pop   ebx
      pop   eax
      ret
print endp

      end   start
```

intel®

6

Numeric
Applications

CHAPTER 6
NUMERIC APPLICATIONS

The Pentium processor contains a high-performance numerics processing element that provides significant numeric capabilities and direct support for floating-point, extended-integer, and BCD data types. The Pentium Floating-point Unit (FPU) easily supports powerful and accurate numeric applications through its implementation, with radix 2, of the IEEE Standard 754 for Floating-Point Arithmetic. The Pentium FPU provides floating-point performance comparable to that of large minicomputers while offering compatibility with object code for 8087, Intel287™, Intel387 DX, Intel387 SX, and Intel487 DX math coprocessors and the Intel486 DX processor.

6.1.   INTRODUCTION TO NUMERIC APPLICATIONS

6.1.1.   History

The 8087 numeric processor extension (NPX) was designed for use in 8086-family systems. The 8086 was the first microprocessor family to partition the processing unit to permit high-performance numeric capabilities. The 8087 NPX for this processor family implemented a complete numeric processing environment in compliance with an early proposal for IEEE Standard 754 for Binary Floating-Point Arithmetic.

With the Intel287 NPX, high-speed numeric computations were extended to 80286 high-performance multitasking and multiuser systems. Multiple tasks using the numeric processor extension were afforded the full protection of the 80286 memory management and protection features.

The Intel387 DX and SX math coprocessors are Intel's third generation numerics processors. They implement the final IEEE Std 754, adding new trigonometric instructions, and using a new design and CHMOS-III process to allow higher clock rates and require fewer clocks per instruction. Together, the Intel387 math coprocessor with additional instructions and the improved standard brought even more convenience and reliability to numerics programming and made this convenience and reliability available to applications that need the high-speed and large memory capacity of the 32-bit environment of the Intel386 microprocessor.

The Intel486 FPU is an on-chip equivalent of the Intel387 DX CPU conforming to both IEEE Std 754 and the more recent, generalized IEEE Std 854. Having the FPU on chip results in a considerable performance improvement in numerics-intensive computation.

The Pentium FPU has been completely redesigned over the Intel486 FPU while maintaining conformance to both the IEEE Std 754 and 854. Faster algorithms provide at least three times the performance over the Intel486 FPU for common operations including ADD, MUL, and LOAD. Many applications can achieve five times the performance of the Intel486 FPU or more with instruction scheduling and pipelined execution.

6.1.2. Performance

Today, floating-point performance is more important than ever. Applications of personal computer workstations, no longer limited to simple spreadsheets and business applications, now include sophisticated algorithms such as lab data analysis and three-dimensional graphics.

Table 6-1 compares the execution times of several Pentium processor numeric instructions with the equivalent operations executed on a 66-MHz Intel486 DX2 processor. As indicated in the table, the 66-MHz Pentium CPU provides about three times the floating-point performance of a 66-MHz Intel486 DX2 CPU. A 66-MHz Pentium processor multiplies 32-bit and 64-bit floating-point numbers in about 45 nanoseconds. Of course, the actual performance of the processor in a given system depends on the characteristics of the individual application.

Table 6-1. Numeric Processing Speed Comparisons

Floating-Point Instruction			Approximate Performance Ratio: 66 MHz Pentium™ Processor ÷ 66 MHz Intel486™ DX2
FADD	ST, ST(i)	Addition	3.8
FDIV	dword_var	Division	2.2
FYL2X	ST(0),ST(1) assumed	Logarithm	3.1
FPATAN	ST(0) assumed	Arctangent	2.6
F2XM1	ST(0) assumed	Exponentiation	4.8
FLD	ST(0), ST(i)	Data Transfer	4.0

The processor coordinates its integer and floating-point activities in a manner transparent to software. Moreover, built-in coordination facilities allow the integer pipe(s) to proceed with other instructions while the FPU is simultaneously executing numeric instructions. See Appendix H on how to obtain more information on floating-point instruction pairing as programs can exploit this concurrency of execution to further increase system performance and throughput.

6.1.3. Ease of Use

The 32-bit Intel architectures, with their on-chip FPU (such as the Pentium and Intel486 CPU's) or NPX's (such as the Intel386 CPU with an Intel387 math coprocessor) are explicitly designed to deliver stable, accurate results when programmed using straightforward "pencil and paper" algorithms, bringing the functionality and power of accurate numeric computation into the hands of the general user. IEEE Std 754 specifically addresses this issue, recognizing the fundamental importance of making numeric computations both easy and safe to use.

These NPX's and FPU's provide more than raw execution speed for computation-intensive tasks; bringing the functionality and power of accurate numeric computation into the hands of the general user. These features are available in most high-level languages available for these processors.

For example, most computers can overflow when two single-precision floating-point numbers are multiplied together and then divided by a third, even if the final result is a perfectly valid 32-bit number. The FPU delivers the correctly rounded result. Other typical examples of undesirable machine behavior in straightforward calculations occur when computing financial rate of return, which involves the expression $(1 + i)^n$ or when solving for roots of a quadratic equation:

$$\frac{-b \pm \sqrt{b^2 - 4ac}}{2a}$$

If a does not equal 0, the formula is numerically unstable when the roots are nearly coincident or when their magnitudes are wildly different. The formula is also vulnerable to spurious over/underflows when the coefficients a, b, and c are all very big or all very tiny. When single-precision (4-byte) floating-point coefficients are given as data and the formula is evaluated in the FPU's normal way, keeping all intermediate results in its stack, the FPU produces impeccable single-precision roots. This happens because, by default and with no effort on the programmer's part, the FPU evaluates all those subexpressions with so much extra precision and range as to overwhelm almost any threat to numerical integrity.

If double-precision data and results were at issue, a better formula would have to be used, and once again the FPU's default evaluation of that formula would provide substantially enhanced numerical integrity over mere double-precision evaluation.

On most machines, straightforward algorithms will not deliver consistently correct results (and will not indicate when they are incorrect). To obtain correct results on traditional machines under all conditions usually requires sophisticated numerical techniques that go beyond typical programming practice. General application programmers using straightforward algorithms will produce much more reliable programs using the Intel architectures. This simple fact greatly reduces the software investment required to develop safe, accurate computation-based products.

Beyond traditional numerics support for scientific applications, the Intel architectures have built-in facilities for commercial computing. They can process decimal numbers of up to 18 digits without round-off errors, performing *exact arithmetic* on integers as large as 2^{64} or 10^{18}. Exact arithmetic is vital in accounting applications where rounding errors may introduce monetary losses that cannot be reconciled.

The Intel FPU's contain a number of optional numerical facilities that can be invoked by sophisticated users. These advanced features include directed rounding, gradual underflow, and programmed exception-handling facilities.

These automatic exception-handling facilities permit a high degree of flexibility in numeric processing software, without burdening the programmer. While performing numeric calculations, the processor automatically detects exception conditions that can potentially damage a calculation (for example, $X \div 0$ or $\sqrt{X}$ when $X < 0$). By default, on-chip exception logic handles these exceptions so that a reasonable result is produced and execution may proceed without program interruption. Alternatively, the processor can invoke a software exception handler to provide special results whenever various types of exceptions are detected.

6.1.4. Applications

The Pentium FPU's versatility and performance make it appropriate for a broad array of numeric applications. In general, applications that exhibit any of the following characteristics can benefit by implementing numeric processing :

- Numeric data vary over a wide range of values, or include nonintegral values.
- Algorithms produce very large or very small intermediate results.
- Computations must be very precise; i.e., a large number of significant digits must be maintained.
- Performance requirements exceed the capacity of traditional microprocessors.
- Consistently safe, reliable results must be delivered using a programming staff that is not expert in numerical techniques.

Note also that the software development costs can be reduced and performance of systems improved that use not only real numbers, but operate on multiprecision binary or decimal integer values as well.

A few examples, which show how the Pentium processor might be used in specific numerics applications, are described below.

- Business data processing—The FPU's ability to accept decimal operands and produce *exact* decimal results of up to 18 digits greatly simplifies accounting programming. Financial calculations that use power functions can take advantage of the Intel architecture's exponentiation and logarithmic instructions. Many business software packages can benefit from the speed and accuracy of the FPU.
- Simulation—The large (32-bit) memory space and raw speed of the processor make it suitable for attacking large simulation problems, which heretofore could only be executed on expensive mini and mainframe computers. For example, complex electronic circuit simulations using SPICE can be performed. Simulation of mechanical systems using finite element analysis can employ more elements, resulting in more detailed analysis or simulation of larger systems.
- Graphics transformations—The FPU can be used in graphics applications such as computer-aided design (CAD), with the FPU performing many functions concurrently with the execution of integer instructions; these functions include rotation, scaling, and interpolation.
- Process control—The FPU solves dynamic range problems automatically, and its extended precision allows control functions to be fine-tuned for more accurate and efficient performance. Using the Pentium processor to implement control algorithms also contributes to improved reliability and safety, while the processor's speed can be exploited in real-time operations.
- Computer numerical control (CNC)—The FPU can move and position machine tool heads with accuracy in real-time. Axis positioning also benefits from the hardware trigonometric support provided by the FPU.

- Robotics—The powerful computational abilities of the Pentium FPU are ideal for on-board six-axis positioning.

- Navigation—Very small, lightweight, and accurate inertial guidance systems can be implemented with the FPU. Its built-in trigonometric functions can speed and simplify the calculation of position from bearing data.

- Data acquisition—The FPU can be used to scan, scale, and reduce large quantities of data as it is collected, thereby lowering storage requirements and time required to process the data for analysis.

- Digital Signal Processing (DSP)—All DSP-related applications, such as matrix multiplication and convolution, can benefit from the pipelined instruction implementation of the Pentium processor.

The preceding examples are oriented toward traditional numerics applications. There are, in addition, many other types of systems that do not appear to the end user as computational, but can employ the 32-bit Intel architecture's numerical capabilities to advantage. The imaginative system designer has an opportunity similar to that created by the introduction of the microprocessor itself. Many applications can be viewed as numerically-based if sufficient computational power is available to support this view (e.g., character generation for a laser printer). This is analogous to the thousands of successful products that have been built around "buried" microprocessors, even though the products themselves bear little resemblance to computers.

6.1.5.   Programming Interface

The Intel x86 architectures have a class of instructions known as ESCAPE instructions, all having a common format. These ESC instructions are numeric instructions for the FPU. These numeric instructions are part of a single integrated instruction set.

Numeric processing centers around the floating-point register stack. Programmers can treat these eight 80-bit registers either as a fixed register set, with instructions operating on explicitly-designated registers, or as a classical stack, with instructions operating on the top one or two stack elements.

Internally, the FPU holds all numbers in a uniform 80-bit extended format. Operands that may be represented in memory as 16-, 32-, or 64-bit integers, 32-, 64-, or 80-bit floating-point numbers, or 18-digit packed BCD numbers, are automatically converted into extended format as they are loaded into the FPU registers. Computation results are subsequently converted back into one of these destination data formats when they are stored into memory from the FPU registers.

Table 6-2 lists each of the seven numeric data types supported by the FPU, showing the data format for each type. The table also shows the approximate range of normalized values that can be represented with each type. Denormal values are also supported in each of the real types, as required by IEEE Std 854. Denormals are discussed later in this chapter.

Table 6-2. Numeric Data Types

Data Type	Bits	Significant Digits (Decimal)	Approximate Normalized Range (Decimal)
Word integer	16	4	$-32{,}768 \leq x \leq +32{,}767$
Short integer	32	9	$-2 \times 10^9 \leq x \leq +2 \times 10^9$
Long integer	64	18	$-9 \times 10^{18} \leq x \leq +9 \times 10^{18}$
Packed decimal	80	18	$-99...99 \leq x \leq +99...99$ (18 digits)
Single real	32	7	$1.18 \times 10^{-38} < \lvert x \rvert < 3.40 \times 10^{38}$
Double real	64	15-16	$2.23 \times 10^{-308} < \lvert x \rvert < 1.79 \times 10^{308}$
Extended real*	80	19	$3.37 \times 10^{-4932} < \lvert x \rvert < 1.18 \times 10^{4932}$

* Equivalent to *double extended* format of IEEE Std 854.

All operands are stored in memory with the least significant digits starting at the initial (lowest) memory address. Numeric instructions access and store memory operands using only this initial address. See Chapter 24 for alignment strategies for the different processors.

Table 6-3 lists the numeric instructions by class. No special programming tools are necessary to use the numerical capabilities, because all of the numeric instructions and data types are directly supported by the Intel ASM386/ASM486 Assembler, by high-level languages from Intel, and by assemblers and compilers produced by many independent software vendors. Numeric routines can be written in assembly language or any of the following higher-level languages from Intel:

- PL/M-386/486
- C-386/486
- FORTRAN-386/486
- ADA-386/486

Table 6-3. Principal Numeric Instructions

Class	Instruction Types
Data Transfer	Load (all data types), Store (all data types), Exchange
Arithmetic	Add, Subtract, Multiply, Divide, Subtract Reversed, Divide Reversed, Square Root, Scale, Extract, Remainder, Integer Part, Change Sign, Absolute Value
Comparison	Compare, Examine, Test
Transcendental	Tangent, Arctangent, Sine, Cosine, Sine and Cosine, $2^x -1$, $Y \cdot Log_2(X)$, $Y \cdot Log_2(X+1)$
Constants	0, 1, π, $Log_{10}2$, Log_e2, $Log_2 10$, $Log_2 e$
Processor Control	Load Control Word, Store Control Word, Store Status Word, Load Environment, Store Environment, Save, Restore, Clear Exceptions, Initialize

All of these high-level languages provide programmers with access to the computational power and speed of the 32-bit Intel architectures without requiring an understanding of its architecture. Such architectural considerations as concurrency and synchronization are handled automatically by these high-level languages. For the assembly language programmer, specific rules for handling these issues are discussed in a later section of this manual.

6.2. ARCHITECTURE OF THE FLOATING-POINT UNIT

To the programmer, the FPU appears as a set of additional registers, data types, and instructions. Refer to Chapter 25 for detailed explanations of the numerical instruction set. This section explains the numerical registers and data types of the FPU architecture.

6.2.1. Numerical Registers

The numerical registers consist of:

- Eight individually-addressable 80-bit numeric registers, organized as a register stack.
- Three 16-bit registers containing:
  — The FPU status word.
  — The FPU control word.
  — The tag word.
- Error pointers, consisting of:
  — Two 16-bit registers containing selectors for the last instruction and operand.
  — Two 32-bit registers containing offsets for the last instruction and operand.
  — One 11-bit register containing the opcode of the last non-control FPU instruction.

All of the numeric instructions focus on the contents of these FPU registers.

6.2.1.1. THE FPU REGISTER STACK

The FPU register stack is shown in Figure 6-1. Each of the eight numeric registers in the stack is 80 bits wide and is divided into fields corresponding to the processor's extended real data type.

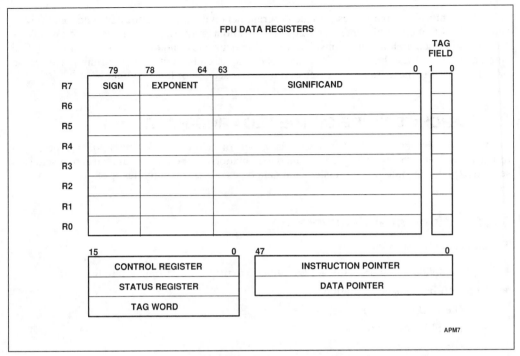

Figure 6-1. Floating-point Unit Register Set

Numeric instructions address the data registers relative to the register on the top of the stack. At any point in time, this top-of-stack register is indicated by the TOP (stack TOP) field in the FPU status word. Load or push operations decrement TOP by one and load a value into the new top register. A store-and-pop operation stores the value from the current TOP register and then increments TOP by one. Like stacks in memory, the FPU register stack grows *down* toward lower-addressed registers.

Many numeric instructions have several addressing modes that permit the programmer to implicitly operate on the top of the stack, or to explicitly operate on specific registers relative to the TOP. The ASM386/486 Assembler supports these register addressing modes, using the expression ST(0), or simply ST, to represent the current Stack Top and ST(i) to specify the ith register from TOP in the stack ($0 \leq i \leq 7$). For example, if TOP contains 011B (register 3 is the top of the stack), the following statement would add the contents of two registers in the stack (registers 3 and 5):

```
FADD    ST, ST(2)
```

The stack organization and top-relative addressing of the numeric registers can simplify subroutine programming by allowing routines to pass parameters on the register stack. By using the stack to pass parameters rather than using "dedicated" registers, calling routines gain flexibility in how they use the stack. As long as the stack is not full, each routine simply loads the parameters onto the stack before calling a particular subroutine to perform a numeric calculation. The subroutine then addresses its parameters as ST, ST(1), etc., even though TOP may, for example, refer to physical register 3 in one invocation and physical register 5 in another. Programmers can use the numeric registers like a conventional stack as described herein, or by using the pipelined architecture of the Pentium processor in conjunction with the FXCH instruction, reduce stack bottleneck and move towards a random register machine.

6.2.1.2. THE FPU STATUS WORD

The 16-bit status word shown in Figure 6-2 reflects the overall state of the FPU. This status word may be stored into memory using the FSTSW/FNSTSW, FSTENV/FNSTENV, and FSAVE/FNSAVE instructions, and can be transferred into the AX register with the FSTSW AX/FNSTSW AX instructions, allowing the FPU status to be inspected by the Integer Unit.

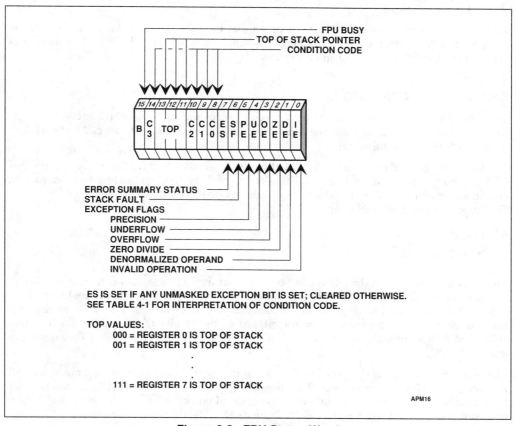

Figure 6-2. FPU Status Word

The four FPU condition code bits (C_3-C_0) are similar to the flags in a CPU: the processor updates these bits to reflect the outcome of arithmetic operations. The effect of these instructions on the condition code bits is summarized in Table 6-4. These condition code bits are used principally for conditional branching. The FSTSW AX instruction stores the FPU status word directly into the AX register, allowing these condition codes to be inspected efficiently. The SAHF instruction can copy C_3-C_0 directly to the CPU's flag bits to simplify conditional branching. Table 6-5 shows the mapping of these bits to the CPU flag bits.

Bits 11-13 of the status word point to the FPU register that is the current Top of Stack (TOP). The significance of the stack top has been described in the prior section on the register stack.

Figure 6-2 shows the six exception flags in bits 0-5 of the status word. Bit 7 is the exception summary status (ES) bit. ES is set if any unmasked exception bits are set, and is cleared otherwise. Bits 0-5 indicate whether the FPU has detected one of six possible exception conditions since these status bits were last cleared or reset. (For definitions of exceptions, refer to Chapter 7.) They are "sticky" bits, and can only be cleared by the instructions FINIT, FCLEX, FLDENV, FSAVE, and FRSTOR.

The B-bit (bit 15) is included for 8087 compatibility only. It reflects the contents of the ES bit (bit 7 of the status word).

Bit 6 is the stack fault (SF) bit. This bit distinguishes invalid operations due to stack overflow or underflow from other kinds of invalid operations. When SF is set, bit 9 (C_1) distinguishes between stack overflow ($C_1 = 1$) and underflow ($C_1 = 0$).

6.2.1.3.   CONTROL WORD

The FPU provides the programmer with several processing options, which are selected by loading a word from memory into the control word. Figure 6-3 shows the format and encoding of the fields in the control word.

The low-order byte of this control word configures the numerical exception masking. Bits 0–5 of the control word contain individual masks for each of the six floating-point exception conditions recognized by the processor. The high-order byte of the control word configures the FPU processing options, including

- Precision control
- Rounding control

The precision-control bits (bits 8–9) can be used to set the FPU internal operating precision at less than the default precision (64-bit significand). These control bits can be used to provide compatibility with the earlier-generation arithmetic processors having less precision than the Intel 32-bit FPU's. The precision-control bits affect the results of only the following five arithmetic instructions: ADD, SUB(R), MUL, DIV(R), and SQRT. No other operations are affected by PC.

The rounding-control bits (bits 10–11) provide for the common round-to-nearest mode, as well as directed rounding and true chop. Rounding control affects the arithmetic instructions (refer to Section 6.3. in this chapter for lists of arithmetic and nonarithmetic instructions) and certain non arithmetic instructions, namely (FLD constant) and (FST(P)mem) instructions.

Table 6-4. Condition Code Interpretation

Instruction	C0	C3	C2	C1
FCOM, FCOMP, FCOMPP, FTST, FUCOMPP, FICOM, FICOMP	Result of Comparison		Operands is not Comparable	Zero or O/U#
FXAM	Operand class			Sign or O/U#
FPREM, FPREM1	Q2	Q1	0=reduction complete 1=reduction incomplete	Q0 or O/U#
FIST, FBSTP, FRINDINT, FST, FSTP, FADD, FMUL, FDIV, FDIVR, FSUB, FSUBR, FSCALE, FSQRT, FPATAN, F2XM1, FYL2X, FYL2XP1	UNDEFINED			Roundup or O/U#
FPTAN, FSIN, FCOS, FSINCOS	UNDEFINED		0=reduction complete 1=reduction incomplete	Roundup or O/U# (UNDEFINED) if C2=1)
FCHS, FABS, FXCH, FINCSTP, FDECSTP, Constant Loads, FXTRACT, FLD, FILD, FBLD, FSTP (ext. real)	UNDEFINED			Zero or O/U#
FLDENV, FRSTOR	Each bit loaded from memory			
FLDCW, FSTENV, FSTCW, FSTSW, FCLEX	UNDEFINED			
FINIT, FSAVE	Zero	Zero	Zero	Zero

NOTES

O/U# — When both IE and SF bits of status word are set, indicating a stack exception, this bit distinguishes between stack overflow (C1=1) and underflow (C1=0).

Reduction — If FPREM and FPREM1 produces a remainder that is les than the modulus, reduction is complete. When reduction is incomplete the value at the top of the stack is a partial remainder, which can be used as input to further reduction. For FPTAN, FSIN, FCOS and FSINCOS, the reduction bit is set if the operand at the top of the stack is too large. In this case, the original operand remains at the top of the stack.

Roundup — When the PE bit of the status word is set, this bit indicates whether the last rounding in the instruction was upward.

UNDEFINED — Do not rely on any specific value in these bits.

Table 6-5. Correspondence Between FPU and IU Flag Bits

FPU Flag	IU Flag
C0	CF
C1	(none)
C2	PF
C3	ZF

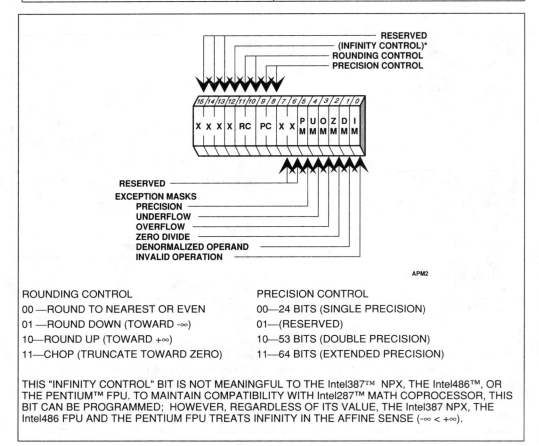

Figure 6-3. FPU Control Word Format

6.2.1.4.   THE FPU TAG WORD

The tag word (TW) indicates the contents of each register in the register stack, as shown in Figure 6-4. The TW is used by the FPU itself to distinguish between empty and nonempty register locations. Programmers of exception handlers may use this tag information to check the contents of a numeric register without performing complex decoding of the actual data in the register. The tag values from the TW correspond to physical registers 0–7. Programmers must use the current top-of-stack (TOP) pointer stored in the FPU status word to associate these tag values with the relative stack registers ST(0) through ST(7).

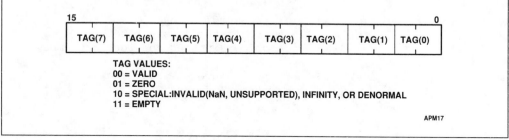

Figure 6-4. Tag Word Format

The exact values of the tags are generated during execution of the FSTENV and FSAVE instructions according to the actual contents of the nonempty stack locations. During execution of other instructions, the processor updates the TW only to indicate whether a stack location is empty or nonempty. As a result, the FPU tag word may not be the same as previously written when saving the FPU state, modifying the tag word, and reloading the FPU state. This can be demonstrated using the following steps to modify the FPU tag word. This example assumes FPU register 0 has the value 0 and tag(0)=11 (empty). Example 6-1 contains the actual assembly code to perform these steps.

1. FSAVE/FSTENV stores FPU state to memory M. M[tag(0)]=11 (empty).

2. Modify memory such that M[tag(0)]=10 (i.e., special, infinity, or denormal).

3. FLDENV loads fp state from memory M to FPU.

4. FSAVE/FSTENV stores FPU state to memory M again. The value of M[tag(0)] will be 01 (i.e., indicates zero because FPU register 0 has the value of 0).

Example 6-1. Modifying the Tag Word

```
    name tagword

stack stackseg 100

data segment rw use16
fpstate    dw    7  dup (?)
fpstate2   dw    7  dup (?)
data ends

code segment er public use16
   assume ds:data, ss:stack
start:
mov      ax,data
```

```
mov      ds,ax                          ; set segment register

finit                                   ; initialize FPU
fldz                                    ; load zero
mov      bx, offset fpstate
fsave    [bx]                           ; save FPU state

mov      ax,[bx+4]                      ; tag word, AX should be 7FFFh,
                                        ; top of the fp stack has
                                        ; zero value and the rest are empty

mov      word ptr [bx+4], 3FFFh         ; now change the zero tag (01) to
                                        ; the valid tag (00)

fldenv   [bx]
mov      bx, offset fpstate2            ; now the tag word is 3FFFh
fsave    [bx]                           ; but we are saving 7FFFh to tag
                                        ; word
code     ends
   end start, ds:data, ss:stack
```

6.2.1.5.   OPCODE FIELD OF LAST INSTRUCTION

The opcode field in Figure 6-5 describes the 11-bit format of the last non-control FPU instruction executed. The first and second instruction bytes (after all prefixes) are combined to form the opcode field. Since all floating-point instructions share the same five upper bits in the first instruction byte (following prefixes), they are not stored in the opcode field. Note that the second instruction byte is actually located in the low-order byte of the stored opcode field.

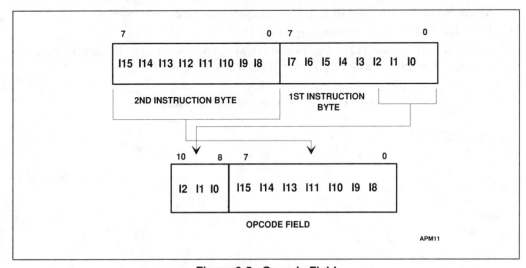

Figure 6-5. Opcode Field

6.2.1.6. THE NUMERIC INSTRUCTION AND DATA POINTERS

The instruction and data pointers provide support for programmed exception-handlers. Whenever the processor decodes an ESC instruction other than FINIT, FCLEX, FLDCW, FSTCW, FSTSW, FSTSWAX, FSTENV, FLDENV, FSAVE, FRSTOR, and FWAIT, it saves the instruction address opcode and the oeprand address (if present) in registers than can be accessed by the user. Contents of these registers remain unchanged when any of the control instructions listed above is executed. Contents of the operand address register are undefined if the prior ESC instruction (which is not one of the above) did not have a memory operand.

These registers can be accessed by the ESC instructions FSTENV, FLDENV, FSAVE and FRSTOR. The FINIT and FSAVE instructions clear these registers after writing them to memory.

When stored in memory, the instruction and data pointers appear in one of four formats, depending on the operating mode of the processor (protected mode or real-address mode) and depending on the operand-size attribute in effect (32-bit operand or 16-bit operand). In virtual-8086 mode, the real-address mode formats are used. Figures 6-6 through Figure 6-9 show these pointers as they are stored following an FSTENV instruction. The FSTENV and FSAVE instructions store this data into memory, allowing exception handlers to determine the precise nature of any numeric exceptions that may be encountered.

For all the Intel x86 FPU and NPX architectures, the instruction address saved points to any prefixes that preceded the instruction, except the 8087, for which the instruction address points only to the ESC instruction opcode.

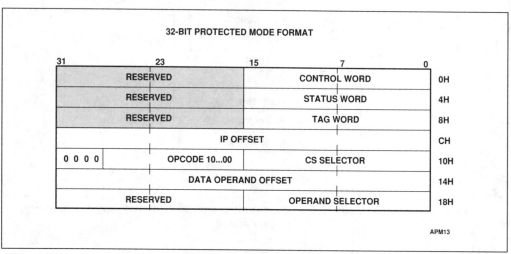

Figure 6-6. Protected Mode Numeric Instruction and Data Pointer Image in Memory, 32-Bit Format

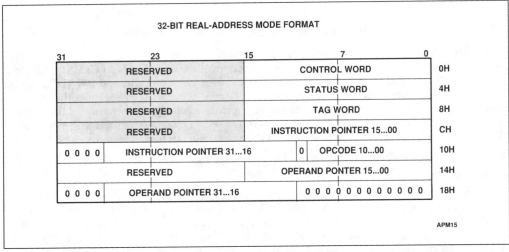

Figure 6-7. Real Mode Numeric Instruction and Data Pointer Image in Memory, 32-Bit Format

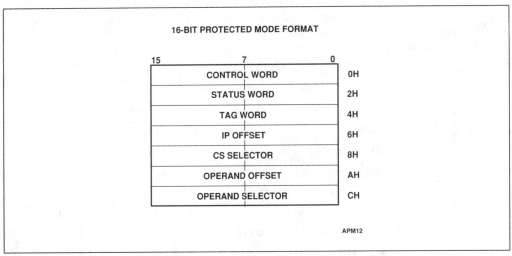

Figure 6-8. Protected Mode Numeric Instruction and Data Pointer Image in Memory, 16-Bit Format

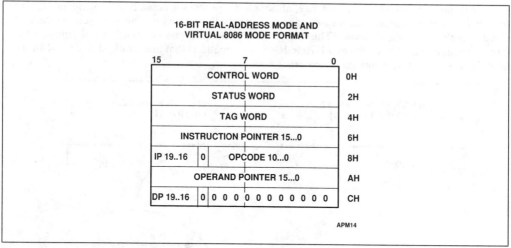

Figure 6-9. Real Mode Numeric Instruction and Data Pointer Image in Memory, 16-Bit Format

6.2.2.   Computation Fundamentals

This section covers numeric programming concepts that are common to all applications. It describes the FPU's internal number system and the various types of numbers that can be employed in numeric programs. The most commonly used options for rounding and precision (selected by fields in the control word) are described, with exhaustive coverage of less frequently used facilities deferred to later sections. Exception conditions that may arise during execution of floating-point instructions are also described along with the options that are available for responding to these exceptions.

6.2.2.1.   NUMBER SYSTEM

The system of real numbers that people use for pencil and paper calculations is conceptually infinite and continuous. There is no upper or lower limit to the magnitude of the numbers one can employ in a calculation, or to the precision (number of significant digits) that may be required to represent them. For any given real number, there are always arbitrarily many numbers both larger and smaller. There are also arbitrarily many numbers between any two real numbers. For example, between 2.5 and 2.6 are 2.51, 2.5897, 2.500001, etc.

While ideally it would be desirable for a computer to be able to operate on the entire real number system, in practice this is not possible. Computers, no matter how large, ultimately have fixed-size registers and memories that limit the system of numbers that can be accommodated. These limitations determine both the range and the precision of numbers. The result is a set of numbers that is finite and discrete, rather than infinite and continuous. This sequence is a subset of the real numbers that is designed to form a useful approximation of the real number system.

Figure 6-10 superimposes the basic floating-point number system on a real number line (decimal numbers are shown for clarity, although the processor actually represents numbers in binary). The dots indicate the subset of real numbers the processor can represent as data and final results of calculations. The range of double-precision, normalized numbers is approximately $\pm 2.23 \times 10^{-308}$ to $\pm 1.79 \times 10^{308}$. Applications that are required to deal with data and final results outside this range are rare.

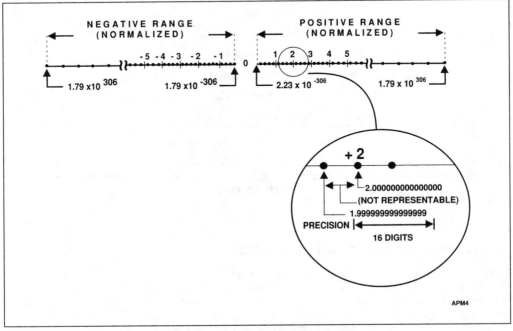

Figure 6-10. Double-Precision Number System

The finite spacing in Figure 6-10 illustrates that the FPU can represent a great many, but not all, of the real numbers in its range. There is always a gap between two adjacent floating-point numbers, and it is possible for the result of a calculation to fall in this space. When this occurs, the FPU rounds the true result to a number that it can represent. Thus, a real number that requires more digits than the FPU can accommodate (e.g., a 20-digit number) is represented with some loss of accuracy. Notice also that the representable numbers are not distributed evenly along the real number line. In fact, the same number of representable numbers exists between any two successive powers of 2 (i.e., as many representable numbers exist between 2 and 4 as between 65,536 and 131,072). Therefore, the gaps between representable numbers are larger as the numbers increase in magnitude. All integers in the range $\pm 2^{64}$ (approximately $\pm 10^{19}$), however, are exactly representable.

In its internal operations, the FPU actually employs a number system that is a substantial superset of that shown in Figure 6-10. The internal format (called extended real) extends the representable (normalized) range to about $\pm 3.37 \times 10^{-4932}$ to $\pm 1.18 \times 10^{4932}$, and its precision to about 19 (equivalent decimal) digits. This format is designed to provide extra range and precision for constants and intermediate results, and is not normally intended for data or final results.

From a practical standpoint, the processor's set of real numbers is sufficiently large and dense so as not to limit the vast majority of applications. Compared to most computers, including mainframes, the processor provides a very good approximation of the real number system. It is important to remember, however, that it is not an exact representation, and that computer arithmetic on real numbers is inherently approximate.

6.2.2.2. DATA TYPES AND FORMATS

The processor recognizes seven numeric data types for memory-based values, divided into three classes: binary integers, packed decimal integers, and binary reals. How these formats are stored in memory are discussed later in this section (the sign is always located in the highest-addressed byte).

Figure 6-11 summarizes the format of each data type. In the figure, the most significant digits of all numbers (and fields within numbers) are the leftmost digits.

6.2.2.2.1. Binary Integers

The three binary integer formats are identical except for length, which governs the range that can be accommodated in each format. The leftmost bit is interpreted as the number's sign: 0=positive and 1=negative. Negative numbers are represented in standard two's complement notation (the binary integers are the only format to use two's complement). The quantity zero is represented with a positive sign (all bits are 0). The word integer format is identical to the 16-bit signed integer data type; the short integer format is identical to the 32-bit signed integer data type.

The binary integer formats exist in memory only. When used by the FPU, they are automatically converted to the 80-bit extended real format. All binary integers are exactly representable in the extended real format.

6.2.2.2.2. Decimal Integers

Decimal integers are stored in packed decimal notation, with two decimal digits "packed" into each byte, except the leftmost byte, which carries the sign bit (0=positive, 1=negative). Negative numbers are not stored in two's complement form and are distinguished from positive numbers only by the sign bit. The most significant digit of the number is the leftmost digit. All digits must be in the range 0–9.

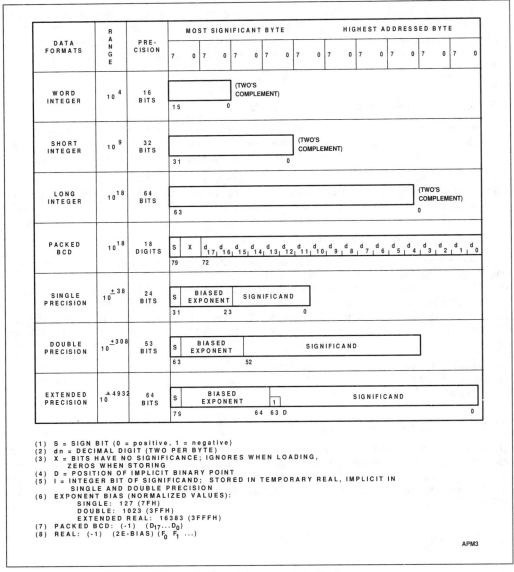

Figure 6-11. Numerical Data Formats

The decimal integer format exists in memory only. When used by the FPU, it is automatically converted to the 80-bit extended real format. All decimal integers are exactly representable in the extended real format.

6.2.2.2.3. Real Numbers

The processor represents real numbers of the form:

$$(-1)^s 2^E (b_0 \Delta b_1 b_2 b_3 .. b_{p-1})$$

where:

s = 0 or 1

E = any integer between Emin and Emax, inclusive

b_i = 0 or 1

p = number of bits of precision

Table 6-6 summarizes the parameters for each of the three real-number formats.

The Pentium processor stores real numbers in a three-field binary format that resembles scientific, or exponential, notation. The format consists of the following fields:

- The *significand* field, $b_0 \Delta b_1 b_2 b_3 .. b_{p-1}$, is the number's significant digits. (The term "significand" is analogous to the term "mantissa" used to describe floating-point numbers on some computers.)

- The *exponent* field, e = E+bias, locates the binary point within the significant digits (and therefore determines the number's magnitude). (The term "exponent" is analogous to the term "characteristic" used to describe floating-point numbers on some computers.)

- The 1-bit *sign* field, which indicates whether the number is positive or negative. Negative numbers differ from positive numbers only in the sign bits of their significands.

Table 6-6. Summary of Format Parameters

Parameter	Format		
	Single	Double	Extended
Format width in bits	32	64	80
p (bits of precision)	24	53	64
Exponent width in bits	8	11	15
Emax	+127	+1023	+16383
Emin	-126	-1022	-16382
Exponent bias	+127	+1023	+16383

Table 6-7 shows how the real number 178.125 (decimal) is stored in the single real format. The table lists a progression of equivalent notations that express the same value to show how a number can be converted from one form to another. (The ASM386/486 and PL/M386/486 language translators perform a similar process when they encounter programmer-defined real number constants.) Note that not every decimal fraction has an exact binary equivalent. The decimal number 1/10, for example, cannot be expressed exactly in binary (just as the number 1/3 cannot be expressed exactly in decimal). When a translator encounters such a value, it produces a rounded binary approximation of the decimal value.

Table 6-7. Real Number Notation

Notation	Value		
Ordinary Decimal	178.125		
Scientific Decimal	1 ∆ 78125E2		
Scientific Binary	1 ∆ 0110010001E111		
Scientific Binary Biased Exponent)	1∆0110010001E10000110		
Single Format (Normalized)	Sign	Biased Exponent	Signifcand
	0	10000110	01100100010000000000000 1 ∆ (implict)

The FPU usually carries the digits of the significand in normalized form. This means that, except for the value zero, the significand contains an *integer* bit and fraction bits as follows:

1∆fff...ff

where ∆ indicates an assumed binary point. The number of fraction bits varies according to the real format: 23 for single, 52 for double, and 63 for extended real. By normalizing real numbers so that their integer bit is always a 1, the processor eliminates leading zeros in small values ($|X| < 1$). This technique maximizes the number of significant digits that can be accommodated in a significand of a given width. Note that, in the single and double formats, the integer bit is *implicit* and is not actually stored; the integer bit is physically present in the extended format only.

If one were to examine only the significand with its assumed binary point, all normalized real numbers would have values greater than or equal to one and less than two. The exponent field locates the *actual* binary point in the significant digits. Just as in decimal scientific notation, a positive exponent has the effect of moving the binary point to the right, and a negative exponent effectively moves the binary point to the left, inserting leading zeros as necessary. An unbiased exponent of zero indicates that the position of the assumed binary point is also the position of the actual binary point. The exponent field, then, determines a real number's magnitude.

In order to simplify comparing real numbers (e.g., for sorting), the processor stores exponents in a biased form. This means that a constant, called a bias, is added to the *true exponent* described above. As Table 6-6 shows, the value of this *bias* is different for each real format. It has been chosen so as to force the *biased exponent* to be a positive value. This allows two real numbers (of the same format and sign) to be compared as if they are unsigned binary integers. That is, when comparing them bitwise from left to right (beginning with the leftmost exponent bit), the first bit position that differs orders the numbers; there is no need to proceed further with the comparison. A number's true exponent can be determined simply by subtracting the bias value of its format.

The single and double real formats exist in memory only. If a number in one of these formats is loaded into an FPU register, it is automatically converted to extended format, the format used for all internal operations. Likewise, data in registers can be converted to single or double real for storage in memory. The extended real format may be used in memory also, typically to store intermediate results that cannot be held in registers.

Most applications should use the double format to store real-number data and results; it provides sufficient range and precision to return correct results with a minimum of programmer attention. The single real format is appropriate for applications that are constrained by memory, but it should be recognized that this format provides a smaller margin of safety. It is also useful for the debugging of algorithms, because roundoff problems will manifest themselves more quickly in this format. The extended real format should normally be reserved for holding intermediate results, loop accumulations, and constants. Its extra length is designed to shield final results from the effects of rounding and overflow/underflow in intermediate calculations. However, the range and precision of the double format are adequate for most microcomputer applications.

6.2.2.3.   ROUNDING CONTROL

Internally, the FPU employs three extra bits (guard, round, and sticky bits) that enable it to round numbers in accord with the infinitely precise true result of a computation; these bits are not accessible to programmers. Whenever the destination can represent the infinitely precise true result, the FPU delivers it. Rounding occurs in arithmetic and store operations when the format of the destination cannot exactly represent the infinitely precise true result. For example, a real number may be rounded if it is stored in a shorter real format, or in an integer format. Or, the infinitely precise true result may be rounded when it is returned to a register.

The FPU has four rounding modes, selectable by the RC field in the control word (see Figure 6-3). Given a true result b that cannot be represented by the target data type, the FPU determines the two representable numbers a and c that most closely bracket b in value ($a < b < c$). The processor then rounds (changes) b to a or to c according to the mode selected by the RC field as shown in Table 6-8. Rounding introduces an error in a result that is less than one unit in the last place to which the result is rounded.

- "Round to nearest" is the default mode and is suitable for most applications; it provides the most accurate and statistically unbiased estimate of the true result.
- The "chop" or "round toward zero" mode is provided for integer arithmetic applications.
- "Round up" and "round down" are termed *directed rounding* and can be used to implement interval arithmetic. Interval arithmetic is used to determine upper and lower bounds for the true result of a multistep computation, when the intermediate results of the computation are subject to rounding.

Rounding control affects only the arithmetic instructions (refer to Section 6.3. in this chapter for lists of arithmetic and nonarithmetic instructions).

Table 6-8. Rounding Modes

RC Field	Rounding Mode	Rounding Action
00	Round to Nearest	Closer to *b* of *a* or *c*; if equally close, select even number (the one whose least significant bit is zero).
01	Round Down (toward -∞)	*a*
10	Round up (toward +∞)	*c*
11	Chop (toward 0)	Smaller in magnitude of *a* or *c*.

NOTE: *a* < *b* < *c*; *a* and *c* are successive representable numbers; *b* is not representable

6.2.2.4. PRECISION CONTROL

The FPU allows results to be calculated with either 64, 53, or 24 bits of precision in the significand as selected by the precision control (PC) field of the control word. The default setting (following FINIT), and the one that is best suited for most applications, is the full 64 bits of significance provided by the extended real format. The other settings are required by the IEEE standard and are provided to obtain compatibility with the specifications of certain existing programming languages. Specifying less precision nullifies the advantages of the extended format's extended fraction length. When reduced precision is specified, the rounding of the fractional value clears the unused bits on the right to zeros. Precision Control affects only the instructions FADD, FSUB, FMUL, FDIV, and FSQRT.

6.3. FLOATING-POINT INSTRUCTION SET

The floating-point instructions available on the Pentium processor can be grouped into six functional classes:

- Data Transfer Instructions
- Nontranscendental Instructions
- Comparison Instructions
- Transcendental Instructions
- Constant Instructions
- Control Instructions

In this chapter, the instruction classes are described as a collection of resources available to programmers. For details of format, encoding, and execution times, see the instruction reference pages in Chapter 25.

The Intel387 math coprocessors and the Intel486 and Pentium FPU's have more instructions than the 8087/Intel287 math coprocessors. Some Intel386 DX microprocessor systems use an Intel287 math coprocessor. See Chapter 5 for examples of how to identify the processor type and determine what instructions are available.

6.3.1. Source and Destination Operands

The typical floating-point instruction takes one or two operands, which can come from the FPU register stack or from memory. Many instructions, such as FSIN, automatically operate on the top FPU stack element. Others allow, or require, the programmer to code the operand(s) explicitly along with the instruction mnemonic. Still others accept one explicit operand and one implicit operand (usually the top FPU stack element).

Whether specified by the programmer or supplied by default, floating-point operands are of two basic types, *sources* and *destinations*. A source operand provides an input to an instruction, but is not altered by its execution. Even when an instruction converts the source operand from one format to another (e.g., real to integer), the conversion is performed in an internal work area to avoid altering the source operand. A destination operand may also provide an input to an instruction; on execution, however, the instruction returns a result to the destination, overwriting its previous contents.

Many instructions allow their operands to be coded in more than one way. For example, FADD (add real) may be written without operands, with only a source, or with a destination and a source. When both destination and source operands are specified, the destination must precede the source on the command line, and both must come from the FPU stack.

Memory operands can be coded with any of the memory-addressing methods provided by the ModR/M byte. To review these methods (BASE = (INDEX X SCALE) + DISPLACEMENT), refer to Chapter 3. Floating-point instructions with memory operands either read from memory or write to it; no floating-point instruction does both. For a detailed description of each instruction, including its range of possible encodings, see the reference pages in Chapter 25.

6.3.2. Data Transfer Instructions

These instructions (summarized in Table 6-9) move operands among elements of the register stack, and between the stack top and memory. Any of the seven data types can be converted to extended-real and loaded (pushed) onto the stack in a single operation; they can be stored to memory in the same manner. The data transfer instructions automatically update the FPU tag word to reflect whether the register is empty or full following the instruction.

Table 6-9. Data Transfer Instructions

Real		Integer		Packed Decimal	
FLD	Load Real	FILD	Load Integer	FBLD	Load Packed Decimal
FST	Store Real	FIST	Store Integer		
FSTP	Store Real and Pop	FISTP	Store Integer and Pop	FBSTP	Store Packed Decimal and Pop
FXCH	Exchange register Contents				

6.3.3. Nontranscendental Instructions

The nontranscendental instruction set provides a wealth of variations on the basic add, subtract, multiply, and divide operations, and a number of other useful functions. These range from a simple absolute value instruction to instructions which perform exact modulo division, round real numbers to integers, and scale values by powers of two. Table 6-10 shows the nontranscendental operations provided, apart from basic arithmetic.

Table 6-10. Nontranscendental Instructions (Besides Arithmetic)

Mnemonic	Operation
FSQRT	Square Root
FSCALE	Scale
FXTRACT	Extract Exponent and Significand
FPREM	Partial Remainder
FPREM1*	IEEE Standard Partial Remainder
FRNDINT	Round to Integer
FABS	Absolute Value
FCHS	Change Sign

* Not available on 8087 or Intel287™ math coprocessor.

The basic arithmetic instructions (addition, subtraction, multiplication and division) are designed to encourage the development of very efficient algorithms. In particular, they allow the programmer to reference memory as easily as the FPU register stack. Table 6-11 summarizes the available operation/operand forms that are provided for basic arithmetic. In addition to the four normal operations, there are "reversed" subtraction and division instructions which eliminate the need for many exchanges between ST(0) and ST(1). The variety of instruction and operand forms give the programmer unusual flexibility:

- Operands can be located in registers or memory.
- Results can be deposited in a choice of registers.
- Operands can be a variety of numerical data types: extended real, double real, single real, short integer or word integer, with automatic conversion to extended real performed by the FPU.

Table 6-11. Basic Arithmetic Instructions and Operands

Instruction Form	Mnemonic Form	Operand Forms: Destination, Source
Classical Stack	F*op*	{ST(1), ST}
Classical Stack, extra pop	F*op*P	{ST(1), ST}
Register	F*op*	ST(i), ST or ST, ST(i)
Register, pop	F*op*P	ST(i), ST
Real Memory	F*op*	{ST} single-real/double-real
Integer Memory	FI*op*	{ST} word-integer/short-integer

NOTES:

Braces ({ }) surround implicit operands; these are not coded, but are supplied by the assembler.

op =

	ADD	DEST ← DEST + SRC
	SUB	DEST ← ST – Other Operand
	SUBR	DEST ← Other Operand – ST
	MUL	DEST ← DEST × SRC
	DIV	DEST ← DEST ÷ SRC
	DIVR	DEST ← SRC ÷ DEST

Five basic instruction forms can be used across all six operations, as shown in Table 6-11. The classical stack form can be used to make the FPU operate like a classical stack machine. No operands are coded in this form, only the instruction mnemonic. The FPU picks the source operand from the stack top (ST) and the destination from the next stack element (ST(1)). After performing its calculation, it returns the result to ST(1) and then pops ST, effectively replacing the operands by the result.

The register form is a generalization of the classical stack form; the programmer specifies the stack top as one operand and any register on the stack as the other operand. Coding the stack top as the destination provides a convenient way to access a constant, held elsewhere in the stack, from the top stack. The destination need not always be ST, however. The basic two-operand instructions allow the use of another register as the destination. Using ST as the source allows, for example, adding the stack top into a register used as an accumulator.

Often the operand in the stack top is needed for one operation but then is of no further use in the computation. The register pop form can be used to pick up the stack top as the source operand, and then discard it by popping the stack. Coding operands of ST(1), ST with a register pop mnemonic is equivalent to a classical stack operation: the top is popped and the result is left at the new top.

The two memory forms increase the flexibility of the nontranscendental instructions. They permit a real number or a binary integer in memory to be used directly as a source operand. This is useful in situations where operands are not used frequently enough to justify holding them in registers. Note that any memory-addressing method can be used to define these operands, so they can be elements in arrays, structures, or other data organizations, as well as simple scalars.

6.3.4. Comparison Instructions

The instructions of this class allow numbers of all supported real and integer data types to be compared. Each of these instructions (Table 6-12) analyzes the top stack element, often in relationship to another operand, and reports the result as a condition code (flags C0, C2, and C3) in the status word.

Table 6-12. Comparison Instructions

Mnemonic	Operation
FCOM	Compare Real
FCOMP	Compare Real and Pop
FCOMPP	Compare Real and Pop Twice
FICOM	Compare Integer
FICOMP	Compare Integer and Pop
FTST	Test
FUCOM*	Unordered Compare Real
FUCOMP*	Unordered Compare Real and Pop
FUCOMPP*	Unordered Compare Real and Pop Twice
FXAM	Examine

The basic operations are compare, test (compare with zero), and examine (report type, sign, and normalization). Special forms of the compare operation are provided to optimize algorithms by allowing direct comparisons with binary integers and real numbers in memory, as well as popping the stack after a comparison.

The FSTSW AX (store status word) instruction can be used after a comparison to transfer the condition code to the AX register for inspection. The TEST instruction is recommended for using the FPU flags (once they are in the AX register) to control conditional branching. First check to see if the comparison resulted in *unordered*. This can happen, for instance, if one of the operands is a NaN. TEST the contents of the AX register against the constant 0400H; this will clear ZF (the Zero Flag of the EFLAGS register) if the original comparison was unordered, and set ZF otherwise. The JNZ instruction can then be used to transfer control (if necessary) to code that handles the case of unordered operands. With the unordered case now filtered out, TEST the contents of the AX register against the appropriate constant from Table 6-13, and then use the corresponding conditional branch.

Table 6-13. TEST Constants for Conditional Branching

Order	Constant	Branch
ST > Operand	4500H	JZ
ST < Operand	0100H	JNZ
ST = Operand	4000H	JNZ
Unordered	0400H	JNZ

It is not always necessary to filter out the unordered case when using this algorithm for conditional jumps. If the software has been thoroughly tested, and incorporates periodic checks for QNaN results (as recommended previously), then it is not necessary to check for *unordered* every time a comparison is made.

Instructions other than those in the comparison group can update the condition code. To ensure that the status word is not altered inadvertently, store it immediately following a comparison operation.

6.3.5. Transcendental Instructions

The instructions in this group (Table 6-14) perform the time-consuming core calculations for all common trigonometric, inverse trigonometric, hyperbolic, inverse hyperbolic, logarithmic, and exponential functions. The transcendentals operate on the top one or two stack elements, and they return their results to the stack. The trigonometric operations assume their arguments are expressed in radians. The logarithmic and exponential operations work in base 2.

Table 6-14. Transcendental Instructions

Mnemonic	Operation
FSIN*	Sine
FCOS*	Cosine
FSINCOS*	Sine and Cosine
FPTAN**	Tangent
FPATAN	Arctangent of ST(1) ÷ ST
F2XM1**	$2^X - 1$; X is in ST
FYL2X	$Y \times \log_2 X$; Y is in ST(1), X is in ST
FYL2XP1	$Y \times \log_2(X + 1)$; Y is in ST(1), X is in ST

NOTES:
*Not available on 8087/Intel287™ math coprocessor.
**Operand range extended over 8087/Intel287 math coprocessor.

The Pentium processor uses new algorithms for transcendental instructions, achieving a higher level of accuracy for the same instructions than the Intel486 processor. Accuracy is measured in terms of units in the last place (ulp). For a given argument x, let $f(x)$ and $F(x)$ be the correct and computed (approximate) function values respectively. The error in ulps is defined to be

$$\left| \frac{f(x) - F(x)}{2^{k - 63}} \right|$$

where k is an integer such that $1 \le 2^{-k}f(x) < 2$.

On the Pentium processor, the worst case error on functions is less than 1 ulp when rounding to the nearest-even and less than 1.5 ulps when rounding in other modes. The functions are guaranteed to be monotonic, with respect to the input operands, throughout the domain supported by the instruction. See Appendix G for detailed information on transcendental accuracy.

The trigonometric functions accept a practically unrestricted range of operands, whereas the other transcendental instructions require that arguments be more restricted in range. FPREM or FPREM1 can be used to bring the otherwise valid operand of a periodic function into range. Prologue and epilogue software can be used to reduce arguments for other instructions to the expected range and to adjust the result to correspond to the original arguments if necessary. The instruction descriptions in the reference pages of Chapter 25 document the allowed operand range for each instruction.

When the argument of a trigonometric function is in range, it is automatically reduced by the appropriate multiple of 2π (in 66-bit precision), by means of the same mechanism used in the FPREM and FPREM1 instructions. The value of π used in the automatic reduction has been chosen so as to guarantee no loss of significance in the operand, provided it is within the specified range. The internal value of π in hexadecimal is:

$$4 * 0.C90FDAA22168C234C$$

A program may use an explicit value for π in computations whose results later appear as arguments to trigonometric functions. In such a case (in explicit reduction of a trigonometric operand outside the specified range, for example), the value used for π should be the same as the full 66-bit internal π. This will insure that the results are consistent with the automatic argument reduction performed by the trigonometric functions. The 66-bit π cannot be represented as an extended-real value, so it must be encoded as two or more numbers. A common solution is to represent π as the sum of a highπ which contains the 33 most-significant bits and a lowπ which contains the 33 least-significant bits. When using this two-part π, all computations should be performed separately on each part, with the results added only at the end.

The complications of maintaining a consistent value of π for argument reduction can be avoided, either by applying the trigonometric functions only to arguments within the range of the automatic reduction mechanism, or by performing all argument reductions (down to a magnitude less than $\pi/4$) explicitly in software.

6.3.6.   Constant Instructions

Each of these instructions, shown in Table 6-15, pushes a commonly used constant onto the stack. (ST(7) must be empty to avoid an invalid exception.) The values have full extended real precision (64 bits) and are accurate to approximately 19 decimal digits. Because an external real constant occupies 10 memory bytes, the constant instructions, which are only two bytes long, save storage and improve execution speed, in addition to simplifying programming.

Table 6-15. Constant Instructions

Mnemonic	Operation
FLDZ	Load +0.0
FLD1	Load +1.0
FLDPI	Load π
FLDL2T	Load $\log_2 10$
FLDL2E	Load $\log_2 e$
FLDLG2	Load $\log_{10} 2$
FLDLN2	Load $\log_e 2$

The constants used by these instructions are stored internally in a format more precise than extended real. When loading the constant, the FPU rounds the more precise internal constant according the RC (rounding control) bit of the control word. However, in spite of this rounding, the precision exception is not raised (to maintain compatibility). When the rounding control is set to round to nearest, the FPU produces the same constant that is produced by the 8087 and Intel287 numeric coprocessors.

6.3.7.   Control Instructions

The FPU control instructions are shown in Table 6-16. The FSTSW instruction is commonly used for conditional branching. The remaining instructions are not typically used in calculations; they provide control over the FPU for system-level activities. These activities include initialization of the FPU, numeric exception handling, and task switching.

As shown in Table 6-16, certain instructions have alternative mnemonics. The instructions which initialize the FPU, clear exceptions, or store (all or part of) the FPU environment come in two forms:

- *Wait*—the mnemonic is prefixed only with an F, such as FSTSW. This form checks for unmasked numeric exceptions.
- *No-wait*—the mnemonic is prefixed with an FN, such as FNSTSW. This form ignores unmasked numeric exceptions.

When a control instruction is coded using the no-wait form of the mnemonic, the ASM386/Intel486 assembler does not precede the ESC instruction with a WAIT instruction. The processor does not test for a floating-point error condition before executing a control instruction.

The only no-wait instructions are those shown in Table 6-16. All other floating-point instructions are automatically synchronized by the processor; all operands are transferred before the next instruction is initiated. Because of this automatic synchronization, non-control floating-point instructions need not be preceded by a WAIT instruction in order to execute correctly.

Exception synchronization relies on the WAIT instruction. Since the Integer Unit and the FPU operate in parallel, it is possible in the case of a floating-point exception for the processor to disturb information vital to exception recovery before the exception-handler can be invoked. Coding a WAIT or FWAIT instruction in the proper place can prevent this. See the next section for details.

Table 6-16. Control Instructions

Mnemonic	Operation
FINIT / FNINIT	Initialize FPU
FLDCW	Load Control Word
FSTCW/FNSTCW	Store Control Word
FSTSW/FNSTSW	Store Status Word
FSTSW AX/FNSTSW AX*	Store Status Word to AX Register
FCLEX/FNCLEX	Clear Exceptions
FSTENV/FNSTENV	Store Environment
FLDENV	Load Environment
FSAVE/FNSAVE	Save State
FRSTOR	Restore State
FINCSTP	Increment Stack Top Pointer
FDECSTP	Decrement Stack Top Pointer
FFREE	Free Regiser
FNOP	No Operation
FWAIT	Report FPU Error

NOTE:
*Not available on 8087 math coprocessor.

It should also be noted that the 8087 instructions FENI and FDISI and the Intel287 math coprocessor instruction FSETPM perform no function in the Pentium, Intel486 and Intel386/Intel387 processors. If these opcodes are detected in the instruction stream, the 32-bit processors perform no specific operation and no internal states are affected. Chapter 23 contains a more complete description of the differences between floating-point operations on the Pentium and Intel486 processors and on the 8087, Intel287, and Intel387 DX numeric coprocessors.

6.4. NUMERIC APPLICATIONS

This section describes how programmers in assembly language and in a variety of higher-level languages can make use of the Intel486 processor's numerics capabilities.

The level of detail in this section is intended to give programmers a basic understanding of the software tools that can be used for numeric programming, but this information does not document the full capabilities of these facilities. Complete documentation is available with each program development product.

6.4.1. High-Level Languages

A variety of Intel high-level languages are available that automatically make use of the numeric instruction set when appropriate. These languages include C-386/486 and PL/M-386/486. In addition, many high-level language compilers optimized for the Pentium processor are available from independent software vendors.

Each of these high-level languages has special numeric libraries allowing programs to take advantage of the capabilities of the FPU. No special programming conventions are necessary to make use of the FPU when programming numeric applications in any of these languages.

Programmers in PL/M-386/486 and ASM386/486 can also make use of many of these library routines by using routines contained in the Support Library. These libraries implement many of the functions provided by higher-level languages, including exception handlers, ASCII-to-floating-point conversions, and a more complete set of transcendental functions than that provided by the processor's numeric instruction set.

6.4.1.1. C PROGRAMS

C programmers automatically cause the C compiler to generate Intel486 numeric instructions when they use the **double** and **float** data types. The **float** type corresponds to the single real format; the **double** type corresponds to the double real format. The statement **#include ⟨ math.h⟩** causes mathematical functions such as **sin** and **sqrt** to return values of type **double**. Example 6-2 illustrates the ease with which C programs can make use of the processor's numerics capabilities.

6.4.1.2. PL/M-386/486

Programmers in PL/M-386/486 can access a very useful subset of the FPU's numeric capabilities. The PL/M-386/486 REAL data type corresponds to the single real (32-bit) format. This data type provides a range of about $8.43 \times 10^{-37} \leq \mid X \mid \leq 3.38 \times 10^{38}$, with about seven significant decimal digits. This representation is adequate for the data manipulated by many microcomputer applications.

Example 6-2. Sample C Program

```
/*************************************************************
*                                                           *
*                   SAMPLE C PROGRAM                        *
*************************************************************/

/** Include stdio.h if necessary **/
/** Include math declarations for transcendentals and others **/

#include <math.h>
#define PI 3.1415926535897943

main()
double sin_result, cos_result;
double angle_deg = 0.0, angle_rad;
int i, no_of_trial=4;

for (i = 1; i <= no_of_trial; i++) {
    angle_rad = angle_deg * PI / 180.0;
    sin_result = sin (angle_rad);
    cos_result = cos (angle_rad);
    printf("sine of %f degrees equals %f\n", angle_deg, sin_result);
    printf("cosine of %f degrees equals %f\n\n", angle_deg,
cos_result);
    angle_deg = angle_deg + 30.0;
    }
/** etc. **/
}
```

The utility of the REAL data type is extended by the PL/M-386/486 compiler's practice of holding intermediate results in the extended real format. This means that the full range and precision of the processor are utilized for intermediate results. Underflow, overflow, and rounding exceptions are most likely to occur during intermediate computations rather than during calculation of an expression's final result. Holding intermediate results in extended-precision real format greatly reduces the likelihood of overflow and underflow and eliminates roundoff as a serious source of error until the final assignment of the result is performed.

The compiler generates floating-point instructions to evaluate expressions that contain REAL data types, whether variables or constants or both. This means that addition, subtraction, multiplication, division, comparison, and assignment of REALs will be performed by the FPU. INTEGER expressions, on the other hand, are evaluated by the Integer Unit.

Five built-in procedures (Table 6-17) give the PL/M-Intel386/Intel486 programmer access to FPU control instructions. Prior to any arithmetic operations, a typical PL/M-386/486 program will set up the FPU using the INIT$REAL$MATH$UNIT procedure and then issue SET$REAL$MODE to configure the FPU. SET$REAL$MODE loads the FPU control word, and its 16-bit parameter has the format shown previously for the control word. The recommended value of this parameter is 033EH (round to nearest, 64-bit precision, all exceptions masked except invalid operation). Other settings may be used at the programmer's discretion.

Table 6-17. PL/M-386/486 Built-In Procedures

Procedure	FPU Control Instruction	Description
INIT$REAL$MATH$UNIT	FINIT	Initialize FPU
SET$REAL$MODE	FLDCW	Set exception masks, rounding precision, and infinity controls.
GET$REAL$ERROR	FNSTSW& FNCLEX	Store, then clear, exception flags.
SAVE$REAL$STATUS	FNSAVE	Save FPU state.
RESTORE$REAL$STATUS	FRSTOR	Restore FPU state.

If any exceptions are unmasked, an exception handler must be provided in the form of an interrupt procedure that is designated to be invoked via interrupt vector number 16. The exception handler can use the GET$REAL$ERROR procedure to obtain the low-order byte of the FPU status word and to then clear the exception flags. The byte returned by GET$REAL$ERROR contains the exception flags; these can be examined to determine the source of the exception.

The SAVE$REAL$STATUS and RESTORE$REAL$STATUS procedures are provided for multitasking environments where a running task that uses the FPU may be preempted by another task that also uses the FPU. It is the responsibility of the operating system to issue SAVE$REAL$STATUS before it executes any statements that affect the FPU; these include the INIT$REAL$MATH$UNIT and SET$REAL$MODE procedures as well as arithmetic expressions. SAVE$REAL$STATUS saves the FPU state (registers, status, and control words, etc.) on the memory stack. RESTORE$REAL$STATUS reloads the state information; the preempting task must invoke this procedure before terminating in order to restore the FPU to its state at the time the running task was preempted. This enables the preempted task to resume execution from the point of its preemption.

6.4.1.3.   ASM386/486

The ASM386/486 assembly language provides programmers with complete access to all of the facilities of the processor.

6.4.1.3.1.   Defining Data

The ASM386/486 directives shown in Table 6-18 allocate storage for numeric variables and constants. As with other storage allocation directives, the assembler associates a type with any variable defined with these directives. The type value is equal to the length of the storage unit in bytes (10 for DT, 8 for DQ, etc.). The assembler checks the type of any variable coded in an instruction to be certain that it is compatible with the instruction. For example, the coding FIADD ALPHA will be flagged as an error if ALPHA's type is not 2 or 4, because integer addition is only available for word and short integer (doubleword) data types. The operand's type also tells the assembler which machine instruction to produce; although to the programmer there is only an FIADD instruction, a different machine instruction is required for each operand type.

Table 6-18. ASM386/486 Storage Allocation Directives

Directives	Interpretation	Data Types
DW	Define Word	Word integer
DD	Define Doubleword	Short integer, short real
DQ	Define Quadword	Long integer, long real
DT	Define Tenbyte	Packed decimal, temporary real

On occasion it is desirable to use an instruction with an operand that has no declared type. For example, if register BX points to a short integer variable, a programmer may want to code FIADD [BX]. This can be done by informing the assembler of the operand's type in the instruction, coding FIADD DWORD PTR [BX]. The corresponding overrides for the other storage allocations are WORD PTR, QWORD PTR, and TBYTE PTR.

The assembler does not, however, check the types of operands used in processor control instructions. Coding FRSTOR [BP] implies that the programmer has set up register BP to point to the location (probably in the stack) where the processor's 94-byte state record has been previously saved.

The initial values for numeric constants may be coded in several different ways. Binary integer constants may be specified as bit strings, decimal integers, octal integers, or hexadecimal strings. Packed decimal values are normally written as decimal integers, although the assembler will accept and convert other representations of integers. Real values may be written as ordinary decimal real numbers (decimal point required), as decimal numbers in scientific notation, or as hexadecimal strings. Using hexadecimal strings is primarily intended for defining special values such as infinities, NaNs, and denormalized numbers. Most programmers will find that ordinary decimal and scientific decimal provide the simplest way to initialize numeric constants. Example 6-3 compares several ways of setting the various numeric data types to the same initial value.

Example 6-3. Sample Numeric Constants

```
; THE FOLLOWING ALL ALLOCATE THE CONSTANT: -126
; NOTE TWO'S COMPLEMENT STORAGE OF NEGATIVE BINARY INTEGERS.
;
EVEN                      ;FORCE WORD ALIGNMENT
WORD_INTEGER    DW 1111111110000010b       ;BIT STRING
SHORT_INTEGER   DD 0FFFFFF82H              ;HEX STRING MUST START
                                          ;WITH DIGIT
LONG_INTEGER    DQ -126                    ;ORDINAL DECIMAL
SINGLE_REAL     DD -126.0                  ;NOTE PRESENCE OF .
DOUBLE_REAL     DD -1.26e2                 ;SCIENTIFIC
PACKED_DECIMAL  DT -126                    ;ORDINARY DECIMAL INTEGER
;
; IN THE FOLLOWING, SIGN AND EXPONENT IS 'C005'
;     SIGNIFICAND IS '7300...00', 'R' INFORMS ASSEMBLER THAT
```

```
;    THE STRING REPRESENTS A REAL DATA TYPE.
;
EXTENDED_REAL  DT 0C0057E00000000000000R   ;HEX STRING
```

Note that preceding numeric variables and constants with the ASM386/486 EVEN directive ensures that the operands will be word-aligned in memory. The best performance is obtained when data transfers are aligned. See Chapter 24 for alignment strategies for the different processors. All numeric data types occupy integral numbers of words so that no storage is "wasted" if blocks of variables are defined together and preceded by a single EVEN declarative.

6.4.1.3.2.   Records and Structures

The ASM386/486 RECORD and STRUC (structure) declaratives can be very useful in numeric programming. The record facility can be used to define the bit fields of the control, status, and tag words. Example 6-4 shows one definition of the status word and how it might be used in a routine that polls the FPU until it has completed an instruction.

Example 6-4. Status Word Record Definition

```
; RESERVE SPACE FOR STATUS WORD
STATUS_WORD
; LAY OUT STATUS WORD FIELDS
STATUS RECORD
&    BUSY:           1,
&    COND_CODE3:     1,
&    STACK_TOP: 3,
&    COND_CODE2:     1,
&    COND_CODE1:     1,
&    COND_CODE0:     1,
&    INT_REQ:        1,
&    S_FLAG:         1,
&    P_FLAG:         1,
&    U_FLAG:         1,
&    O_FLAG:         1,
&    Z_FLAG:         1,
&    D_FLAG:         1,
&    I_FLAG:         1
; REDUCE UNTIL COMPLETE
REDUCE:
    FPREM1
    FNSTSW      STATUS_WORD
    TEST STATUS_WORD, MASK_COND_CODE2
    JNZ   REDUCE
```

Because structures allow different but related data types to be grouped together, they often provide a natural way to represent "real world" data organizations. The fact that the structure template may be "moved" about in memory adds to its flexibility. Example 6-5 shows a simple structure that might be used to represent data consisting of a series of test score samples. This sample structure can be reorganized, if necessary, for the sake of more efficient execution. If the two double real fields were listed before the integer fields, then (provided that the structure is instantiated only at addresses divisible by eight) all the fields would be optimally aligned for efficient memory access and caching. A structure could also be used to define the organization of the information stored and loaded by the FSTENV and FLDENV instructions.

Example 6-5. Structure Definition

```
SAMPLE STRUC
      N_OBS DD ?        ; SHORT INTEGER
      MEAN  DQ ?        ; DOUBLE REAL
      MODE  DW ?        ; WORD INTEGER
      STD_DEV    DQ ? ; DOUBLE REAL
      ; ARRAY OF OBSERVATIONS -- WORD INTEGER
      TEST_SCORES DW 1000 DUP (?)
SAMPLE ENDS
```

6.4.1.3.3.   Addressing Methods

Numeric data in memory can be accessed with any of the memory addressing methods provided by the ModR/M byte and (optionally) the SIB byte. This means that numeric data types can be incorporated in data aggregates ranging from simple to complex according to the needs of the application. The addressing methods and the ASM386/486 notation used to specify them in instructions make the accessing of structures, arrays, arrays of structures, and other organizations direct and straightforward. Table 6-19 gives several examples of numeric instructions coded with operands that illustrate different addressing methods.

Table 6-19. Addressing Method Examples

Coding	Interpretation
FIADD ALPHA	ALPHA is a simple scalar (mode is direct).
FDIVR ALPHA.BETA	BETA is a field in a structure that is "overlaid" on ALPHA (mode is direct).
FMUL QWORD PTR [BX]	BX contains the address of a long real variable (mode is register indirect).
FSUB ALPHA [SI]	ALPHA is an array and SI contains the offset of an array element from the start of the array (mode is indexed).
FILD [BP].BETA	BP contains the address of a structure on the CPU stack and BETA is a field in the structure (mode is based).
FBLD TBYTE PTR [BX] [DI]	BX contains the address of a packed decimal array and DI contains the offset of an array element (mode is based indexed).

6.4.1.4. COMPARATIVE PROGRAMMING EXAMPLE

The following code examples show the PL/M-386/486 and ASM386/486 code for a simple numeric program, called ARRSUM. The program references an array (X$ARRAY), which contains 0–100 single real values; the integer variable NOFX indicates the number of array elements the program is to consider. ARRSUM steps through X$ARRAY accumulating three sums:

- SUM$X, the sum of the array values
- SUM$INDEXES, the sum of each array value times its index, where the index of the first element is 1, the second is 2, etc.
- SUM$SQUARES, the sum of each array element squared

Example 6-6. Sample PL/M-386/486 Program

```
/******************************************************************
*                                                                *
*                      ARRAYSUM MODULE                           *
*                                                                *
******************************************************************/

array$sum:   do;
    declare (sum$x, sum$indexes, sum$squares) real;
    declare x$array(100) real;
    declare (n$of$x, i) integer;
    declare control $ FPU literally '033eh';

    / *Assume x$array and n$of$x are initialized */
    call init$real$math$unit;
    call set$real$mode(control $ FPU);

    /* Clear sums */
    sum$x, sum$indexes, sum$squares = 0.0;

    /* Loop through array, accumulating sums */
    do i = 0 to n$of$x - 1;
        sum$x = sum$x + x$array(i);
        sum$indexes = sum$indexes + (x$array(i)*float(i+1));
        sum$squares = sum$squares + (x$array(i)*x$array(i));
    end;

    /* etc. */
end array$sum;
```

Example 6-7. Sample ASM386/486 Program

```
name arraysum

; Define initialization routine
```

```
extrn initFPU:far

; Allocate space for data

data segment rw public
        control_FPU     dw 033eh
        n_of_x          dd ?
        x_array         dd 100 dup(?)
        sum_squares     dd ?
        sum_indexes     dd ?
        sum_x           dd ?
data ends

; Allocate CPU stack space

stack stackseg 400

; Begin code

code segment er public
        assume ds:data, ss:stack

start:
        mov   ax, data
        mov   ds, ax
        mov   ax, stack
        mov   ss, ax
        mov   esp, stackstart stack

; Assume x_array and n_of_x have been initialized

; Prepare the FPU or its emulator

        call  initFPU
        fldcw control_FPU

; Clear three registers to hold running sums

        fldz
        fldz
        fldz

; Setup ECX as loop counter and ESI as index into x_array

        mov   ecx, n_of_x
        imul  ecx
        mov   esi, eax

; ESI now contains index of last element + 1
; Loop through x_array and accumulate sum

sum_next:
; Back up one element and push on the stack

        sub   esi, type x_array
        fld   x_array[esi]
```

```
; Add to the sum and duplicate x on the stack

    fadd  st(3), st
    fld   st

; Square it and add into the sum of (index+1) and discard

    fmul  st, st
    faddp st(2), st
    fmul  n_of_x
    faddp st(2), st

; Reduce index for next iteration

    loop  sum_next

; Pop sums into memory

pop_results:
    fstp  sum_squares
    fstp  sum_indexes
    fstp  sum_x
    fwait

;
; Etc.
;
code ends
end start, ds:data, ss:stack
```

(A true program, of course, would go beyond these steps to store and use the results of these calculations.) The control word is set with the recommended values: round to nearest, 64-bit precision, interrupts enabled, and all exceptions masked except invalid operation. It is assumed that an exception handler has been written to field the invalid operation if it occurs, and that it is invoked by interrupt pointer 16.

The PL/M-386/486 version of ARRAYSUM is very straightforward and illustrates how easily the numerics capabilities of the Intel486 processor can be used in this language. After declaring variables, the program calls built-in procedures to initialize the FPU and to load to the control word. The program clears the sum variables and then steps through X$ARRAY with a DO-loop. The loop control takes into account PL/M-386/486's practice of considering the index of the first element of an array to be 0. In the computation of SUM$INDEXES, the built-in procedure FLOAT converts I+1 from integer to real because the language does not support "mixed mode" arithmetic. One of the strengths of the Intel486 FPU, of course, is that it *does* support arithmetic on mixed data types (because all values are converted internally to the 80-bit extended-precision real format).

The ASM386/486 version defines the external procedure INITFPU, which makes the different initialization requirements of the processor and its emulator transparent to the source code. After defining the data and setting up the segment registers and stack pointer, the program calls INITFPU and loads the control word. The computation begins with the next three instructions, which clear three registers by loading (pushing) zeros onto the stack. As shown in Figure 6-12, these registers remain at the bottom of the stack throughout the computation while temporary values are pushed on and popped off the stack above them.

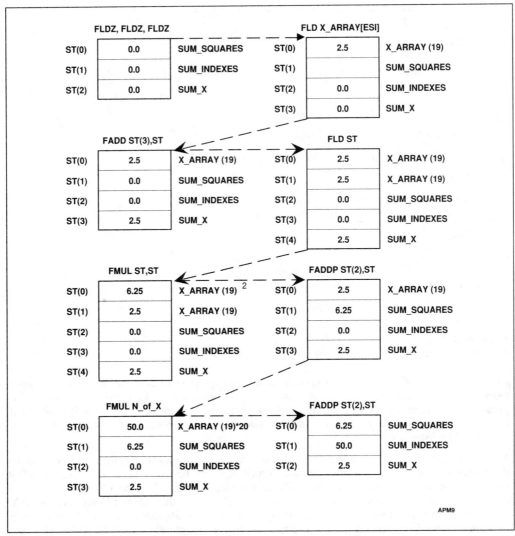

Figure 6-12. Instructions and Register Stack

The program uses the LOOP instruction to control its iteration through X_ARRAY; register ECX, which LOOP automatically decrements, is loaded with n_of_x the number of array elements to be summed. Register ESI is used to select (index) the array elements. The program steps through X_ARRAY from back to front, so ESI is initialized to point at the element just beyond the first element to be processed. The ASM386/486 TYPE operator is used to determine the number of bytes in each array element. This permits changing X_ARRAY to a double-precision real array by simply changing its definition (DD to DQ) and reassembling.

Figure 6-12 shows the effect of the instructions in the program loop on the FPU register stack. The figure assumes that the program is in its first iteration, that N_OF_X is 20, and that

X_ARRAY(19) (the 20th element) contains the value 2.5. When the loop terminates, the three sums are left as the top stack elements so that the program ends by simply popping them into memory variables.

6.4.1.5.   CONCURRENT PROCESSING

Because the Intel Pentium Processor Integer Unit (IU) and FPU execution units are separate, it is possible for the FPU to execute numeric instructions in parallel with integer instructions. This simultaneous execution of different instructions is called concurrency.

No special programming techniques are required to gain the advantages of concurrent execution; numeric instructions are simply placed in line with the integer instructions. Integer and numeric instructions are initiated in the same order as they are encountered in the instruction stream. However, because numeric operations performed by the FPU generally require more time than integer operations, the IU can often execute several instructions before the FPU completes a numeric instruction previously initated.

This concurrency offers obvious advantages in terms of execution performance, but concurrency also imposes several rules that must be observed in order to assure proper synchronization of the IU and FPU .

All Intel high-level languages automatically provide for and manage concurrency in the FPU. Assembly-language programmers, however, must understand and manage some areas of concurrency in exchange for the flexibility and performance of programming in assembly language. This section is for the assembly-language programmer or well-informed high-level-language programmer.

6.4.1.6.   MANAGING CONCURRENCY

The activities of numeric programs can be split into two major areas: program control and arithmetic. The program control part performs activities such as deciding what functions to perform, calculating addresses of numeric operands, and loop control. The arithmetic part simply adds, subtracts, multiplies, and performs other operations on the numeric operands. The processor is designed to handle these two parts separately and efficiently.

Concurrency management is required to check for an exception before letting the processor change a value just used by the FPU. Almost any numeric instruction can, under the wrong circumstances, produce a numeric exception. For programmers in higher-level languages, all required synchronization is automatically provided by the appropriate compiler. For assembly-language programmers exception synchronization remains the responsibility of the programmer.

A complication is that a programmer may not expect their numeric program to cause numeric exceptions, but in some systems, they may regularly happen. To better understand these points, consider what can happen when the FPU detects an exception.

Depending on options determined by the software system designer, the processor can perform one of two things when a numeric exception occurs:

- The FPU can provide a default fix-up for selected numeric exceptions. Programs can mask individual exception types to indicate that the FPU should generate a safe, reasonable result whenever that exception occurs. The default exception fix-up activity is treated by the FPU as part of the instruction causing the exception; no external indication of the exception is given. When exceptions are detected, a flag is set in the numeric status register, but no information regarding where or when is available. If the FPU performs its default action for all exceptions, then the need for exception synchronization is not manifest. However, as will be shown later, this is not sufficient reason to ignore exception synchronization when designing programs that use the FPU.

- As an alternative to the default fix-up of numeric exceptions, the IU can be notified whenever an exception occurs. When a numeric exception is unmasked and the exception occurs, the FPU stops further execution of the numeric instruction and signals this event. On the next occurrence of an ESC or WAIT instruction, the processor traps to a software exception handler. The exception handler can then implement any sort of recovery procedures desired for any numeric exception detectable by the FPU. Some ESC instructions do not check for exceptions. These are the nonwaiting forms FNINIT, FNSTENV, FNSAVE, FNSTSW, FNSTCW, and FNCLEX.

When the FPU signals an unmasked exception condition, it is requesting help. The fact that the exception was unmasked indicates that further numeric program execution under the arithmetic and programming rules of the FPU is unreasonable.

If concurrent execution is allowed, the state of the processor when it recognizes the exception is undefined. It may have changed many of its internal registers and be executing a totally different program by the time the exception occurs. To handle this situation, the FPU has special registers updated at the start of each numeric instruction to describe the state of the numeric program when the failed instruction was attempted.

Exception synchronization ensures that the FPU is in a well-defined state after an unmasked numeric exception occurs. Without a well-defined state, it would be impossible for exception recovery routines to determine why the numeric exception occurred, or to recover successfully from the exception.

The following two sections illustrate the need to always consider exception synchronization when writing numeric code, even when the code is initially intended for execution with exceptions masked. If the code is later moved to an environment where exceptions are unmasked, the same code may not work correctly. An example of how some instructions written without exception synchronization will work initially, but fail when moved into a new environment, is shown in the following section.

6.4.1.7.   EXCEPTION SYNCHRONIZATION

In the following examples, three instructions are shown to load an integer, calculate its square root, then increment the integer. The synchronous execution of the FPU will allow this program to execute correctly when no exceptions occur on the FILD instruction.

Incorrect Error Synchronization:

```
FILD  COUNT      ; FPU instruction
INC   COUNT      ; integer instruction alters operand
FSQRT            ; subsequent FPU instruction -- error
            ; from previous FPU
            ; instruction detected here
```

Proper Error Synchronization:

```
FILD COUNT            ; FPU instruction
FSQRT                 ; subsequent FPU instruction -- error from
                      ; previous FPU
                      ; instruction detected here
INC COUNT             ; integer instruction alters operand
```

This situation changes if the numeric register stack is extended to memory. To extend the FPU stack to memory, the invalid exception is unmasked. A push to a full register or pop from an empty register sets SF and causes an invalid exception.

The recovery routine for the exception must recognize this situation, fix up the stack, then perform the original operation. The recovery routine will not work correctly in the first example shown in the figure. The problem is that the value of COUNT is incremented before the exception handler is invoked, so that the recovery routine will load an incorrect value of COUNT, causing the program to fail or behave unreliably.

6.4.1.8.   PROPER EXCEPTION SYNCHRONIZATION

Exception synchronization relies on the WAIT instruction. Whenever an unmasked numerical exception occurs, the FPU asserts an error-condition signal internal to the processor. When the next WAIT instruction (or an ESC instruction other than FNINIT, FNCLEX, FNSTSW, FNSTSW AX, FNSTCW, FNSTENV, FNSAVE) is encountered, the error-condition signal is acknowledged and a software exception handler is invoked. (See Chapter 7 for a more detailed discussion of the various floating-point error-reporting mechanisms.) If this WAIT or ESC instruction is properly placed, the processor will not yet have disturbed any information vital to recovery from the exception. A WAIT instruction should also be placed after the last floating point instruction in an application so that any unmasked exceptions will be serviced before the task completes.

intel®

7

Special
Computational
Situations

Besides being able to represent positive and negative numbers, the numerical data formats may be used to describe other entities. These special values provide extra flexibility, but most users will not need to understand them in order to use the numerics capabilities of the processor successfully. This section describes the special values that may occur in certain cases and the significance of each. The numeric exceptions are also described, for writers of exception handlers and for those interested in probing the limits of numeric computation.

The material presented in this section is mainly of interest to programmers concerned with writing exception handlers. Many readers will only need to skim this section.

When discussing these special computational situations, it is useful to distinguish between *arithmetic instructions* and *nonarithmetic instructions*. Nonarithmetic instructions are those that have no operands or transfer their operands without substantial change; arithmetic instructions are those that make significant changes to their operands. Table 7-1 defines these two classes of instructions.

7.1. SPECIAL NUMERIC VALUES

The numerical data formats encompass encodings for a variety of special values in addition to the typical real or integer data values that result from normal calculations. These special values have significance and can express relevant information about the computations or operations that produced them. The various types of special values are:

- Denormal real numbers
- Zeros
- Positive and negative infinity
- NaN (Not-a-Number)
- Indefinite
- Unsupported formats

The following sections explain the origins and significance of each of these special values. Tables 7-2 through Tables 7-6 show how each of these special values is encoded for each of the numeric data types.

Table 7-1. Arithmetic and Nonarithmetic Instructions

Nonarithmetic Instructions	Arithmetic Instructions
FABS	F2XM1
FCHS	FADD (P)
FCLEX	FBLD
FDECSTP	FBSTP
FFREE	FCOMP(P)(P)
FINCSTP	FCOS
FINIT	FDIV(R)(P)
FLD (register-to-register)	FIADD
FLD (extended format from memory)	FICOM(P)
FLD constant	FIDIV(R)
FLDCW	FILD
FLDENV	FIMUL
FNOP	FIST(P)
FRSTOR	FISUB(R)
FSAVE	FLD (conversion)
FST(P) (register-to-register)	FMUL(P)
FSTP (extended format to memory)	FPATAN
FSTCW	FPREM
FSTENV	FPREM1
FSTSW	FPTAN
FWAIT	FRNDINT
FXAM	FSCALE
FXCH	FSIN
	FSINCOS
	FSQRT
	FST(P) (conversion)
	FSUB(R)(P)
	FTST
	FUCOM(P)(P)
	FXTRACT
	FYL2X
	FYL2XP1

Table 7-2. Binary Integer Encodings

Class	Sign	Magnitude
Positives		
(Largest)	0	11..11
	.	.
	.	.
	.	.
(Smallest)	0	00..01
Zero	0	00..00
Negatives		
(Smallest)	1	11..11
	.	.
	.	.
	.	.
	.	.
(Largest/Indefinite*)	1	00..00
	Word:	15 bits
	Short:	31 bits
	Long:	63 bits

NOTES:

*If this encoding is used as a source operand (as in an integer load or integer arithmetic instruction), the FPU interprets it as the largest negative number representable in the format... -2^{15}, -2^{31}, or -2^{63}. The FPU delivers this encoding to an integer destination in two cases:

1. If the result is the largest negative number.

2. As the response to a masked invalid operation exception, in which case it represents the special value *integer indefinite*.

Table 7-3. Packed Decimal Encodings

Class	Sign		Magnitude					
			digit	digit	digit	digit	...	digit
Positives								
Largest	0	0000000	1001	1001	1001	1001	...	1001
	.	.			.			
	.	.			.			
	.	.			.			
Smallest	0	0000000	0000	0000	0000	0000	...	0001
Zero	0	0000000	0000	0000	0000	0000	...	0000
Negatives								
Zero	1	0000000	0000	0000	0000	0000	...	0000
Smallest	1	0000000	0000	0000	0000	0000	...	0000
	.	.			.			
	.	.			.			
	.	.			.			
					.			
Largest	1	0000000	1001	1001	1001	1001	...	1001
Indefinite*	1	1111111	1111	1111	UUUU**	UUUU	...	UUUU
	—1 byte—		—9 bytes—					

NOTES:

*   The packed decimal indefinite is stored by FBSTP in response to a masked invalid operation exception. Attempting to load this value via FBLD produces an undefined result.

**   UUUU means bit values are undefined and may contain any value.

Table 7-4. Single and Double Real Encodings

Class	Sign	Biased Exponent	Significand ff-ff*
Positive NaNs			
Quiet	0 . . 0	11..11 . . 11..11	11..11 . . 10..00
Signaling	0 . . 0	11..11 . . 11..11	01..11 . . 00..01
Infinity	0	11..11	00..00
Positive Reals			
Normals	0 . . 0	11..10 . . 00..01	11..11 . . 00..00
Denormals	0 . . 0	00..00 . . 00..00	11.11 . . 00..01
Zero	0	00..00	00..00
Negative Reals			
Zero	1	00..00	00..00
Denormals	1 . . 1	00..00 . . 00..00	00..01 . . 11..11
Normals	1 . . 1	00..01 . . 11..10	00..00 . . 11..11
Infinity	1	11..11	00..00
Negative NaNs			
Signaling	1 . . 1	11..11 . . 11..11	00..01 . . 01..11
Quiet	1 (Indefinite) . . 1	11..11 . . 11..11	10..00 . . 11..11
Single: Double:		—8 bits— —11 bits—	—23 bits— —52 bits—

NOTE: *Integer bit is implied and not stored.

Table 7-5. Extended Real Encodings

Class	Sign	Biased Exponent	Significand ff-ff*
Positive NaNs			
Quiet	0 . . 0	11..11 . . 11..11	1 11..11 . . 1 10..00
Signaling	0 . . 0	11..11 . . 11..11	1 01..11 . . 1 00..01
Infinity	0	11..11	1 00..00
Positive Reals			
Normals	0 . . 0	11..10 . . 00..01	1 11..11 . . 1 00..00
Pseudodenormals	0 . 0	00..00 . 00..00	1 11.11 . 1 00..01
Denormals	0 . . 0	00..00 . . 00..00	0 11.11 . . 0 00..01
Zero	0	00..00	0 00..00
Negative Reals			
Zero	1	00..00	0 00..00
Denormals	1 . . 1	00..00 . . 00..00	0 00..01 . . 0 11..11
Pseudodenormals	0 . 0	00..00 . 00..00	1 11..11 . 1 00..00
Normals	1 . . 1	00..01 . . 11..10	1 00..00 . . 1 11..11
Infinity	1	11..11	1 00..00
Negative NaNs			
Signaling	1 . . 1	11..11 . . 11..11	1 00..01 . . 1 01..11
Quiet	1 (Indefinite) . . 1	11..11 . . 11..11	1 10..00 . . 1 11..11
		—15 bits—	—64 bits—

Table 7-6. Unsupported Formats

Class	Sign	Biased Exponent	Significand f△ff-ff*
Positive Pseudo-NaNs			
Quiet	0 . . 0	11..11 . . 11..11	0△ 11..11 . . 0 10..00
Signaling	0 . . 0	11..11 . . 11..11	0 01..11 . . 0 00..01
Pseudoinfinity	0	11..11	1 00..00
Positive Reals			
Unnormals	0 . . 0	11..10 . . 00..01	0 11..11 . . 0 00..00
Negative Reals			
Unnormals	1 . . 1	11..10 . . 00..01	0 11..01 . . 0 00..00
Pseudoinfinity	1	11..11	0 00..00
Negative Pseudo NaNs			
Signaling	1 . . 1	11..11 . . 11..11	0 01..11 . . 0 00..01
Quiet	1 . . 1	11..11 . . 11..11	0 11..11 . . 0 10..00
		—15 bits—	—64 bits—

7.1.1. Denormal Real Numbers

The processor generally stores nonzero real numbers in normalized floating-point form; that is, the integer (leading) bit of the significand is always a one. (Refer to the previous section for a review of operand formats.) This bit is explicitly stored in the extended format, and is implicitly assumed to be a one ($1_\triangle$) in the single and double formats. Since leading zeros are eliminated, normalized storage allows the maximum number of significant digits to be held in a significand of a given width.

When a numeric value becomes very close to zero, normalized floating-point storage cannot be used to express the value accurately. The term *tiny* is used here to precisely define what values require special handling. A number R is said to be *tiny* when $-2^{Emin} < R < 0$ or $0 < R < +2^{Emin}$. (As defined in the previous section, Emin is -126 for single format, -1022 for double format, and -16382 for extended format.) In other words, a nonzero number is *tiny* if its exponent would be too negative to store in the destination format.

To accommodate these instances, the processor can store and operate on reals that are not normalized, i.e., whose significands contain one or more leading zeros. Denormals typically arise when the result of a calculation yields a value that is *tiny*.

Denormal values have the following properties:

- The biased floating-point exponent is stored at its smallest value (zero)
- The integer bit of the significand (whether explicit or implicit) is zero

The leading zeros of denormals permit smaller numbers to be represented, at the possible cost of some lost precision (the number of significant bits is reduced by the leading zeros). In typical algorithms, extremely small values are most likely to be generated as intermediate, rather than final, results. By using the extended real format for holding intermediate values, quantities as small as $\pm 3.37 \times 10^{-4932}$ can be represented; this makes the occurrence of denormal numbers a rare phenomenon in numerical applications. Nevertheless, the processor can load, store, and operate on denormalized real numbers when they do occur.

Denormals receive special treatment by the processor in three respects:

- The processor avoids creating denormals whenever possible. In other words, it always normalizes real numbers except in the case of tiny numbers.
- The processor provides the unmasked underflow exception to permit programmers to detect cases when denormals would be created.
- The processor provides the denormal operand exception to permit programmers to detect cases when denormals enter into calculations.

Denormalizing means incrementing the true result's exponent and inserting a corresponding leading zero in the significand, shifting the rest of the significand one place to the right. Denormal values may occur in any of the single, double, or extended formats. Table 7-7 shows the range of denormalized values in each format.

Table 7-7. Denormalized Values

Format	Smallest Magnitude		Largest Magnitude	
	(Exact)	(Approx.)	(Exact)	(Approx.)
Single Precision	2^{-149}	10^{-46}	$2^{-126}\text{--}2^{-150}$	10^{-38}
Double Precision	2^{-1074}	10^{-324}	$2^{-1022}\text{--}2^{-1075}$	10^{-308}
Extended	2^{-16445}	10^{-4951}	$2^{-16382}\text{--}2^{-16445}$	10^{-4932}

Denormalization produces either a denormal or a zero. Denormals are readily identified by their exponents, which are always the minimum for their formats; in biased form, this is always the bit string: 00..00. This same exponent value is also assigned to the zeros, but a denormal has a nonzero significand. A denormal in a register is tagged *special*. Tables 7-2 through Table 7-6 show how denormal values are encoded in each of the real data formats.

The denormalization process causes loss of significance if low-order one-bits are shifted off the right of the significand. In a severe case, *all* the significand bits of the true result are shifted out and replaced by the leading zeros. In this case, the result of denormalization is a true zero, and, if the value is in a register, it is tagged as a zero.

Denormals are rarely encountered in most applications. Typical debugged algorithms generate extremely small results only during the evaluation of intermediate subexpressions; the final result is usually of an appropriate magnitude for its single or double format real destination. If intermediate results are held in temporary real, as is recommended, the greater range of this format makes underflow very unlikely. Denormals are likely to arise only when an application generates a great many intermediates, so many that they cannot be held on the register stack or in extended format memory variables. If storage limitations force the use of single or double format reals for intermediates, and small values are produced, underflow may occur, and, if masked, may generate denormals.

When a denormal number in single or double format is used as a source operand and the denormal exception is masked, the FPU automatically *normalizes* the number when it is converted to extended format.

7.1.2. Zeros

The value *zero* in the real and decimal integer formats may be signed either positive or negative, although the sign of a binary integer zero is always positive. For computational purposes, the value of zero always behaves identically, regardless of sign, and typically the fact that a zero may be signed is transparent to the programmer. If necessary, the FXAM instruction may be used to determine a zero's sign.

A programmer can code a zero, or it can be created by the FPU as its masked response to an underflow exception. If a zero is loaded or generated in a register, the register is tagged *zero*. Table 7-8 lists the results of instructions executed with zero operands and also shows how a zero may be created from nonzero operands.

7.1.3. Infinity

The real formats support signed representations of infinities. These values are encoded with a biased exponent of all ones and a significand of $1_\Delta00..00$; if the infinity is in a register, it is tagged *special*.

A programmer can code an infinity, or it can be created by the FPU as its masked response to an overflow or a zero divide exception. Note that depending on rounding mode, the masked response may create the largest valid value representable in the destination rather than infinity.

The signs of the infinities are observed, and comparisons are possible. Infinities are always interpreted in the affine sense; that is, $-\infty <$ (any finite number) $< +\infty$. Arithmetic on infinities is always exact and, therefore, signals no exceptions, except for the invalid operations specified in Table 7-9.

Table 7-8. Zero Operands and Results

Operation	Operands	Result
FLD, FLBD	±0	$*0$
FILD	$+0$	$+0$
FST, FSTP, FRNDINT	±0	$*0$
	$+X$	$+0^1$
	$-X$	-0^1
FBSTP	±0	$*0$
FIST,FISTP	±0	$*0$
	$+X$	-0^3
	$-X$	-0^4
FCHS	$+0$	-0
	-0	$+0$
FABS	±0	$+0$
Addition	$+0$ plus $+0$	$+0$
	-0 plus -0	-0
	±0 plus -0, -0 plus$+0$	$+0^2$
	$-X$ plus $+X$, $+X$ plus$-X$	±0
	±0 plus $\pm X$, $\pm X$ plus ±0	$\#X$
Subtraction	$+0$ minus $- 0$	$+0$
	-0 minus $+ 0$	-0
	$+0$ minus $+ 0$, -0 minus	$\pm0^2$
	-0	$\pm0^2$
	$+X$ minus $+X$, $-X$ minus	$-\#X$
	$-X$	$\#X$
	±0 minus $\pm X$	
	$\pm X$ minus ±0	

Table 7-8. Zero Operands and Results (Contd.)

Operation	Operands	Result
Multiplication	$\pm 0 \times \pm 0$	0
	$\pm 0 \times \pm X$, $\pm X \times \pm 0$	0
	$+X \times +Y$, $-X \times -Y$	$+0^1$
	$+X \times -Y$, $-X \times +Y$	-0^1
Division	$\pm 0 \div \pm 0$	Invalid Operation
	$\pm X \div \pm 0$	∞ (Zero Divide)
	$\pm X \div \pm\infty$	0
	$+0 \div +X$, $-0 \div -X$	$+0$
	$+0 \div -X$, $-0 \div +X$	-0
	$-X \div -Y$, $+X \div +Y$	$+0^1$
	$-X \div -Y$, $+X \div +Y$	-0^1
FPREM, FPREM1	± 0 rem ± 0	Invalid Operation
	$\pm X$ rem ± 0	Invalid Operation
	$+0$ rem $\pm X$	$+0$
	-0 rem $\pm X$	-0
	$+X$ rem $\pm Y$	$+0$ Y exactly divides X
	$-X$ rem $\pm Y$	-0 Y exactly divides X
FSQRT	± 0	*0
Compare	$\pm 0 : +X$	$\pm 0 < +X$
	$\pm 0 : \pm 0$	$\pm 0 = \pm 0$
	$\pm 0 : -X$	$\pm 0 > -X$
FTST	± 0	$\pm 0 = 0$
FXAM	$+0$	$C_3 = 1$; $C_2 = C_1 = C_0 = 0$
	-0	$C_3 = C_1 = 1$; $C_2 = C_0 = 0$
FSCALE	± 0 scaled by $-\infty$	*0
	± 0 scaled by $+\infty$	Invalid Operation
	± 0 scaled by X	*0
FXTRACT	$+0$	$ST = +0, ST(1) = \infty$, Zero divide
	-0	$ST = -0, ST(1) = -\infty$, Zero divide

Table 7-8. Zero Operands and Results (Contd.)

Operation	Operands	Result
FPTAN	±0	*0
FSIN (or SIN result of FSINCOS)	±0	*0
FCOS (or COS result of FSINCOS)	±0	+1
FPATAN	±0 ÷ + X	*0
	±0 ÷ − X	*π
	±X ÷ ±0	#π/2
	±0 ÷ +0	*0
	±0 ÷ −0	*π
	+∞ ÷ ±0	+π/2
	−∞ ÷ ±0	−π/2
	±0 ÷ + ∞	*0
	±0 ÷ − ∞	*π
F2XM1	+0	+0
	−0	−0
FYL2X	±Y × log(±0)	Zero Divide
	±0 × log(±0)	Invalid Operation
FYL2XP1	+ Y × log(±0+1)	*0
	− Y × log(±0+1)	−*0

NOTES:

X and Y denote nonzero positive operands

1 When extreme underflow denormalizes the result to zero.
2 Sign determined by rounding mode: + for nearest, up, or chop, − for down
3 When 0 < X < 1 and rounding mode is not up.
4 When −1 < X < 0 and rounding mode is not down.
* Sign of original zero operand.
# Sign of original X operand.
−# Complement of sign of original X operand.
⊕ Exclusive OR of the signs of the operands

Table 7–9. Infinity Operands and Results

Operation	Operands	Result
FLD,FBLD	$\pm\infty$	$*\infty$
FST,FSTP,FRNDINT	$\pm\infty$	$*\infty$
FCHS	$+\infty$	$-\infty$
	$-\infty$	$+\infty$
FABS	$\pm\infty$	$+\infty$
Addition	$+\infty$ plus $+\infty$	$+\infty$
	$-\infty$ plus $-\infty$	$-\infty$
	$+\infty$ plus $-\infty$	Invalid Operation
	$-\infty$ plus $+\infty$	Invalid Operation
	$\pm\infty$ plus $\pm X$	$*\infty$
	$\pm X$ plus $\pm\infty$	$*\infty$
Subtraction	$+\infty$ minus $-\infty$	$+\infty$
	$-\infty$ minus $+\infty$	$-\infty$
	$+\infty$ minus $+\infty$	Invalid Operation
	$-\infty$ minus $-\infty$	Invalid Operation
	$\pm\infty$ minus $\pm X$	$*\infty$
	$\pm X$ minus $\pm\infty$	$-*\infty$
Multiplication	$\pm\infty \times \pm\infty$	∞
	$\pm\infty \times \pm Y, \pm Y \times \pm\infty$	∞
	$\pm\infty \times \pm Y, \pm Y \times \pm\infty$	∞
	$\pm 0 \times \pm\infty, \pm\infty \times \pm 0$	Invalid Operation
Division	$\pm\infty \div \pm\infty$	Invalid Operation
	$+\infty \div \pm X$	∞
	$\pm X \div \pm\infty$	0
FPREM,FPREM1	$+\infty$ rem $\pm\infty$	Invalid Operation
	$\pm\infty$ rem $\pm X$	Invalid Operation
	$\pm X$ rem $\pm\infty$	$\$X$, Q = 0
FSQRT	$-\infty$	Invalid Operation
	$+\infty$	$+\infty$

Table 7-9. Infinity Operands and Results (Contd.)

Operation	Operands	Result
Compare	$+\infty : +\infty$	$+\infty = +\infty$
	$-\infty : -\infty$	$-\infty = -\infty$
	$+\infty : -\infty$	$+\infty > -\infty$
	$-\infty : +\infty$	$-\infty < +\infty$
	$+\infty : \pm X$	$+\infty > X$
	$-\infty : \pm X$	$-\infty < X$
	$\pm X : +\infty$	$X < +\infty$
	$\pm X : -\infty$	$X > +\infty$
	$+\infty$	$+\infty > 0$
FTST	$-\infty$	$-\infty < 0$
FSCALE	$\pm\infty$ scaled by $-\infty$	Invalid Operation
	$\pm\infty$ scaled by $+\infty$	$*\infty$
	$\pm\infty$ scaled by $\pm X$	$*\infty$
	± 0 scaled by $-\infty$	$\pm 0_1$
	± 0 scaled by ∞	Invalid Operation
	$\pm Y$ scaled by $+\infty$	$\#\infty$
	$\pm Y$ scaled by $-\infty$	$\#0$
FXTRACT	$\pm\infty$	$ST = *\infty$, $ST(1) = +\infty$
FXAM	$+\infty$	$C0 = C2 = 1; C1 = C3 = 0$
	$-\infty$	$C0 = C1 = C2 = 1; C3 = 0$
FPATAN	$\pm\infty \div \pm X$	$*\pi/2$
	$\pm Y \div +\infty$	$\#0$
	$\pm Y \div -\infty$	$\#\pi$
	$\pm\infty \div +\infty$	$*\pi/4$
	$\pm\infty \div -\infty$	$*3\pi/4$
	$\pm\infty \div \pm 0$	$*\pi/2$
	$+0 \div +\infty$	$+0$
	$+0 \div -\infty$	$+\pi$
	$-0 \div +\infty$	-0
	$-0 \div -\infty$	$-\pi$

Table 7-9. Operands and Results (Contd.)

Operation	Operands	Result
F2XM1	$+\infty$	$+\infty$
	$-\infty$	-1
FYL2X	$\pm\infty \times \log\,(1)$	Invalid Operation
	$\pm\infty \times \log\,(X>1)$	$*\infty$
	$\pm\infty \times \log\,(0<X<1)$	$-*\infty$
	$\pm Y \times \log\,(+\infty)$	$\#\infty$
	$\pm 0 \times \log\,(+\infty)$	Invalid Operation
	$\pm Y \times \log\,(-\infty)$	Invalid Operation
FYL2XP1	$\pm\infty \times \log\,(1)$	Invalid Operation
	$\pm\infty \times \log\,(X>0)$	$*\infty$
	$\pm\infty \times \log$	$-*\infty$
	$(-1<X<0)$	$\#\infty$
	$\pm Y \times \log\,(+\infty)$	Invalid Operation
	$\pm 0 \times \log\,(+\infty)$	Invalid Operation
	$\pm Y \times \log\,(-\infty)$	

NOTES:

X	Zero or nonzero, positive, finite operand
Y	Nonzero positive, finite operand
*	Sign of original infinity operand.
$-*$	Complement of sign of original infinity operand
$	Sign of original operand.
$\oplus$	Exclusive OR of the signs of the operands
#	Sign of the original Y operand.
1	Sign of original zero operand.

7.1.4. NAN (Not-A-Number)

A NaN (Not a Number) is a member of a class of special values that exists in the real formats only. A NaN has an exponent of 11..11B, may have either sign, and may have any significand except $1_\Delta 00..00B$, which is assigned to the infinities. A NaN in a register is tagged *special*.

There are two classes of NaN: signaling (SNaN) and quiet (QNaN). Among the QNaNs, the value *real indefinite* is of special interest.

7.1.4.1.   SIGNALING NANS

A signaling NaN is a NaN that has a zero as the most significant bit of its fraction. The rest of the significand may be set to any value. The FPU never generates a signaling NaN as a result; however, it recognizes signaling NaNs when they appear as operands. Arithmetic operations (as defined at the beginning of this chapter) on a signaling NaN cause an invalid-operation exception (except for load operations from the stack, FXCH, FCHS, and FABS).

By unmasking the invalid operation exception, the programmer can use signaling NaNs to trap to the exception handler. The generality of this approach and the large number of NaN values that are available provide the sophisticated programmer with a tool that can be applied to a variety of special situations.

For example, a compiler could use signaling NaNs as references to uninitialized (real) array elements. The compiler could preinitialize each array element with a signaling NaN whose significand contained the index (relative position) of the element. If an application program attempted to access an element that it had not initialized, it would use the NaN placed there by the compiler. If the invalid operation exception were unmasked, an interrupt would occur, and the exception handler would be invoked. The exception handler could determine which element had been accessed, since the operand address field of the exception pointers would point to the NaN, and the NaN would contain the index number of the array element.

7.1.4.2.   QUIET NANS

A quiet NaN is a NaN that has a one as the most significant bit of its significand. The processor creates the quiet NaN *real indefinite* (defined below) as its default response to certain exceptional conditions. The processor may derive other QNaNs by converting an SNaN. The processor converts a SNaN by setting the most significant bit of its significand to one, thereby generating a QNaN. The remaining bits of the significand are not changed; therefore, diagnostic information that may be stored in these bits of the SNaN is propagated into the QNaN.

The processor will generate the special QNaN, *real indefinite,* as its masked response to an invalid operation exception. This NaN is signed negative; its significand is encoded $1_\Lambda100..00$. All other NaNs represent values created by programmers or derived from values created by programmers.

Both quiet and signaling NaNs are supported in all operations. A QNaN is generated as the masked response for invalid-operation exceptions and as the result of an operation in which at least one of the operands is a QNaN. The processor applies the rules shown in Table 7-10 when generating a QNaN.

Table 7-10. Rules for Generating QNaNs

Operation	Action
Real operation on an SNaN and a QNaN.	Deliver the QNaN operand.
Real operation on two SNaNs.	Deliver the QNaN that results from converting the SNaN that has the larger significand.
Real operation on two QNaNs.	Deliver the QNaN that has the larger significand.
Real operation on an SNaN and another number.	Deliver the QNaN that results from converting the SNaN.
Real operation on a QNaN and another number.	Deliver the QNaN.
Invalid operation that does not involve NaNs.	Deliver the default QNaN *real indefinite*.

Note that handling of a QNaN operand has greater priority than all exceptions except certain invalid-operation exceptions (refer to the section "Exception Priority" in this chapter).

Quiet NaNs could be used, for example, to speed up debugging. In its early testing phase, a program often contains multiple errors. An exception handler could be written to save diagnostic information in memory whenever it was invoked. After storing the diagnostic data, it could supply a quiet NaN as the result of the erroneous instruction, and that NaN could point to its associated diagnostic area in memory. The program would then continue, creating a different NaN for each error. When the program ended, the NaN results could be used to access the diagnostic data saved at the time the errors occurred. Many errors could thus be diagnosed and corrected in one test run.

In embedded applications which use computed results in further computations, an undetected QNaN can invalidate all subsequent results. Such applications should therefore periodically check for QNaNs and provide a recovery mechanism to be used if a QNaN result is detected.

7.1.5.   Indefinite

For each numeric data type, one unique encoding is reserved for representing the special value *indefinite*. The processor produces this encoding as its response to a masked invalid-operation exception.

In the case of reals, the *indefinite* value is a QNaN as discussed in the prior section.

Packed decimal *indefinite* may be stored with a FBSTP instruction; attempting to use this encoding in a FBLD instruction, however, will have an undefined result; thus *indefinite* cannot be loaded from a packed decimal integer.

In the binary integers, the same encoding may represent either *indefinite* or the largest negative number supported by the format (-2^{15}, -2^{31}, or -2^{63}). The processor will store this encoding as its masked response to an invalid operation, or when the value in a source register represents or rounds to the largest negative integer representable by the destination. In situations where its origin may be ambiguous, the invalid-operation exception flag can be examined to see if the value was produced by an exception response. When this encoding is loaded or used by an integer arithmetic or compare operation, it is always interpreted as a negative number; thus, *indefinite* cannot be loaded from a binary integer.

7.1.6. Encoding of Data Types

Table 7-2 through Table 7-5 show how each of the special values just described is encoded for each of the numeric data types. In these tables, the least-significant bits are shown to the right and are stored in the lowest memory addresses. The sign bit is always the left-most bit of the highest-addressed byte.

7.1.6.1. UNSUPPORTED FORMATS

The extended format permits many bit patterns that do not fall into any of the previously mentioned categories. Table 7-6 shows these unsupported formats. Some of these encodings were supported by the Intel287 math coprocessor; however, most of them are not supported by the Intel387, Intel486, and Pentium FPUs. These changes are required due to changes made in the final version of IEEE Std 754 that eliminated these data types.

The categories of encodings formerly known as pseudo-NaNs, pseudoinfinities, and unnormal numbers are not supported. The Intel387, Intel486 and Pentium FPU's raise the invalid-operation exception when they are encountered as operands.

The encodings formerly known as pseudodenormal numbers are not generated by the Pentium processor; however, they are correctly utilized when encountered as operands. The exponent is treated as if it were 00..01 and the mantissa is unchanged. The denormal exception is raised.

7.1.7. Numeric Exceptions

The FPU can recognize six classes of numeric exception conditions while executing numeric instructions:

1. I — Invalid operation
   — Stack fault
   — IEEE standard invalid operation
2. Z—Divide-by-zero
3. D—Denormalized operand
4. O—Numeric overflow

5. U—Numeric underflow

6. P—Inexact result (precision)

7.1.8. Handling Numeric Exceptions

When numeric exceptions occur, the processor takes one of two possible courses of action:

- The FPU can itself handle the exception, producing the most reasonable result and allowing numeric program execution to continue undisturbed.
- A software exception handler can be invoked to handle the exception.

Each of the six exception conditions described above has a corresponding flag bit in the FPU status word and a mask bit in the FPU control word. If an exception is masked (the corresponding mask bit in the control word = 1), the processor takes an appropriate default action and continues with the computation. If the exception is unmasked (mask = 0), a software exception handler is invoked immediately before execution of the next WAIT or a floating-point instruction other than FNINIT, FNCLEX, FNSTSW, FNSTSW AX, FNSTCW, FNSTENV, FNSAVE. Depending on the value of the NE bit of the CR0 control register, the exception handler is invoked either (NE = 1) through interrupt vector 16 or (NE = 0) through an external interrupt.

Note that when exceptions are masked, the FPU may detect multiple exceptions in a single instruction, because it continues executing the instruction after performing its masked response. For example, the FPU could detect a denormalized operand, perform its masked response to this exception, and then detect an underflow.

7.1.8.1. AUTOMATIC EXCEPTION HANDLING

The processor has a default fix-up activity for every possible exception condition it may encounter. These masked-exception responses are designed to be safe and are generally acceptable for most numeric applications.

As an example of how even severe exceptions can be handled safely and automatically using the default exception responses, consider a calculation of the parallel resistance of several values using only the standard formula (Figure 7-1). If R1 becomes zero, the circuit resistance becomes zero. With the divide-by-zero and precision exceptions masked, the processor will produce the correct result.

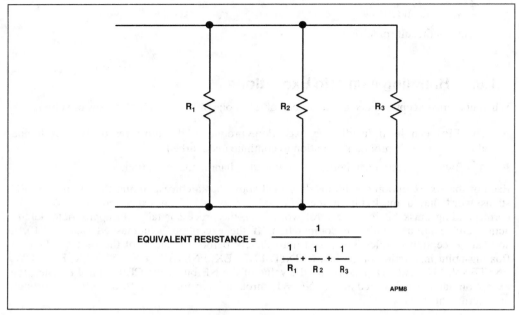

Figure 7-1. Arithmetic Example Using Infinity

By masking or unmasking specific numeric exceptions in the FPU control word, programmers can delegate responsibility for most exceptions to the processor, reserving the most severe exceptions for programmed exception handlers. Exception-handling software is often difficult to write, and the masked responses have been tailored to deliver the most reasonable result for each condition. For the majority of applications, masking all exceptions yields satisfactory results with the least programming effort. Certain exceptions can usefully be left unmasked during the debugging phase of software development, and then masked when the clean software is actually run. An invalid-operation exception for example, typically indicates a program error that must be corrected.

The exception flags in the FPU status word provide a cumulative record of exceptions that have occurred since these flags were last cleared. Once set, these flags can be cleared only by executing the FCLEX (clear exceptions) instruction, by reinitializing the FPU with FINIT, or by overwriting the flags with an FRSTOR or FLDENV instruction. This allows a programmer to mask all exceptions, run a calculation, and then inspect the status word to see if any exceptions were detected at any point in the calculation.

7.1.8.2. SOFTWARE EXCEPTION HANDLING

If the Pentium and Intel486 FPU encounters an unmasked exception condition, a software exception handler is invoked immediately before execution of the next WAIT or non-control floating-point instruction. The exception handler is invoked either through interrupt vector 16 or through an external interrupt, depending on the value of the NE bit of the CR0 control register.

If NE = 1, an unmasked floating-point exception results in interrupt 16, immediately before the execution of the next non-control floating-point or WAIT instruction. Interrupt 16 is an operating-system call that invokes the exception handler. Chapter 14 contains a general discussion of exceptions and interrupts.

If NE = 0 (and the IGNNE# input is inactive), an unmasked floating-point exception causes the processor to freeze immediately before executing the next non-control floating-point or WAIT instruction. The frozen processor waits for an external interrupt, which must be supplied by external hardware in response to the FERR# output of the processor. (Regardless of the value of NE, an unmasked numerical exception causes the FERR# output to be activated.) In this case, the external interrupt invokes the exception-handling routine. If NE = 0 but the IGNNE# input is active, the processor disregards the exception and continues. Error reporting via external interrupt is supported for DOS compatibility. Chapter 23 contains further discussion of compatibility issues.

If the Intel387 NPX encounters an unmasked exception condition, it signals the exception to the Intel386 CPU using the ERROR# status line between the two processors. See Chapter 23 for differences in FPU exception handling.

The exception-handling routine is normally a part of the systems software. Typical exception responses may include:

- Incrementing an exception counter for later display or printing
- Printing or displaying diagnostic information (e.g., the FPU environment and registers)
- Aborting further execution, or using the exception pointers to build an instruction that will run without exception and executing it

Applications programmers should consult their operating system's reference manuals for the appropriate system response to numerical exceptions. For systems programmers, some details on writing software exception handlers are provided in Chapter 14.

7.1.9. Invalid Operation

This exception may occur in response to two general classes of operations:

1. Stack operations
2. Arithmetic operations

The stack flag (SF) of the status word indicates which class of operation caused the exception. When SF is 1 a stack operation has resulted in stack overflow or underflow; when SF is 0, an arithmetic instruction has encountered an invalid operand.

7.1.9.1. STACK EXCEPTION

When SF is 1, indicating a stack operation, the O/U# bit of the condition code (bit C1) distinguishes between stack overflow and underflow as follows:

O/U# = 1   Stack overflow—an instruction attempted to push down a nonempty stack location.

O/U# = 0   Stack underflow—an instruction attempted to read an operand from an empty stack location.

When the invalid-operation exception is masked, the FPU returns the QNaN *indefinite*. This value overwrites the destination register, destroying its original contents.

When the invalid-operation exception is not masked, an exception handler is invoked. TOP is not changed, and the source operands remain unaffected.

7.1.9.2. INVALID ARITHMETIC OPERATION

This class includes the invalid operations defined in IEEE Std 854. The FPU reports an invalid operation in any of the cases shown in Table 7-11. Also shown in this table are the FPU's responses when the invalid exception is masked. When unmasked, an exception handler is invoked, and the operands remain unaltered. An invalid operation generally indicates a program error.

Table 7-11. Masked Responses to Invalid Operations

Condition	Masked Response
Any arithmetic operation on an unsupported format.	Return the QNaN *indefinite*.
Any arithmetic operation on a signaling NaN.	Return a QNaN (refer to the section "Rules for Generating QNaNs").
Compare and test operations: one or both operands is a NaN.	Set condition codes "not comparable."
Addition of opposite-signed infinities or subtraction of like-signed infinities.	Return the QNaN *indefinite*.
Multiplication: $\infty \times 0$; or $0 \times \infty$.	Return theQNaN *indefinite*.
Division: $\infty \div \infty$; or $0 \div 0$.	Return the QNaN *indefinite*.
Remainder instructions FPREM, FPREM1 when modulus (divisor) is zero or dividend is ∞.	Return the QNaN *indefinite*; set $C_2 = 0$.
Trigonometric instructions FCOS, FPTAN, FSIN, FSINCOS when argument is ∞.	Return theQNaN *indefinite*; set $C_2 = 0$.
FSQRT of negative operand (except FSQRT $(-0) = -0$), FYL2X of negative operand (except FYL2X $(-0) = -\infty$), FYL2XP1 of operand more negative than -1.	Return the QNaN *indefinite*
FIST(P) instructions when source register is empty, a NaN, ∞, or exceeds representable range of destination.	Store integer *indefinite*.
FBSTP instruction when source register is empty, a NaN, ∞, or exceeds 18 decimal digits.	Store packed decimal *indefinite*.
FXCH instruction when one or both registers are tagged empty.	Change empty registers to the QNaN *indefinite* and then perform exchange.

7.1.10. Division by Zero

If an instruction attempts to divide a finite nonzero operand by zero, the FPU will report a zero-divide exception. This is possible for F(I)DIV(R)(P) as well as the other instructions that perform division internally: FYL2X and FXTRACT. The masked response for FDIV is to return an infinity signed with the exclusive OR of the sign of the two operands. FYL2X returns an infinity signed with the opposite sign of the non-zero operand. For FXTRACT, ST(1) is set to $-\infty$; ST is set to zero with the same sign as the original operand. If the divide-by-zero exception is unmasked, an exception handler is invoked; the operands remain unaltered.

7.1.11. Denormal Operand

If an arithmetic instruction attempts to operate on a denormal operand, the FPU reports the denormal-operand exception. Denormal operands may have reduced significance due to lost low-order bits, therefore it may be advisable in certain applications to preclude operations on these operands. This can be accomplished by an exception handler that responds to unmasked denormal operand exceptions. Most users will mask this exception so that computation may proceed; any loss of accuracy will be analyzed by the user when the final result is delivered.

When this exception is masked, the FPU sets the DE-bit in the status word, then proceeds with the instruction. Gradual underflow and denormal numbers will produce results at least as good as, and often better than what could be obtained from a machine that flushes underflows to zero. In fact, a denormal operand in single- or double-precision format will be normalized to the extended-real format when loaded into the FPU. Subsequent operations will benefit from the additional precision of the extended-real format used internally.

When this exception is not masked, the DE-bit is set and the exception handler is invoked. The operands are not changed by the instruction and are available for inspection by the exception handler.

The Pentium FPU, Intel486 FPU, and Intel387 math coprocessors handle denormal values differently than the 8087 and Intel287 math coprocessors. This change is due to revisions in the IEEE standard before being approved. The difference in operation occurs when the denormal exception is masked. The Pentium FPU, Intel486 FPU, and Intel387 math coprocessors will automatically normalize denormals. The 8087 and Intel287 math coprocessors will generate a denormal result.

The difference in denormal handling is usually not an issue. The denormal operand exception is normally masked for the Intel387, Intel486, and Pentium FPUs. For programs that also run on an Intel287 math coprocessor, the denormal exception is often unmasked and an exception handler is provided to normalize any denormal values. Such an exception handler is redundant for the Pentium, Intel486 and Intel387 DX FPUs. The default exception handler should be used. See Chapter 23 for more information on the handling of exceptions by the various Intel architectures.

A program can detect at run-time whether it is running on an Pentium, Intel486, or Intel387 FPU or the older 8087/Intel287 math coprocessors. See Chapter 5 for example code sequences to determine the presence of 8087/Intel287 and Intel387 math coprocessors, as well as processor type. This example can be used to selectively mask the denormal exception for Intel387 DX, Intel486 or Pentium FPUs. A denormal exception handler should also be provided to support 8087/Intel287 math coprocessors. This code example can also be used to set a flag to allow use of new instructions added to the Intel387, Intel486, and Pentium FPUs beyond the instructions of the 8087/Intel287 math coprocessors.

7.1.12. Numeric Overflow and Underflow

If the exponent of a numeric result is too large for the destination real format, the FPU signals a numeric overflow. Conversely, if the exponent of a result is too small to be represented in the destination format, a numeric underflow is signaled. If either of these exceptions occur, the result of the operation is outside the range of the destination real format.

Typical algorithms are most likely to produce extremely large and small numbers in the calculation of intermediate, rather than final, results. Because of the great range of the extended-precision format, overflow and underflow are relatively rare events in most numerical applications.

7.1.12.1. OVERFLOW

The overflow exception can occur whenever the rounded true result would exceed in magnitude the largest finite number in the destination format. The exception can occur in the execution of most of the arithmetic instructions and in some of the conversion instructions; namely, FST(P), F(I)ADD(P), F(I)SUB(R)(P), F(I)MUL(P), FDIV(R)(P), FSCALE, FYL2X, and FYL2XP1.

The response to an overflow condition depends on whether the overflow exception is masked:

- Overflow exception masked. The value returned depends on the rounding mode as Table 7-12 illustrates.

- Overflow exception not masked. The unmasked response depends on whether the instruction is supposed to store the result on the stack or in memory:

  — If the destination is the stack, then true result is divided by $2^{24,576}$ and rounded. (The bias 24,576 is equal to 3×2^{13}.) The significand is rounded to the appropriate precision (according to the precision control (PC) bit of the control word, for those instructions controlled by PC, otherwise to extended precision). The roundup bit (C1) of the status word is set if the significand was rounded upward. The biasing of the exponent by 24,576 normally translates the number as nearly as possible to the middle of the exponent range so that, if desired, it can be used in subsequent scaled operations with less risk of causing further exceptions. With the instruction FSCALE, however, it can happen that the result is too large and overflows even after biasing. In this case, the unmasked response is exactly the same as the masked round-to-nearest response, namely ± infinity. The intention of this feature is to ensure the trap handler will discover that a translation of the exponent by −24574 would not work correctly without obliging the programmer of Decimal-to-Binary or Exponential functions to determine which trap handler, if any, should be invoked.

  — If the destination is memory (this can occur only with the store instructions), then no result is stored in memory. Instead, the operand is left intact in the stack. Because the data in the stack is in extended-precision format, the exception handler has the option either of reexecuting the store instruction after proper adjustment of the operand or of rounding the significand on the stack to the destination's precision as the standard requires. The exception handler should ultimately store a value into the destination location in memory if the program is to continue.

Table 7-12. Masked Overflow Results

Rounding Mode	Sign of True Result	Result
To nearest	+	$+\infty$
	−	$-\infty$
Toward $-\infty$	+	Largest finite positive number
	−	$-\infty$
Toward $+\infty$	+	$+\infty$
	−	Largest finite negative number
Toward zero	+	Largest finite positive number
	−	Largest finite negative number

7.1.12.2. UNDERFLOW

Underflow can occur in the execution of the instructions FST(P), FADD(P), FSUB(RP), FMUL(P), F(I)DIV(RP), FSCALE, FPREM(1), FPTAN, FSIN, FSINCOS, FPATAN, F2XM1, FYL2X, and FYL2XP1.

Two related events contribute to underflow:

1. Creation of a tiny (denormal) result which, because it is so small, may cause some other exception later (such as overflow upon division).
2. Creation of an inexact result; i.e. the delivered result differs from what would have been computed were both the exponent range and precision unbounded.

Which of these events triggers the underflow exception depends on whether the underflow exception is masked:

1. Underflow exception masked. The underflow exception is signaled when the result is both tiny and inexact.
2. Underflow exception not masked. The underflow exception is signaled when the result is tiny, regardless of inexactness.

The response to an underflow exception also depends on whether the exception is masked:

1. Masked response. The result is denormal or zero. The precision exception is also triggered.
2. Unmasked response. The unmasked response depends on whether the instruction is supposed to store the result on the stack or in memory
   — If the destination is the stack, then the true result is multiplied by $2^{24,576}$ and rounded. (The bias 24,576 is equal to 3×2^{13}.) The significand is rounded to the appropriate precision (according to the precision control (PC) bit of the control word, for those instructions controlled by PC, otherwise to extended precision). The roundup bit (C1)

of the status word is set if the significand was rounded upward.

The biasing of the exponent by 24,576 normally translates the number as nearly as possible to the middle of the exponent range so that, if desired, it can be used in subsequent scaled operations with less risk of causing further exceptions. With the instruction FSCALE, however, it can happen that the result is too tiny and underflows even after biasing. In this case, the unmasked response is exactly the same as the masked round-to-nearest response, namely ±0. The intention of this feature is to ensure the trap handler will discover that a translation by +24576 would not work correctly without obliging the programmer of Decimal-to-Binary or Exponential functions to determine which trap handler, if any, should be invoked.

— If the destination is memory (this can occur only with the store instructions), then no result is stored in memory. Instead, the operand is left intact in the stack. Because the data in the stack is in extended-precision format, the exception handler has the option either of reexecuting the store instruction after proper adjustment of the operand or of rounding the significand on the stack to the destination's precision as the standard requires. The exception handler should ultimately store a value into the destination location in memory if the program is to continue.

7.1.13. Inexact (Precision)

This exception condition occurs if the result of an operation is not exactly representable in the destination format. For example, the fraction 1/3 cannot be precisely represented in binary form. This exception occurs frequently and indicates that some (generally acceptable) accuracy has been lost.

By their nature, the transcendental instructions cause the inexact exception for their core cases. Table 7-13 lists the core cases for each of the transcendental instructions.

Table 7-13. Transcendental Core Ranges

Instruction	Core Range
FSIN	$\lvert \theta \rvert < 2^{63}$
FCOS	$\lvert \theta \rvert < 2^{63}$
FSINCOS	$\lvert \theta \rvert < 2^{63}$
FPTAN	$\lvert \theta \rvert < 2^{63}$
FPATAN	no restriction
F2XM1	$-1 < X < 1$
FYL2X*	$X > 0$
FYL2XP1*	$-(1-(\sqrt{2}/2)) \leq ST \leq \sqrt{2}-1$

NOTES: For these 2-operand instructions, Y should be normal for the core cases.

The C1 (roundup) bit of the status word indicates whether the inexact result was rounded up (C1 = 1) or chopped (C1 = 0).

The inexact exception accompanies the underflow exception when there is also a loss of accuracy. When underflow is masked, the underflow exception is signaled only when there is a loss of accuracy; therefore the precision flag is always set as well. When underflow is unmasked, there may or may not have been a loss of accuracy; the precision bit indicates which is the case.

This exception is provided for applications that need to perform exact arithmetic only. Most applications will mask this exception. The FPU delivers the rounded or over/underflowed result to the destination, regardless of whether a trap occurs.

7.1.14. Exception Priority

The processor deals with exceptions according to a predetermined precedence. Precedence in exception handling means that higher-priority exceptions are flagged and results are delivered according to the requirements of that exception. Lower-priority exceptions may not be flagged even if they occur. For example, dividing an SNaN by zero causes an invalid-operand exception (due to the SNaN) and not a zero-divide exception; the masked result is the QNaN *real indefinite*, not ∞. A denormal or inexact (precision) exception, however, can accompany a numeric underflow or overflow exception.

The precedence among numeric exceptions is as follows:

1. Invalid operation exception, subdivided as follows:
    a. Stack underflow.
    b. Stack overflow.
    c. Operand of unsupported format.
    d. SNaN operand.
2. QNaN operand. Though this is not an exception, if one operand is a QNaN, dealing with it has precedence over lower-priority exceptions. For example, a QNaN divided by zero results in a QNaN, not a zero-divide exception.
3. Any other invalid-operation exception not mentioned above or zero divide.
4. Denormal operand. If masked, then instruction execution continues, and a lower-priority exception can occur as well.
5. Numeric overflow and underflow. Inexact result (precision) can be flagged as well.
6. Inexact result (precision).

7.1.15. Standard Underflow/Overflow Exception Handler

As long as the underflow and overflow exceptions are masked, no additional software is required to cause the output of the processor to conform to the requirements of IEEE Std 854. When unmasked, these exceptions give the exception handler an additional option in the case of store instructions. No result is stored in memory; instead, the operand is left intact on the stack. The handler may round the significand of the operand on the stack to the destination's precision as the standard requires, or it may adjust the operand and reexecute the faulting instruction.

intel ®

8

Numeric
Programming
Examples

The following sections contain examples of numeric programs written in ASM386/Intel486. These examples are intended to illustrate some of the techniques useful for programming numeric applications.

8.1. CONDITIONAL BRANCHING EXAMPLE

As discussed earlier, several numeric instructions post their results to the condition code bits of the FPU status word. Although there are many ways to implement conditional branching following a comparison, the basic approach is as follows:

- Execute the comparison.
- Store the status word. (The FPU status word can be stored directly into AX register.)
- Inspect the condition code bits.
- Jump on the result.

Example 8-1 is a code fragment that illustrates how two memory-resident double-format real numbers might be compared (similar code could be used with the FTST instruction). The numbers are called A and B, and the comparison is A to B.

Example 8-1. Conditional Branching for Compares

```
        .
        .
A    DQ     ?
B    DQ     ?
        .
        .

    FLD     A  ; LOAD A ONTO TOP OF FPU STACK
    FCOMP B    ; COMPARE A;B POP A
    FSTSW AX   ; STORE  RESULT TO AX REGISTER
;
; CPU AX REGISTER CONTAINS CONDITION CODES
;          (RESULTS OF COMPARE)
; LOAD CONDITION CODES INTO FLAGS
;
    SAHF
;
; USE CONDITONAL JUMPS TO DETERMINE ORDERING OF A TO B
;
    JP A_B_UNORDERED;  TEST C2 (PF)
```

```
   JB    A_LESS        ;  TEST CO (CF)
   JE A_EQUAL          ;  TEST C3 (ZF)
A_GREATER:             ;  C0 (CF) = 0, C3 (ZF) = 0
       .
       .
       .
A_EQUAL :              ;  C0 (CF) 1, C3 (ZF) = 0
       .
       .
       .
A_LESS                 ;  CD (CF) = 1, C3 (ZF) = 0
       .
       .
       .
A_B_UNORDERED:         ;  C2 (PF) = 1
       .
       .
       .
```

The comparison itself requires loading A onto the top of the FPU register stack and then comparing it to B, while popping the stack with the same instruction. The status word is then written into the AX register.

A and B have four possible orderings, and bits C3, C2, and C0 of the condition code indicate which ordering holds. These bits are positioned in the upper byte of the FPU status word so as to correspond to the zero, parity, and carry flags (ZF, PF, and CF), when the byte is written into the flags. The code fragment sets ZF, PF, and CF of the EFLAGS register to the values of C3, C2, and C0 of the FPU status word, and then uses the conditional jump instructions to test the flags. The resulting code is extremely compact, requiring only seven instructions.

The FXAM instruction updates all four condition code bits. Example 8-2 shows how a jump table can be used to determine the characteristics of the value examined. The jump table (FXAM_TBL) is initialized to contain the 32-bit displacement of 16 labels, one for each possible condition code setting. Note that four of the table entries contain the same value, "EMPTY." The first two condition code settings correspond to "EMPTY." The two other table entries that contain "EMPTY" will never be used on the 32-bit processors with integrated FPU or the Intel387 math coprocessor, but may be used if the code is executed with an Intel287 math coprocessor.

Example 8-2. Conditional Branching for FXAM

```
;    JUMP TABLE FOR EXAMINE ROUTINE
;
FXAM-TBL   DD POSS_UNNORM, POS NAN, NEG_UNNORN, NEG_NAN,
&        POS_NORM, POS_INFINITY, NEG_NORM,
&        NEG_NFINITY, POS_ZERO, EMPTY, NEG_ZERO
&        EMPTY, POS_DENORM, EMPTY, NEG_DENORM, EMPTY
       .
       .
       .
    ; EXAMINE ST AND STORE RESULT (CONDITION CODES)
FXAM
XOR      EAX, EAX     ; CLEAR EAX
FSTSWAX

    ; CALCULATE OFFSET INTO JUMP TABLE
```

```
AND      AX, 0100011100000000B   ; CLEAR ALL BITS EXCEPT C3, C2-C0
SHR      EAX, 6             ; SHIFT C2-C0 INTO PLACE (000XXX00)
SAL      AH, 5              ; POSITION C3 (00X00000)
OR       AL, AH             ; DROP C3 IN ADJACENT TO C2
                           (00XXXX00)
XOR      AH, AH             ; CLEAR OUT THE OLD COPY OF C3

; JUMP TO THE ROUTINE ' ADDRESSED' BY CONDITION CODE

JMP      FXAM_TBL[EAX]

;   HERE ARE THE JUMP TARGETS, ONE TO HANDLE
;             EACH POSSIBLE RESULT OF FXAM

POS_UNNORM:
         .
POS_NAM:
         .
NEG_UNNOM:
         .
NEG_NAM:
         .
POS_NORM:
         .
POS_INFINITY:
         .
NEG_NORM:
         .
NEG_INFINITY:
         .
POS_ZERO:
         .
EMPTY:
         .
NEG_ZERO:
         .
POS_DENORM:
         .
NEG_DENORM:
```

The program fragment performs the FXAM and stores the status word. It then manipulates the condition code bits to finally produce a number in register AX that equals the condition code times 2. This involves zeroing the unused bits in the byte that contains the code, shifting C3 to the right so that it is adjacent to C2, and then shifting the code to multiply it by 2. The resulting value is used as an index that selects one of the displacements from FXAM_TBL (the multiplication of the condition code is required because of the 2-byte length of each value in FXAM_TBL). The unconditional JMP instruction effectively vectors through the jump table to the labeled routine that contains code (not shown in the example) to process each possible result of the FXAM instruction.

8.2. EXCEPTION HANDLING EXAMPLES

There are many approaches to writing exception handlers. One useful technique is to consider the exception handler procedure as consisting of "prologue," "body," and "epilogue" sections of code. This procedure is invoked via interrupt number 16.

In the transfer of control to the exception handler due to an INTR, NMI, or SMI, interrupts have been disabled by hardware. The prologue performs all functions that must be protected from possible interruption by higher-priority sources. Typically, this involves saving registers and transferring diagnostic information from the FPU to memory. When the critical processing has been completed, the prologue may re-enable interrupts to allow higher-priority interrupt handlers to preempt the exception handler.

The body of the exception handler examines the diagnostic information and makes a response that is necessarily application-dependent. This response may range from halting execution, to displaying a message, to attempting to repair the problem and proceed with normal execution.

The epilogue essentially reverses the actions of the prologue, restoring the processor so that normal execution can be resumed. The epilogue must *not* load an unmasked exception flag into the FPU or another exception will be requested immediately.

The following code examples show the ASM386/Intel486 coding of three skeleton exception handlers. They show how prologues and epilogues can be written for various situations, but provide comments indicating only where the application dependent exception handling body should be placed.

The first two are very similar; their only substantial difference is their choice of instructions to save and restore the FPU. The tradeoff here is between the increased diagnostic information provided by FNSAVE and the faster execution of FNSTENV. For applications that are sensitive to interrupt latency or that do not need to examine register contents, FNSTENV reduces the duration of the "critical region," during which the processor does not recognize another interrupt request.

After the exception handler body, the epilogues prepare the processor to resume execution from the point of interruption (i.e., the instruction following the one that generated the unmasked exception). Notice that the exception flags in the memory image that is loaded into the FPU are cleared to zero prior to reloading (in fact, in these examples, the entire status word image is cleared).

Example 8-3 and Example 8-4 assume that the exception handler itself will not cause an unmasked exception. Where this is a possibility, the general approach shown in Example 8-5 can be employed. The basic technique is to save the full FPU state and then to load a new control word in the prologue. Note that considerable care should be taken when designing an exception handler of this type to prevent the handler from being reentered endlessly.

Example 8-3. Full-State Exception Handler

```
SAVE_ALL    PROC
;
; SAVE REGISTERS, ALLOCATE STACK SPACE
; FOR FPU STATE IMAGE
```

```
   PUSH EBP
    .
    .
   MOV   EBP, ESP
   SUB   ESP, 108
;SAVE FULL FPU STATE, ENABLE INTERRUPTS
   FNSAVE  [EBP-108]
   STI
;
; APPLICATION-DEPENDENT EXCEPTION HANDLING
; CODE GOES HERE
;
; CLEAR EXCEPTION FLAGS IN STATUS WORD
; (WHICH IS IN MEMORY)
; RESTORE MODIFIED STATE IMAGE
   MOV      BYTE PTR [EBP-104], 0H
   FRSTOR  [EBP-108]
; DEALLOCATE STACK SPACE, RESTORE REGISTERS
   MOV      ESP, EBP
    .
    .
   POP      EBP
;
; RETURN TO INTERRUPTED CALCULATION
   IRET
SAVE_ALL    ENDP
```

Example 8-4. Reduced-Latency Exception Handler

```
SAVE_ENVIRONMENT    PROC
;
; SAVE REGISTERS, ALLOCATE STACK SPACE
; FOR FPU ENVIRONMENT
   PUSH     EBP
    .
    .
   MOV   EBP, ESP
   SUB   ESP, 28
;SAVE ENVIRONMENT, ENABLE INTERRUPTS
   FNSTENV ..[EBP-28]
   STI
;
; APPLICATION-DEPENDENT EXCEPTION HANDLING
; CODE GOES HERE
;
; CLEAR EXCEPTION FLAGS IN STATUS WORD
; (WHICH IS IN MEMORY)
; RESTORE MODIFIED ENVIRONEMNT IMAGE
   MOV      BYTE PTR [EBP-24], 0H
```

```
   FLDENV  [EBP-28]
; DEALLOCATE STACK SPACE, RESTORE REGISTERS
   MOV     ESP, EBP
   .
   .
   .
   POP     EBP
;
; RETURN TO INTERRUPTED CALCULATION
   IRET
SAVE_ENVRIONEMNT   ENDP
```

Example 8-5. Reentrant Exception Handler

```
   .
   .
LOCAL_CONTROL DW ? ; ASSUME INITIALIZED
   .
   .
REENTRANT  PROC
;
; SAVE REGISTERS, ALLOCATE STACK SPACE
; FOR FPU STATE IMAGE
   PUSH EBP
   .
   .
   MOV     EBP, ESP
   SUB     ESP, 108
; SAVE STATE, LOAD NEW CONTROL WORD,
; ENABLE INTERRUPTS
   FNSAVE  [EBP-108]
   FLDCW   LOCAL_CONTROL
   STI
   .
   .
   .
;
; APPLICATION-DEPENDENT EXCEPTION HANDLING
; CODE GOES HERE
; AN UNMASKED EXCEPTION GENERATED HERE WILL
; CAUSE THE EXCEPTION HANDLER TO BE REENTERED.
; IF LOCAL STORAGE IS NEEDED, IT MUST BE ALLOCATED
; ON THE STACK.
;
   .
   .
; CLEAR EXCEPTION FLAGS IN STATUS WORD
; (WHICH IS IN MEMORY)
; RESTORE MODIFIED STATE IMAGE
   MOV     BYTE PTR [EBP-104], 0H
   FRSTOR  [EBP-108]
```

```
; DEALLOCATE STACK SPACE, RESTORE REGISTERS
   MOV     ESP, EBP
     .
     .
     .
   POP     EBP
;
; RETURN TO POINT OF INTERRUPTION
   IRET
REENTRANT  ENDP
```

8.3. FLOATING-POINT TO ASCII CONVERSION EXAMPLES

Numeric programs must typically format their results at some point for presentation and inspection by the program user. In many cases, numeric results are formatted as ASCII strings for printing or display. This example shows how floating-point values can be converted to decimal ASCII character strings. Example 8-6 was developed using Intel's assemblers. Modification will need to be made to meet the requirements of other vendor's assemblers or their interface to high level languages.

Shortness, speed, and accuracy were chosen rather than providing the maximum number of significant digits possible. An attempt is made to keep integers in their own domain to avoid unnecessary conversion errors.

Using the extended precision real number format, this routine achieves a worst case accuracy of three units in the 16th decimal position for a noninteger value or integers greater than 10^{18}. This is double precision accuracy. With values having decimal exponents less than 100 in magnitude, the accuracy is one unit in the 17th decimal position.

Higher precision can be achieved with greater care in programming, larger program size, and lower performance.

Example 8-6. Floating-Point to ASCII Conversion Routine

```
SOURCE

+1 $title ('Convert a floating point number to ASCII')


   name    floating_to_ascil

   public  floating_to_ascii
   extrn   get_power_10:near, tos_status:near

;
; This subroutine will convert the floating point
; number in the top of the NPX stack to an ASCII
; string and separate power of 10 scaling value
; (in binary). The maximum width of the ASCII string
; formed is controlled by a parameter which must be
; >1. Unnormal values, denormal values, and pseudo
```

```
; zeros will be correctly converted. However,
; unnormals and pseudo zeros are no longer supported
; formats on the Intel486 processor in conformance with
; the IEEE floating point standard) and hence
; not generated internally. A returned value will
; indicate how many binary bits of precision were lost
; in an unnormal or denormal value. The magnitude
; (in terms of binary power) of a psuedo zero will also
; be indicated. Integers less than 10**18 in magnitude
; are accurately converted if the destination ASCII
; string field is wide enough to hold all the digits.
; Otherwise the value is converted to scientific notation.
;
; The status of the conversion is indentified by the
; return value, it can be:
;
;  0 Conversion complete, string size is defined
;  1 invalid arguments
;  2 exact integer conversion, string_size is defined
;  3 indefinite
;  4 + NAN (Not A Number)
;  5 - NAN
;  6 + Infinity
;  7 - Infinity
;  8 pseudo zero found, string_size is defined
;
; The PLM-386/486 calling convention is:
;
; floating_to_ascii:
;    procedure (number, denormal_ptr,string_ptr, size_ptr,
; field_size, power_ptr) word external:
; declare (denormal_ptr, string_ptr, size_ptr)
; pointer;
; declare field_size word,
; string_size based size_ptr word;
; declare number real;
; declare denormal integer based denormal_ptr;
; declare power integer based power_ptr;
; end floating_to_ascii;
;
; The floating point value is expected  to be
; on the top of the FPU stack. This subroutine
; expects 3 free entries on the FPU stack and
; will pop the passed value off when done. The
; generated ASCII string will have a leading
; character either '-' or '+' indicating the sign
; of the value. The ASCII decimal digits will
; immediately follow. The numeric value of the
; ASCII string is (ASCII STRING.)*10 power. If
; the given number was zero, the ASCII string will
```

```
; contain a sign and a single zero character. The
; value string_size indicates the total length of
; ASCII string including the sign character.
; String(0) will always hold the sign. It is
; possible for string_size to be less than
; field_size. This occurs for zeroes of integer
; values. A psuedo zero will return a special
; return code. The denormal count will indicate
; the power of two originally associated with the
; value. The power of ten and ASCII string will
; be as if the value was an ordinary zero.
;
; This subroutine is accurate up to a maximum of
; 18 decimal digits for integers. Integer values
; will have a decimal power of zero associated
; with the item. For non-integers, the result will be
; accurate to within 2 decimal digits of the 16th
; decimal place(double precision). The exponeniate
; instruction is also  used for scaling the value into
; the range acceptable for the BCD data type. The
; rounding mode in effect on entry to the
; subroutine is used for the conversion.
;
;  The following registers are not transparent:
;
;     eax ebx edx esi edi eflags
;
;
;  Define the stack layout.
;
ebp_save        equ     dword ptr [ebp]
es_save         equ     ebp_save + size ebp_save
return_ptr      equ     es_save + size es_save
power_ptr       equ     return_ptr + size return_ptr
field_size      equ     power_ptr + size power_ptr
size_ptr        equ     field_size + size field_size
string_ptr      equ     size_ptr + size size_ptr
denormal_ptr equ        string_ptr + size string_ptr

parms_size      equ     size power_ptr + size field_size +
&                       size size_ptr + size string_ptr +
&                       size denormal_ptr


;
; Define Constants used
;
BCD DIGITS      equ     18 ; number of digits in bcd_value
WORD_SIZE       equ     4
BCD_SIZE        equ     10
MINUS           equ     1  ; Define return values
```

```
NAN            equ  4  ; The exact values chosen
INFINITY       equ  6  ; here are important. They must
INDEFINITE     equ  3  ; correspond to the possible return
PSUDO-ZERO     equ  8  ; values and be in the same numeric
INVALID        equ  -2 ; order as tested by the program.
ZERO           equ  -4
DENORMAL       equ  -6
UNNORMAL       equ  -8
NORMAL         equ  0
EXACT          equ  2
;
; Define layout of temporary storage area.
;
power_two      equ  word ptr [EBP - WORD_SIZE]
bcd_value      equ  tbyte ptr power_two - BCD_SIZE
bcd_byte       equ  byte ptr bcd_value
fraction       equ  bcd_value

local_size     equ  size power_two + size bcd_value
;
; Allocate stack space for the temporaries so
; the stack will be big enough
;
stack stackseg (local_size+6)    ; allocate stack
; space for locals


code    segment public er
   extrn power_table:qword
;
;Constants used by this function
;
      even              ; Optimize for 16 bits
const10 dw              ; Adjustment value for
                        ; too big BCD

; Convert the C3,C2, C1, C0 encoding from tos_status
; into meaningful bit flags and values.
;
status_table db UNNORMAL, NAN, UNNORMAL + MINUS,
& NAN + MINUS, NORMAL, INFINITY,
& NORMAL + MINUS, INFINITY + MINUS,
& ZERO, INVALID, ZERO + MINUS, INVALID,
& DENORMAL, INVALID, DENORMAL + MINUS, INVALID
floating_to_ascii proc

   call tos_status    ; Look at status of ST(0)

; Get descriptor from table
   movzx eax, staus_table[eax]
```

```
        cmp     al, INVALID      ; Look for empty ST(0)
        jne     not_empty
;
; ST(0) is empty!  Return the status value.
        ret     parms_size
;
; Remove infinity from stack and exit.
;
found_infinity:
        fstp st(0)           ; OK to leave fstp running
        jmp   short exit_proc
;
; String space is too small
; Return invalid code.
;
small_string:
        mov     al,INVALID
exit_proc:
        leave                ; Restore stack setup

        pop     es
        ret     parms_size
;
; ST(0) is NAN or indefinite. Store the
; value in memory and look at the fraction
; field to separate indefinite from an ordinary NAN.
;
NAN_or_indefinite:
        fstp fraction        ; remove value from stack
                             ; for examination
        test al, MINUS       ; Look at sign bit
        fwait                ; Insure store is done
        jz   exit_proc       ; Can't be indefinite if positive

        mov  ebx,0C0000000H  ; Match against upper 32 bits of fraction

; Compare bits 63-32
        sub  ebx, dword ptr fraction + 4

; Bits 31-0 must be zero
        or   ebx, dword ptr fraction
        jnz  exit_proc

; Set return value for idefinite value
        mov  al, INDEFINITE
        jmp  exit_proc
;
; Allocate stack space for local variables
; and establish parameter addressability.
;
```

```
not_empty:
  push  es                ; Save working register
  enter local_size, 0; Setup stack addressing


; check for enough string space
  mov   ecx, field_size
  cmp   ecx, 2
  jl    small_string

  dec   ecx             ;adjust for sign character

; See if string is too large for BCD
  cmp   ecx,BCD_DIGITS
  jbe   size_ok

; Else set maximum string size
  mov   ecx, BCD_DIGITS
size_ok:
  cmp   al,INFINITY      ;Look for infinity

; Return status value for + or - inf
  jge   found_infinity
  cmp   al, NAN          ; Look for NAN INDEFINITE
  jge   NAN_or_indefinite
;
; Set default return values and check that
; the number is normalized.
;
  fabs                       ;use positive value only
                             ; sign bit in al has true sign of
                             ; value
  xor   edx,edx              ; form 0 constant
  mov   edi, denormal_ptr    ; zero denormal count
  mov   [edi], dx
  mov   ebx, power_ptr       ; zero power of ten value
  mov   [ebx], dx
  mov   dl, al
  and   dl, 1
  add   dl, EXACT
  cmp   al, ZERO             ; Test for zero
  jae   convert_integer      ; skip power code if value is zero
  fstp  fraction
  fwait
  mov   al, bcd_byte +7
  or    byte ptr bcd_byte +7, 80h
  fld   fraction
  fxtract
  test  al, 80h
  jnz   normal_value
```

```
      fld1
      fsub
      ftst
      fstsw ax
      sahf
      jnz   set_unnormal_count
;
; Found a psuedo zero
;
      fldlg2                    ; Develop power of ten estimate
      add   dl, PSUEDO_ZERO - EXACT
      fmul p st(2), st
      fxch                      ; Get power of ten
      fistp word ptr [ebx]      ; set power of ten
      jmp   convert_integer

set_unnormal_count:
      fxtract                   ; Get original fraction,
                                ; now normalized
      fxch                      ; Get unnormal count
      fchs
      fistp word ptr [edi]      ; set unnormal count


; Calculate the decimal magnitude associated
; with this number to within one order. This
; error will always be inevitable due to
; rounding and lost precision. As a result,
; we will deliberately fail to consider the
; LOG10 of the fraction value in calculating
; the order. Since the fraction will always
; be 1 <= f < 2, its LOG10 will not change
; the basic accuracy of the function. To
; get the decimal order of magnitude, simply
; multiply the power of two by LOG10(2) and
; truncate the result to an integer.
;
normal_value:
      fstp fraction             ; Save the fraction field
                                ; for later use
      fist power_two            ; Save  power of two
      fldlg2                    ; Get LOG10(2)
                                ; Power_two is now safe to use
      fmul                      ; Form LOG10(of exponent of number)
      fistp word ptr [ebx]      ; Any rounding mode will work here
;
; Check if the magnitude of the number rules
; out treating it is an integer.
;
```

```
; CX has the maximum number of decimal digits
; allowed.
;
   fwait                    ; Wait for power-ten to be valid

;  Get power of ten of value
   movsx si, word ptr [ebx]
   sub   esi, ecx          ; Form scaling factor necessary in ax
   ja    adjust_result; Jump if number will not fit
;
; The number is between 1 and 10**(field_size).
; Test if it is an integer.
;
   fild power_two ; Restore original number
   sub  dl, NORMAL_EXACT   ; Convert to exact return value
   fld   fraction
   fscale              ; Form full value, this
                       ; is safe here
   fst   st(1)         ; Copy value for compare
   frndint             ; Test if its an integer
   fcomp               ; Compare values
   fstsw ax            ; Save status
   sahf                ; C3=1 implies it was an integer
   jnz   convert_integer

   fstp st(0)          ; Remove non integer value
   add  dl, NORMAL_EXACT   ; Restore original return

; Scale the number to within the range allowed
; by the BCD format. The scaling operation should
; produce a number within one decimal order of
; magnitude of the largest decimal number
; representative within the given string width.
;
; The scaling power of ten value is in si.
;
adjust_result:
   mov   eax,esi            ; Setup for pow10
   mov   word ptr [ebx], ax; Set initial power
                            ; of ten return value
   neg   eax                ; Subtract one for each  order of
                            ; magnitude the value is scaled by
   call  get_power_10       ; Scaling factor is returned as
                            ; exponent and fraction
   fld   fraction           ; Get fraction
   fmul                     ; Combine fractions
   mov   esi, ecx           ; Form power of ten of the maximum
   shl   esi, 3             ; BCD value to fit in
                            ; the string
   fild  power_two          ; combine powers of two
```

```
        faddp st(2),st
        fscale                  ; Form full value
                                ; exponent was safe
        fstp st(1)              ; remove exponent
;
; Test the adjusted value against a table
; of exact powers of ten. The combined errors
; of the magnitude estimate and power function
; can result in a value one order of magnitude
; too small or too large to fit correctly in
; the BCD field. To handle this problem, pretest
; the adjusted value, if it is too small or
; large, then adjust it by ten and adjust the
; power of ten value.
;
test_power:

; compare against exact power entry. Use the next
; entry since cx has been decremenated by one

        fcom power_table[esi]+type power_table
        fstsw ax                ; No wait is necessary
        sahf                    ; If C3 = C0 = 0 then
        jb    test_for_small    ; too big

        fdiv const10            ; Else adjust value
        and   dl, not EXACT; Remove exact flag
        inc   word ptr [ebx]    ; Adjust power of ten value
        jmp   short in_range    ; Convert the value to a BCD
                                ; integer
test_for_small:
        fcom power_table[esi]; Test relative size
        fstsw ax                ; no wait is nessesary
        sahf                    ; If C0 = 0 then
                                ;   st (0) >= lower_bound
        jc    in_range          ; Convert the value to a
                                ; BCD integer
        fimul const10           ; Adjust value into range
        dec   word ptr [ebx]    ; Adjust power of ten value
in_range:
        frndint                 ; Form integer value
;
; Assert: 0 <= TOS <= 999,999,999,999,999,999
; The TOS number will be exactly representable
; in 18 digit BCD format.
;
convert_integer:
        fbstp bcd_value         ; Store as BCD format number
;
; While the store BCD runs, setup registers
```

```
; for the conversion to ASCII.
;
    mov   esi, BCD_SIZE-2   ; Initial BCD index value
    mov   cx, 0F04h         ; Set shift count and mask
    mov   ebx, 1            ; Set initial size of ASCII
; Field for sign
    mov   edi, string_ptr   ; Get address of start of
                            ; ASCII string
    mov   ax,ds             ; Copy ds to es
    mov   es, ax
    cld                     ; Set autoincrement mode
    mov   al, '+'           ; Clear sign field
    test  dl, MINUS         ; Look for negative value
    jz    positive_result

    mov   al, '-'
positive_result:
    stosb                   ; Bump string pointer
                            ; past sign
    and   dl, not MINUS;    Turn off sign bit
    fwait                   ; Wait for fbstp to finish
;
;Register usage:
; ah:     BCD byte value in use
; al:     ASCII character value
; dx:     Return value
; ch:     BCD mask = 0Fh
; cl:     BCD shift count = 4
; ebx:    ASCII string field width
; esi:    BCD field index
; edi:    ASCII string field pointer
; ds,es:  ASCII string segment base
;
;Remove leading zereos from the number.
;
skip_leading_zeroes:
    mov   ah, bcd_byte[esi] ; Get BCD byte
    mov   al,ah             ; Copy value
    shr   al,cl             ; Get high order digit
    and   al, 0Fh           ; Set zero flag
    jnz   enter_odd         ; Exit loop if leading
                            ; non zero found

    mov   al, ah            ; Get BCD byte again
    and   al, 0fh           ; Get low order digit
    jnz   enter_even        ; Exit loop if non zero
                            ; digit found

    dec   esi               ; Decrement BCD index
    jns   skip_leading_zeroes
```

```
;
;   The significand was all zeroes.
;
   mov     al, '0'          ; Set initial zero
   stosb
   inc     ebx              ; Bump string length
   jmp     short exit_with_value
;
; Now expand the BCD string into digit
; per byte values 0-9.
;
digit_loop:
   mov ah,bcd_byte[esi]     ; Get BCD byte
   mov al,ah
   shr al,cl                ; Get high order digit

enter_odd:
   add al, '0'              ; Convert to ASCII
   stosb                    ; Put digit into ASCII
                            ; string area
   mov al,ah                ; Get low order digit
   and al,0Fh
   inc ebx                  ; Bump field size counter
enter_even:
   add al, '0'              ; Convert to ASCII
   stosb                    ; Put digit into ASCII area
   inc ebx                  ; Bump field size counter
   dec esi                  ; Go to next BCD byte
   jns digit_loop
;
; Conversion complete. set the string
; size and reminder.
;
exit_with_value:
   mov edi,size_ptr
   mov word ptr [edi],bx
   mov eax,edx              ; set return value
   jmp exit_proc

floating_to_ascii endp
          code ends
              end

+ 1 $title(calculate the value of 10**eax)
; This subroutine will calculate the
; value of 10**eax. For values of
; 0 <= eax <19, the result will exact.
; All registers are transparent
; and results are returned on the TOS
; as two numbers, exponent in st(1) and
```

```
; fraction is st(0). The exponent value
; can be larger than the largest
; exponent of an extended real format
; number. Three stack entries are used.
;

   name        get_power 10
   public      get_power_10, power_table

stack stackseg 8

code    segment public er
;
;   Use exact values from 1.0 to 1e18.
;
     even            ; optimize 16 bit access
power_table  dq 1.0,1e,1e2,1e3
             dq 1e4,1e5,1e6,1e7
             dq 1e8,1e9,1e10,1e11
             dq 1e12, 1e13, 1e14,1e15
             dq 1e16,1e17, 1e18

get_power_10 proc

   cmp      eax,18            ; Test for 0 <= ax < 19
   ja       out_of_range

   fld      power_table[eax*8] ; Get exact value
   fxtract                     ; Separate power
                               ; and fraction
   ret                         ; OK to leave fxtract running
;
; Calculate the value using the
; exponentiate instruction. The following
; relations are used:
;   10**x= 2**(log2(10)*x)
;   2**(I+F) = 2**I * 2**F
; if st(1) - I and st(0) = 2**F then
; fscale produces 2**(I+F)
;
out_of-range:
   fldl2t                       ; TOS = LOG2(10)
   enter 4,0

; Save power of 10 value, P
   mov    [edp-4], eax

; TOS,X= LOG2(10)*P = LOG2(10**P)
   fimul dword ptr[edp-4]
   fld1                         ; Set TOS =  1.0
```

```
        fchs
        fld    st(1)              ; Copy power value
                                  ; in base two
        frndint                   ; TOS = I: -inf < I <= x
                                  ; where I is an integer
                                  ; Rounding mode does
                                  ; not matter
        fxch   st(2)                ; TOS = x, st(1) = 1.0
                                  ; st(2) = I
        fsub   st,st(2)           ; TOS,F = x - I:
                                  ; -1.0 < TOS <= 1.0

; Restore original rounding control
        pop    eax
        fx2m1                     ; TOS = 2**(F) - 1.0
        leave                     ; Restore stack
        fsubr                     ; Form 2**(F)
        ret                       ; OK to leave fsubr running

get_power_10 endp

code        ends
        end


+1 $Title(Determine TOS register contents)
;
; This subroutine will return a value
; from 0-15 in eax corresponding
; to the contents of FPU TOS. All
; registers are transparent and no
; errors are possible. The return
; value corresponds to c3,c2,c1,c0
; of FXAM instuction.
;
    name    tos_status
    public  tos_status

stack stackseg   6

code segment public er

tos_status proc

    fxam                ; Get status of TOS register
    fstsw ax            ; Get current status
    mov   al,ah         ; Put bits 10-8 into bits 2-0
    and   eax,4007h     ; Mask out bits c3,c2,c1,c0
    shr   ah, 3         ; Put bits c3 into bit 11
    or    al, ah        ; Put c3 into bit 3
```

```
    mov   ah, 0          ; Clear return value
    ret

tos_status endp

code      ends
     end
```

8.3.1.   Function Partitioning

Three separate modules implement the conversion. Most of the work of the conversion is done in the module FLOATING__TO_ASCII. The other modules are provided separately, because they have a more general use. One of them, GET_POWER_10, is also used by the ASCII to floating-point conversion routine. The other small module, TOS_STATUS, identifies what, if anything, is in the top of the numeric register stack.

8.3.2.   Exception Considerations

Care is taken inside the function to avoid generating exceptions. Any possible numeric value is accepted. The only possible exception is insufficient space on the numeric register stack.

The value passed in the numeric stack is checked for existence, type (NaN or infinity), and status (denormal, zero, sign). The string size is tested for a minimum and maximum value. If the top of the register stack is empty, or the string size is too small, the function returns with an error code.

Overflow and underflow is avoided inside the function for very large or very small numbers.

8.3.3.   Special Instructions

The functions demonstrate the operation of several numeric instructions, different data types, and precision control. Shown are instructions for automatic conversion to BCD, calculating the value of 10 raised to an integer value, establishing and maintaining concurrency, data synchronization, and use of directed rounding on the FPU.

Without the extended precision data type and built-in exponential function, the double precision accuracy of this function could not be attained with the size and speed of the shown example.

The function relies on the numeric BCD data type for conversion from binary floating-point to decimal. It is not difficult to unpack the BCD digits into separate ASCII decimal digits. The major work involves scaling the floating-point value to the comparatively limited range of BCD values. To print a 9-digit result requires accurately scaling the given value to an integer between 10^8 and 10^9. For example, the number +0.123456789 requires a scaling factor of 10^9 to produce the value +123456789.0, which can be stored in 9 BCD digits. The scale factor must be an exact power of 10 to avoid changing any of the printed digit values.

These routines should exactly convert all values exactly representable in decimal in the field size given. Integer values that fit in the given string size are not be scaled, but directly stored into the BCD form. Noninteger values exactly representable in decimal within the string size limits are also exactly converted. For example, 0.125 is exactly representable in binary or decimal. To convert this floating-point value to decimal, the scaling factor is 1000, resulting in 125. When scaling a value, the function must keep track of where the decimal point lies in the final decimal value.

8.3.4. Description of Operation

Converting a floating-point number to decimal ASCII takes three major steps: identifying the magnitude of the number, scaling it for the BCD data type, and converting the BCD data type to a decimal ASCII string.

Identifying the magnitude of the result requires finding the value X such that the number is represented by $I \times 10^X$, where $1.0 \le I < 10.0$. Scaling the number requires multiplying it by a scaling factor 10^S, so that the result is an integer requiring no more decimal digits than provided for in the ASCII string.

Once scaled, the numeric rounding modes and BCD conversion put the number in a form easy to convert to decimal ASCII by host software.

Implementing each of these three steps requires attention to detail. To begin with, not all floating-point values have a numeric meaning. Values such as infinity, indefinite, or NaN may be encountered by the conversion routine. The conversion routine should recognize these values and identify them uniquely.

Special cases of numeric values also exist. Denormals have numeric values, but should be recognized because they indicate that precision was lost during some earlier calculations.

Once it has been determined that the number has a numeric value, and it is normalized (setting appropriate denormal flags, if necessary, to indicate this to the calling program), the value must be scaled to the BCD range.

8.3.5. Scaling the Value

To scale the number, its magnitude must be determined. It is sufficient to calculate the magnitude to an accuracy of 1 unit, or within a factor of 10 of the required value. After scaling the number, a check is made to see if the result falls in the range expected. If not, the result can be adjusted one decimal order of magnitude up or down. The adjustment test after the scaling is necessary due to inevitable inaccuracies in the scaling value.

Because the magnitude estimate for the scale factor need only be close, a fast technique is used. The magnitude is estimated by multiplying the power of 2, the unbiased floating-point exponent, associated with the number by $\log_{10}2$. Rounding the result to an integer produces an estimate of sufficient accuracy. Ignoring the fraction value can introduce a maximum error of 0.32 in the result.

Using the magnitude of the value and size of the number string, the scaling factor can be calculated. Calculating the scaling factor is the most inaccurate operation of the conversion process. The relation $10^X = 2^{(X*\log_2 10)}$ is used for this function. The exponentiate instruction F2XM1 is used.

Due to restrictions on the range of values allowed by the F2XM1 instruction, the power of 2 value is split into integer and fraction components. The relation $2^{(I + F)} = 2^I \times 2^F$ allows using the FSCALE instruction to recombine the 2^F value, calculated through F2XM1, and the 2^I part.

8.3.5.1.   INACCURACY IN SCALING

The inaccuracy in calculating the scale factor arises because of the trailing zeros placed into the fraction value of the power of two when stripping off the integer valued bits. For each integer valued bit in the power of 2 value separated from the fraction bits, one bit of precision is lost in the fraction field due to the zero fill occurring in the least significant bits.

Up to 14 bits may be lost in the fraction because the largest allowed floating point exponent value is $2^{14}-1$. These bits directly reduce the accuracy of the calculated scale factor, thereby reducing the accuracy of the scaled value. For numbers in the range of $10^{\pm 30}$, a maximum of 8 bits of precision are lost in the scaling process.

8.3.5.2.   AVOIDING UNDERFLOW AND OVERFLOW

The fraction and exponent fields of the number are separated to avoid underflow and overflow in calculating the scaling values. For example, to scale 10^{-4932} to 10^8 requires a scaling factor of 10^{4950}, which cannot be represented by the the Intel FPU's.

By separating the exponent and fraction, the scaling operation involves adding the exponents separate from multiplying the fractions. The exponent arithmetic involves small integers, all easily represented by the Intel FPU's.

8.3.5.3.   FINAL ADJUSTMENTS

It is possible that the power function (Get_Power_10) could produce a scaling value such that it forms a scaled result larger than the ASCII field could allow. For example, scaling $9.9999999999999999 \times 10^{4900}$ by $1.0000000000000010 \times 10^{-4883}$ produces $1.0000000000000009 \times 10^{18}$. The scale factor is within the accuracy of the FPU and the result is within the conversion accuracy, but it cannot be represented in BCD format. This is why there is a post-scaling test on the magnitude of the result. The result can be multiplied or divided by 10, depending on whether the result was too small or too large, respectively.

8.3.6.   Output Format

For maximum flexibility in output formats, the position of the decimal point is indicated by a binary integer called the power value. If the power value is zero, then the decimal point is assumed to be at the right of the rightmost digit. Power values greater than zero indicate how many trailing zeros are not shown. For each unit below zero, move the decimal point to the left in the string.

The last step of the conversion is storing the result in BCD and indicating where the decimal point lies. The BCD string is then unpacked into ASCII decimal characters. The ASCII sign is set corresponding to the sign of the original value.

8.4. TRIGONOMETRIC CALCULATION EXAMPLES

In this example, the kinematics of a robot arm is modeled with the 4×4 homogeneous transformation matrices proposed by Denavit and Hartenberg[1,2]. The translational and rotational relationships between adjacent links are described with these matrices using the D-H matrix method. For each link, there is a 4×4 homogeneous transformation matrix that represents the link's coordinate system (L_i) at the joint (J_i) with respect to the previous link's coordinate system (J_{i-1}, L_{i-1}). The following four geometric quantities completely describe the motion of any rigid joint/link pair (J_i, L_i), as Figure 8-1 illustrates.

$\theta_i =$ The angular displacement of the x_i axis from the x_{i-1} axis by rotating around the z_{i-1} axis (anticlockwise).

$d_i =$ The distance from the origin of the $(i-1)^{th}$ coordinate system along the z_{i-1} axis to the x_i axis.

$a_i =$ The distance of the origin of the ith coordinate system from the z_{i-1} axis along the $-x_i$ axis.

$\alpha_i =$ The angular displacement of the z_i axis from the z_{i-1} about the x_i axis (anticlockwise).

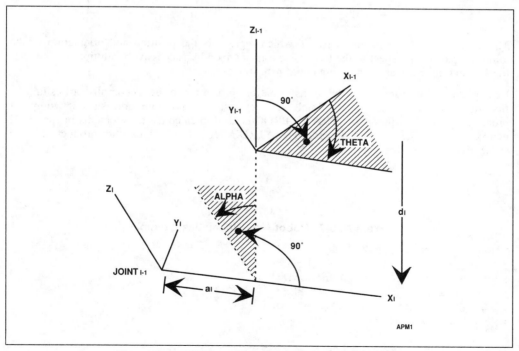

Figure 8-1. Relationships Between Adjacent Joints

The D-H transformation matrix $\mathbf{A}^{i}_{i-1}$ for adjacent coordinate frames (from joint$_{i-1}$ to joint$_i$ is calculated as follows:

$$\mathbf{A}^{i}_{i-1} = \mathbf{T}_{z,d} \times \mathbf{T}_{z,\theta} \times \mathbf{T}_{x,a} \times \mathbf{T}_{x,\alpha}$$

where:

$\mathbf{T}_{z,d}$ represents a translation along the $\mathbf{z}_{i-1}$ axis

$\mathbf{T}_{z,\theta}$ represents a rotation of angle θ about the $\mathbf{z}_{i-1}$ axis

$\mathbf{T}_{x,a}$ represents a translation along the $\mathbf{x}_i$ axis

$\mathbf{T}_{x,\alpha}$ represents a rotation of angle α about the $\mathbf{x}_i$ axis

$$\mathbf{A}^{i}_{i-1} = \begin{bmatrix} \cos\theta_i & -\cos\alpha_i \sin\theta_i & \sin\alpha_i \sin\theta_i & \cos\theta_i \\ \sin\theta_i & \cos\alpha_i \cos\theta_i & -\sin\alpha_i \cos\theta_i & \sin\theta_i \\ 0 & \sin\alpha_i & \cos\alpha_i & d_i \\ 0 & 0 & 0 & 1 \end{bmatrix}$$

The composite homogeneous matrix $\mathbf{T}$ which represents the position and orientation of the joint/link pair with respect to the base system is obtained by successively multiplying the D-H transformation matrices for adjacent coordinate frames.

Example 8-7 illustrates how the transformation process can be accomplished using the floating-point capabilities of the Intel architectures. The program consists of two major procedures. The first procedure TRANS_PROC is used to calculate the elements in each D-H matrix, $\mathbf{A}^{i}_{i-1}$. The second procedure MATRIXMUL_PROC finds the product of two successive D-H matrices.

$$\mathbf{T}^{i}_{0} = \mathbf{A}^{1}_{0} \times \mathbf{A}^{2}_{1} \times \ldots \times \mathbf{A}^{i}_{i-1}$$

Example 8-7. Robot Arm Kinematics Example

```
NAME ROT_MATRIX_CAL
; This example illustrates the use
; of the Intel486™ floating point
; instuctions, in paticular, the
; FSINCOS function which gives both
; the SIN and COS values.
; The program calculates the
; composite matrix for base to end-
; effector transformation.
;
; Only the kinematics is considered in
; this example.
;
```

```
; If the composite matrix mentioned above
; is given by:
; t1n = A1 x A2 ... x An
; T1n is found by successively calling
; trans_proc and matrixmul_proc until
; all matrices have been exhausted.
;
; trans_proc calculates entries in each
; A(A1,...,An) while matrixmul_proc
; performs the matrix multiplication for
; Ai and Ai+1. matrixmul_proc in turn
; calls matrix_row and matrix_elem to
; do the multiplication.


; Define stack space

trans_stack stackseg 400

; Define the matrix structure for
; 4x4 transformational matrices

a_matrix struc
    a11    dq    ?
    a12    dq    ?
    a13    dq    ?
    a14    dq    ?
    a21    dq    ?
    a22    dq    ?
    a23    dq    ?
    a24    dq    ?
    a31    dq 0h
    a32    dq    ?
    a33    dq    ?
    a34    dq    ?
    a41    dq 0h
    a42    dq 0h
    a43    dq 0h
    a44    dq 1h

a_matrix ends

; Assume  One joint in the storage
; allocation and hence for
; two seats of parameters; however,
; more joints are possible
;
alp_deg struc
    alpha_deg1 dd ?
    alpha_deg2 dd ?
```

```
alp_deg ends

tht_deg struc
   theta_deg  dd ?
tht_deg ends

a_array struc
   A1 dd ?
   A2 dd ?
A_array ends

D_array struc
   D1 dq ?
   D2 dq ?
D_array ends

; trans-data is the data segment
;

trans_data segment rw public

   Amx         a_matrix<>
   Bmx         a_matrix<>
   Tmx         a _marix<>
   ALPHA_DEG   alp_deg<>
   THETA_DEG   tht_deg<>
   A_VECTOR    A_array<>
   D_VECTOR    D_array<>
   ZERO        dd 0
   d180        dd 180
   NUM_JOINT   equ   1
   NUM_ROW     equ   4
   NUM_COL     equ   4
   REVERSE     db 1h
trans_data ends

assume ds:trans_data, es:trans_data

; Trans code contains the procedures
; for calculating matrix elements and
; matrix multiplications

trans_code segment er publlic
trans_proc proc far

; Calculate alpha and theta in radians
; from their values in degrees

   fldpi
   fdiv d180
```

```
; Duplicate pi/180
   fld   st(0)

   fmul  qword ptr ALPHA_DEG[ecx*8]
   fxch  st(1)
   fmul  qword ptr THETA_DEG[ecx*8]


; theta(radians) in ST and
; alpha(radians) in ST(1)

; Calculate matrix elements
; a11 = cos theta
; a12 = -cos alpha * sin thet
; a13 = sin alpha * sin theta
; a14 = A *cos theta
; a21 = sin theta
; a22 = cos alpha * cos theta
; a23 = sin alpha * cos theta
; a24 = A * sin theta
; a32 = sin alpha
; a33 = cos alpha
; a34 = D
; a31 = a41 = a2 = a43 = 0.0
; a44 = 1

; ebx contains the offset for the matrix

   fsincos                 ; cos theta in ST
                           ; sin theta inst(1)
   fld   st(0)             ; duplicate cos theta
   fst   [ebx].all         ; cos theta in all
   fmul  qword ptr A_VECTOR[ecx*8]
   fstp  [ebx].a14         ; A* cos theta in a14
   fxch  st(1)             ; sin theta in ST
   fst   [exb].a21         ; sin theta in a21
   fld   st                ; duplicate sin theta
   fmul  qword ptr A_VECTOR[ecx*8]
   fstp  [ebx].a24         ; A * sin theta in a24
   fld   st(2)             ; alpha in ST
   fsincos                 ; cos alpha in ST
                           ;sin alpha in ST(1)
                           ;sin theta in ST(2)
                           ;cos theta in ST (3)
   fst   [ebx].a33         ;cos alpha in a33
   fxch  st(1)             ;sin alpha in ST
   fst   [ebx].a32         ;sin sin alpha in a32
   .fld  st (2)            ;sin theta in ST
                           ;sin alpha in ST (1)
```

```
        fmul  st,st(1)              ;sin alpha  * sin theta
        fstp  [ebx].a13            ;stored in a 13a
        fmul  st,st(3)             ;costheta * sin alpha
        fchs                        ;cos theta * sin alpha
        fstp  [ebx].a23            ;stored in a23
        fld   st(2)                ;cos theta in ST
                                    ;cos alpha in ST(1)
                                    ;sin theta in ST(2)
                                    ;cos theta in ST(3)
        fmul  st,st(1)             ;cos theta * cos alpha
        fstp  [ebx].a22            ;stored in a22
        fmul  st,st(1)             ;cos alpha * sin theta
;
; To take advantage of parallel operations
; between the IU and FPU
        push  eax                   ;save eax
;
; also move D into a34 in a faster way
        mov   eax, dword ptr D_VECTOR[ecx*8]
        mov   dword ptr [ebx + 88], eax
        mov   eax, dword ptr D_VECTOR[ecx * 8 + 4]
        mov   dword ptr [ebx + 92], eax
        pop   eax                   ;restore eax
        fchs                        ;cos alpha * sin theta
        fstp  [ebx].a12            ;stored in a12
                                    ;and all nonzero elements
                                    ;have been calculated

        ret

trans_proc endp

matrix_elem proc far

; This procedure calculates the dot product of the ith row
; of the first matrix and the jth column of the second
; matrix:

; TIJ where TIJ = sum of Aik x Bkj over k
;
; parameters passed from the calling routine,
; matrix_row:
; ESI = (i-1)*8
; EDI = (j-1)*8
; local register, EBP = (k-1)*8

        push  ebp           ; save ebp
        push  ecx           ; ecx to be used as a tmp reg
        mov   ecx, esi      ; save it for later indexing

; locating the element in the first matrix, A
```

```
      imul  ecx, NUM_COL   ; ecx contains offset due
                           ; to preceding rows; the
                           ; offset is from the beginning
                           ; of the matrix

      xor ebp, ebp         ; clear ebp, which will be
                           ; used as a temp reg to index(k)
                           ; across the ith row of the first
                           ; matrix as well as down the jth
                           ; column of the second matrix

; clear Tij for accumulating Aik*Bkj
   mov  dword ptr [edx][edi], ebp
   mov  dword ptr [edx][edi+4], ebp

      push ecx             ; save on stack:  esi * num_col =
                           ; the offset of the beginning of
                           ; the ith row from the
                           ; beginning of the A matrix

NXT_k:
   add   ecx, ebp          ;get to the kth column entry
                           ;of the ith row of the A matrix

; load Aik into FPU
   fld   qword ptr [eax][ecx]

; locating Bkj
   mov   ecx, ebp
   imul  ecx, NUM_ROW       ; ecx contains the offset of the
                            ; beginning of the kth row from
                            ; the beginning of the B matrix
   add   ecx, edi           ; get to the jth column
                            ; of the kth row of the B matrix
   fmul qword ptr [ebx][ecx] ;Aik & Bkj
   pop   ecx                ;esi * num_col in ecx again
   push ecx                 ;also at top of program stack

; add to the result in the output matrix, Tij
   add   ecx, edi

; accumulating the sum of Aik * Bkj
   fadd qword ptr [edx][ecx]
   fstp qword ptr [edx][ecx]

; increment k by 1, i.e., ebp by 8
   add   ebp, 8

; Has k reached the width of the matrix yet?
   cmp   ebp, NUM_COL*8
```

```
        jl    NXT_k

; Restore registers
        pop   ecx          ;clear esi_num_col from stack
        pop   ecx          ;restore ecx
        pop   ebp          ;restore ebp
        ret

matrix_elem endp

matrix_row proc far
        xor   edi, edi
        ;scan across a row

NXT_COL:
        call  matrix_elem
        add   edi, 8
        cmp   edi, NUM_COL*8
        jl    NXT_COL
        ret

matrix_row endp

matrixmul_proc proc far
; This procedure does the matrix multiplication by calling
; matrix_row to calculate entries in each row.
;
; The matrix multiplication is performed in the following
; manner,
; Tij = Aik x Bkj
; where i and j denote the row and column
; respectively and k is the index for scanning
; across the ith row of the first matrix and
; the jth column of the second matrix.

        mov   ebp, esp                ; use base pointer for indexing
        mov   edx, dword ptr [ebp+4]  ; offset Tmx in edx
        mov   ebx, dword ptr [ebp+8]  ; offset Bmx in ebx
        mov   eax, dword ptr [ebp+12] ; offset Amx in eax

; setup esi and edi
; edi points to the column
; esi points to the row

        xor     esi, esi            ; clear esi

NXT_ROW:
        call  matrix_row
        add     esi, 8
        cmp     esi, NUM_ROW*8
```

```
      jl    NXT_ROW
      ret   12                    ;pop off matrix pointers

matrixmul_proc endp

trans_code ends
```

```
;*********************************************
;                                           ;
;          Main Program                     ;
;                                           ;
;*********************************************
```

```
main_code segment er

START:
   mov   esp, stackstart trans_stack


      pushad                     ;save all registers
```

```
; ECX denotes the number of joints where
; number of matrices = NUM_JOINT + 1
; Find the first matrix (from the base of the
; system to the first joint) and call it Bmx
   xor   ecx, ecx            ;1st matrix
   mov   ebx, offset Bmx
   call trans_proc        ; is Bmx
   inc   ecx
```

```
NXT_MATRIX:
; From the 2nd matrix and on, it will be stored in Amx.
; The result from the first matrix mult. is stored in
; Tmx but will be accessed as Bmx in the next multiplication.
; As a matter of fact, the roles of Bmx and Tmx alternate in
; successive multiplications.  This is achieved by reversing
; the order of the Bmx and Tmx pointers being passed onto the
; program stack.  Thus, this is invislbe to the matrix
; mutliplication procedure.
; REVERSE serves as the indicator
; REVERSE = 0 means that the result is to be placed in Tmx

   mov      ebx, offset Amx       ;find Amx
   call     trans_proc
   inc      ecx
   xor      REVERSE, 1h
   jnz      Bmx_as_Tmx
```

```
; No reversing.  Bms as the second input
; matrix while Tmx as the output matrix.
```

```
    push  offset Amx
    push  offset Bmx
    push  offset Tmx
    jmp   CONTINUE

; Reversing.  Tmx as the second input
; matrix while Bms as the output matrix.
Bmx_as_Tmx:
    push  offset Amx
    push  offset Tmx           ;reversing the
    push  offset Bmx           ;pointers passed

CONTINUE:
    call matrixmul_proc
    cmp  ecx, NUM_JOINT
    jle  NXT_MATRIX

; if REVERSE = 1 then the final answer
; will be in Bmx, otherwise in Tmx.

    popad

main_code ends

end START, ds:trans_data, ss:trans_stack
```

---

[1] J. Denavit and R.S. Hartenberg, "A Kinematic Notation for Lower-Pair Mechanisms Based on Matrices", *J. Applied Mechanics*, June 1955, pp. 215-221.

[2] C.S. George Lee, "Robot Arm Kinematics, Dynamics, and Control," *IEEE Computer*, Dec. 1982.

Part II

System Programming

Part II

System Programming

intel ®

9

Real-Address Mode
System Architecture

CHAPTER 9
REAL-ADDRESS MODE SYSTEM ARCHITECTURE

The real-address mode of the Pentium processor runs programs written for the 8086, 8088, 80186, or 80188 processors, or for the real-address mode of an Intel 286, Intel386, or Intel486 processor.

The architecture of the processor in this mode is almost identical to that of the 8086, 8088, 80186, and 80188 processors. To a programmer, a 32-bit processor in real-address mode appears as a high-speed 8086 processor or real-mode Intel 286 processor with extensions to the instruction set and registers. The principal features of this architecture are defined in Chapter 3 and Chapter 4.

This chapter discusses certain additional topics which complete the system programmer's view of real-address mode:

- Address formation.
- Interrupt and exception handling.
- Real-address mode exceptions.

For information on input and output both in real-address mode and protected mode, refer to Chapter 15.

9.1. ADDRESS TRANSLATION

In real-address mode, the processor does not interpret selectors by referring to descriptors; instead, it forms linear addresses as an 8086 processor would. It shifts the selector left by four bits to form a 20-bit base address. The effective address is extended with four clear bits in the upper bit positions and added to the base address to create a linear address, as shown in Figure 9-1.

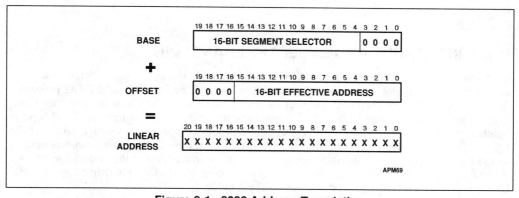

Figure 9-1. 8086 Address Translation

Because of the possibility of a carry, the resulting linear address may have as many as 21 significant bits. An 8086 program may generate linear addresses anywhere in the range 0 to 10_FFEFH (1 megabyte plus approximately 64K bytes) of the linear address space. (Note, however, that on the Intel486 and Pentium processors, the A20M# signal can be used in real-address mode to mask address signal A20, thereby mimicking the 20-bit wrap-around behavior of the 8086 processor) Because paging is not available in real-address mode, the linear address is used as the physical address.

Unlike the 8086 and Intel 286 processors, but like the Intel386 and Intel486 processors, the Pentium processor can generate 32-bit effective addresses using an address override prefix; however in real-address mode, the value of a 32-bit address may not exceed 65,535 without causing an exception. For full compatibility with Intel 286 real-address mode, pseudo-protection faults (interrupt 12 or 13 with no error code) occur if an effective address is generated outside the range 0 through 65,535.

9.2.   REGISTERS AND INSTRUCTIONS

The register set available in real-address mode includes all the registers defined for the 8086 processor plus the new registers introduced with the Intel386 processor and Intel387 coprocessor: FS, GS, debug registers, control registers, test registers, and floating-point unit registers. New instructions which explicitly operate on the segment registers FS and GS are available, and the new segment-override prefixes can be used to cause instructions to use the FS and GS registers for address calculations.

The instruction codes which generate invalid-opcode exceptions include instructions from protected mode which move or test protected-mode segment selectors and segment descriptors, i.e., the VERR, VERW, LAR, LSL, LTR, STR, LLDT, and SLDT instructions. Programs executing in real-address mode are able to take advantage of the new application-oriented instructions added to the architecture with the introduction of the 80186, 80188, Intel 286, Intel386, Intel486, and Pentium processors.

Unlike the 8086 and Intel 286 processors, but like the Intel386 and Intel486 processors, the Pentium processor offers an operand-size override prefixe which enables access to 32-bit operands. This prefix should not be used, however, if compatibility with the 8086 or Intel 286 processors is desired.

9.3.   INTERRUPT AND EXCEPTION HANDLING

Interrupts and exceptions in real-address mode work much as they do on an 8086 processor. Interrupts and exceptions call interrupt procedures through an interrupt table. The processor scales the interrupt or exception identifier by four to obtain an index into the interrupt table. The entries of the interrupt table are far pointers to the entry points of interrupt or exception handler procedures. When an interrupt occurs, the processor pushes the current values of the CS and IP registers onto the stack, disables interrupts, clears the TF flag, and transfers control to the location specified in the interrupt table. An IRET instruction at the end of the handler procedure reverses these steps before returning control to the interrupted procedure. Exceptions do not return error codes in real-address mode.

The primary difference in the interrupt handling of the 32-bit processors in real-address mode compared to the 8086 processor is that the location and size of the interrupt table depend on the contents of the IDTR register. Ordinarily, this fact is not apparent to programmers, because, after reset initialization, the IDTR register contains a base address of 0 and a limit of 3FFH, which is compatible with the 8086 processor. However, the LIDT instruction can be used in real-address mode to change the base and limit values in the IDTR register. See Chapter 9 for details on the IDTR register, and the LIDT and SIDT instructions. If an interrupt occurs and its entry in the interrupt table is beyond the limit stored in the IDTR register, a double-fault exception is generated.

9.4.   REAL-ADDRESS MODE EXCEPTIONS

The processor reports some exceptions differently when executing in real-address mode than when executing in protected mode. Table 9-1 details the real-address-mode exceptions.

Table 9-1. Exceptions and Interrupts

Description	Vector	Source of the Exception	Does the Return Address Point to the Instruction Which Caused the Exception?
Divide Error	0	DIV and IDIV instructions	yes
Debug	1	Any	*1
NMI	2	Nonmaskable Interrupt	yes
Breakpoint	3	INT instruction	no
Overflow	4	INTO instruction	no
Bounds Check	5	BOUND instruction	yes
Invalid Opcode	6	Reserved opcodes and improper use of LOCK prefix	yes
Device not available	7	ESC or WAIT instructions	yes
Double Fault	8	Interrupt table limit too small, fault occurring while handling another fault	yes
Reserved	9		
Invalid Task State Segment[3]	10	JMP, CALL, IRET instructions, interrupts and exceptions	yes
Segment not present[3]	11	Any instruction which changes segments	yes
Stack Exception	12	Stack operation crosses address limit (beyond offset FFFFH)	yes
CS, DS, ES, FS, GS Segment Overrun	13	Word memory reference beyond offset FFFFH. An attempt to execute past the end of CS segment.	yes
Page Fault[3]	14	Any instruction that references memory	yes
Reserved	15		
Floating-Point Error	16	ESC or WAIT instructions	yes[2]
Alignment Check[3]	17	Any data reference	no
Intel Reserved	18–31		
Software Interrupt	0–255	INT n instructions	no
Maskable Interrupt	32–255		yes

NOTES:

1. Some debug exceptions point to the faulting instruction, others point to the following instruction. The exception handler can test the DR6 register to determine which has occurred.

2. Floating-point errors are reported on the first ESC or WAIT instruction after the ESC instruction which generated the error.

3. Exceptions 10, 11, 14 and 17 do not occur in Real Mode, but are possible in virtual 8086 mode.

intel®

10

Protected Mode System Architecture Overview

10

CHAPTER 10
PROTECTED MODE SYSTEM ARCHITECTURE
OVERVIEW

Many of the architectural features of the processor are used only by system programmers. This chapter presents an overview of these features. Application programmers may need to read this chapter, and the following chapters which describe the use of these features, in order to understand the hardware facilities used by system programmers to create a reliable and secure environment for application programs. The system-level architecture also supports powerful debugging features which application programmers may wish to use during program development.

The system-level features of the architecture include:

- Memory Management
- Protection
- Multitasking
- Exceptions and Interrupts
- Input/Output
- Initialization and Mode Switching
- FPU Management
- Debugging
- Cache Management
- Multiprocessing

These features are supported by registers and instructions, all of which are introduced in the following sections. The purpose of this chapter is not to explain each feature in detail, but rather to place the remaining chapters about protected mode and systems programming in perspective. When a register or instruction is mentioned, it is accompanied by an explanation or a reference to a following chapter.

10.1. SYSTEM REGISTERS

The registers intended for use by system programmers fall into these categories:

- EFLAGS Register
- Memory-Management Registers
- Control Registers
- Debug Registers

The system registers control the execution environment of application programs. Most systems restrict access to these facilities by application programs (although systems can be built where all programs run at the most privileged level, in which case application programs are allowed to modify these facilities).

10.1.1. System Flags

The system flags of the EFLAGS register control I/O, maskable interrupts, debugging, task switching, and the virtual-8086 mode. An application program should ignore these system flags, and should not attempt to change their state. In some systems, an attempt to change the state of a system flag by an application program results in an exception. These flags are shown in Figure 10-1.

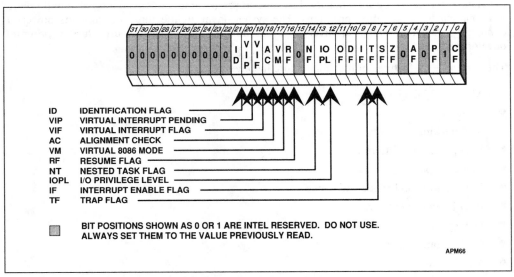

Figure 10-1. System Flags

ID (Identification Flag, bit 21)

The ability of a program to set and clear the ID flag indicates that the processor supports the CPUID instruction. Refer to Chapter 25 for details about CPUID.

VIP (Virtual Interrupt Pending Flag, bit 20)

The VIP flag together with the VIF enable each applications program in a multitasking environment to have virtualized versions of the system's IF flag. For more on the use of these flags in virtual-8086 mode and in protected mode, refer to Appendix H.

VIF (Virtual Interrupt Flag, bit 19)

The VIF is a virtual image of IF (the interrupt flag) used with VIP.

AC (Alignment Check Mode, bit 18)

Setting the AC flag and the AM bit in the CR0 register enables alignment checking on memory references. An alignment-check exception is generated when reference is made to an unaligned operand, such as a word at an odd byte address or a doubleword at an address which is not an integral multiple of four. Alignment-check exceptions are generated only in user mode (privilege level 3). Memory references which default to privilege level 0, such as segment descriptor loads, do not generate this exception even when caused by a memory reference in user-mode.

The alignment-check exception can be used to check alignment of data. This is useful when exchanging data with other processors, such as the i860™ microprocessor, which require all data to be aligned. The alignment-check exception can also be used by interpreters to flag some pointers as special by misaligning the pointer. This eliminates overhead of checking each pointer and only handles the special pointer when used.

VM (Virtual-8086 Mode, bit 17)

Setting the VM flag places the processor in virtual-8086 mode, which is an emulation of the programming environment of an 8086 processor. See Chapter 22 for more information.

RF (Resume Flag, bit 16)

The RF flag temporarily disables debug faults so that an instruction can be restarted after a debug fault without immediately causing another debug fault. The debugger sets this flag with the IRETD instruction when returning to the interrupted program. The RF flag is not affected by the POPF, POPFD or IRET instructions. See Chapter 14 and Chapter 17 for details.

NT (Nested Task, bit 14)

The processor sets and tests the nested task flag to control chaining of interrupted and called tasks. The NT flag affects the operation of the IRET instruction. The NT flag is affected by the POPF, POPFD, and IRET instructions. Improper changes to the state of this flag can generate unexpected exceptions in application programs. See Chapter 13 and Chapter 14 for more information on nested tasks.

IOPL (I/O Privilege Level, bits 12 and 13)

The I/O privilege level is used by the protection mechanism to control access to the I/O address space. The privilege level of the code segment currently executing (CPL) and the IOPL determine whether this field can be modified by the POPF, POPFD, and IRET instructions. See Chapter 15 for more information.

IF (Interrupt-Enable Flag, bit 9)

Setting the IF flag puts the processor in a mode in which it responds to maskable interrupt requests (INTR interrupts). Clearing the IF flag disables these interrupts. The IF flag has no effect on either exceptions or nonmaskable interrupts (NMI interrupts). The CPL and IOPL determine whether this field can be modified by the CLI, STI, POPF, POPFD, and IRET instructions. See Chapter 14 for more details about interrupts.

TF (Trap Flag, bit 8)

Setting the TF flag puts the processor into single-step mode for debugging. In this mode, the processor generates a debug exception after each instruction, which allows a program to be inspected as it executes each instruction. Single-stepping is just one of several debugging features of the processor. If an application program sets the TF flag using the POPF, POPFD, or IRET instructions, a debug exception is generated. See Chapter 14 and Chapter 17 for more information.

10.1.2. Memory-Management Registers

Four registers of the processor specify the locations of the data structures which control segmented memory management, as shown in Figure 10-2. Special instructions are provided for loading and storing these registers. The GDTR and IDTR registers can be loaded with instructions which get a six-byte block of data from memory. The LDTR and TR registers can be loaded with instructions which take a 16-bit segment selector as an operand. The remaining bytes of these registers are then loaded automatically by the processor from the descriptor referenced by the operand.

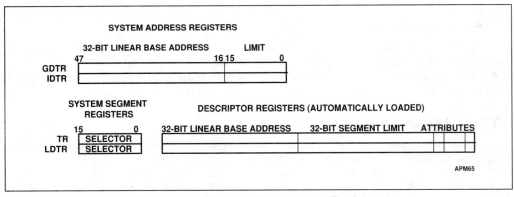

Figure 10-2. Memory Management Registers

Most systems protect the instructions which load memory-management registers from use by application programs (although a system in which no protection is used is possible).

GDTR Global Descriptor Table Register

This register holds the 32-bit base address and 16-bit segment limit for the global descriptor table (GDT). When a reference is made to data in memory, a segment selector is used to find a segment descriptor in the GDT or LDT. A segment descriptor contains the base address for a segment. See Chapter 11 for an explanation of segmentation.

LDTR Local Descriptor Table Register

This register holds the 32-bit base address, 32-bit segment limit, descriptor attributes, and 16-bit segment selector for the local descriptor table (LDT). The segment which contains the LDT has a segment descriptor in the GDT. There is no segment selector for the GDT. When a reference is made to data in memory, a segment selector is used to find a segment descriptor in the GDT or LDT. A segment descriptor contains the base address for a segment. See Chapter 11 for an explanation of segmentation.

IDTR Interrupt Descriptor Table Register

This register holds the 32-bit base address and 16-bit segment limit for the interrupt descriptor table (IDT). When an interrupt occurs, the interrupt vector is used as an index to get a gate descriptor from this table. The gate descriptor contains a pointer used to start up the interrupt handler. See Chapter 14 for details of the interrupt mechanism.

TR Task Register

This register holds the 32-bit base address, 32-bit segment limit, descriptor attributes, and 16-bit segment selector for the task currently being executed. It references a task state segment (TSS) descriptor in the global descriptor table. See Chapter 13 for a description of the multitasking features of the processor.

10.1.3. Control Registers

Figure 10-3 shows the format of the control registers CR0, CR1, CR2, CR3, and CR4. Most systems prevent application programs from loading the control registers (although an unprotected system would allow this). Application programs can read these registers; for example, reading CR0 to determine if a numerics coprocessor is present. Forms of the MOV instruction allow these registers to be loaded from or stored in general registers. For example:

```
MOV     EAX,    CR0
MOV     CR3,    EBX
```

Refer to Chapter 16 for a list of the initial values of all these registers.

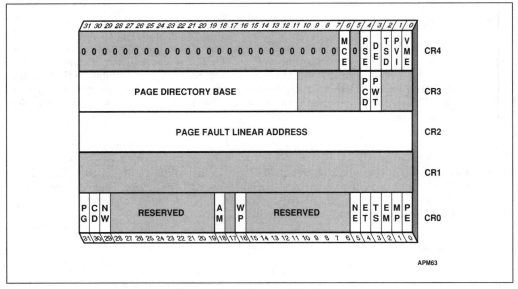

Figure 10-3. Control Registers

The CR0 register contains system control flags, which control modes or indicate states which apply generally to the processor, rather than to the execution of an individual task. A program should not attempt to change any of the reserved bit positions. Reserved bits should always be set to the value previously read.

PG (Paging, bit 31 of CR0)

This bit enables paging when set and disables paging when clear. See Chapter 11 for more information about paging. See Chapter 16 for information on how to enable paging.

When an exception is generated during paging, the CR2 register has the 32-bit linear address which caused the exception. See Chapter 14 for more information about handling exceptions generated during paging (page faults).

When paging is used, the CR3 register has the 20 most-significant bits of the address of the page directory (the first-level page table). The CR3 register is also known as the page-directory base register (PDBR). Note that the page directory must be aligned to a page boundary, so the low 12 bits of the register are not used as address bits. Unlike the Intel386 DX processor, the Intel486 and Pentium processors assign functions to two of these bits. These are:

- PCD (Page-Level Cache Disable, bit 4 of CR3)

  The state of this bit is driven on the PCD pin during bus cycles which are not paged, such as interrupt acknowledge cycles, when paging is enabled. It is driven during all bus cycles when paging is not enabled. The PCD pin is used to control caching in an external cache on a cycle-by-cycle basis.

- PWT (Page-Level Writes Transparent, bit 3 of CR3)

  The state of this bit is driven on the PWT pin during bus cycles which are not paged, such as interrupt acknowledge cycles, when paging is enabled. It is driven during all bus cycles when paging is not enabled. The PWT pin is used to control write-through in an external cache on a cycle-by-cycle basis.

CD (Cache Disable, bit 30 of CR0)

This bit enables the internal cache fill mechanism when clear and disables it when set. Cache misses do not cause cache line fills when the bit is set. Note that cache hits are not disabled; to completely disable the cache, the cache must be invalidated. See Chapter 18 for information on caching.

NW (Not Write-through, bit 29 of CR0)

This bit enables write-throughs and cache invalidation cycles when clear and disables invalidation cycles and write-throughs which hit in the cache when set. See Chapter 18 for information on caching.

AM (Alignment Mask, bit 18 of CR0)

This bit allows alignment checking when set and disables alignment checking when clear. Alignment checking is performed only when the AM bit is set, the AC flag is set, and the CPL is 3 (user mode).

WP (Write Protect, bit 16 of CR0)

When set, this bit write-protects user-level pages against supervisor-level writes. When this bit is clear, read-only user-level pages can be written by a supervisor process. This feature is useful for implementing the copy-on-write method of creating a new process (forking) used by some operating systems, such as UNIX.

NE (Numeric Error, bit 5 of CR0)

This bit enables the standard mechanism for reporting floating-point numeric errors when set. When NE is clear and the IGNNE# input is active, numeric errors are ignored. When the NE bit is clear and the IGNNE# input is inactive, a numeric error causes the processor to stop and wait for an interrupt. The interrupt is generated by using the FERR# pin to drive an input to the interrupt controller (the FERR# pin emulates the ERROR# pin of the Intel287 and Intel387 DX math coprocessors). The NE bit, IGNNE# pin, and FERR# pin are used with external logic to implement PC-style error reporting.

ET (Extension Type, bit 4 of CR0)

This bit is one to indicate support of Intel387 DX math coprocessor instructions (on the Pentium microprocessor, this bit is reserved).

TS (Task Switched, bit 3 of CR0)

The processor sets the TS bit with every task switch and tests it when interpreting floating-point arithmetic instructions. This bit allows delaying save/restore of numeric context until the numeric data is actually used. The CLTS instruction clears this bit.

39EM (Emulation, bit 2 of CR0)

When the EM bit is set, execution of a numeric instruction generates the coprocessor-not-available exception. The EM bit must be set when the processor does not have a floating-point unit.

MP (Monitor coProcessor, bit 1 of CR0)

On the Intel 286 and Intel386 DX processors, the MP bit controls the function of the WAIT instruction, which is used to synchronize with a coprocessor. When running Intel 286 and Intel386 DX CPU programs on processors with the Intel486 and Pentium FPUs, this bit should be set. The MP bit should be reset in the Intel486 SX CPU.

PE (Protection Enable, bit 0 of CR0)

Setting the PE bit enables segment-level protection. See Chapter 12 for more information about protection. See Chapter 16 for information on how to enable paging.

The CR4 register contains bits that enable certain architectural extensions. This register is new with the Pentium microprocessor.

VME (Virtual-8086 Mode Extensions, bit 0 of CR4)

Setting this bit to 1 enables support for a virtual interrupt flag in virtual-8086 mode. This feature can improve the performance of virtual-8086 applications by eliminating the overhead of faulting to a virtual-8086 monitor for emulation of certain operations. Refer to Appendix H for more information on this feature.

PVI (Protected-Mode Virtual Interrupts, bit 1 of CR4)

Setting this bit to 1 enables support for a virtual interrupt flag in protected mode. This feature can enable some programs designed for execution at privilege level 0 to execute at privilege level 3. Refer to Appendix H for more information on this feature.

TSD (Time Stamp Disable, bit 2 of CR4)

Setting this bit to 1 makes RDTSC (read from time stamp counter) a privileged instruction. Refer to Chapter 25 for details on the RDTSC instruction.

DE (Debugging Extensions, bit 3 of CR4)

Setting this bit to 1 enables I/O breakpoints. Refer to Chapter 17 for more information on debugging.

PSE (Page Size Extensions, bit 4 of CR4)

Setting this bit to 1 enables four-megabyte pages. Refer to Appendix H for information about this feature.

MCE (Machine Check Enable, bit 6 of CR4)

Setting this bit to 1 enables the machine check exception.

10.1.4. Debug Registers

The debug registers bring advanced debugging abilities to the processor, including data breakpoints and the ability to set instruction breakpoints without modifying code segments (useful in debugging ROM-based software). Only programs executing at the highest privilege level can access these registers. See Chapter 17 for a complete description of their formats and use. The debug registers are shown in Figure 10-4.

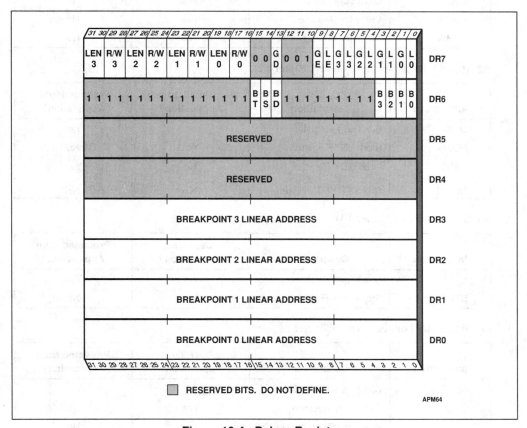

Figure 10-4. Debug Registers

10.2. SYSTEM INSTRUCTIONS

System instructions deal with functions such as:

1. Verfication of pointer parameters (see Chapter 12):

Instruction	Description	Useful to Application?	Protected from Application?
ARPL	Adjust RPL	No	No
LAR	Load Access Rights	Yes	No
LSL	Load Segment Limit	Yes	No
VERR	Verify for Reading	Yes	No
VERW	Verify for Writing	Yes	No

2. Addressing descriptor tables (see Chapter 11):

Instruction	Description	Useful to Application?	Protected from Application?
LLDT	Load LDT Register	No	Yes
SLDT	Store LDT Register	Yes	No
LGDT	Load GDT Register	No	Yes
SGDT	Store GDT Register	No	No

3. Multitasking (see Chapter 13):

Instruction	Description	Useful to Application?	Protected from Application?
LTR	Load Task Register	No	Yes
STR	Store Task Register	Yes	No

4. Floating-Point Numerics (see Chapter 6):

Instruction	Description	Useful to Application?	Protected from Application?
CLTS	Clear TS bit in CR0	No	Yes
ESC	Escape Instructions	Yes	No
WAIT	Wait Until Coprocessor Not Busy	Yes	No

5. Input and Output (see Chapter 15):

Instruction	Description	Useful to Application?	Protected from Application?
IN	Input	Yes	Can be
OUT	Output	Yes	Can be
INS	Input String	Yes	Can be
OUTS	Output String	Yes	Can be

6. Interrupt control (see Chapter 14):

Instruction	Description	Useful to Application?	Protected from Application?
CLI	Clear IF flag	Can be	Can be
STI	Set IF flag	Can be	Can be
LIDT	Load IDT Register	No	Yes
SIDT	Store IDT Register	No	No

7. Debugging (see Chapter 17):

Instruction	Description	Useful to Application?	Protected from Application?
MOV	Load and store debug registers	No	Yes

8. Cache Management (see Chapter 18):

Instruction	Description	Useful to Application?	Protected from Application?
INVD	Invalidate cache, no write-back	No	Yes
WBINVD	Invalidate cache, with write-back	No	Yes
INVLPG	Invalidate TLB entry	No	Yes

9. System Control:

Instruction	Description	Useful to Application?	Protected from Application?
SMSW	Store MSW	Yes	No
LMSW	Load MSW	No	Yes
MOV	Load And Store Control Register	No	Yes
HLT	Halt Processor	No	Yes
LOCK	Bus Lock	No	No
RSM	Return from system management mode	No	Yes

The SMSW and LMSW instructions are provided for compatibility with the 16-bit Intel 286 processor. Programs for 32-bit processors such as the Pentium microprocessor should not use these instructions. Instead, they should access the Control Registers using forms of the MOV instruction. The LMSW instruction does not affect the PG, CD, NW, AM, WP, NE or ET bits, and it cannot be used to clear the PE bit.

The HLT instruction stops the processor until an enabled interrupt or RESET signal is received. (Note that the NMI and SMI interrupts are always enabled.) A special bus cycle is generated by the processor to indicate halt mode has been entered. Hardware may respond to this signal in a number of ways. An indicator light on the front panel may be turned on. An NMI interrupt for recording diagnostic information may be generated. Reset initialization may be invoked. Software designers may need to be aware of the response of hardware to halt mode.

The LOCK instruction prefix is used to invoke a locked (atomic) read-modify-write operation when modifying a memory operand. The LOCK# signal is asserted and the processor does not respond to requests for bus control during a locked operation. This mechanism is used to allow reliable communications between processors in multiprocessor systems.

In addition to the chapters mentioned above, detailed information about each of these instructions can be found in the instruction reference chapter, Chapter 25.

intel®

11

Protected Mode Memory Management

Memory management is a hardware mechanism which lets operating systems create simplified environments for running programs. For example, when several programs are running at the same time, they must each be given an independent address space. If they all had to share the same address space, each would have to perform difficult and time-consuming checks to avoid interfering with the others.

Memory management consists of segmentation and paging. Segmentation is used to give each program several independent, protected address spaces. Paging is used to support an environment where large address spaces are simulated using a small amount of RAM and some disk storage. System designers can choose to use either or both of these mechanisms. When several programs are running at the same time, either mechanism can be used to protect programs against interference from other programs.

Segmentation allows memory to be completely unstructured and simple, like the memory model of an 8-bit processor, or highly structured with address translation and protection. The memory management features apply to units called segments. Each segment is an independent, protected address space. Access to segments is controlled by data which describes its size, the privilege level required to access it, the kinds of memory references which can be made to it (instruction fetch, stack push or pop, read operation, write operation, etc.), and whether it is present in memory.

Segmentation is used to control memory access, which is useful for catching bugs during program development and for increasing the reliability of the final product. It also is used to simplify the linkage of object code modules. There is no reason to write position-independent code when full use is made of the segmentation mechanism, because all memory references can be made relative to the base addresses of a module's code and data segments. Segmentation can be used to create ROM-based software modules, in which fixed addresses (fixed, in the sense that they cannot be changed) are offsets from a segment's base address. Different software systems can have the ROM modules at different physical addresses because the segmentation mechanism will direct all memory references to the right place.

In a simple memory architecture, all addresses refer to the same address space. This is the memory model used by 8-bit microprocessors, such as the 8080 processor, where the logical address is the physical address. The 32-bit processors in protected mode can be used in this way by mapping all segments into the same address space and keeping paging disabled. This might be done where an older design is being updated to 32-bit technology without also adopting the new architectural features.

An application also could make partial use of segmentation. A frequent cause of software failures is the growth of the stack into the instruction code or data of a program. Segmentation can be used to prevent this. The stack can be put in an address space separate from the address space for either code or data. Stack addresses always would refer to the memory in the stack segment, while data addresses always would refer to memory in the data segment. The stack segment would have a maximum size enforced by hardware. Any attempt to grow the stack beyond this size would generate an exception.

A complex system of programs can make full use of segmentation. For example, a system in which programs share data in real time can have precise control of access to that data. Program bugs appear as exceptions generated when a program makes improper access. This is useful as an aid to debugging during program development, and it also can be used to trigger error-recovery procedures in systems delivered to the end user.

Segmentation hardware translates a segmented (logical) address into an address for a continuous, unsegmented address space, called a linear address. If paging is enabled, paging hardware translates a linear address into a physical address. If paging is not enabled, the linear address is used as the physical address. The physical address appears on the address bus coming out of the processor.

Paging is a mechanism used to simulate a large, unsegmented address space using a small, fragmented address space and some disk storage. Paging provides access to data structures larger than the available memory space by keeping them partly in memory and partly on disk.

Paging is applied to units of 4 kilobytes called pages. When a program attempts to access a page which is on disk, the program is interrupted in a special way. Unlike other exceptions and interrupts, an exception generated due to address translation restores the contents of the processor registers to values which allow the exception-generating instruction to be re-executed. This special treatment enables instruction restart; that is, it allows the operating system to read the page from disk, update the mapping of linear addresses to physical addresses for that page, and restart the program. This process is transparent to the program.

Paging is optional. If an operating system never enables the paging mechanism, linear addresses will be used as physical addresses. This might be done where a design using a 16-bit processor is being updated to use a 32-bit processor. An operating system written for a 16-bit processor does not use paging because the size of its address space is so small (64K bytes) that it is more efficient to swap entire segments between RAM and disk, rather than individual pages.

Paging would be enabled for operating systems, such as UNIX, which can support demand-paged virtual memory. Paging is transparent to application software, so an operating system intended to support application programs written for 16-bit processors can run those programs with paging enabled. Unlike paging, segmentation is not transparent to application programs. Programs which use segmentation must be run with the segments they were designed to use.

11.1. SELECTING A SEGMENTATION MODEL

A model for the segmentation of memory is chosen on the basis of reliability and performance. For example, a system which has several programs sharing data in real time would get maximum performance from a model which checks memory references in hardware. This would be a multisegment model.

At the other extreme, a system which has just one program may get higher performance from an unsegmented or "flat" model. The elimination of "far" pointers and segment-override prefixes reduces code size and increases execution speed. Context switching is faster, because the contents of the segment registers no longer have to be saved or restored.

Some of the benefits of segmentation also can be provided by paging. For example, data can be shared by mapping the same pages onto the address space of each program.

11.1.1. Flat Model

The simplest model is the flat model. In this model, all segments are mapped to the entire physical address space. A segment offset can refer to either code or data areas. To the greatest extent possible, this model removes the segmentation mechanism from the architecture seen by either the system designer or the application programmer. This might be done for a programming environment like UNIX, which supports paging but does not support segmentation.

A segment is defined by a segment descriptor. At least two segment descriptors must be created for a flat model, one for code references and one for data references. Both descriptors have the same base address value. Whenever memory is accessed, the contents of one of the segment registers are used to select a segment descriptor. The segment descriptor provides the base address of the segment and its limit, as well as access control information (see Figure 11-1).

ROM usually is put at the top of the physical address space, because the processor begins execution at FFFF_FFF0H. RAM is placed at the bottom of the address space because the initial base address for the DS data segment after reset initialization is 0.

For a flat model, each descriptor has a base address of 0 and a segment limit of 4 gigabytes. By setting the segment limit to 4 gigabytes, the segmentation mechanism is kept from generating exceptions for memory references which fall outside of a segment. Exceptions could still be generated by the paging or segmentation protection mechanisms, but these also can be removed from the memory model.

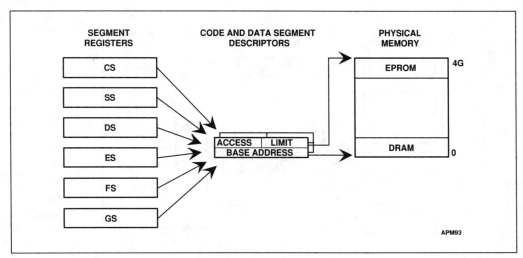

Figure 11-1. Flat Model

11.1.2. Protected Flat Model

The protected flat model is like the flat model, except the segment limits are set to include only the range of addresses for which memory actually exists. A general-protection exception will be generated on any attempt to access unimplemented memory. This might be used for systems in which the paging mechanism is disabled, because it provides a minimum level of hardware protection against some kinds of program bugs.

In this model, the segmentation hardware prevents programs from addressing nonexistent memory locations. The consequences of being allowed access to these memory locations are hardware-dependent. For example, if the processor does not receive a READY# signal (the signal used to acknowledge and terminate a bus cycle), the bus cycle does not terminate and program execution stops.

Although no program should make an attempt to access these memory locations, an attempt may occur as a result of program bugs. Without hardware checking of addresses, it is possible that a bug could suddenly stop program execution. With hardware checking, programs fail in a controlled way. A diagnostic message can appear and recovery procedures can be attempted.

An example of a protected flat model is shown in Figure 11-2. Here, segment descriptors have been set up to cover only those ranges of memory which exist. A code and a data segment cover the EPROM and DRAM of physical memory. The code segment base and limit can optionally be set to allow access to DRAM area. The data segment limit must be set to the sum of EPROM and DRAM sizes. If memory-mapped I/O is used, it can be addressed just beyond the end of DRAM area.

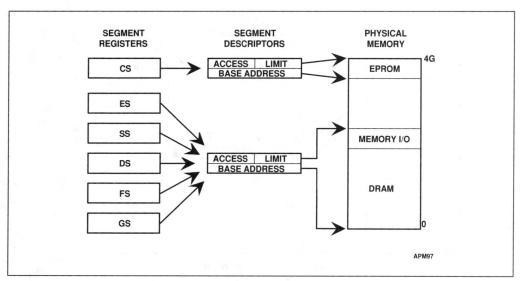

Figure 11-2. Protected Flat Model

11.1.3. Multisegment Model

The most sophisticated model is the multisegment model. Here, the full capabilities of the segmentation mechanism are used. Each program is given its own table of segment descriptors, and its own segments. The segments can be completely private to the program, or they can be shared with specific other programs. Access between programs and particular segments can be individually controlled.

Up to six segments can be ready for immediate use. These are the segments which have segment selectors loaded in the segment registers. Other segments are accessed by loading their segment selectors into the segment registers (see Figure 11-3).

Each segment is a separate address space. Even though they may be placed in adjacent blocks of physical memory, the segmentation mechanism prevents access to the contents of one segment by reading beyond the end of another. Every memory operation is checked against the limit specified for the segment it uses. An attempt to address memory beyond the end of the segment generates a general-protection exception.

The segmentation mechanism only enforces the address range specified in the segment descriptor. It is the responsibility of the operating system to allocate separate address ranges to each segment. There may be situations in which it is desirable to have segments which share the same range of addresses. For example, a system can have both code and data stored in a ROM. A code segment descriptor would be used when the ROM is accessed for instruction fetches. A data segment descriptor would be used when the ROM is accessed as data.

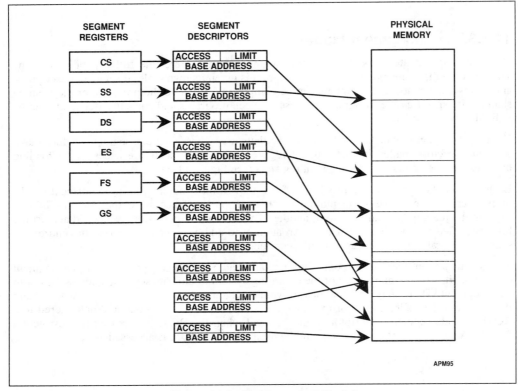

Figure 11-3. Multisegment Model

11.2. SEGMENT TRANSLATION

A logical address consists of the 16-bit segment selector for its segment and a 32-bit offset into the segment. The logical address is checked for access rights and range. If it passes these tests, the logical address is translated into a linear address by adding the offset to the base address of the segment. The base address comes from the segment descriptor, a data structure in memory which provides the size and location of a segment, as well as access control information. The segment descriptor comes from one of two tables, the global descriptor table (GDT) or the local descriptor table (LDT). There is one GDT for all programs in the system and one LDT for each separate program being run. If the operating system allows, different programs can share the same LDT. The system also can be set up with no LDTs; all programs will then use the GDT.

Every logical address is associated with a segment (even if the system maps all segments into the same linear address space). Although a program can have thousands of segments, only six can be available for immediate use. These are the six segments whose segment selectors are loaded in the processor. The segment selector holds information used to translate the logical address into the corresponding linear address.

Separate segment registers exist in the processor for each kind of memory reference (code space, stack space, and data spaces). They hold the segment selectors for the segments currently in use. Access to other segments requires loading a segment register using a form of the MOV instruction. Up to four data spaces can be available at the same time, thus providing a total of six segment registers.

When a segment selector is loaded, the base address, segment limit, and access control information also are loaded into the segment register. The processor does not reference the descriptor tables in memory again until another segment selector is loaded. The information saved in the processor allows it to translate addresses without making extra bus cycles. In systems in which multiple processors have access to the same descriptor tables, it is the responsibility of software to reload the segment registers when the descriptor tables are modified. If this is not done, an old segment descriptor cached in a segment register might be used after its memory-resident version has been modified.

The segment selector contains a 13-bit index into one of the descriptor tables. The index is scaled by eight (the number of bytes in a segment descriptor) and added to the 32-bit base address of the descriptor table. The base address comes from either the global descriptor table register (GDTR) or the local descriptor table register (LDTR). These registers hold the linear address of the beginning of the descriptor tables. A bit in the segment selector specifies which table to use, as shown in Figure 11-4.

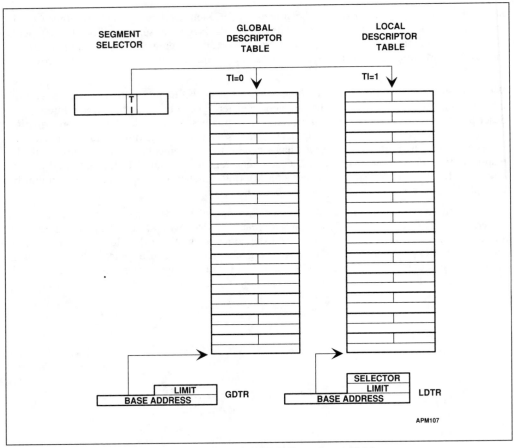

Figure 11-4. TI Bit Selects Descriptor Table

The translated address is the linear address, as shown in Figure 11-5. If paging is not used, it is also the physical address. If paging is used, a second level of address translation produces the physical address. This translation is described in Section 11.3.

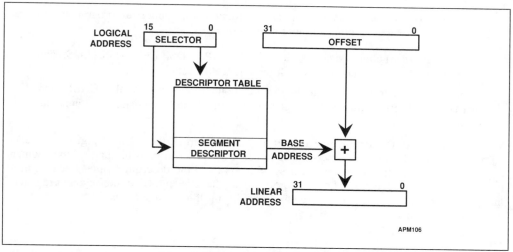

Figure 11-5. Segment Translation

11.2.1. Segment Registers

Each kind of memory reference is associated with a segment register. Code, data, and stack references each access the segments specified by the contents of their segment registers. More segments can be made available by loading their segment selectors into these registers during program execution.

Every segment register has a "visible" part and an "invisible" part, as shown in Figure 11-6. There are forms of the MOV instruction to load the visible part of these segment registers. The invisible part is loaded by the processor.

VISIBLE PART	INVISIBLE PART	
SELECTOR	BASE ADDRESS, LIMIT, ETC.	CS
		SS
		DS
		ES
		FS
		GS

APM104

Figure 11-6. Segment Registers

The operations which load these registers are instructions for application programs (described in Chapter 4). There are two kinds of these instructions:

1. Direct load instructions such as the MOV, POP, LDS, LES, LSS, LGS, and LFS instructions. These instructions explicitly reference the segment registers.

2. Implied load instructions such as the far pointer versions of the CALL and JMP instructions. These instructions change the contents of the CS register as an incidental part of their function.

When one of these instructions is executed, the visible part of the segment register is loaded with a segment selector. The processor automatically loads the invisible part of the segment register with information (such as the base address) from the descriptor table. Because most instructions refer to segments whose selectors already have been loaded into segment registers, the processor can add the logical-address offset to the segment base address with no performance penalty.

11.2.2. Segment Selectors

A segment selector points to the information which defines a segment, called a segment descriptor. A program may have more segments than the six whose segment selectors occupy segment registers. When this is true, the program uses forms of the MOV instruction to change the contents of these registers when it needs to access a new segment.

A segment selector identifies a segment descriptor by specifying a descriptor table and a descriptor within that table. Segment selectors are visible to application programs as a part of a pointer variable, but the values of selectors are usually assigned or modified by link editors or linking loaders, not application programs. Figure 11-7 shows the format of a segment selector.

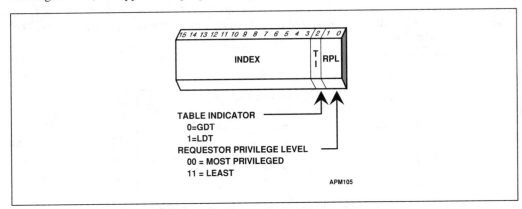

Figure 11-7. Segment Selector

Index: Selects one of 8192 descriptors in a descriptor table. The processor multiplies the index value by 8 (the number of bytes in a segment descriptor) and adds the result to the base address of the descriptor table (from the GDTR or LDTR register).

Table Indicator bit: Specifies the descriptor table to use. A clear bit selects the GDT; a set bit selects the current LDT.

Requestor Privilege Level: When this field of a selector contains a privilege level having a greater value (i.e., less privileged) than the program, it effectively overrides the program's privilege level for accesses that use that selector. When a program uses a less privileged segment selector, memory accesses take place at the lesser privilege level. This is used to guard against a security violation in which a less privileged program uses a more privileged program to access protected data.

For example, system utilities or device drivers must run with a high level of privilege in order to access protected facilities such as the control registers of peripheral interfaces. But they must not interfere with other protected facilities, even if a request to do so is received from a less privileged program. If a program requested reading a sector of disk into memory occupied by a more privileged program, such as the operating system, the RPL can be used to generate a general-protection exception when the less privileged segment selector is used. This exception occurs even though the program using the segment selector would have a sufficient privilege level to perform the operation on its own.

Because the first entry of the GDT is not used by the processor, a selector which has an index of 0 and a table indicator of 0 (i.e., a selector which points to the first entry of the GDT) is used as a "null selector." The processor does not generate an exception when a segment register (other than the CS or SS registers) is loaded with a null selector. It does, however, generate an exception when a segment register holding a null selector is used to access memory. This feature can be used to initialize unused segment registers.

11.2.3. Segment Descriptors

A segment descriptor is a data structure in memory which provides the processor with the size and location of a segment, as well as control and status information. Descriptors typically are created by compilers, linkers, loaders, or the operating system, but not application programs. Figure 11-8 illustrates the general descriptor format. All types of segment descriptors use a variation of this basic format.

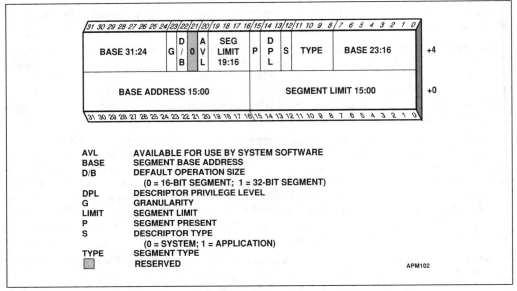

AVL   AVAILABLE FOR USE BY SYSTEM SOFTWARE
BASE   SEGMENT BASE ADDRESS
D/B   DEFAULT OPERATION SIZE
         (0 = 16-BIT SEGMENT; 1 = 32-BIT SEGMENT)
DPL   DESCRIPTOR PRIVILEGE LEVEL
G   GRANULARITY
LIMIT   SEGMENT LIMIT
P   SEGMENT PRESENT
S   DESCRIPTOR TYPE
         (0 = SYSTEM; 1 = APPLICATION)
TYPE   SEGMENT TYPE
■   RESERVED   APM102

Figure 11-8. Segment Descriptors

Base: Defines the location of the segment within the 4 gigabyte physical address space. The processor puts together the three base address fields to form a single 32-bit value. Segment base values should be aligned to 16 byte boundaries to allow programs to maximize performance by aligning code/data on 16 byte boundaries.

Granularity bit: Turns on scaling of the Limit field by a factor of 4096 (2^{12}). When the bit is clear, the segment limit is interpreted in units of one byte; when set, the segment limit is interpreted in units of 4K bytes. Note that the twelve least significant bits of the address are not tested when scaling is used. For example, a limit of 0 with the Granularity bit set results in valid offsets from 0 to 4095. Also note that only the Limit field is affected. The base address remains byte granular.

Limit: Defines the size of the segment. The processor puts together the two limit fields to form a 20-bit value. The processor interprets the segment size in one of two ways, depending on the setting of the Granularity bit:

1. If the Granularity bit is clear, the segment size is from 1 byte to 1 megabyte, in increments of 1 byte.

2. If the Granularity bit is set, the segment size is from 4 kilobytes to 4 gigabytes, in increments of 4K bytes.

For expand-up segments, a logical address can have an offset ranging from 0 to the limit. Other offsets generate exceptions. Expand-down segments reverse the sense of the Limit field; they can be addressed with any offset except those from 0 to the limit (see the Type field, below). This is done to allow segments to be created in which increasing the value held in the Limit field allocates new memory at the bottom of the segment's address space, rather than at the top. Expand-down segments are intended to hold stacks, but it is not necessary to use them. If a stack is going to be put in a segment which does not need to change size, it can be a normal data segment.

S bit: Determines whether a given segment is a system segment or a code or data segment. If the S bit is set, then the segment is either a code or a data segment. If it is clear, then the segment is a system segment.

D bit/B bit: In a code segment, this bit is called the D bit, and it indicates the default length for operands and effective addresses. If the D bit is set, then 32-bit operands and 32-bit effective addressing modes are assumed. If it is clear, then 16-bit operands and addressing modes are assumed. In a data segment, this bit is called the B bit, and it controls two aspects of stack operation:

1. The size of the stack pointer register. If B = 1, pushes, pops and calls all use 32-bit ESP register; if B = 0, stack operations use the 16-bit SP register.

2. The upper bound of an expand-down stack. In expand-down segments, the Limit field specifies the lower bound of the stack segment, while the upper bound is an address of all 1-bits. If B = 1, the upper bound is FFFF_FFFFH; if B = 0, the upper bound is FFFFH.

Type: The interpretation of this field depends on whether the segment descriptor is for an application segment or a system segment. System segments have a slightly different descriptor format, discussed in Chapter 12. The Type field of a memory descriptor specifies the kind of access which may be made to a segment, and its direction of growth (see Table 11-1).

For data segments, the three lowest bits of the type field can be interpreted as expand-down (E), write enable (W), and accessed (A). For code segments, the three lowest bits of the type field can be interpreted as conforming (C), read enable (R), and accessed (A).

Data segments can be read-only or read/write. Stack segments are data segments which must be read/write. Loading the SS register with a segment selector for any other type of segment generates a general-protection exception. If the stack segment needs to be able to change size, it can be an expand-down data segment. The meaning of the segment limit is reversed for an expand-down segment. The valid offsets in an expand-down segment are those which generate exceptions in expand-up segments. Expand-up segments must be addressed by offsets which are equal or less than the segment limit. Offsets into expand-down segments always must be greater than the segment limit. This interpretation of the segment limit causes memory space to be allocated at the bottom of the segment when the segment limit is decreased, which is correct for stack segments because they grow toward lower addresses. If the stack is given a segment which does not change size, the segment does not need to be expand-down.

Table 11-1. Application Segment Types

Type	11	10 E	9 W	8 A	Descriptor Type	Description
0	0	0	0	0	Data	Read-Only
1	0	0	0	1	Data	Read-Only, accessed
2	0	0	1	0	Data	Read/Write
3	0	0	1	1	Data	Read/Write, accessed
4	0	1	0	0	Data	Read-Only, expand-down
5	0	1	0	1	Data	Read-Only, expand-down, accessed
6	0	1	1	0	Data	Read/Write, expand-down
7	0	1	1	1	Data	Read/Write, expand-down, accessed
Type	11	10 C	9 R	8 A	Descriptor Type	Description
8	1	0	0	0	Code	Execute-Only
9	1	0	0	1	Code	Execute-Only, accessed
10	1	0	1	0	Code	Execute/Read
11	1	0	1	1	Code	Execute/Read, accessed
12	1	1	0	0	Code	Execute-Only, conforming
13	1	1	0	1	Code	Execute-Only, conforming, accessed
14	1	1	1	0	Code	Execute/Read-Only, conforming
15	1	1	1	1	Code	Execute/Read-Only, conforming, accessed

Code segments can be execute-only or execute/read. An execute/read segment might be used, for example, when constants have been placed with instruction code in a ROM. In this case, the constants can be read either by using an instruction with a CS override prefix or by placing a segment selector for the code segment in a segment register for a data segment.

Code segments can be either conforming or non-conforming. A transfer of execution into a more privileged conforming segment keeps the current privilege level. A transfer into a non-conforming segment at a different privilege level results in a general-protection exception, unless a task gate is used (see Chapter 13 for a discussion of multitasking). System utilities which do not access protected facilities, such as data-conversion functions (e.g., EBCDIC/ASCII translation, Huffman encoding/decoding, math library) and some types of exceptions (e.g., Divide Error, INTO-detected overflow, and BOUND range exceeded) may be loaded in conforming code segments.

The A (accessed) bit of the Type field is set by the processor to indicate that a segment has been loaded into a segment register. By clearing the A-bit initially, then testing it later, software can monitor segment usage. For example, a program development system might clear all of the Accessed bits for the segments of an application. If the application crashes, the states of these bits can be used to generate a map of all the segments accessed by the application. Unlike the breakpoints provided by the debugging mechanism (Chapter 17), the usage information applies to segment usage rather than linear address matches.

The processor may update the Type field when a segment is accessed, even if the access is a read cycle. If the descriptor tables have been put in ROM, it may be necessary for hardware to prevent the ROM from being enabled onto the data bus during a write cycle. It also may be necessary to return the READY# signal to the processor when a write cycle to ROM occurs, otherwise the cycle does not terminate. These features of the hardware design are necessary for using ROM-based descriptor tables with the Intel386 DX processor, which always sets the

Accessed bit when a segment descriptor is loaded. The Intel486 and Pentium processors, however, only set the Accessed bit if it is not already set. Writes to descriptor tables in ROM can be avoided by setting the Accessed bits in every descriptor.

DPL (Descriptor Privilege Level): Defines the privilege level of the segment. This is used to control access to the segment, using the protection mechanism described in Chapter 12.

Segment-Present bit: If this bit is clear, the processor generates a segment-not-present exception when a selector for the descriptor is loaded into a segment register. This is used to detect access to segments which have become unavailable. A segment can become unavailable when the system needs to create free memory. Items in memory, such as character fonts or device drivers, which currently are not being used are deallocated. An item is deallocated by marking the segment "not present" (this is done by clearing the Segment-Present bit). The memory occupied by the segment then can be put to another use. The next time the deallocated item is needed, the segment-not-present exception will indicate the segment needs to be loaded into memory. When this kind of memory management is provided in a manner invisible to application programs, it is called virtual memory. A system can maintain a total amount of virtual memory far larger than physical memory by keeping only a few segments present in physical memory at any one time.

Figure 11-9 shows the format of a descriptor when the Segment-Present bit is clear. When this bit is clear, the operating system is free to use the locations marked Available to store its own data, such as information regarding the whereabouts of the missing segment.

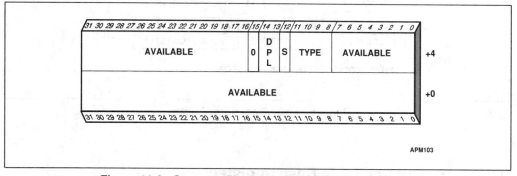

Figure 11-9. Segment Descriptor (Segment Not Present)

11.2.4. Segment Descriptor Tables

A segment descriptor table is an array of segment descriptors. There are two kinds of descriptor tables:

- The global descriptor table (GDT)
- The local descriptor tables (LDT)

There is one GDT for all tasks, and an LDT for each task being run. A descriptor table is an array of segment descriptors, as shown in Figure 11-10. A descriptor table is variable in length and can contain up to 8192 (2^{13}) descriptors. The first descriptor in the GDT is not used by the processor. A segment selector to this "null descriptor" does not generate an exception when loaded into a data segment register (DS, ES, FS, or GS), but it always generates an exception when an attempt is made to access memory using the descriptor. By initializing the segment registers with this segment selector, accidental reference to unused segment registers can be guaranteed to generate an exception.

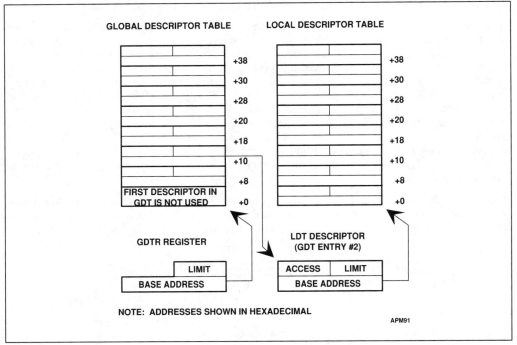

Figure 11-10. Descriptor Tables

11.2.5. Descriptor Table Base Registers

The processor finds the global descriptor table (GDT) and interrupt descriptor table (IDT) using the GDTR and IDTR registers. These registers hold 32-bit base addresses for tables in the linear address space. They also hold 16-bit limit values for the size of these tables.

When the IDTR and GDTR registers are loaded or stored, a 48-bit "pseudo-descriptor" is accessed in memory, as shown in Figure 11-11. To avoid alignment check faults in user mode (privilege level 3). the pseudo-descriptor should be located at an odd word address (i.e., an address which is 2 MOD 4). This causes the processor to store an aligned word, followed by an aligned doubleword. User-mode programs normally do not store pseudo-descriptors, but the possibility of generating an alignment check fault can be avoided by aligning pseudo-descriptors in this way.

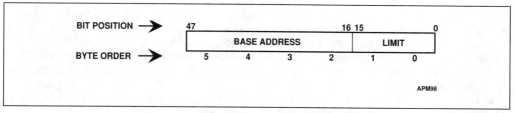

Figure 11-11. Pseudo-Descriptor Format

The base addresses of the GDT and IDT should be aligned on an eight-byte boundary to maximize performance of cache line fills.

The limit values for both the GDT and IDT are expressed in bytes. As with segments, the limit value is added to the base address to get the address of the last valid byte. A limit value of zero results in exactly one valid byte. Because segment descriptors are always eight bytes long, the limit should always be one less than an integral multiple of eight (i.e., $8N - 1$). The LGDT and SGDT instructions write and read the GDTR register; the LIDT and SIDT instructions write and read the IDTR register.

A third descriptor table is the local descriptor table (LDT). It is identified by a 16-bit segment selector held in the LDTR register. The LLDT and SLDT instructions write and read the segment selector in the LDTR register. The LDTR register also holds the base address and limit for the LDT, but these are loaded automatically by the processor from the segment descriptor for the LDT (which is taken from the GDT). The LDT should be aligned on an eight-byte boundary to maximize performance of cache line fills.

11.3. PAGE TRANSLATION

A linear address is a 32-bit address into a uniform, unsegmented address space. This address space can be a large physical address space (i.e., an address space composed of several gigabytes of RAM), or paging can be used to simulate this address space using a small amount of RAM and some disk storage. When paging is used, a linear address is translated into its corresponding physical address, or an exception is generated. The exception gives the operating system a chance to read the page from disk (perhaps sending a different page out to disk in the process), then restart the instruction which generated the exception.

Paging is different from segmentation through its use of fixed-size pages. Unlike segments, which usually are the same size as the code or data structures they hold, pages have a fixed size. If segmentation is the only form of address translation which is used, a data structure which is present in physical memory will have all of its parts in memory. If paging is used, a data structure can be partly in memory and partly in disk storage.

The information which either maps linear addresses into physical addresses or raises exceptions is held in data structures in memory called page tables. As with segmentation, this information is cached within the CPU to minimize the number of bus cycles required for address translation. Unlike segmentation, the address translation caches are completely invisible to application programs. The processor's caches for address translation information are called translation lookaside buffers (TLB). The TLBs satisfy most requests for reading the page tables. Extra bus cycles occur only when the TLBs cannot satisfy a request. This typically happens when a page has not been accessed for a long time.

11.3.1. Paging Options

Paging is enabled when bit 31 (the PG bit) of the CR0 register is set. This bit usually is set by the operating system during software initialization. (Refer to Chapter 16 for information on how to change PG.) When paging is enabled, a second stage of address translation is used to generate the physical address from the linear address. If paging is not enabled, the linear address is used as the physical address. The PG bit must be set if the operating system is running more than one program in virtual-8086 mode or if demand-paged virtual memory is used.

11.3.2. Linear Address

Figure 11-12 shows the format of a linear address for a 4K page.

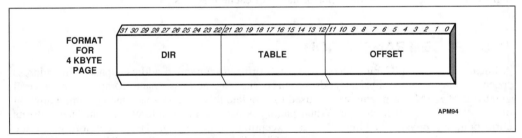

Figure 11-12. Format of a Linear Address

Figure 11-13 shows how the processor translates the DIRECTORY, TABLE, and OFFSET fields of a linear address into the physical address by consulting page tables. The addressing mechanism uses the DIRECTORY field as an index into a page directory. It uses the TABLE field as an index into the page table determined by the page directory. It uses the OFFSET field to address an operand within the page specified by the page table.

11.3.3. Page Tables

A page table is an array of 32-bit entries. A page table is itself a page, and contains 4096 bytes of data or at most 1K 32-bit entries. Four kilobyte pages, including page directories and page tables, are aligned to 4K-byte boundaries. Two levels of tables are used to address a page of memory. At the highest level is a page directory. A page directory holds up to 1K entries that address page tables of the second level. A page table of the second level addresses up to 1K pages in physical memory. All the tables addressed by one page directory, therefore, can address 1M (2^{20}) four-Kbyte pages. If each page contains 4K (2^{12}) bytes, the tables of one page directory can span a linear address space of four gigabytes ($2^{20} \times 2^{12} = 2^{32}$). For information on support of page sizes larger than 4K, see Appendix H.

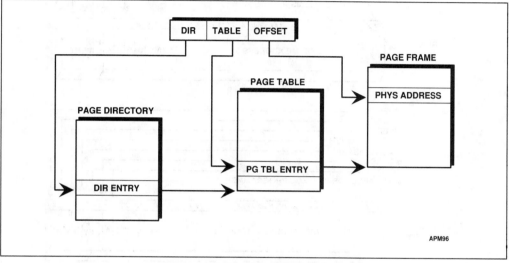

Figure 11-13. Page Translation

The physical address of the current page directory is stored in the CR3 register, also called the page directory base register (PDBR). Memory management software has the option of using one page directory for all tasks, one page directory for each task, or some combination of the two. See Chapter 16 for information on initialization of the CR3 register. See Chapter 13 for how the contents of the CR3 register can change for each task.

11.3.4. Page-Table Entries

Page-table and page-directory entries for 4K pages have one of the formats shown by Figure 11-14. For information on page-table and page-directory formats for pages larger than 4K, see Appendix H.

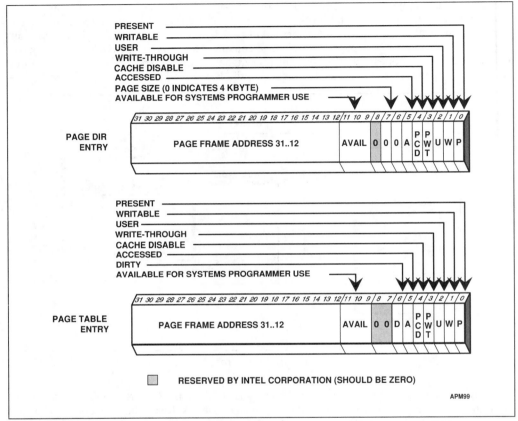

Figure 11-14. Format of Page Directory and Page Table Entries for 4K Pages

11.3.4.1. PAGE FRAME ADDRESS

The page frame address specifies the physical starting address of a page. In a page directory, the page frame address is the address of a page table. In a second-level page table, the page frame address is the address of the four kilobyte page that contains the desired memory operand or instructions.

11.3.4.2. PRESENT BIT

The Present bit indicates whether the page frame address in a page table entry maps to a page in physical memory. When set, the page is in memory.

When the Present bit is clear, the page is not in memory, and the rest of the page table entry is available for the operating system, for example, to store information regarding the whereabouts of the missing page. Figure 11-15 illustrates the format of a page table entry when the Present bit is clear.

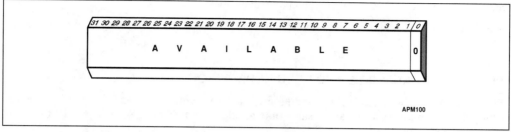

APM100

Figure 11-15. Format of a Page Table Entry for a Not-Present Page

If the Present bit is clear in either level of page tables when an attempt is made to use a page table entry for address translation, a page-fault exception is generated. In systems which support demand-paged virtual memory, the following sequence of events then occurs:

1. The operating system copies the page from disk storage into physical memory.

2. The operating system loads the page frame address into the page table entry and sets its Present bit. Other bits, such as the dirty and accessed bits, may be set, too.

3. Because a copy of the old page table entry may still exist in a translation lookaside buffer (TLB), the operating system invalidates them. See Section 11.3.5. for a discussion of TLBs and how to invalidate them.

4. The program which caused the exception is then restarted.

Note that there is no Present bit in CR3 for the page directory itself. The page directory may be not-present while the associated task is suspended, but the operating system must ensure that the page directory indicated by the CR3 image in a process's TSS is present in physical memory before the process is dispatched. The page directory must also remain in memory as long as the task is active.

11.3.4.3. ACCESSED AND DIRTY BITS

These bits provide data about page usage in both levels of page tables. The Accessed bit is used to report read or write access to a page or to a second-level page table. The Dirty bit is used to report write access to a page. These bits are set by the hardware; however, the processor does not implicitly clear either of these bits.

The processor sets the Accessed bit in both levels of page table before a read or write operation to a page. The processor sets the Dirty bit before a write operation to an address mapped by that page table entry. Only the Dirty bit in the second-level page table is used; the processor does not use the Dirty bit of the page directory.

The operating system may use the Accessed bit when it needs to create some free memory by sending a page or second-level page table to disk storage. By periodically clearing the Accessed bits in the page tables, it can see which pages have been used recently. Pages which have not been used are candidates for sending out to disk.

The operating system may use the Dirty bit when a page is sent back to disk. By clearing the Dirty bit when the page is brought into memory, the operating system can see if it has received any write access. If there is a copy of the page on disk and the copy in memory has not received any writes, there is no need to update disk from memory.

See Chapter 19 for how the processor updates the Accessed and Dirty bits in multiprocessor systems.

11.3.4.4. READ/WRITE AND USER/SUPERVISOR BITS

The Read/Write and User/Supervisor bits are used for protection checks applied to pages, which the processor performs at the same time as address translation. See Chapter 12 for more information on protection.

11.3.4.5. PAGE-LEVEL CACHE CONTROL BITS

The PCD and PWT bits are used for page-level cache management. Software can control the caching of individual pages or second-level page tables using these bits. See Chapter 18 for more information on caching.

11.3.5. Translation Lookaside Buffers

The processor stores the most recently used page table entries in on-chip caches called translation lookaside buffers or TLBs. The Pentium microprocessor has separate TLB's for the data and instruction caches. Most paging is performed using the contents of the TLBs. Bus cycles to the page tables in memory are performed only when the TLBs do not contain the translation information for a requested page.

The TLBs are invisible to application programs (with PL>0), but not to operating systems (PL=0). Operating-system programmers must invalidate the TLBs (dispose of their page table entries) immediately following and every time there are changes to entries in the page tables (including when the present bit is set to zero). If this is not done, old data which has not received the changes might be used for address translation and as a result, subsequent page table references could be incorrect.

The operating system can invalidate the TLBs by loading the CR3 register. The CR3 register can be loaded in either of two ways:

1. Explicit loading using MOV instructions, such as:

```
MOV CR3, EAX
```

2. Implicit loading by a task switch which changes the contents of the CR3 register. (See Chapter 13 for more information on task switching.)

When the mapping of an individual page is changed, the operating system should use the INVLPG instruction. Where possible, INVLPG invalidates only an individual TLB entry; however, in some cases, INVLPG invalidates the entire instruction-cache TLB.

11.4. COMBINING SEGMENT AND PAGE TRANSLATION

Figure 11-16 combines Figure 11-5 and Figure 11-13 to summarize both stages of translation from a logical address to a physical address when paging is enabled. Options available in both stages of address translation can be used to support several different styles of memory management.

11.4.1. Flat Model

When a 32-bit processor is used to run software written without segments, it may be desirable to remove the segmentation features of the processor. The 32-bit processors do not have a mode bit for disabling segmentation, but the same effect can be achieved by mapping the stack, code, and data spaces to the same range of linear addresses. The 32-bit offsets used by 32-bit processor instructions can cover a four-gigabyte linear address space.

When paging is used, the segments can be mapped to the entire linear address space. If more than one program is being run at the same time, the paging mechanism can be used to give each program a separate address space.

11.4.2. Segments Spanning Several Pages

The architecture allows segments which are larger than the size of a page. For example, a large data structure may span thousands of pages. If paging were not used, access to any part of the data structure would require the entire data structure to be present in physical memory. With paging, only the page containing the part being accessed needs to be in memory.

11.4.3. Pages Spanning Several Segments

Segments also can be smaller than the size of a page. If one of these segments is placed in a page which is not shared with another segment, the extra memory is wasted. For example, a small data structure, such as a 1-byte semaphore, occupies 4K bytes if it is placed in a page by itself. If many semaphores are used, it is more efficient to pack them into a single page.

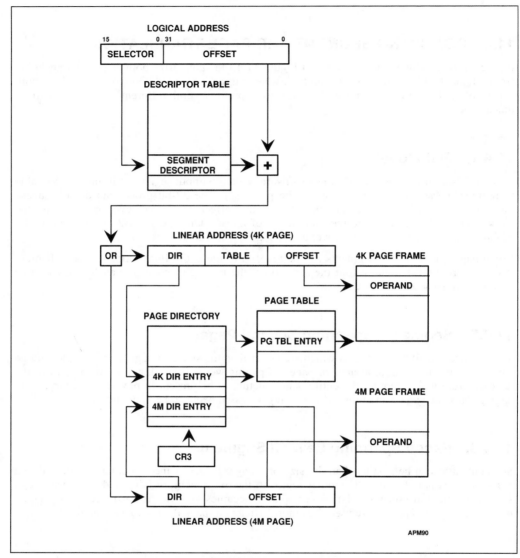

Figure 11-16. Combined Segment and Page Address Translation

11.4.4. Non-Aligned Page and Segment Boundaries

The architecture does not enforce any correspondence between the boundaries of pages and segments. A page can contain the end of one segment and the beginning of another. Likewise, a segment can contain the end of one page and the beginning of another.

11.4.5. Aligned Page and Segment Boundaries

Memory-management software may be simpler and more efficient if it enforces some alignment between page and segment boundaries. For example, if a segment which can fit in one page is placed in two pages, there may be twice as much paging overhead to support access to that segment.

11.4.6. Page-Table Per Segment

An approach to combining paging and segmentation which simplifies memory-management software is to give each segment its own page table, as shown in Figure 11-17. This gives the segment a single entry in the page directory which provides the access control information for paging the segment.

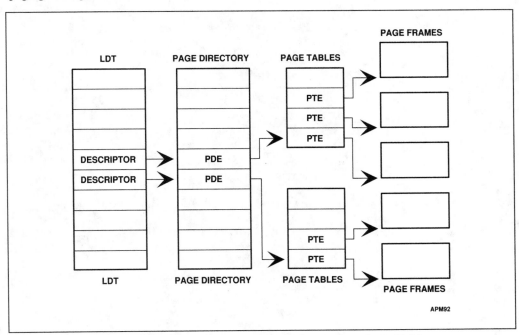

Figure 11-17. Each Segment Can Have Its Own Page Table

intel®

12

Protection

CHAPTER 12
PROTECTION

Protection is necessary for reliable multitasking. Protection can be used to prevent tasks from interfering with each other. For example, protection can keep one task from overwriting the instructions or data of another task.

During program development, the protection mechanism can give a clearer picture of program bugs. When a program makes an unexpected reference to the wrong memory space, the protection mechanism can block the event and report its occurrence.

In end-user systems, the protection mechanism can guard against the possibility of software failures caused by undetected program bugs. If a program fails, its effects can be confined to a limited domain. The operating system can be protected against damage, so diagnostic information can be recorded and automatic recovery attempted.

Protection can be applied to segments and pages. Two bits in a processor register define the privilege level of the program currently running (called the current privilege level or CPL). The CPL is checked during address translation for segmentation and paging.

Although there is no control register or mode bit for turning off the protection mechanism, the same effect can be achieved by assigning privilege level 0 (the highest level of privilege) to all segment selectors, segment descriptors, and page table entries.

12.1. SEGMENT-LEVEL PROTECTION

Protection provides the ability to limit the amount of interference a malfunctioning program can inflict on other programs and their data. Protection is a valuable aid in software development because it allows software tools (operating system, debugger, etc.) to survive in memory undamaged. When an application program fails, the software is available to report diagnostic messages, and the debugger is available for post-mortem analysis of memory and registers. In production, protection can make software more reliable by giving the system an opportunity to initiate recovery procedures.

Each memory reference is checked to verify that it satisfies the protection checks. All checks are made before the memory cycle is started; any violation prevents the cycle from starting and results in an exception. Because checks are performed in parallel with address translation, there is no performance penalty. There are five protection checks:

1. Type check

2. Limit check

3. Restriction of addressable domain

4. Restriction of procedure entry points

5. Restriction of instruction set

A protection violation results in an exception. See Chapter 14 for an explanation of the exception mechanism. This chapter describes the protection violations which lead to exceptions.

12.2. SEGMENT DESCRIPTORS AND PROTECTION

Figure 12-1 shows the fields of a segment descriptor which are used by the protection mechanism. Individual bits in the Type field also are referred to by the names of their functions.

When the operating system creates a descriptor, its sets the protection parameters. In general, application programmers do not need to be concerned about protection parameters.

When a program loads a segment selector into a segment register, the processor loads both the base address of the segment and the protection information. The invisible part of each segment register has storage for the base, limit, type, and privilege level. While this information is resident in the segment register, subsequent protection checks on the same segment can be performed with no performance penalty.

12.2.1. Type Checking

In addition to the descriptors for application code and data segments, the processor has descriptors for system segments and gates. These are data structures used for managing tasks (Chapter 13) and exceptions and interrupts (Chapter 14). Table 12-1 lists all the types defined for system segments and gates. Note that not all descriptors define segments; gate descriptors hold pointers to procedure entry points.

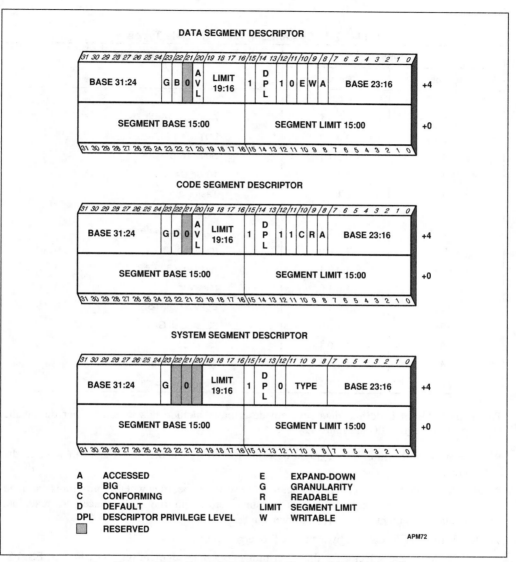

Figure 12-1. Descriptor Fields Used for Protection

Table 12-1. System Segment and Gate Types

Type		Description
Decimal	**Binary**	
0	0 0 0 0	reserved
1	0 0 0 1	Available 16-Bit TSS
2	0 0 1 0	LDT
3	0 0 1 1	Busy 16-Bit TSS
4	0 1 0 0	16-Bit Call Gate
5	0 1 0 1	Task Gate
6	0 1 1 0	16-Bit Interrupt Gate
7	0 1 1 1	16-Bit Trap Gate
8	1 0 0 0	reserved
9	1 0 0 1	Available 32-Bit TSS
10	1 0 1 0	reserved
11	1 0 1 1	Busy 32-Bit TSS
12	1 1 0 0	32-Bit Call Gate
13	1 1 0 1	reserved
14	1 1 1 0	32-Bit Interrupt Gate
15	1 1 1 1	32-Bit Trap Gate

The Type fields of code and data segment descriptors include bits which further define the purpose of the segment (see Figure 12-1):

- The Writable bit in a data-segment descriptor controls whether programs can write to the segment.

- The Readable bit in an executable-segment descriptor specifies whether programs can read from the segment (e.g., to access constants stored in the code space). A readable, executable segment may be read in two ways:

  1. With the CS register, by using a CS override prefix.

  2. By loading a selector for the descriptor into a data-segment register (the DS, ES, FS, or GS registers).

Type checking can be used to detect programming errors which would attempt to use segments in ways not intended by the programmer. The processor examines type information on two kinds of occasions:

1. When a selector for a descriptor is loaded into a segment register. Certain segment registers can contain only certain descriptor types; for example:

   — The CS register only can be loaded with a selector for an executable segment.

   — Selectors of executable segments which are not readable cannot be loaded into data-segment registers.

— Only selectors of writable data segments can be loaded into the SS register.

2. When instructions access segments whose descriptors are already loaded into segment registers. Certain segments can be used by instructions only in certain predefined ways; for example:

    — No instruction may write into an executable segment.

    — No instruction may write into a data segment if the writable bit is not set.

    — No instruction may read an executable segment unless the readable bit is set.

12.2.2. Limit Checking

The Limit field of a segment descriptor prevents programs from addressing outside the segment. The effective value of the limit depends on the setting of the G bit (Granularity bit). For data segments, the limit also depends on the E bit (Expansion Direction bit). The E bit is a designation for one bit of the Type field, when referring to data segment descriptors.

When the G bit is clear, the limit is the value of the 20-bit Limit field in the descriptor. In this case, the limit ranges from 0 to F_FFFFH ($2^{20} - 1$ or 1 megabyte). When the G bit is set, the processor scales the value in the Limit field by a factor of 2^{12}. In this case the limit ranges from 0FFFH ($2^{12} - 1$ or 4K bytes) to FFFF_FFFFH ($2^{32} - 1$ or 4 gigabytes). Note that when scaling is used, the lower twelve bits of the address are not checked against the limit; when the G bit is set and the segment limit is 0, valid offsets within the segment are 0 through 4095.

For all types of segments except expand-down data segments, the value of the limit is one less than the size, in bytes, of the segment. The processor causes a general-protection exception in any of these cases:

- Attempt to access a memory byte at an address > limit
- Attempt to access a memory word at an address > (limit − 1)
- Attempt to access a memory doubleword at an address > (limit − 3)
- Attempt to access a memory quadword at an address > (limit − 7)

For expand-down data segments, the limit has the same function but is interpreted differently. In these cases the range of valid offsets is from (limit + 1) to $2^{32} - 1$ if B-bit = 1 and $2^{16} - 1$ if B-bit = 0. An expand-down segment has maximum size when the segment limit is 0.

Limit checking catches programming errors such as runaway subscripts and invalid pointer calculations. These errors are detected when they occur, so identification of the cause is easier. Without limit checking, these errors could overwrite critical memory in another module, and the existence of these errors would not be discovered until the damaged module crashed, an event which may occur long after the actual error. Protection can block these errors and report their source.

In addition to limit checking on segments, there is limit checking on the descriptor tables. The GDTR, LDTR, and IDTR registers contain a 16-bit limit value. It is used by the processor to prevent programs from selecting a segment descriptor outside the descriptor table. The limit of a descriptor table identifies the last valid byte of the table. Because each descriptor is eight bytes long, a table which contains up to N descriptors should have a limit of 8N − 1.

A selector may be given a zero value. Such a selector refers to the first descriptor in the GDT, which is not used. Although this descriptor can be loaded into a segment register, any attempt to reference memory using this descriptor will generate a general-protection exception.

12.2.3. Privilege Levels

The protection mechanism recognizes four privilege levels, numbered from 0 to 3. The greater numbers mean lesser privileges. If all other protection checks are satisfied, a general-protection exception is generated if a program attempts to access a segment using a less privileged level (greater privilege number) than that applied to the segment.

Although no control register or mode bit is provided for turning off the protection mechanism, the same effect can be achieved by assigning all privilege levels the value of 0. (The PE bit in the CR0 register is not an enabling bit for the protection mechanism alone; it is used to enable protected mode, the mode of program execution in which the full 32-bit architecture is available. When protected mode is disabled, the processor operates in real-address mode, where it appears as a fast, enhanced 8086 processor.)

Privilege levels can be used to improve the reliability of operating systems. By giving the operating system the greatest privilege (numerically lowest privilege level), it is protected from damage by bugs in other programs. If a program crashes, the operating system has a chance to generate a diagnostic message and attempt recovery procedures.

Another level of privilege can be established for other parts of the system software, such as the programs which handle peripheral devices. If a device driver crashes, the operating system should be able to report a diagnostic message, so it makes sense to protect the operating system against bugs in device drivers. A device driver, however, may service an important peripheral such as a disk drive. If the application program crashes, the device driver should not corrupt the directory structure of the disk, so it makes sense to protect device drivers against bugs in applications. Device drivers should be given an intermediate privilege level between the operating system and the application programs. Application programs are given the least privilege (numerically greatest level).

Figure 12-2 shows how these levels of privilege can be interpreted as rings of protection. The center is for the segments containing the most critical software, usually the kernel of an operating system. Outer rings are for less critical software.

The following data structures contain privilege levels:

- The lowest two bits of the CS segment register hold the current privilege level (CPL). This is the privilege level of the program being run. The lowest two bits of the SS register also hold a copy of the CPL. Normally, the CPL is equal to the privilege level of the code segment from which instructions are being fetched. The CPL changes when control is transferred to a code segment with a different privilege level.

- Segment descriptors contain a field called the descriptor privilege level (DPL). The DPL is the privilege level applied to a segment.

- Segment selectors contain a field called the requestor privilege level (RPL). The RPL is intended to represent the privilege level of the procedure which created the selector. If the RPL is a less privileged level than the CPL, it overrides the CPL. When a more privileged program receives a segment selector from a less privileged program, the RPL causes the memory access to take place at the less privileged level.

Privilege levels are checked when the selector of a descriptor is loaded into a segment register. The checks used for data access differ from those used for transfers of execution among executable segments; therefore, the two types of access are considered separately in the following sections.

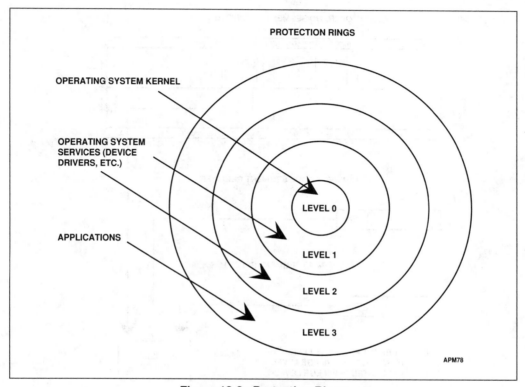

Figure 12-2. Protection Rings

12.3. RESTRICTING ACCESS TO DATA

To address operands in memory, a segment selector for a data segment must be loaded into a data-segment register (the DS, ES, FS, GS, or SS registers). The processor checks the segment's privilege levels. The check is performed when the segment selector is loaded. As Figure 12-3 shows, three different privilege levels enter into this type of privilege check.

The three privilege levels which are checked are:

1. The CPL (current privilege level) of the program. This is held in the two least-significant bit positions of the CS register.

2. The DPL (descriptor privilege level) of the segment descriptor of the segment containing

the operand.

3. The RPL (requestor's privilege level) of the selector used to specify the segment containing the operand. This is held in the two lowest bit positions of the segment register used to access the operand (the SS, DS, ES, FS, or GS registers). If the operand is in the stack segment, the RPL is the same as the CPL.

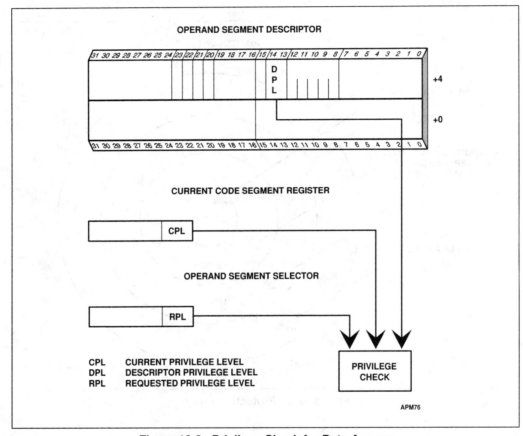

Figure 12-3. Privilege Check for Data Access

Instructions may load a segment register only if the DPL of the segment is the same or a less privileged level (greater privilege number) than the less privileged of the CPL and the selector's RPL.

The addressable domain of a task varies as its CPL changes. When the CPL is 0, data segments at all privilege levels are accessible; when the CPL is 1, only data segments at privilege levels 1 through 3 are accessible; when the CPL is 3, only data segments at privilege level 3 are accessible.

Systems that use only two of the four possible privilege levels should use levels 0 and 3.

12.3.1. Accessing Data in Code Segments

It may be desirable to store data in a code segment, for example, when both code and data are provided in ROM. Code segments may legitimately hold constants; it is not possible to write to a segment defined as a code segment, unless a data segment is mapped to the same address space. The following methods of accessing data in code segments are possible:

1. Load a data-segment register with a segment selector for a nonconforming, readable, executable segment.
2. Load a data-segment register with a segment selector for a conforming, readable, executable segment.
3. Use a code-segment override prefix to read a readable, executable segment whose selector already is loaded in the CS register.

The same rules for access to data segments apply to case 1. Case 2 is always valid because the privilege level of a code segment with a set Conforming bit is effectively the same as the CPL, regardless of its DPL. Case 3 is always valid because the DPL of the code segment selected by the CS register is the CPL.

12.4. RESTRICTING CONTROL TRANSFERS

Control transfers are provided by the JMP, CALL, RET, INT, and IRET instructions, as well as by the exception and interrupt mechanisms. Exceptions and interrupts are special cases discussed in Chapter 14. This chapter discusses only the JMP, CALL, and RET instructions.

The near forms of the JMP, CALL, and RET instructions transfer program control within the current code segment, and therefore are subject only to limit checking. The processor checks that the destination of the JMP, CALL, or RET instruction does not exceed the limit of the current code segment. This limit is cached in the CS register, so protection checks for near transfers do not degrade performance .

The operands of the far forms of the JMP and CALL instruction refer to other segments, so the processor performs privilege checking. There are two ways a JMP or CALL instruction can refer to another segment:

1. The operand selects the descriptor of another executable segment.
2. The operand selects a call gate descriptor.

As Figure 12-4 shows, two different privilege levels enter into a privilege check for a control transfer which does not use a call gate:

1. The CPL (current privilege level).
2. The DPL of the descriptor of the destination code segment.

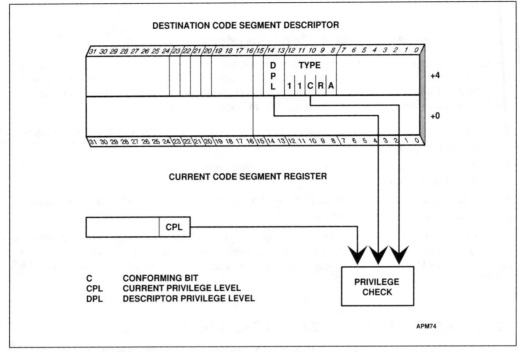

Figure 12-4. Privilege Check for Control Transfer Without Gate

Normally the CPL is equal to the DPL of the segment which the processor is currently executing. The CPL may, however, be greater (less privileged) than the DPL if the current code segment is a conforming segment (as indicated by the Type field of its segment descriptor). A conforming segment runs at the privilege level of the calling procedure. The processor keeps a record of the CPL cached in the CS register; this value can be different from the DPL in the segment descriptor of the current code segment.

The processor only permits a JMP or CALL instruction directly into another segment if either of the following privilege rules is satisfied:

- The DPL of the segment is equal to the CPL.

- The segment is a conforming code segment, and its DPL is less (more privileged) than the CPL.

Conforming segments are used for programs, such as math libraries and some kinds of exception handlers, which support applications but do not require access to protected system facilities. When control is transferred to a conforming segment, the CPL does not change, even if the selector used to address the segment has a different RPL. This is the only condition in which the CPL may be different from the DPL of the current code segment.

Most code segments are not conforming. For these segments, control can be transferred without a gate only to other code segments at the same level of privilege. It is sometimes necessary, however, to transfer control to higher privilege levels. This is accomplished with the

CALL instruction using call-gate descriptors, which is explained in Chapter 13. The JMP instruction may never transfer control to a nonconforming segment whose DPL does not equal the CPL.

12.5. GATE DESCRIPTORS

To provide protection for control transfers among executable segments at different privilege levels, the processor uses gate descriptors. There are four kinds of gate descriptors:

- Call gates
- Trap gates
- Interrupt gates
- Task gates

Task gates are used for task switching and are discussed in Chapter 13. Chapter 14 explains how trap gates and interrupt gates are used by exceptions and interrupts. This chapter is concerned only with call gates. Call gates are a form of protected control transfer. They are used for control transfers between different privilege levels. They only need to be used in systems in which more than one privilege level is used. Figure 12-5 illustrates the format of a call gate.

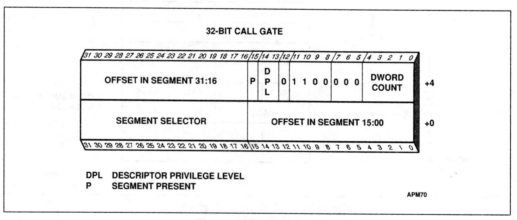

Figure 12-5. Call Gate

A call gate has two main functions:

1. To define an entry point of a procedure.
2. To specify the privilege level required to enter a procedure.

CALL and JMP instructions use call gate descriptors in the same manner as code segment descriptors. When the hardware recognizes that the segment selector for the destination refers to a gate descriptor, the operation of the instruction is determined by the contents of the call gate. A call gate descriptor may reside in the GDT or in an LDT, but not in the interrupt descriptor table (IDT).

The selector and offset fields of a gate form a pointer to the entry point of a procedure. A call gate guarantees that all control transfers to other segments go to a valid entry point, rather than to the middle of a procedure (or worse, to the middle of an instruction). The operand of the control transfer instruction is not the segment selector and offset within the segment to the procedure's entry point. Instead, the segment selector points to a gate descriptor, and the offset is not used. Figure 12-6 shows this form of addressing.

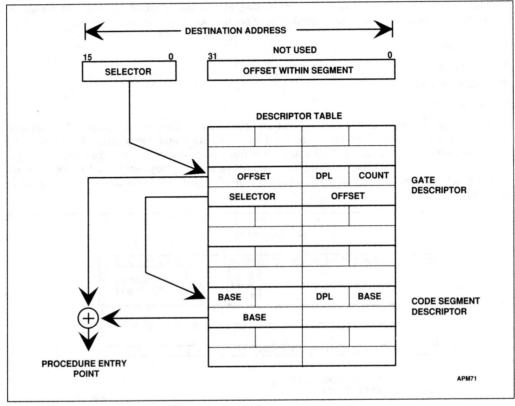

Figure 12-6. Call Gate Mechanism

As shown in Figure 12-7, four different privilege levels are used to check the validity of a control transfer through a call gate.

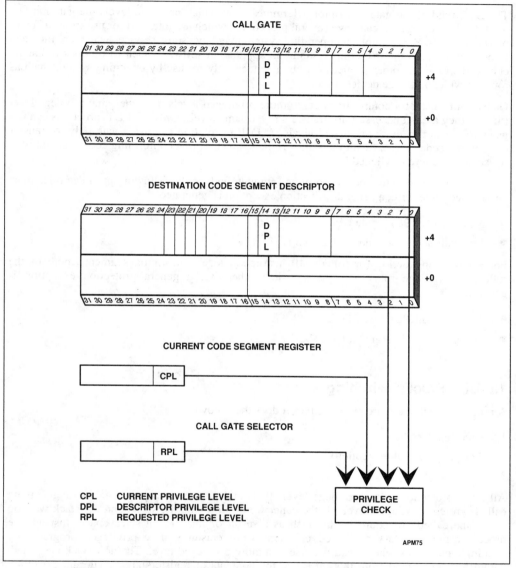

Figure 12-7. Privilege Check for Control Transfer with Call Gate

The privilege levels checked during a transfer of execution through a call gate are:

1. The CPL (current privilege level).
2. The RPL (requestor's privilege level) of the segment selector used to specify the call gate.
3. The DPL (descriptor privilege level) of the gate descriptor.
4. The DPL of the segment descriptor of the destination code segment.

The DPL field of the gate descriptor determines from which privilege levels the gate may be used. One code segment can have several procedures which are intended for use from different privilege levels. For example, an operating system may have some services which are intended to be used by both the operating system and application software, such as routines to handle character I/O, while other services may be intended only for use by operating system, such as routines which initialize device drivers.

Gates can be used for control transfers to more privileged levels or to the same privilege level (though they are not necessary for transfers to the same level). Only CALL instructions can use gates to transfer to more privileged levels. A JMP instruction can use a gate only to transfer control to a code segment with the same privilege level, or to a conforming code segment with the same or a more privileged level.

For a JMP instruction to a nonconforming segment, both of the following privilege rules must be satisfied; otherwise, a general-protection exception is generated.

- MAX (CPL,RPL) ≤ gate DPL
- Destination code segment DPL = CPL

For a CALL instruction (or for a JMP instruction to a conforming segment), both of the following privilege rules must be satisfied; otherwise, a general-protection exception is generated.

- MAX (CPL,RPL) ≤ gate DPL
- Destination code segment DPL ≤ CPL

12.5.1. Stack Switching

A procedure call to a more privileged level does the following:

1. Changes the CPL.
2. Transfers control (execution).
3. Switches stacks.

All inner protection rings (privilege levels 0, 1, and 2), have their own stacks for receiving calls from less privileged levels. If the caller were to provide the stack, and the stack was too small, the called procedure might crash as a result of insufficient stack space. Instead, the processor prevents less privileged programs from crashing more privileged programs by creating a new stack when a call is made to a more privileged level. The new stack is created, parameters are copied from the old stack, the contents of registers are saved, and execution proceeds normally. When the procedure returns, the contents of the saved registers restore the original stack.

The processor finds the space to create new stacks using the task state segment (TSS), as shown in Figure 12-8. (Chapter 13 discusses the TSS in more detail.) Each task has its own TSS. The TSS contains initial stack pointers for the inner protection rings. The operating system is responsible for creating each TSS and initializing its stack pointers. (If the operating system does not use TSSs for multitasking, it still must allocate at least one TSS for this stack-related purpose.) An initial stack pointer consists of a segment selector and an initial value for the ESP register (an initial offset into the segment). The initial stack pointers are strictly read-only values. The processor does not change them while the task runs. These stack pointers are used only to create new stacks when calls are made to more privileged levels. These stacks disappear when the called procedure returns. The next time the procedure is called, a new stack is created using the initial stack pointer.

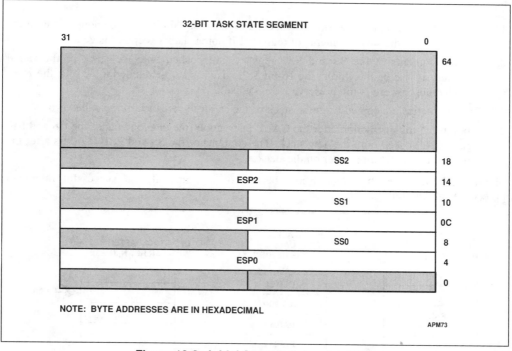

Figure 12-8. Initial Stack Pointers in a TSS

When a call gate is used to change privilege levels, a new stack is created by loading an address from the TSS. The processor uses the DPL of the destination code segment (the new CPL) to select the initial stack pointer for privilege level 0, 1, or 2.

The DPL of the new stack segment must equal the new CPL; if not, a TSS fault is generated. It is the responsibility of the operating system to create stacks and stack-segment descriptors for all privilege levels which are used. The stacks must be read/write as specified in the Type fields of their segment descriptors. They must contain enough space, as specified in the Limit fields, to hold the contents of the SS and ESP registers, the return address, and the parameters and temporary variables required by the called procedure.

As with calls within a privilege level, parameters for the procedure are placed on the stack. The parameters are copied to the new stack. The parameters can be accessed within the called procedure using the same relative addresses which would have been used if no stack switching had occurred. The count field of a call gate tells the processor how many doublewords (up to 31) to copy from the caller's stack to the stack of the called procedure. If the count is 0, no parameters are copied.

If more than 31 doublewords of data need to be passed to the called procedure, one of the parameters can be a pointer to a data structure, or the saved contents of the SS and ESP registers may be used to access parameters in the old stack space.

The processor performs the following stack-related steps in executing a procedure call between privilege levels.

1. The stack of the called procedure is checked to make certain it is large enough to hold the parameters and the saved contents of registers; if not, a stack exception is generated.

2. The old contents of the SS and ESP registers are pushed onto the stack of the called procedure as two doublewords (the 16-bit SS register is zero-extended to 32 bits; the zero-extended upper word is Intel reserved; do not use).

3. The parameters are copied from the stack of the caller to the stack of the called procedure.

4. A pointer to the instruction after the CALL instruction (the old contents of the CS and EIP registers) is pushed onto the new stack. The contents of the SS and ESP registers after the call point to this return pointer on the stack.

Figure 12-9 illustrates the stack frame before, during, and after a successful interlevel procedure call and return.

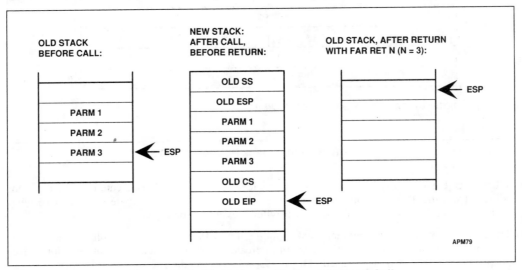

Figure 12-9. Stack Frame During Interlevel Call

The TSS does not have a stack pointer for a privilege level 3 stack, because a procedure at privilege level 3 cannot be called by a less privileged procedure. The stack for privilege level 3 is preserved by the contents of the SS and EIP registers which have been saved on the stack of the privilege level called from level 3.

A call using a call gate does not check the values of the words copied onto the new stack. The called procedure should check each parameter for validity. A later section discusses how the ARPL, VERR, VERW, LSL, and LAR instructions can be used to check pointer values.

12.5.2. Returning from a Procedure

The near forms of the RET instruction only transfer control within the current code segment, therefore are subject only to limit checking. The offset to the instruction following the CALL instruction is popped from the stack into the EIP register. The processor checks that this offset does not exceed the limit of the current code segment.

The far form of the RET instruction pops the return address which was pushed onto the stack by an earlier far CALL instruction. Under normal conditions, the return pointer is valid, because it was generated by a CALL or INT instruction. Nevertheless, the processor performs privilege checking because of the possibility that the current procedure altered the pointer or failed to maintain the stack properly. The RPL of the code-segment selector popped off the stack by the return instruction should have the privilege level of the calling procedure.

A return to another segment can change privilege levels, but only toward less privileged levels. When a RET instruction encounters a saved CS value whose RPL is numerically greater (less privileged) than the CPL, a return across privilege levels occurs. A return of this kind performs these steps:

1. The checks shown in Table 12-2 are made, and the CS, EIP, SS, and ESP registers are loaded with their former values, which were saved on the stack.

2. The old contents of the SS and ESP registers (from the top of the current stack) are adjusted by the number of bytes indicated in the RET instruction. The resulting ESP value is not checked against the limit of the stack segment. If the ESP value is beyond the limit, that fact is not recognized until the next stack operation. (The contents of the SS and ESP registers for the returning procedure are not preserved; normally, their values are the same as those contained in the TSS.)

3. The contents of the DS, ES, FS, and GS segment registers are checked. If any of these registers refer to segments whose DPL is less than the new CPL (excluding conforming code segments), the segment register is loaded with the null selector (Index = 0, TI = 0). The RET instruction itself does not signal exceptions in these cases; however, any subsequent memory reference using a segment register containing the null selector will cause a general-protection exception. This prevents less privileged code from accessing more privileged segments using selectors left in the segment registers by a more privileged procedure.

Table 12-2. Interlevel Return Checks

Type of Check	Exception Type	Error Code
Top-of-stack + 7 must be within stack segment limit	stack	0
RPL of return code segment must be greater than the CPL	protection	Return CS
Return code segment selector must be non-null	protection	Return CS
Return code segment descriptor must be within descriptor table limit	protection	Return CS
Return segment descriptor must be a code segment	protection	Return CS
Return code segment is present	segment not present	Return CS
DPL of return non-conforming code segment must equal RPL of return code segment selector, or DPL of return conforming code segment must be less than or equal to RPL of return code segment selector	protection	Return CS
ESP + N + 15* must be within the stack segment limit	stack fault	0
Segment selector at ESP + N + 12* must be non-null	protection	Return SS
Segment descriptor at ESP + N + 12* must be within descriptor table limit	protection	Return SS
Stack segment descriptor must be read/write	protection	Return SS
Stack segment must be present	stack fault	Return SS
Old stack segment DPL must be equal to RPL of old code segment	protection	Return SS
Old stack segment selector must have an RPL equal to the DPL of the old stack segment	protection	Return SS

* N is the value of the immediate operand supplied with the RET instruction.

12.6. INSTRUCTIONS RESERVED FOR THE OPERATING SYSTEM

Instructions which can affect the protection mechanism or influence general system performance can only be executed by trusted procedures. The processor has two classes of such instructions:

1. Privileged instructions—those used for system control.

2. Sensitive instructions—those used for I/O and I/O-related activities.

12.6.1. Privileged Instructions

The instructions which affect protected facilities can be executed only when the CPL is 0 (most privileged). If one of these instructions is executed when the CPL is not 0, a general-protection exception is generated. These instructions include:

CLTS   —Clear Task-Switched Flag

HLT	—Halt Processor
INVD	—Invalidate Cache
INVLPG	—Invalidate TLB Entry
LGDT	—Load GDT Register
LIDT	—Load IDT Register
LLDT	—Load LDT Register
LMSW	—Load Machine Status Word
LTR	—Load Task Register
MOV to/from CRn	—Move to Control Register n
MOV to/from DRn	—Move to Debug Register n
WBINVD	—Write Back and Invalidate Cache

12.6.2. Sensitive Instructions

Instructions which deal with I/O need to be protected, but they also need to be used by procedures executing at privilege levels other than 0 (the most privileged level). The mechanisms for protection of I/O operations are covered in detail in Chapter 15.

12.7. INSTRUCTIONS FOR POINTER VALIDATION

Pointer validation is necessary for maintaining isolation between privilege levels. It consists of the following steps:

1. Check whether the supplier of the pointer is allowed to access the segment.
2. Check whether the segment type is compatible with its use.
3. Check whether the pointer offset exceeds the segment limit.

Although the processor automatically performs checks 2 and 3 during instruction execution, software must assist in performing the first check. The ARPL instruction is provided for this purpose. Software also can use steps 2 and 3 to check for potential violations, rather than waiting for an exception to be generated. The LAR, LSL, VERR, and VERW instructions are provided for this purpose.

LAR (Load Access Rights) is used to verify that a pointer refers to a segment of a compatible privilege level and type. The LAR instruction has one operand: a segment selector for the descriptor whose access rights are to be checked. Conforming code segments may be accessed from any privilege level. Any other segment descriptor must be readable at a privilege level which is numerically greater (less privileged) than the CPL and the selector's RPL. If the descriptor is readable, the LAR instruction gets the second doubleword of the descriptor, masks this value with 00FxFF00H, stores the result into the specified 32-bit destination register, and sets the ZF flag. (The x indicates that the corresponding four bits of the stored value are undefined.) Once loaded, the access rights can be tested. All valid descriptor types can be tested by the LAR instruction. If the RPL or CPL is greater than the DPL, or if the segment selector would exceed the limit for the descriptor table, zero is returned, and the ZF flag is cleared.

LSL (Load Segment Limit) allows software to test the limit of a segment descriptor. If the descriptor referenced by the segment selector (in memory or a register) is readable at the CPL, the LSL instruction loads the specified 32-bit register with a 32-bit, byte granular limit calculated from the concatenated limit fields and the G bit of the descriptor. This only can be done for descriptors which describe segments (data, code, task state, and local descriptor tables); gate descriptors are inaccessible. (Table 12-3 lists in detail which types are valid and which are not.) Interpreting the limit is a function of the segment type. For example, downward-expandable data segments (stack segments) treat the limit differently than other kinds of segments. For both the LAR and LSL instructions, the ZF flag is set if the load was successful; otherwise, the ZF flag is cleared.

Table 12-3. Valid Descriptor Types for LSL Instruction

Type Code	Descriptor Type	Valid?
0	reserved	no
1	reserved	no
2	LDT	yes
3	reserved	no
4	reserved	no
5	Task Gate	no
6	reserved	no
7	reserved	no
8	reserved	no
9	Available 32-bit TSS	yes
A	reserved	no
B	Busy 32-bit TSS	yes
C	32-bit Call Gate	no
D	reserved	no
E	32-bit Interrupt Gate	no
F	32-bit Trap Gate	no

An additional check, the alignment check, can be applied at CPL = 3. When both the AM bit in CR0 and the AC flag are set, unaligned memory references generate exceptions. This is useful for programs which use the low two bits of pointers to identify the type of data structure they address. For example, a subroutine in a math library may accept pointers to numeric data structures. If the type of this structure is assigned a code of 10 (binary) in the lowest two bits of pointers to this type, math subroutines can correct for the type code by adding a displacement of −10 (binary). If the subroutine should ever receive the wrong pointer type, an unaligned reference would be produced, which would generate an exception. Alignment checking accelerates the processing of programs written in symbolic-processing (i.e., Artificial Intelligence) languages such as Lisp, Prolog, Smalltalk, and C++. It can be used to speed up pointer tag type checking.

12.7.1. Descriptor Validation

The processor has two instructions, VERR and VERW, which determine whether a segment selector points to a segment which can be read or written using the CPL. Neither instruction causes a protection fault if the segment cannot be accessed.

VERR (Verify for Reading) verifies a segment for reading and sets the ZF flag if that segment is readable using the CPL. The VERR instruction checks the following:

- The segment selector points to a segment descriptor within the bounds of the GDT or an LDT.
- The segment selector indexes to a code or data segment descriptor.
- The segment is readable and has a compatible privilege level.

The privilege check for data segments and nonconforming code segments verifies that the DPL must be a less privileged level than either the CPL or the selector's RPL. Conforming segments are not checked for privilege level.

VERW (Verify for Writing) provides the same capability as the VERR instruction for verifying writability. Like the VERR instruction, the VERW instruction sets the ZF flag if the segment can be written. The instruction verifies the descriptor is within bounds, is a segment descriptor, is writable, and has a DPL which is a less privileged level than either the CPL or the selector's RPL. Code segments are never writable, whether conforming or not.

12.7.2. Pointer Integrity and RPL

The requestor's privilege level (RPL) can prevent accidental use of pointers which crash more privileged code from a less privileged level.

A common example is a file system procedure, FREAD (file_id, n_bytes, buffer_ptr). This hypothetical procedure reads data from a disk file into a buffer, overwriting whatever is already there. It services requests from programs operating at the application level, but it must run in a privileged mode in order to read from the system I/O buffer. If the application program passed this procedure a bad buffer pointer, one which pointed at critical code or data in a privileged address space, the procedure could cause damage which would crash the system.

Use of the RPL can avoid this problem. The RPL allows a privilege override to be assigned to a selector. This privilege override is intended to be the privilege level of the code segment which generated the segment selector. In the above example, the RPL would be the CPL of the application program which called the system level procedure. The processor automatically checks any segment selector loaded into a segment register to determine whether its RPL allows access.

To take advantage of the processor's checking of the RPL, the called procedure need only check that all segment selectors passed to it have an RPL for the same or a less privileged level as the original caller's CPL. This guarantees that the segment selectors are not more privileged than their source. If a selector is used to access a segment which the source would not be able to access directly, i.e. the RPL is less privileged than the segment's DPL, a general-protection exception is generated when the selector is loaded into a segment register.

ARPL (Adjust Requested Privilege Level) adjusts the RPL field of a segment selector to be the larger (less privileged) of its original value and the value of the RPL field for a segment selector stored in a general register. The RPL fields are the two least significant bits of the segment selector and the register. The latter normally is a copy of the caller's CS register on the stack. If the adjustment changes the selector's RPL, the ZF flag is set; otherwise, the ZF flag is cleared.

12.8. PAGE-LEVEL PROTECTION

Protection applies to both segments and pages. When the flat model for memory segmentation is used, page-level protection prevents programs from interfering with each other.

Each memory reference is checked to verify that it satisfies the protection checks. All checks are made before the memory cycle is started; any violation prevents the cycle from starting and results in an exception. Because checks are performed in parallel with address translation, there is no performance penalty. There are two page-level protection checks:

1. Restriction of addressable domain.
2. Type checking.

A protection violation results in an exception. See Chapter 14 for an explanation of the protected-mode exception mechanism. This chapter describes the protection violations which lead to exceptions.

12.8.1. Page-Table Entries Hold Protection Parameters

Figure 12-10 highlights the fields of a page table entry which control access to pages. The protection checks are applied for both first- and second-level page tables.

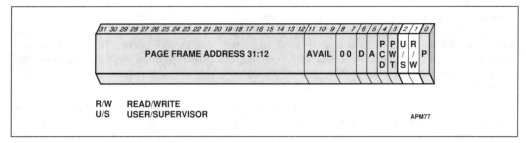

Figure 12-10. Protection Fields of a Page Table Entry

12.8.1.1. RESTRICTING ADDRESSABLE DOMAIN

Privilege is interpreted differently for pages than for segments. With segments, there are four privilege levels, ranging from 0 (most privileged) to 3 (least privileged). With pages, there are two levels of privilege:

1.   Supervisor level (U/S=0)—for the operating system, other system software (such as device drivers), and protected system data (such as page tables).

2.   User level (U/S=1)—for application code and data.

The privilege levels used for segmentation are mapped into the privilege levels used for paging. If the CPL is 0, 1, or 2, the processor is running at supervisor level. If the CPL is 3, the processor is running at user level.When the processor is running at supervisor level, all pages are accessible. When the processor is running at user level, only pages from the user level are accessible.

12.8.1.2.   TYPE CHECKING

Only two types of pages are recognized by the protection mechanism:

1.   Read-only access (R/W=0).

2.   Read/write access (R/W=1).

When the processor is running at supervisor level with the WP bit in the CR0 register clear (its state following reset initialization), all pages are both readable and writable (write-protection is ignored). When the processor is running at user level, only pages which belong to user level and are marked for read/write access are writable. User-level pages which are read/write or read-only are readable. Pages from the supervisor level are neither readable nor writable from user level. A general-protection exception is generated on any attempt to violate the protection rules.

Unlike the Intel386 DX processor, the Intel486 and Pentium processors allow user-mode pages to be write-protected against supervisor mode access. Setting the WP bit in the CR0 register enables supervisor-mode sensitivity to user-mode, write-protected pages.

The supervisor write-protect feature is also useful for implementing the copy-on-write strategy used by some operating systems, such as UNIX, for task creation (also called forking or spawning). When a new task is created, it is possible to copy the entire address space of the parent task. This gives the child task a complete, duplicate set of the parent's segments and pages. An alternative strategy, copy-on-write, saves memory space and time by mapping the child's segments and pages to the same segments and pages used by the parent task. A private copy of a page gets created only when one of the tasks writes to the page. By using the WP bit, the supervisor can detect an attempt to write to a user-level page, and can copy the page at that time.

12.8.2.   Combining Protection of Both Levels of Page Tables

For any one page, the protection attributes of its page directory entry (first-level page table) may differ from those of its second-level page table entry. The processor checks the protection for a page by examining the protection specified in both the page directory (first-level page table) and the second-level page table. Table 12-4 shows the protection provided by the possible combinations of protection attributes when the WP bit is clear.

12.8.3. Overrides to Page Protection

Certain accesses are checked as if they are privilege-level 0 accesses, for any value of CPL:

- Access to segment descriptors (LDT, GDT, TSS and IDT).
- Access to inner stack during a CALL instruction, or exceptions and interrupts, when a change of privilege level occurs.

Table 12-4. Combined Page Directory and Page Table Protection

Page Directory Entry		Page Table Entry		Combined Effect	
Privilege	Access Type	Privilege	Access Type	Privilege	Access Type
User	Read-Only	User	Read-Only	User	Read-Only
User	Read-Only	User	Read-Write	User	Read-Only
User	Read-Write	User	Read-Only	User	Read-Only
User	Read-Write	User	Read-Write	User	Read/Write
User	Read-Only	Supervisor	Read-Only	Supervisor	Read/Write*
User	Read-Only	Supervisor	Read-Write	Supervisor	Read/Write*
User	Read-Write	Supervisor	Read-Only	Supervisor	Read/Write*
User	Read-Write	Supervisor	Read-Write	Supervisor	Read/Write*
Supervisor	Read-Only	User	Read-Only	Supervisor	Read/Write*
Supervisor	Read-Only	User	Read-Write	Supervisor	Read/Write*
Supervisor	Read-Write	User	Read-Only	Supervisor	Read/Write*
Supervisor	Read-Write	User	Read-Write	Supervisor	Read/Write*
Supervisor	Read-Only	Supervisor	Read-Only	Supervisor	Read/Write*
Supervisor	Read-Only	Supervisor	Read-Write	Supervisor	Read/Write*
Supervisor	Read-Write	Supervisor	Read-Only	Supervisor	Read/Write*
Supervisor	Read-Write	Supervisor	Read-Write	Supervisor	Read/Write*

NOTE:
*If the WP bit of CR0 is set, the access type is Read-Only

12.9. COMBINING PAGE AND SEGMENT PROTECTION

When paging is enabled, the processor first evaluates segment protection, then evaluates page protection. If the processor detects a protection violation at either the segment level or the page level, the operation does not go through; an exception occurs instead. If an exception is generated by segmentation, no paging exception is generated for the operation.

For example, it is possible to define a large data segment which has some parts which are read-only and other parts which are read-write. In this case, the page directory (or page table)

entries for the read-only parts would have the U/S and R/W bits specifying no write access for all the pages described by that directory entry (or for individual pages specified in the second-level page tables). This technique might be used, for example, to define a large data segment, part of which is read-only (for shared data or ROMmed constants). This defines a flat data space as one large segment, with flat pointers used to access this flat space, while protecting shared data, shared files mapped into the virtual space, and supervisor areas.

intel®

13

Protected-Mode
Multitasking

CHAPTER 13
PROTECTED-MODE MULTITASKING

The Pentium processor provides hardware support for multitasking. A task is a program which is running, or waiting to run while another program is running. A task is invoked by an interrupt, exception, jump, or call. When one of these forms of transferring execution is used with a destination specified by an entry in one of the descriptor tables, this descriptor can be a type which causes a new task to begin execution after saving the state of the current task. There are two types of task-related descriptors which can occur in a descriptor table: task state segment descriptors and task gates. When execution is passed to either kind of descriptor, a task switch occurs.

A task switch is like a procedure call, but it saves more processor state information. A task switch transfers execution to a completely new environment, the environment of a task. This requires saving the contents of nearly all the processor registers, including the EFLAGS register and the segment registers. Unlike procedures, tasks are not re-entrant. A task switch does not push anything on the stack. The processor state information is saved in a data structure in memory, called a task state segment.

The registers and data structures which support multitasking are:

- Task state segment.
- Task state segment descriptor.
- Task register.
- Task gate descriptor.

With these structures, the processor can switch execution from one task to another, saving the context of the original task to allow the task to be restarted. The processor also offers two other task-management features:

1. Interrupts and exceptions can cause task switches (if needed in the system design). The processor can not only perform a task switch to handle the interrupt or exception, but it can automatically switch back when the interrupt or exception returns. This mechanism can handle interrupts that occur during interrupt tasks.

2. With each switch to another task, the processor also can switch to another LDT. This can be used to give each task a different logical-to-physical address mapping. This is an additional protection feature, because tasks can be isolated and prevented from interfering with one another. The PDBR register also is reloaded. This allows the paging mechanism to be used to enforce the isolation between tasks.

Use of the multitasking mechanism is optional. In some applications, it may not be the best way to manage program execution. Where extremely fast response to interrupts is needed, the time required to save the processor state may be too great. A possible compromise in these situations is to use the task-related data structures, but perform task switching in software. This allows a smaller processor state to be saved. This technique can be one of the optimizations used to enhance system performance after the basic functions of a system have been implemented.

13.1. TASK STATE SEGMENT

The processor state information needed to restore a task is saved in a type of segment, called a task state segment or TSS. Figure 13-1 shows the format of a TSS for tasks designed for 32-bit CPUs (compatibility with 16-bit 80286 tasks is provided by a different kind of TSS; see Chapter 23). The fields of a TSS are divided into two main categories:

1. Dynamic fields the processor updates with each task switch. These fields store:
    — The general registers (EAX, ECX, EDX, EBX, ESP, EBP, ESI, and EDI).
    — The segment registers (ES, CS, SS, DS, FS, and GS).
    — The flags register (EFLAGS).
    — The instruction pointer (EIP).
    — The selector for the TSS of the previous task (updated only when a return is expected).

2. Static fields the processor reads, but does not change. These fields are set up when a task is created. These fields store:
    — The selector for the task's LDT.
    — The PDBR of the task (CR3).
    — The logical address of the stacks for privilege levels 0, 1, and 2.
    — The T-bit (debug trap bit) which, when set, causes the processor to raise a debug exception when a task switch occurs. (See Chapter 17 for more information on debugging.)
    — The base address for the I/O permission bit map and interrupt redirection bitmap. If present, these maps are stored in the TSS at higher addresses. The base address points to the beginning of the I/O map and the end of the 32-byte interrupt map. (See Chapter 15 for more information about the I/O permission bit map and Chapter 22 for more information about interrupt redirection.)

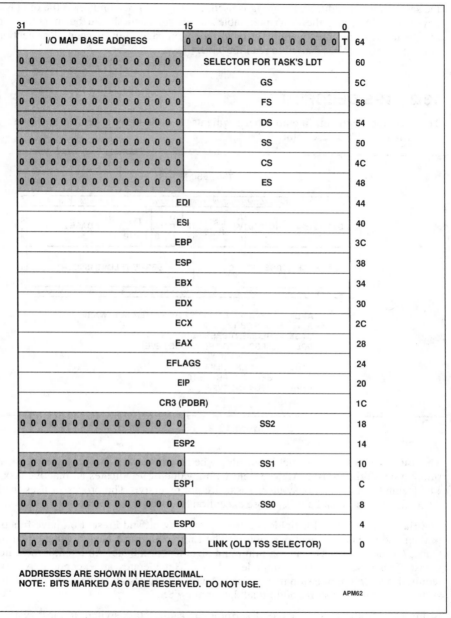

Figure 13-1. 32-Bit Task State Segment

If paging is used, it is important to avoid placing a page boundary within the part of the TSS which is read by the processor during a task switch (the first 104 bytes). If a page boundary is placed within this part of the TSS, the pages on either side of the boundary must be present at the same time. In addition, if paging is used, the pages corresponding to the old task's TSS, the new task's TSS, and the descriptor table entries for each should be marked as present and read/write. It is an unrecoverable error to receive a page fault or general-protection exception after the processor has started to read the TSS.

13.2. TSS DESCRIPTOR

The task state segment, like all other segments, is defined by a descriptor. Figure 13-2 shows the format of a TSS descriptor.

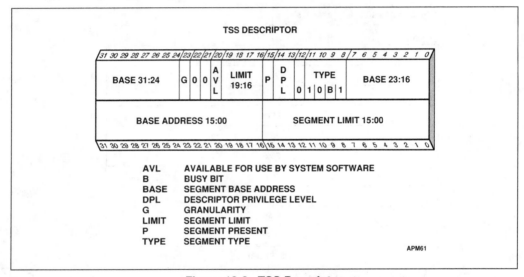

Figure 13-2. TSS Descriptor

The Busy bit in the Type field indicates whether the task is busy. A busy task is currently running or waiting to run. A Type field with a value of 9 indicates an inactive task; a value of 11 (decimal) indicates a busy task. Tasks are not recursive. The processor uses the Busy bit to detect an attempt to call a task whose execution has been interrupted.

The Base, Limit, and DPL fields and the Granularity bit and Present bit have functions similar to their use in data-segment descriptors. The Limit field must have a value equal to or greater than 67H, one byte less than the minimum size of a task state. An attempt to switch to a task whose TSS descriptor has a limit less than 67H generates an exception. A larger limit is required if an I/O permission map is used. A larger limit also may be required for the operating system, if the system stores additional data in the TSS.

A procedure with access to a TSS descriptor can cause a task switch. In most systems, the DPL fields of TSS descriptors should be less than 3, so only privileged software can perform task switching.

Access to a TSS descriptor does not give a procedure the ability to read or modify the descriptor. Reading and modification only can be done using a data descriptor mapped to the same location in memory. Loading a TSS descriptor into a segment register generates an exception. TSS descriptors only may reside in the GDT. An attempt to access a TSS using a selector with a set TI bit (which indicates the current LDT) generates an exception.

13.3. TASK REGISTER

The task register (TR) is used to find the current TSS. Figure 13-3 shows the path by which the processor accesses the TSS.

The task register has both a visible part (i.e., a part which can be read and changed by software) and an invisible part (i.e., a part maintained by the processor and inaccessible to software). The selector in the visible portion indexes to a TSS descriptor in the GDT. The processor uses the invisible portion of the TR register to retain the base and limit values from the TSS descriptor. Keeping these values in a register makes execution of the task more efficient, because the processor does not need to fetch these values from memory to reference the TSS of the current task.

The LTR and STR instructions are used to modify and read the visible portion of the task register. Both instructions take one operand, a 16-bit segment selector located in memory or a general register.

LTR (Load task register) loads the visible portion of the task register with the operand, which must index to a TSS descriptor in the GDT. The LTR instruction also loads the invisible portion with information from the TSS descriptor. The LTR instruction is a privileged instruction; it may be executed only when the CPL is 0. The LTR instruction generally is used during system initialization to put an initial value in the task register; afterwards, the contents of the TR register are changed by events which cause a task switch.

STR (Store task register) stores the visible portion of the task register in a general register or memory. The STR instruction is privileged.

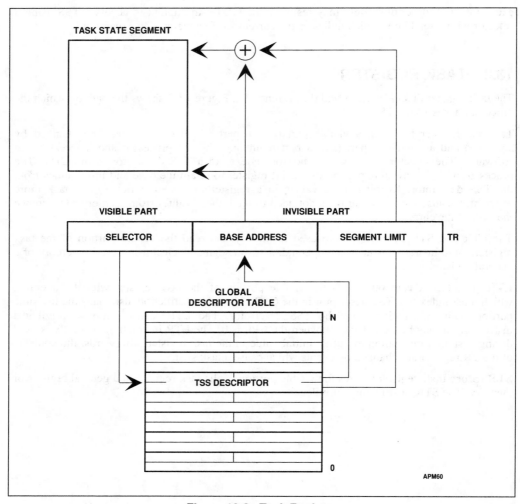

Figure 13-3. Task Register

13.4. TASK GATE DESCRIPTOR

A task gate descriptor provides an indirect, protected reference to a task. Figure 13-4 illustrates the format of a task gate.

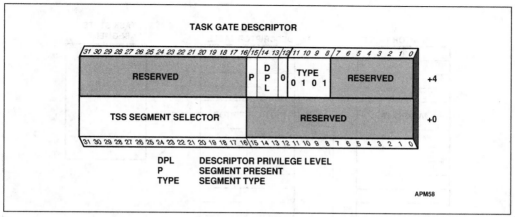

Figure 13-4. Task Gate Descriptor

The Selector field of a task gate indexes to a TSS descriptor. The RPL in this selector is not used.

The DPL of a task gate controls access to the descriptor for a task switch. A procedure may not select a task gate descriptor unless the selector's RPL and the CPL of the procedure are numerically less than or equal to the DPL of the descriptor. This prevents less privileged procedures from causing a task switch. (Note that when a task gate is used, the DPL of the destination TSS descriptor is not used.)

A procedure with access to a task gate can cause a task switch, as can a procedure with access to a TSS descriptor. Both task gates and TSS descriptors are provided to satisfy three needs:

1. The need for a task to have only one Busy bit. Because the Busy bit is stored in the TSS descriptor, each task should have only one such descriptor. There may, however, be several task gates which select a single TSS descriptor.

2. The need to provide selective access to tasks. Task gates fill this need, because they can reside in an LDT and can have a DPL which is different from the TSS descriptor's DPL. A procedure which does not have sufficient privilege to use the TSS descriptor in the GDT (which usually has a DPL of 0) can still call another task if it has access to a task gate in its LDT. With task gates, the operating system can limit task switching to specific tasks.

3. The need for an interrupt or exception to cause a task switch. Task gates also may reside in the IDT, which allows interrupts and exceptions to cause task switching. When an interrupt or exception supplies a vector to a task gate, the processor switches to the indicated task.

Figure 13-5 illustrates how both a task gate in an LDT and a task gate in the IDT can identify the same task.

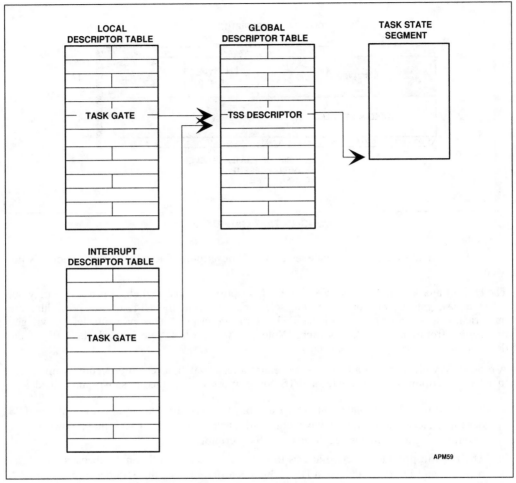

Figure 13-5. Task Gates Reference Tasks

13.5. TASK SWITCHING

The processor transfers execution to another task in any of four cases:

1. The current task executes a JMP or CALL to a TSS descriptor.
2. The current task executes a JMP or CALL to a task gate.
3. An interrupt or exception indexes to a task gate in the IDT.
4. The current task executes an IRET when the NT flag is set.

The JMP, CALL, and IRET instructions, as well as interrupts and exceptions, are all ordinary mechanisms of the processor which can be used in circumstances in which no task switch occurs. The descriptor type (when a task is called) or the NT flag (when the task returns) make the difference between the standard mechanism and the form which causes a task switch.

To cause a task switch, a JMP or CALL instruction can transfer execution to either a TSS descriptor or a task gate. The effect is the same in either case: the processor transfers execution to the specified task.

An exception or interrupt causes a task switch when it indexes to a task gate in the IDT. If it indexes to an interrupt or trap gate in the IDT, a task switch does not occur. See Chapter 14 for more information on the interrupt mechanism.

An interrupt service routine always returns execution to the interrupted procedure, which may be in another task. If the NT flag is clear, a normal return occurs. If the NT flag is set, a task switch occurs. The task receiving the task switch is specified by the TSS selector in the TSS of the interrupt service routine.

A task switch has these steps:

1. Check that the current task is allowed to switch to the new task. Data-access privilege rules apply to JMP and CALL instructions. The DPL of the TSS descriptor and the task gate must be numerically greater (e.g., lower privilege level) than or equal to both the CPL and the RPL of the gate selector. Exceptions, interrupts, and IRET instructions are permitted to switch tasks regardless of the DPL of the destination task gate or TSS descriptor.

2. Check that the TSS descriptor of the new task is marked present and has a valid limit (greater than or equal to 67H). Errors restore any changes made in the processor state when an attempt is made to execute the error-generating instruction. This lets the return address for the exception handler point to the error-generating instruction, rather than the instruction following the error-generating instruction. The exception handler can fix the condition which caused the error, and restart the task. The intervention of the exception handler can be completely transparent to the application program.

3. Save the state of the current task. The processor finds the base address of the current TSS in the task register. The processor registers are copied into the current TSS (the EAX, ECX, EDX, EBX, ESP, EBP, ESI, EDI, ES, CS, SS, DS, FS, GS, and EFLAGS registers, and the instruction pointer).

4. Load the TR register with the selector to the new task's TSS descriptor, set the new task's Busy bit, and set the TS bit in the CR0 register. The selector is either the operand of a JMP or CALL instruction, or it is taken from a task gate.

5. Load the new task's state from its TSS and continue execution. The registers loaded are the LDTR register; the PDBR (CR3); the EFLAGS register; the general registers EIP, EAX, ECX, EDX, EBX, ESP, EBP, ESI, EDI; and the segment registers ES, CS, SS, DS, FS, and GS. Any errors detected in this step occur in the context of the new task. To an exception handler, the first instruction of the new task appears not to have executed.

Note that the state of the old task is always saved when a task switch occurs. If the task is resumed, execution starts with the instruction which normally would have been next. The registers are restored to the values they held when the task stopped running.

Every task switch sets the TS (task switched) bit in the CR0 register. The TS bit is useful to system software for coordinating the operations of the integer unit with the floating-point unit.

The TS bit indicates that the context of the floating-point unit may be different from that of the current task. Chapter 6 discusses the TS bit and the FPU in more detail.

Exception service routines for exceptions caused by task switching (exceptions resulting from steps 5 through 17 shown in Table 13-1 may be subject to recursive calls if they attempt to reload the segment selector which generated the exception. The cause of the exception (or the first of multiple causes) should be fixed before reloading the selector.

The privilege level at which the old task was running has no relation to the privilege level of the new task. Because the tasks are isolated by their separate address spaces and task state segments, and because privilege rules control access to a TSS, no privilege checks are needed to perform a task switch. The new task begins executing at the privilege level indicated by the RPL of the new contents of the CS register, which are loaded from the TSS.

Table 13-1. Checks Made during a Task Switch

Step	Condition Checked	Exception[1]	Error Code Reference
1	TSS descriptor is present in memory	NP	New Task's TSS
2	TSS descriptor is not busy	TS (for IRET); GP (for JMP, CALL, INT)	Task's backlink TSS
3	TSS segment limit greater than or equal to 108	TS	New Task's TSS
4	Registers are loaded from the values in the TSS		
5	LDT selector of new task is valid[2]	TS	New Task's LDT
6	Code segment DPL matches selector RPL	TS	New Code Segment
7	SS selector is valid[2]	TS	New Stack Segment
8	Stack segment is present in memory	SF	New Stack Segment
9	Stack segment DPL matches CPL	TS	New stack segment
10	LDT of new task is present in memory	TS	New Task's LDT
11	CS selector is valid[2]	TS	New Code Segment
12	Code segment is present in memory	NP	New Code Segment
13	Stack segment DPL matches selector RPL	TS	New Stack Segment
14	DS, ES, FS, and GS selectors are valid[2]	TS	New Data Segment
15	DS, ES, FS, and GS segments are readable	TS	New Data Segment
16	DS, ES, FS, and GS segments are present in memory	NP	New Data Segment
17	DS, ES, FS, and GS segment DPL greater than or equal to CPL (unless these are conforming segments)	TS	New Data Segment

NOTES: Future Intel processors may use a different order of checks.

1. NP = Segment-not-present exception, GP = General-protection exception, TS = Invalid-TSS exception, SF = Stack exception.
2. A selector is valid if it is in a compatible type of table (e.g., an LDT selector may not be in any table except the GDT), occupies an address within the table's segment limit, and refers to a compatible type of descriptor (e.g., a selector in the CS register only is valid when it indexes to a descriptor for a code segment; the descriptor type is specified in its Type field).

13.6. TASK LINKING

The Link field of the TSS and the NT flag are used to return execution to the previous task. The NT flag indicates whether the currently executing task is nested within the execution of another task, and the Link field of the current task's TSS holds the TSS selector for the higher-level task, if there is one (see Figure 13-6).

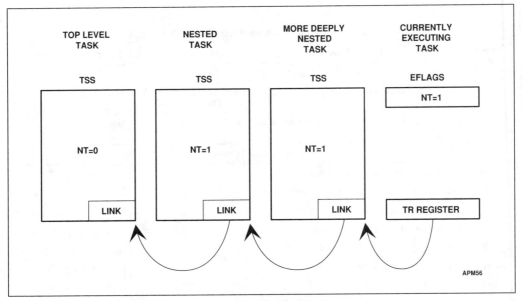

Figure 13-6. Nested Tasks

When an interrupt, exception, jump, or call causes a task switch, the processor copies the segment selector for the current task state segment into the TSS for the new task and sets the NT flag. The NT flag indicates the Link field of the TSS has been loaded with a saved TSS selector. The new task releases control by executing an IRET instruction. When an IRET instruction is executed, the NT flag is checked. If it is set, the processor does a task switch to the previous task. Table 13-2 summarizes the uses of the fields in a TSS which are affected by task switching.

Table 13-2. Effect of a Task Switch on Busy, NT, and Link Fields

Field	Effect of Jump	Effect of CALL Instruction or Interrupt	Effect of IRET Instruction
Busy bit of new task	Bit is set. Must have been clear before.	Bit is set. Must have been clear before.	No change. Must be set.
Busy bit of old task	Bit is cleared.	No change. Bit is currently set.	Bit is cleared.
NT flag of new task	No change.	Flag is set.	No change.
NT flag of old task	No change.	No change.	Flag is cleared.
Link field of new task.	No change.	Loaded with selector for old task's TSS.	No change.
Link field of old task.	No change.	No change.	No change.

Note that the NT flag may be modified by software executing at any privilege level. It is possible for a program to set its NT bit and execute an IRET instruction, which would have the effect of invoking the task specified in the Link field of the current task's TSS. To keep spurious task switches from succeeding, the operating system should initialize the Link field of every TSS it creates.

13.6.1. Busy Bit Prevents Loops

The Busy bit of the TSS descriptor prevents re-entrant task switching. There is only one saved task context, the context saved in the TSS, therefore a task only may be called once before it terminates. The chain of suspended tasks may grow to any length, due to multiple interrupts, exceptions, jumps, and calls. The Busy bit prevents a task from being called if it is in this chain. A re-entrant task switch would overwrite the old TSS for the task, which would break the chain.

The processor manages the Busy bit as follows:

1. When switching to a task, the processor sets the Busy bit of the new task.
2. When switching from a task, the processor clears the Busy bit of the old task if that task is not to be placed in the chain (i.e., the instruction causing the task switch is a JMP or IRET instruction). If the task is placed in the chain, its Busy bit remains set.
3. When switching to a task, the processor generates a general-protection exception if the Busy bit of the new task already is set.

In this way, the processor prevents a task from switching to itself or to any task in the chain, which prevents re-entrant task switching.

The Busy bit may be used in multiprocessor configurations, because the processor asserts a bus lock when it sets or clears the Busy bit. This keeps two processors from invoking the same task at the same time. (See Chapter 19 for more information on multiprocessing.)

13.6.2. Modifying Task Linkages

Modification of the chain of suspended tasks may be needed to resume an interrupted task before the task which interrupted it. A reliable way to do this is:

1. Disable interrupts.
2. First change the Link field in the TSS of the interrupting task, then clear the Busy bit in the TSS descriptor of the task being removed from the chain.
3. Re-enable interrupts.

13.7. TASK ADDRESS SPACE

The LDT selector and PDBR (CR3) field of the TSS can be used to give each task its own LDT and page tables. Because segment descriptors in the LDTs are the connections between tasks and segments, separate LDTs for each task can be used to set up individual control over these connections. Access to any particular segment can be given to any particular task by placing a segment descriptor for that segment in the LDT for that task. If paging is enabled, each task can have its own set of page tables for mapping linear addresses to physical addresses.

It also is possible for tasks to have the same LDT. This is a simple and memory-efficient way to allow some tasks to communicate with or control each other, without dropping the protection barriers for the entire system.

Because all tasks have access to the GDT, it also is possible to create shared segments accessed through segment descriptors in this table.

13.7.1. Task Linear-to-Physical Space Mapping

The choices for arranging the linear-to-physical mappings of tasks fall into two general classes:

1. One linear-to-physical mapping shared among all tasks. When paging is not enabled, this is the only choice. Without paging, all linear addresses map to the same physical addresses. When paging is enabled, this form of linear-to-physical mapping is obtained by using one page directory for all tasks. The linear space may exceed the available physical space if demand-paged virtual memory is supported.

2. Independent linear-to-physical mappings for each task. This form of mapping comes from using a different page directory for each task. Because the PDBR (page directory base register) is loaded from the TSS with each task switch, each task may have a different page directory.

The linear address spaces of different tasks may map to completely distinct physical addresses. If the entries of different page directories point to different page tables and the page tables point to different pages of physical memory, then the tasks do not share any physical addresses.

The task state segments must lie in a space accessible to all tasks so that the mapping of TSS addresses does not change while the processor is reading and updating the TSSs during a task switch. The linear space mapped by the GDT also should be mapped to a shared physical space; otherwise, the purpose of the GDT is defeated. Figure 13-7 shows how the linear spaces of two tasks can overlap in the physical space by sharing page tables.

13.7.2. Task Logical Address Space

By itself, an overlapping linear-to-physical space mapping does not allow sharing of data among tasks. To share data, tasks must also have a common logical-to-linear space mapping; i.e., they also must have access to descriptors which point into a shared linear address space. There are three ways to create shared logical-to-physical address-space mappings:

1. Through the segment descriptors in the GDT. All tasks have access to the descriptors in the GDT. If those descriptors point into a linear-address space which is mapped to a common physical-address space for all tasks, then the tasks can share data and instructions.

2. Through shared LDTs. Two or more tasks can use the same LDT if the LDT selectors in

their TSSs select the same LDT for use in address translation. Segment descriptors in the LDT addressing linear space mapped to overlapping physical space provide shared physical memory. This method of sharing is more selective than sharing by the GDT; the sharing can be limited to specific tasks. Other tasks in the system may have different LDTs which do not give them access to the shared areas.

3. Through segment descriptors in the LDTs which map to the same linear address space. If the linear address space is mapped to the same physical space by the page mapping of the tasks involved, these descriptors permit the tasks to share space. Such descriptors are commonly called aliases. This method of sharing is even more selective than those listed above; other descriptors in the LDTs may point to independent linear addresses which are not shared.

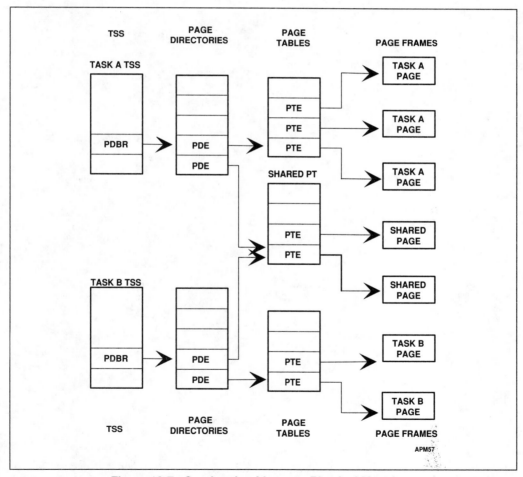

Figure 13-7. Overlapping Linear-to-Physical Mappings

intel®

14

Protected-Mode
Exceptions and
Interrupts

Exceptions and interrupts are forced transfers of execution to a task or a procedure. The task or procedure is called a *handler*. Interrupts occur at random times during the execution of a program, in response to signals from hardware. Exceptions occur when instructions are executed which provoke exceptions. Usually, the servicing of interrupts and exceptions is performed in a manner transparent to application programs. Interrupts are used to handle events external to the processor, such as requests to service peripheral devices. Exceptions handle conditions detected by the processor in the course of executing instructions, such as division by zero.

There are two sources for interrupts and two sources for exceptions:

1. Interrupts

    — Maskable interrupts, which are received on the CPU's INTR input pin. Maskable interrupts do not occur unless the interrupt-enable flag (IF) is set.

    — Nonmaskable interrupts, which are received on the NMI (Non-Maskable Interrupt) input of the processor. The processor does not provide a mechanism to prevent nonmaskable interrupts.

2. Exceptions

    — Processor-detected exceptions. These are further classified as *faults*, *traps*, and *aborts*.

    — Programmed exceptions. The INTO, INT 3, INT *n*, and BOUND instructions may trigger exceptions. These instructions often are called "software interrupts," but the processor handles them as exceptions.

This chapter explains the features of the processor which control and respond to interrupts.

14.1. EXCEPTION AND INTERRUPT VECTORS

The processor associates an identifying number with each different type of interrupt or exception. This number is called a *vector*.

The NMI interrupt and the exceptions are assigned vectors in the range 0 through 31. Not all of these vectors are currently used by the processor; unassigned vectors in this range are reserved for possible future uses. Do not use unassigned vectors.

The vectors for maskable interrupts are determined by hardware. External interrupt controllers (such as Intel's 8259A Programmable Interrupt Controller) put the vector on the processor's bus during its interrupt-acknowledge cycle. Any vectors in the range 32 through 255 can be used. Table 14-1 shows the assignment of exception and interrupt vectors.

Table 14-1. Exception and Interrupt Vectors

Vector Number	Description
0	Divide Error
1	Debug Exception
2	NMI Interrupt
3	Breakpoint
4	INTO-detected Overflow
5	BOUND Range Exceeded
6	Invalid Opcode
7	Device Not Available
8	Double Fault
9	CoProcessor Segment Overrun (reserved)
10	Invalid Task State Segment
11	Segment Not Present
12	Stack Fault
13	General Protection
14	Page Fault
15	(Intel reserved. Do not use.)
16	Floating-Point Error
17	Alignment Check
18	Machine Check*
19-31	(Intel reserved. Do not use.)
32-255	Maskable Interrupts

NOTE:

*Machine check is a model-specific exception, available on the Pentium™ microprocessor only. It may not be continued or may not be continued with a compatible implementation in future processor generations.

Exceptions are classified as *faults*, *traps*, or *aborts* depending on the way they are reported and whether restart of the instruction which caused the exception is supported.

Faults—A fault is an exception which is reported at the instruction boundary prior to the instruction in which the exception was detected. The fault is reported with the machine restored to a state which permits the instruction to be restarted. The return address for the fault handler points to the instruction which generated the fault, rather than the instruction following the faulting instruction.

Traps—A trap is an exception which is reported at the instruction boundary immediately after the instruction in which the exception was detected.

Aborts—An abort is an exception which does not always report the location of the instruction causing the exception and does not allow restart of the program which caused the exception.

Aborts are used to report severe errors, such as hardware errors and inconsistent or illegal values in system tables.

14.2. INSTRUCTION RESTART

For most exceptions and interrupts, transfer of execution does not take place until the end of the current instruction. This leaves the EIP register pointing at the instruction which comes after the instruction which was being executed when the exception or interrupt occurred. If the instruction has a repeat prefix, transfer takes place at the end of the current iteration with the registers set to execute the next iteration. But if the exception is a fault, the processor registers are restored to the state they held before execution of the instruction began. This permits *instruction restart*.

Instruction restart is used to handle exceptions which block access to operands. For example, an application program could make reference to data in a segment which is not present in memory. When the exception occurs, the exception handler must load the segment (probably from a hard disk) and resume execution beginning with the instruction which caused the exception. At the time the exception occurs, the instruction may have altered the contents of some of the processor registers. If the instruction read an operand from the stack, it is necessary to restore the stack pointer to its previous value. All of these restoring operations are performed by the processor in a manner completely transparent to the application program.

When a fault occurs, the EIP register is restored to point to the instruction which received the exception. When the exception handler returns, execution resumes with this instruction.

14.3. ENABLING AND DISABLING INTERRUPTS

Certain conditions and flag settings cause the processor to inhibit certain kinds of interrupts and exceptions.

14.3.1. NMI Masks Further NMIs

While an NMI interrupt handler is executing, the processor disables additional calls to the procedure or task which handles the interrupt until the next IRET instruction is executed. This prevents stacking up calls to the interrupt handler. It is recommended that interrupt gates be used for NMI's in order to disable nested maskable interrupts, since an IRET instruction from the maskable-interrupt handler would re-enable NMI.

14.3.2. IF Masks INTR

The IF flag can turn off servicing of interrupts received on the INTR pin of the processor. When the IF flag is clear, INTR interrupts are ignored; when the IF flag is set, INTR interrupts are serviced. As with the other flag bits, the processor clears the IF flag in response to a RESET signal. The STI and CLI instructions set and clear the IF flag.

CLI (Clear Interrupt-Enable Flag) and **STI (Set Interrupt-Enable Flag)** put the IF flag (bit 9 in the EFLAGS register) in a known state. These instructions may be executed only if the

CPL is an equal or more privileged level than the IOPL. A general-protection exception is generated if they are executed with a lesser privileged level.

The IF flag also is affected by the following operations:

- The PUSHF instruction stores all flags on the stack, where they can be examined and modified. The POPF instruction can be used to load the modified form back into the EFLAGS register.

- Task switches and the POPF and IRET instructions load the EFLAGS register; therefore, they can be used to modify the setting of the IF flag.

- Interrupts through interrupt gates automatically clear the IF flag, which disables interrupts. (Interrupt gates are explained later in this chapter).

14.3.3. RF Masks Debug Faults

The RF flag in the EFLAGS register is used to prevent servicing an instruction breakpoint fault multiple times. RF works as follows:

- Before entry into any fault handler, the processor sets the RF bit in the EFLAGS image that it pushes onto the stack of the handler. Normally the RF image on the stack does not need to be changed by software.

- RF itself is set by the fault handler when it executes the IRETD instruction to return to the faulting instruction. IRETD transfers the EFLAGS image from the stack into the EFLAGS register. (POPF and POPFD do not transfer the RF image into the EFLAGS register.)

- RF is cleared by the processor at successful termination of every instruction, except after the IRET instruction and after JMP, CALL, or INT instructions that cause a task switch. Therefore, RF remains set for no more than one instruction — the one executed immediately after the IRET.

- When set, RF causes the processor to suppress reporting of instruction breakpoint faults.

Because instruction breakpoint faults are the highest priority faults, they are always reported before any other faults for the same instruction. RF is zero for the first attempt to execute the instruction and one for all attempts to restart the instruction after an instruction breakpoint or any other fault. This ensures that an instruction breakpoint fault is reported only once. (See Chapter 17 for more information on debugging.)

14.3.4. MOV or POP to SS Masks Some Exceptions and Interrupts

Software which needs to change stack segments often uses a pair of instructions; for example:

```
MOV          SS, AX
MOV          ESP, StackTop
```

If an interrupt or exception occurs after the segment selector has been loaded but before the ESP register has been loaded, these two parts of the logical address into the stack space are inconsistent for the duration of the interrupt or exception handler.

To prevent this situation, the processor inhibits interrupts, debug exceptions, and single-step trap exceptions after either a MOV to SS instruction or a POP to SS instruction, until the instruction boundary following the next instruction is reached. General-protection faults may still be generated. If the LSS instruction is used to modify the contents of the SS register, the problem does not occur.

14.4. PRIORITY AMONG SIMULTANEOUS EXCEPTIONS AND INTERRUPTS

If more than one exception or interrupt is pending at an instruction boundary, the processor services them in a predictable order. The priority among classes of exception and interrupt sources is shown in Table 14-2. While priority among these classes is consistent throught the architecture, exceptions within each class are implementation-dependent and may vary from processor to processor. The processor first services a pending exception or interrupt from the class which has the highest priority, transferring execution to the first instruction of the handler. Lower priority exceptions are discarded; lower priority interrupts are held pending. Discarded exceptions are re-issued when the interrupt handler returns execution to the point of interruption.

Table 14-2. Priority Among Simultaneous Exceptions and Interrupts

Priority	Class	Descriptions
Highest	Class 1	Traps on the Previous Instruction - Breakpoints - Debug Trap Exceptions (TF flag set, T bit in TSS set, or data/IO breakpoint)
	Class 2	External Interrupts - NMI Interrupts - Maskable Interrupts
	Class 3	Faults from fetching next instruction - Code Breakpoint Fault - Code Segment Limit Violation - Page Fault on Prefetch
	Class 4	Faults from Decoding the next instruction - Illegal Opcode - Instruction length > 15 bytes - Coprocessor Not Available
Lowest	Class 5	Faults on Executing an Instruction - General Detection - FP error (from previous FP instruction) - Interrupt on Overflow - Bound - Invalid TSS - Segment Not Present - Stack Exception - General Protection - Data Page Fault - Alignment Check

14.5. INTERRUPT DESCRIPTOR TABLE

The interrupt descriptor table (IDT) associates each exception or interrupt vector with a descriptor for the procedure or task which services the associated event. Like the GDT and LDTs, the IDT is an array of 8-byte descriptors. Unlike the GDT, the first entry of the IDT may contain a descriptor. To form an index into the IDT, the processor scales the exception or interrupt vector by eight, the number of bytes in a descriptor. Because there are only 256 vectors, the IDT need not contain more than 256 descriptors. It can contain fewer than 256 descriptors; descriptors are required only for the interrupt vectors which may occur.

The IDT may reside anywhere in physical memory. As Figure 14-1 shows, the processor locates the IDT using the IDTR register. This register holds both a 32-bit base address and 16-bit limit for the IDT. The LIDT and SIDT instructions load and store the contents of the IDTR register. Both instructions have one operand, which is the address of six bytes in memory.

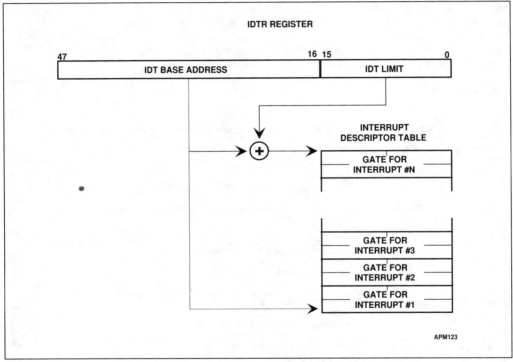

Figure 14-1. IDTR Locates IDT in Memory

If a vector references a descriptor beyond the limit, the processor enters shutdown mode. In this mode, the processor stops executing instructions until an NMI interrupt is received or reset initialization is invoked. The processor generates a special bus cycle to indicate it has entered shutdown mode. Software designers may need to be aware of the response of hardware to receiving this signal. For example, hardware may turn on an indicator light on the front panel, generate an NMI interrupt to record diagnostic information, or invoke reset initialization.

LIDT (Load IDT register) loads the IDTR register with the base address and limit held in the memory operand. This instruction can be executed only when the CPL is 0. It normally is used by the initialization code of an operating system when creating an IDT. An operating system also may use it to change from one IDT to another.

SIDT (Store IDT register) copies the base and limit value stored in IDTR to memory. This instruction can be executed at any privilege level.

14.6. IDT DESCRIPTORS

The IDT may contain any of three kinds of descriptors:

- Task gates
- Interrupt gates
- Trap gates

Figure 14-2 shows the format of task gates, interrupt gates, and trap gates. (The task gate in an IDT is the same as the task gate in the GDT or an LDT already discussed in Chapter 13.)

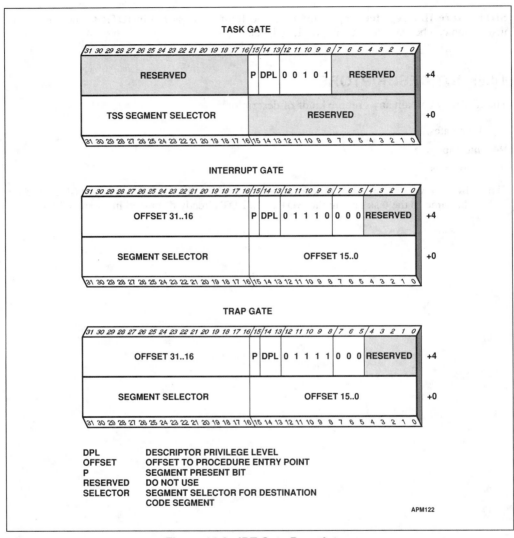

Figure 14-2. IDT Gate Descriptors

14.7. INTERRUPT TASKS AND INTERRUPT PROCEDURES

Just as a CALL instruction can call either a procedure or a task, so an exception or interrupt can "call" an interrupt handler as either a procedure or a task. When responding to an exception or interrupt, the processor uses the exception or interrupt vector to index to a descriptor in the IDT. If the processor indexes to an interrupt gate or trap gate, it calls the handler in a manner similar to a CALL to a call gate. If the processor finds a task gate, it causes a task switch in a manner similar to a CALL to a task gate.

14.7.1. Interrupt Procedures

An interrupt gate or trap gate indirectly references a procedure which runs in the context of the currently executing task, as shown in Figure 14-3. The selector of the gate points to an executable-segment descriptor in either the GDT or the current LDT. The offset field of the gate descriptor points to the beginning of the exception or interrupt handling procedure.

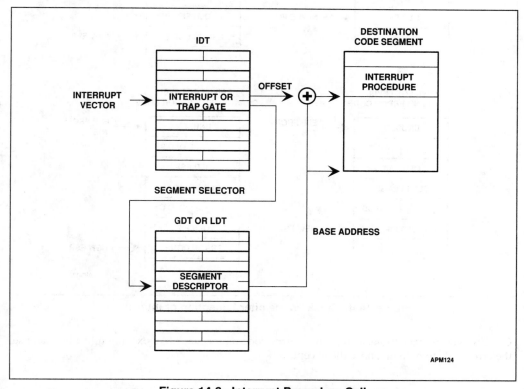

Figure 14-3. Interrupt Procedure Call

The processor calls an exception or interrupt handling procedure in much the same manner as a procedure call; the differences are explained in the following sections.

14.7.1.1. STACK OF INTERRUPT PROCEDURE

Just as with a transfer of execution using a CALL instruction, a transfer to an exception or interrupt handling procedure uses the stack to store the processor state. As Figure 14-4 shows, an interrupt pushes the contents of the EFLAGS register onto the stack before pushing the address of the interrupted instruction.

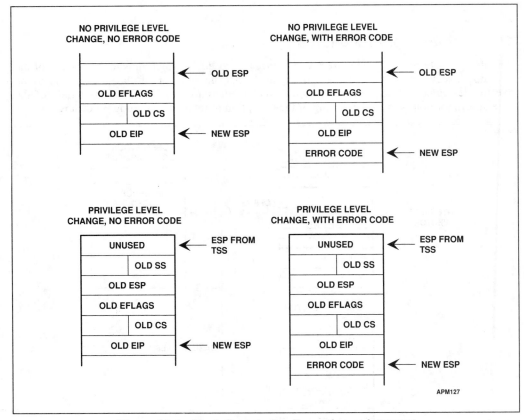

Figure 14-4. Stack Frame after Exception or Interrupt

Certain types of exceptions also push an error code on the stack. An exception handler can use the error code to help diagnose the exception.

14.7.1.2.   RETURNING FROM AN INTERRUPT PROCEDURE

An interrupt procedure differs from a normal procedure in the method of leaving the procedure. The IRET instruction is used to exit from an interrupt procedure. The IRET instruction is similar to the RET instruction except that it increments the contents of the ESP register by an extra four bytes and restores the saved flags into the EFLAGS register. The IOPL field of the EFLAGS register is restored only if the CPL is 0. The IF flag is changed only if CPL ≤ IOPL.

14.7.1.3.   FLAG USAGE BY INTERRUPT PROCEDURE

Interrupts using either interrupt gates or trap gates cause the TF flag to be cleared after its current value is saved on the stack as part of the saved contents of the EFLAGS register. In so doing, the processor prevents instruction tracing from affecting interrupt response. A subsequent IRET instruction restores the TF flag to the value in the saved contents of the EFLAGS register on the stack.

The difference between an interrupt gate and a trap gate is its effect on the IF flag. An interrupt which uses an interrupt gate clears the IF flag, which prevents other interrupts from interfering with the current interrupt handler. A subsequent IRET instruction restores the IF flag to the value in the saved contents of the EFLAGS register on the stack. An interrupt through a trap gate does not change the IF flag.

14.7.1.4.   PROTECTION IN INTERRUPT PROCEDURES

The privilege rule which governs interrupt procedures is similar to that for procedure calls: the processor does not permit an interrupt to transfer execution to a procedure in a less privileged segment (numerically greater privilege level). An attempt to violate this rule results in a general-protection exception.

Because interrupts generally do not occur at predictable times, this privilege rule effectively imposes restrictions on the privilege levels at which exception and interrupt handling procedures can run. Either of the following techniques can be used to keep the privilege rule from being violated.

- The exception or interrupt handler can be placed in a conforming code segment. This technique can be used by handlers for certain exceptions (divide error, for example). These handlers must use only the data available on the stack. If the handler needs data from a data segment, the data segment would have to have privilege level 3, which would make it unprotected.

- The handler can be placed in a code segment with privilege level 0. This handler would always run, no matter what CPL the program has.

14.7.2. Interrupt Tasks

A task gate in the IDT indirectly references a task, as Figure 14-5 illustrates. The segment selector in the task gate addresses a TSS descriptor in the GDT.

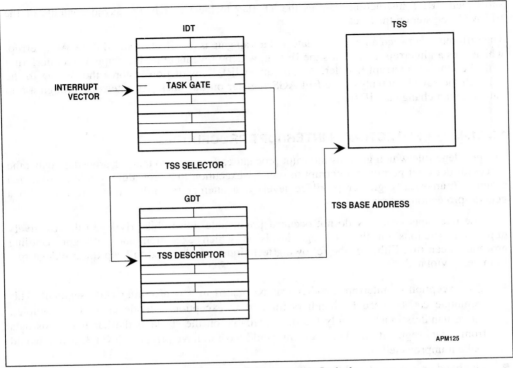

Figure 14-5. Interrupt Task Switch

When an exception or interrupt calls a task gate in the IDT, a task switch results. Handling an interrupt with a separate task offers two advantages:

● The entire context is saved automatically.

● The interrupt handler can be isolated from other tasks by giving it a separate address space. This is done by giving it a separate LDT.

A task switch caused by an interrupt operates in the same manner as the other task switches described in Chapter 13. The interrupt task returns to the interrupted task by executing an IRET instruction.

Some exceptions return an error code. If the task switch is caused by one of these, the processor pushes the code onto the stack corresponding to the privilege level of the interrupt handler.

When interrupt tasks are used in an operating system, there are actually two mechanisms which can dispatch tasks: the software scheduler (part of the operating system) and the hardware scheduler (part of the processor's interrupt mechanism). The software scheduler needs to accommodate interrupt tasks which may be dispatched when interrupts are enabled.

14.8. ERROR CODE

With exceptions related to a specific segment, the processor pushes an error code onto the stack of the exception handler (whether it is a procedure or task). The error code has the format shown in Figure 14-6. The error code resembles a segment selector; however instead of an RPL field, the error code contains two one-bit fields:

1. The processor sets the EXT bit if an event external to the program caused the exception.

2. The processor sets the IDT bit if the index portion of the error code refers to a gate descriptor in the IDT.

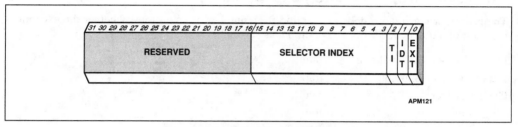

Figure 14-6. Error Code

If the IDT bit is not set, the TI bit indicates whether the error code refers to the GDT (TI bit clear) or to the LDT (TI bit set). The remaining 13 bits are the upper bits of the selector for the segment. In some cases the error code is *null* (i.e., all bits in the lower word are clear).

The error code is pushed on the stack as a doubleword. This is done to keep the stack aligned on addresses which are multiples of four. The upper half of the doubleword is reserved.

14.9. EXCEPTION CONDITIONS

The following sections describe conditions which generate exceptions. Each description classifies the exception as a *fault*, *trap*, or *abort*. This classification provides information needed by system programmers for restarting the procedure in which the exception occurred:

- Faults—The saved contents of the CS and EIP registers point to the instruction which generated the fault.

- Traps—The saved contents of the CS and EIP registers stored when the trap occurs point to the instruction to be executed after the instruction which generated the trap. If a trap is detected during an instruction which transfers execution, the saved contents of the CS and EIP registers reflect the transfer. For example, if a trap is detected in a JMP instruction, the saved contents of the CS and EIP registers point to the destination of the JMP instruction, not to the instruction at the next address above the JMP instruction.

- Aborts—An abort is an exception which permits neither precise location of the instruction causing the exception nor restart of the program which caused the exception. Aborts are used to report severe errors, such as hardware errors and inconsistent or illegal values in system tables.

14.9.1. Interrupt 0—Divide Error

The divide-error fault occurs during a DIV or an IDIV instruction when the divisor is zero.

14.9.2. Interrupt 1—Debug Exceptions

The processor generates a debug exception for a number of conditions; whether the exception is a fault or a trap depends on the condition, as shown below:

Instruction address breakpoint   fault

Data address breakpoint   trap

General detect   fault

Single-step   trap

Task-switch breakpoint   trap

The processor does not push an error code for this exception. An exception handler can examine the debug registers to determine which condition caused the exception. See Chapter 17 for more detailed information about debugging and the debug registers.

14.9.3. Interrupt 3—Breakpoint

The INT 3 instruction generates a breakpoint trap. The INT 3 instruction is one byte long, which makes it easy to replace an opcode in a code segment in RAM with the breakpoint opcode. The operating system or a debugging tool can use a data segment mapped to the same physical address space as the code segment to place an INT 3 instruction in places where it is desired to call the debugger. Debuggers use breakpoints as a way to suspend program execution in order to examine registers, variables, etc.

The saved contents of the CS and EIP registers point to the byte following the breakpoint. If a debugger allows the suspended program to resume execution, it replaces the INT 3 instruction with the original opcode at the location of the breakpoint, and it decrements the saved contents of the EIP register before returning. See Chapter 17 for more information on debugging.

14.9.4. Interrupt 4—Overflow

The overflow trap occurs when the processor executes an INTO instruction with the OF flag set. Because signed and unsigned arithmetic both use some of the same instructions, the processor cannot determine when overflow actually occurs. Instead, it sets the OF flag when the results, if interpreted as signed numbers, would be out of range. When doing arithmetic on signed operands, the OF flag can be tested directly or the INTO instruction can be used.

14.9.5. Interrupt 5—Bounds Check

The bounds-check fault is generated when the processor, while executing a BOUND instruction, finds that the operand exceeds the specified limits. A program can use the BOUND instruction to check a signed array index against signed limits defined in a block of memory.

14.9.6. Interrupt 6—Invalid Opcode

The invalid-opcode fault is generated when an invalid opcode is detected by the execution unit. (The exception is not detected until an attempt is made to execute the invalid opcode; i.e., prefetching an invalid opcode does not cause this exception.) No error code is pushed on the stack. The exception can be handled within the same task.

This exception also occurs when the type of operand is invalid for the given opcode. Examples include an intersegment JMP instruction using a register operand, or an LES instruction with a register source operand.

A third condition which generates this exception is the use of the LOCK prefix with an instruction which may not be locked. Only certain instructions may be used with bus locking, and only forms of these instructions which write to a destination in memory may be used. All other uses of the LOCK prefix generate an invalid-opcode exception.

Following is a list of undefined opcodes that are reserved by Intel. These opcodes, even though undefined, do not generate interrupt 6.

- D6
- F1

14.9.7. Interrupt 7—Device Not Available

The device-not-available fault is generated by either of two conditions:

- The processor executes an ESC instruction, and the EM bit of the CR0 register is set.
- The processor executes a WAIT instruction (with MP=1) or ESC instruction, and the TS bit of the CR0 register is set.

Interrupt 7 thus occurs when the programmer wants ESC instructions to be handled by software (EM set), or when a WAIT or ESC instruction is encountered and the context of the floating-point unit is different from that of the current task.

On the Intel 286 and Intel386 processors, the MP bit in the CR0 register is used with the TS bit to determine if WAIT instructions should generate exceptions. For programs running on the Pentium, Intel486 DX, and Intel487 SX processors, the MP bit should always be set. For programs running on the Intel486 SX, MP should be clear.

14.9.8. Interrupt 8—Double Fault

Normally, when the processor detects an exception while trying to call the handler for a prior exception, the two exceptions can be handled serially. If, however, the processor cannot handle them serially, it signals the double-fault exception instead. To determine when two faults are to be signalled as a double fault, the processor divides the exceptions into three classes: benign exceptions, contributory exceptions, and page faults. Table 14-3 shows this classification. Then, comparing the classes of the first and second exception, the processor signals a double-fault in the cases indicated by Table 14-4.

Table 14-3. Interrupt and Exception Classes

Class	Vector Number	Description
Benign Exceptions and Interrupts	1 2 3 4 5 6 7 16	Debug Exceptions NMI Interrupt Breakpoint Overflow Bounds Check Invalid Opcode Device Not Available Floating-Point Error
Contributory Exceptions	0 10 11 12 13	Divide Error Invalid TSS Segment Not Present Stack Fault General Protection
Page Faults	14	Page Fault

Table 14-4. Double Fault Conditions

First Exception	Second Exception		
	Benign	Contributory	Page Fault
Benign	OK	OK	OK
Contributory	OK	Double Fault	OK
Page Fault	OK	Double Fault	Double Fault

An initial segment or page fault encountered while prefetching instructions is outside the domain of Table 14-4. Any further faults generated while the processor is attempting to transfer control to the appropriate fault handler could still lead to a double-fault sequence.

The processor always pushes an error code onto the stack of the double-fault handler; however, the error code is always 0. The faulting instruction may not be restarted. If any other exception occurs while attempting to call the double-fault handler, the processor enters shutdown mode. This mode is similar to the state following execution of a HLT instruction. No instructions are executed until an NMI interrupt or a RESET signal is received. If the shutdown occurs while the processor is executing an NMI interrupt handler, then only a RESET can restart the processor. The processor generates a special bus cycle to indicate it has entered shutdown mode.

14.9.9. Interrupt 9—(Intel reserved. Do not use.)

Interrupt 9, the coprocessor-segment overrun abort, is generated in Intel386 CPU-based systems with an Intel387 math coprocessor when the Intel386 CPU detects a page or segment violation while transferring the middle portion of an Intel387 math coprocessor operand. This interrupt is generated neither by the Pentium processor nor by the Intel486 processor; interrupt 13 occurs instead.

14.9.10. Interrupt 10—Invalid TSS

An invalid-TSS fault is generated if a task switch to a segment with an invalid TSS is attempted. A TSS is invalid in the cases shown in Table 14-5. An error code is pushed onto the stack of the exception handler to help identify the cause of the fault. The EXT bit indicates whether the exception was caused by a condition outside the control of the program (e.g., if an external interrupt using a task gate attempted a task switch to an invalid TSS).

Table 14-5. Invalid TSS Conditions

Error Code Index	Description
TSS segment	TSS segment limit less than 67H
LDT segment	Invalid LDT or LDT not present
Stack segment	Stack segment selector exceeds descriptor table limit
Stack segment	Stack segment is not writable
Stack segment	Stack segment DPL not compatible with CPL
Stack segment	Stack segment selector RPL not compatible with CPL
Code segment	Code segment selector exceeds descriptor table limit
Code segment	Code segment is not executable
Code segment	Non-conforming code segment DPL not equal to CPL
Code segment	Conforming code segment DPL greater than CPL
Data segment	Data segment selector exceeds descriptor table limit
Data segment	Data segment not readable

This fault can occur either in the context of the original task or in the context of the new task. Until the processor has completely verified the presence of the new TSS, the exception occurs in the context of the original task. Once the existence of the new TSS is verified, the task switch is considered complete; i.e., the TR register is loaded with a selector for the new TSS and, if the switch is due to a CALL or interrupt, the Link field of the new TSS references the old TSS. Any errors discovered by the processor after this point are handled in the context of the new task.

To ensure a TSS is available to process the exception, the handler for an invalid-TSS exception must be a task called using a task gate.

14.9.11. Interrupt 11—Segment Not Present

The segment-not-present fault is generated when the processor detects that the present bit of a descriptor is clear. The processor can generate this fault in any of these cases:

- While attempting to load the CS, DS, ES, FS, or GS registers; loading the SS register, however, causes a stack fault.
- While attempting to load the LDT register using an LLDT instruction; loading the LDT register during a task switch operation, however, causes an invalid-TSS exception.
- While attempting to use a gate descriptor which is marked segment-not-present.

This fault is restartable. If the exception handler loads the segment and returns, the interrupted program resumes execution.

If a segment-not-present exception occurs during a task switch, not all the steps of the task switch are complete. During a task switch, the processor first loads all the segment registers, then checks their contents for validity. If a segment-not-present exception is discovered, the remaining segment registers have not been checked and therefore may not be usable for referencing memory. The segment-not-present handler should not rely on being able to use the segment selectors found in the CS, SS, DS, ES, FS, and GS registers without causing another exception. The exception handler should check all segment registers before trying to resume the new task; otherwise, general protection faults may result later under conditions which make diagnosis more difficult. There are three ways to handle this case:

1. Handle the segment-not-present fault with a task. The task switch back to the interrupted task causes the processor to check the registers as it loads them from the TSS.
2. Use the PUSH and POP instructions on all segment registers. Each POP instruction causes the processor to check the new contents of the segment register.
3. Check the saved contents of each segment register in the TSS, simulating the test which the processor makes when it loads a segment register.

This exception pushes an error code onto the stack. The EXT bit of the error code is set if an event external to the program caused an interrupt which subsequently referenced a not-present segment. The IDT bit is set if the error code refers to an IDT entry (e.g., an INT instruction referencing a not-present gate).

An operating system typically uses the segment-not-present exception to implement virtual memory at the segment level. A not-present indication in a gate descriptor, however, usually does not indicate that a segment is not present (because gates do not necessarily correspond to segments). Not-present gates may be used by an operating system to trigger exceptions of special significance to the operating system.

14.9.12. Interrupt 12—Stack Exception

A stack fault is generated under two conditions:

- As a result of a limit violation in any operation which refers to the SS register. This includes stack-oriented instructions such as POP, PUSH, ENTER, and LEAVE, as well as other memory references which implicitly or explicitly use the SS register (for example, MOV AX, [BP+6] or MOV AX, SS:[EAX+6]). The ENTER instruction generates this exception when there is too little space for allocating local variables.

- When attempting to load the SS register with a descriptor which is marked segment-not-present but is otherwise valid. This can occur in a task switch, a CALL instruction to a different privilege level, a return to a different privilege level, an LSS instruction, or a MOV or POP instruction to the SS register.

When the processor detects a stack exception, it pushes an error code onto the stack of the exception handler. If the exception is due to a not-present stack segment or to overflow of the new stack during an interlevel CALL, the error code contains a selector to the segment which caused the exception (the exception handler can test the present bit in the descriptor to determine which exception occurred); otherwise, the error code is 0.

An instruction generating this fault is restartable in all cases. The return address pushed onto the exception handler's stack points to the instruction which needs to be restarted. This instruction usually is the one which caused the exception; however, in the case of a stack exception from loading a not-present stack-segment descriptor during a task switch, the indicated instruction is the first instruction of the new task.

When a stack exception occurs during a task switch, the segment registers may not be usable for addressing memory. During a task switch, the selector values are loaded before the descriptors are checked. If a stack exception is generated, the remaining segment registers have not been checked and may cause exceptions if they are used. The stack fault handler should not expect to use the segment selectors found in the CS, SS, DS, ES, FS, and GS registers without causing another exception. The exception handler should check all segment registers before trying to resume the new task; otherwise, general protection faults may result later under conditions where diagnosis is more difficult.

14.9.13. Interrupt 13—General Protection

All protection violations which do not cause another exception cause a general-protection exception. This includes (but is not limited to):

- Exceeding the segment limit when using the CS, DS, ES, FS, or GS segments.
- Exceeding the segment limit when referencing a descriptor table.
- Transferring execution to a segment which is not executable.
- Writing to a read-only data segment or a code segment.
- Reading from an execute-only code segment.
- Loading the SS register with a selector for a read-only segment (unless the selector comes

from a TSS during a task switch, in which case an invalid-TSS exception occurs).

- Loading the SS, DS, ES, FS, or GS register with a selector for a system segment.

- Loading the DS, ES, FS, or GS register with a selector for an execute-only code segment.

- Loading the SS register with the selector of an executable segment.

- Accessing memory using the DS, ES, FS, or GS register when it contains a null selector.

- Switching to a busy task.

- Violating privilege rules.

- Exceeding the instruction length limit of 15 bytes (this only can occur when redundant prefixes are placed before an instruction).

- Loading the CR0 register with a set PG bit (paging enabled) and a clear PE bit (protection disabled).

- Interrupt or exception through an interrupt or trap gate from virtual-8086 mode to a handler at a privilege level other than 0.

- Attempting to write a one into a reserved bit of CR4.

The general-protection exception is a fault. In response to a general-protection exception, the processor pushes an error code onto the exception handler's stack. If loading a descriptor causes the exception, the error code contains a selector to the descriptor; otherwise, the error code is null. The source of the selector in an error code may be any of the following:

- An operand of the instruction.

- A selector from a gate which is the operand of the instruction.

- A selector from a TSS involved in a task switch.

14.9.14. Interrupt 14—Page Fault

A page fault occurs when paging is enabled (the PG bit in the CR0 register is set) and the processor detects one of the following conditions while translating a linear address to a physical address:

- The page-directory or page-table entry needed for the address translation has a clear Present bit, which indicates that a page table or the page containing the operand is not present in physical memory.

- The procedure does not have sufficient privilege to access the indicated page.

If a page fault is caused by a page level protection violation, the access bits in the page-directory are set when the faults occur. The access bit in the page table is only set if there are no page level protection violations.

The processor provides the page fault handler two items of information which aid in diagnosing the exception and recovering from it:

- An error code on the stack. The error code for a page fault has a format different from that for other exceptions (see Figure 14-7). The error code tells the exception handler three things:

a. Whether the exception was due to a not-present page, to an access rights violation, or to use of a reserved bit.

b. Whether the processor was executing at user or supervisor level at the time of the exception.

c. Whether the memory access which caused the exception was a read or write.

● The contents of the CR2 register. The processor loads the CR2 register with the 32-bit linear address which generated the exception. The exception handler can use this address to locate the corresponding page directory and page table entries. If another page fault occurs during execution of the page fault handler, the handler will push the contents of the CR2 register onto the stack.

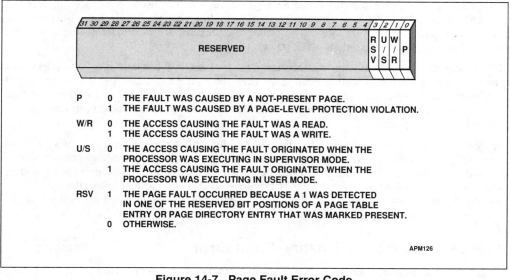

P   0   THE FAULT WAS CAUSED BY A NOT-PRESENT PAGE.
      1   THE FAULT WAS CAUSED BY A PAGE-LEVEL PROTECTION VIOLATION.

W/R   0   THE ACCESS CAUSING THE FAULT WAS A READ.
      1   THE ACCESS CAUSING THE FAULT WAS A WRITE.

U/S   0   THE ACCESS CAUSING THE FAULT ORIGINATED WHEN THE
          PROCESSOR WAS EXECUTING IN SUPERVISOR MODE.
      1   THE ACCESS CAUSING THE FAULT ORIGINATED WHEN THE
          PROCESSOR WAS EXECUTING IN USER MODE.

RSV   1   THE PAGE FAULT OCCURRED BECAUSE A 1 WAS DETECTED
          IN ONE OF THE RESERVED BIT POSITIONS OF A PAGE TABLE
          ENTRY OR PAGE DIRECTORY ENTRY THAT WAS MARKED PRESENT.
      0   OTHERWISE.

APM126

Figure 14-7. Page Fault Error Code

14.9.14.1.   PAGE FAULT DURING TASK SWITCH

These operations during a task switch cause access to memory:

1. Write the state of the original task in the TSS of that task.

2. Read the GDT to locate the TSS descriptor of the new task.

3. Read the TSS of the new task to check the types of segment descriptors from the TSS.

4. May read the LDT of the new task in order to verify the segment registers stored in the new TSS.

A page fault can result from accessing any of these operations. In the last two cases the exception occurs in the context of the new task. The instruction pointer refers to the next instruction of the new task, not to the instruction which caused the task switch (or the last instruction to be executed, in the case of an interrupt). If the design of the operating system permits page faults to occur during task-switches, the page-fault handler should be called through a task gate.

14.9.14.2. PAGE FAULT WITH INCONSISTENT STACK POINTER

Special care should be taken to ensure that a page fault does not cause the processor to use an invalid stack pointer (SS:ESP). Software written for Intel 16-bit processors often uses a pair of instructions to change to a new stack; for example:

```
MOV SS, AX
MOV SP, StackTop
```

With the 32-bit processors, because the second instruction accesses memory, it is possible to get a page fault after the selector in the SS segment register has been changed but before the contents of the SP register have received the corresponding change. At this point, the two parts of the stack pointer SS:SP (or, for 32-bit programs, SS:ESP) are inconsistent. The new stack segment is being used with the old stack pointer.

The processor does not use the inconsistent stack pointer if the handling of the page fault causes a stack switch to a well defined stack (i.e., the handler is a task or a more privileged procedure). However, if the page fault occurs at the same privilege level and in the same task as the page fault handler, the processor will attempt to use the stack indicated by the inconsistent stack pointer.

In systems which use paging and handle page faults within the faulting task (with trap or interrupt gates), software executing at the same privilege level as the page fault handler should initialize a new stack by using the LSS instruction rather than an instruction pair shown above. When the page fault handler is running at privilege level 0 (the normal case), the problem is limited to programs which run at privilege level 0, typically the kernel of the operating system.

14.9.15. Interrupt 16—Floating-Point Error

A floating-point-error fault signals an error generated by a floating-point arithmetic instruction. Interrupt 16 can occur only if the NE bit in the CR0 register is set. Numeric processing exceptions have already been introduced previously in Chapter 7.

If NE = 1, an unmasked floating-point exception results in interrupt 16, immediately before the execution of the next non-control floating-point or WAIT instruction. Interrupt 16 is an operating-system call that invokes the exception handler. Chapter 14 contains a general discussion of exceptions and interrupts.

If NE = 0 (and the IGNNE# input is inactive), an unmasked floating-point exception causes the processor to freeze immediately before executing the next non-control floating-point or WAIT instruction. The frozen processor waits for an external interrupt, which must be supplied by external hardware in response to the FERR# output of the Intel486 or Pentium processor (the FERR# is similar to the ERROR# pin of the Intel387 math coprocessor). Regardless of the value of NE, an unmasked numerical exception causes the FERR# output of the Intel486 and Pentium processors to be activated. In this case, the external interrupt invokes the exception-handling routine. If NE = 0 but the IGNNE# input is active, the processor disregards the exception and continues. Error reporting via external interrupt is supported for DOS compatibility. Chapter 23 contains further discussion of compatibility issues.

When handling numeric errors, the processor has two responsibilities:

- It must not disturb the numeric context when an error is detected.
- It must clear the error and attempt recovery from the error.

Although the manner in which programmers may treat these responsibilities varies from one implementation to the next, most exception handlers will include these basic steps:

- Store the FPU environment (control, status, and tag words, operand and instruction pointers) as it existed at the time of the exception.
- Clear the exception bits in the status word.
- Enable interrupts if disabled due to an INTR, NMI, or SMI exception.
- Identify the exception by examining the status and control words in the saved environment.
- Take some system-dependent action to rectify the exception.
- Return to the interrupted program and resume normal execution.

14.9.15.1. NUMERICS EXCEPTION HANDLING

Recovery routines for numeric exceptions can take a variety of forms. They can change the arithmetic and programming rules of the FPU. These changes may redefine the default fix-up for an error, change the appearance of the FPU to the programmer, or change how arithmetic is defined on the FPU.

A change to an exception response might be to perform denormal arithmetic on denormals loaded from memory. A change in appearance might be extending the register stack into memory to provide an "infinite" number of numeric registers. The arithmetic of the FPU can be changed to automatically extend the precision and range of variables when exceeded. All these functions can be implemented on the processor via numeric exceptions and associated recovery routines in a manner transparent to the application programmer.

Some other possible application-dependent actions might include:

- Incrementing an exception counter for later display or printing
- Printing or displaying diagnostic information (e.g., the FPU environment and registers)
- Aborting further execution
- Storing a diagnostic value (a NaN) in the result and continuing with the computation

Notice that an exception may or may not constitute an error, depending on the application. Once the exception handler corrects the condition causing the exception, the floating-point instruction that caused the exception can be restarted, if appropriate. This cannot be accomplished using the IRET instruction, however, because the trap occurs at the ESC or WAIT instruction following the offending ESC instruction. The exception handler must obtain (using FSAVE or FSTENV) the address of the offending instruction in the task that initiated it, make a copy of it, execute the copy in the context of the offending task, and then return via IRET to the current instruction stream.

In order to correct the condition causing the numeric exception, exception handlers must recognize the precise state of the FPU at the time the exception handler was invoked, and be able to reconstruct the state of the FPU when the exception initially occurred. To reconstruct the state of the FPU, programmers must understand that different classes of exceptions are recognized at different times (before or after) execution of a numeric instruction.

Invalid operation, zero divide, and denormal operand exceptions are detected before an operation begins, whereas overflow, underflow, and precision exceptions are not raised until a true result has been computed. When a *before* exception is detected, the FPU register stack and memory have not yet been updated, and appear as if the offending instructions has not been executed.

When an *after* exception is detected, the register stack and memory appear as if the instruction has run to completion; i.e., they may be updated. (However, in a store or store-and-pop operation, unmasked over/underflow is handled like a *before* exception; memory is not updated and the stack is not popped.) The following programming examples include an outline of several exception handlers to process numeric exceptions.

14.9.15.2. SIMULTANEOUS EXCEPTION RESPONSE

In cases where multiple exceptions arise simultaneously, the FPU signals one exception according to the precedence list below. This means, for example, that an SNaN divided by zero results in an invalid operation, not in a zero-divide exception; the masked result is the QNaN *real indefinite*, not ∞. A denormal or inexact (precision) exception, however, can accompany a numeric underflow or overflow exception.

The precedence among numeric exceptions is as follows:

1. Invalid operation exception, subdivided as follows:
    — Stack underflow.
    — Stack overflow.
    — Operand of unsupported format.
    — SNaN operand.
2. QNaN operand. Though this is not an exception, if one operand is a QNaN, dealing with it has precedence over lower-priority exceptions. For example, a QNaN divided by zero results in a QNaN, not a zero-divide exception.
3. Any other invalid-operation exception not mentioned above or zero divide.
4. Denormal operand. If masked, then instruction execution continues, and a lower-priority exception can occur as well.
5. Numeric overflow and underflow. Inexact result (precision) can be flagged as well.
6. Inexact result (precision).

14.9.16. Interrupt 17—Alignment Check

An alignment-check fault can be generated for access to unaligned operands. For example, a word stored at an odd byte address, or a doubleword stored at an address which is not an integer multiple of four. Table 14-6 lists the alignment requirements by data type. To enable alignment checking, the following conditions must be true:

- AM bit in the CR0 register is set
- AC flag is set
- CPL is 3 (user mode)

Table 14-6. Alignment Requirements by Data Type

Data Type	Address Must Be Divisible By
WORD	2
DWORD	4
Short REAL	4
Long REAL	8
TEMPREAL	8
Selector	2
48-bit Segmented Pointer	4
32-bit Flat Pointer	4
32-bit Segmented Pointer	2
48-bit "Pseudo-Descriptor"	4
FSTENV/FLDENV save area	4 or 2, depending on operand size
FSAVE/FRSTOR save area	4 or 2, depending on operand size
Bit String	4

Alignment checking is useful for programs which use the low two bits of pointers to identify the type of data structure they address. For example, a subroutine in a math library may accept pointers to numeric data structures. If the type of this structure is assigned a code of 10 (binary) in the lowest two bits of pointers to this type, math subroutines can correct for the type code by adding a displacement of −10 (binary). If the subroutine should ever receive the wrong pointer type, an unaligned reference would be produced, which would generate an exception.

Alignment-check faults are generated only in user mode (privilege level 3). Memory references which default to privilege level 0, such as segment descriptor loads, do not generate alignment-check faults, even when caused by a memory reference made in user mode.

Storing a 48-bit pseudo-descriptor (the memory image of the contents of a descriptor table base register) in user mode can generate an alignment-check fault. Although user-mode programs do not normally store pseudo-descriptors, the fault can be avoided by aligning the pseudo-descriptor to an odd word address (i.e., an address which is 2 MOD 4).

FSAVE and FRSTOR instructions generate unaligned references which can cause alignment-check faults. These instructions are rarely needed by application programs.

14.9.17. Interrupt 18—Machine Check

Machine check is a model-specific exception, available only on the Pentium microprocessor. It may not be continued or may not be continued with a compatible implementation on future processor generations. Refer to the *Pentium™ Processor Data Book* for an explanation of its implementation and use.

14.10. EXCEPTION SUMMARY

Table 14-7 summarizes the exceptions recognized by the Pentium processor.

Table 14-7. Exception Summary

Description	Vector Number	Return Address Points to Faulting Instruction?	Exception Type	Source of the Exception
Division by Zero	0	Yes	FAULT	DIV and IDIV instructions
Debug Exceptions	1	*1	*1	Any code or data reference
Breakpoint	3	No	TRAP	INT 3 instruction
Overflow	4	No	TRAP	INTO instruction
Bounds Check	5	Yes	FAULT	BOUND instruction
Invalid Opcode	6	Yes	FAULT	Reserved Opcodes
Device Not Available	7	Yes	FAULT	ESC and WAIT instructions
Double Fault	8	Yes	ABORT	Any instruction
Invalid TSS	10	Yes[2]	FAULT	JMP, CALL, IRET instructions, interrupts, and exceptions
Segment Not Present	11	Yes[2]	FAULT	Any instruction which changes segments
Stack Fault	12	Yes	FAULT	Stack operations
General Protection	13	Yes	FAULT/TRAP[3]	Any code or data reference
Page Fault	14	Yes	FAULT	Any code or data reference
Floating-Point Error	16	Yes	FAULT[4]	ESC and WAIT instructions
Alignment Check	17	Yes	FAULT	Any data reference
Machine Check	18	–	–	*(model dependent)*
Software Interrupt	0 to 255	No	TRAP	INT n instructions

NOTES:

1. Debug exceptions are either traps or faults. The exception handler can distinguish between traps and faults by examining the contents of the DR6 register.

2. Restartability is conditional during task switches as documented in section 7.5.

3. All general-protection faults are restartable. If the fault occurs while attempting to call the handler, the interrupted program is restartable, but the interrupt may be lost.

4. Floating-point errors are not reported until the first ESC or WAIT instruction following the ESC instruction which generated the error.

14.11. ERROR CODE SUMMARY

Table 14-8 summarizes the error information that is available with each exception.

Table 14-8. Error Code Summary

Description	Vector Number	Is an Error Code Generated?
Divide Error	0	No
Debug Exceptions	1	No
Breakpoint	3	No
Overflow	4	No
Bounds Check	5	No
Invalid Opcode	6	No
Device Not Available	7	No
Double Fault	8	Yes (always zero)
Invalid TSS	10	Yes
Segment Not Present	11	Yes
Stack Fault	12	Yes
General Protection	13	Yes
Page Fault	14	Yes (special format)
Floating-Point Error	16	No
Alignment Check	17	Yes (always zero)
Machine Check	18	*(model dependent)*
Software Interrupt	0–255	No

intel®

15

Input/Output

CHAPTER 15
INPUT/OUTPUT

Input/output is accomplished through I/O ports, which are registers connected to peripheral devices. An I/O port can be an input port, an output port, or a bidirectional port. Some I/O ports are used for carrying data, such as the transmit and receive registers of a serial interface. Other I/O ports are used to control peripheral devices, such as the control registers of a disk controller.

The input/output architecture is the programmer's model of how these ports are accessed. The discussion of this model includes:

- Methods of addressing I/O ports.
- Instructions which perform I/O operations.
- The I/O protection mechanism.

15.1. I/O ADDRESSING

The processor allows I/O ports to be addressed in either of two ways:

- Through a separate I/O address space accessed using I/O instructions.
- Through memory-mapped I/O, where I/O ports appear in the address space of physical memory.

The use of a separate I/O address space is supported by special instructions and a hardware protection mechanism. When memory-mapped I/O is used, the general-purpose instruction set can be used to access I/O ports, and protection is provided using segmentation or paging. Some system designers may prefer to use the I/O facilities built into the processor, while others may prefer the simplicity of a single physical address space.

Hardware designers use these ways of mapping I/O ports into the address space when they design the address decoding circuits of a system. I/O ports can be mapped so that they appear in the I/O address space or the address space of physical memory (or both).

15.1.1. I/O Address Space

The processor provides a separate I/O address space, distinct from the address space for physical memory, where I/O ports can be placed. The I/O address space consists of 2^{16} (64K) individually addressable 8-bit ports; any two consecutive 8-bit ports can be treated as a 16-bit port, and any four consecutive ports can be a 32-bit port. Extra bus cycles are required if a port crosses the boundary between two doublewords in physical memory.

The M/IO# pin of the processor indicates when a bus cycle to the I/O address space occurs. When a separate I/O address space is used, it is the responsibility of the hardware designer to make use of this signal to select I/O ports rather than memory. In fact, the use of the separate

I/O address space simplifies the hardware design because these ports can be selected by a single signal; unlike other processors, it is not necessary to decode a number of upper address lines in order to set up a separate I/O address space.

A program can specify the address of a port in two ways. With an immediate byte constant, the program can specify:

- 256 8-bit ports numbered 0 through 255.
- 128 16-bit ports numbered 0, 2, 4, . . . , 252, 254.
- 64 32-bit ports numbered 0, 4, 8, . . . , 248, 252.

Using a value in the DX register, the program can specify:

- 8-bit ports numbered 0 through 65535.
- 16-bit ports numbered 0, 2, 4, . . . , 65532, 65534.
- 32-bit ports numbered 0, 4, 8, . . . , 65528, 65532.

The processor can transfer 8, 16, or 32 bits to a device in the I/O space. Like words in memory, 16-bit ports should be aligned to even addresses so that all 16 bits can be transferred in a single bus cycle. Like doublewords in memory, 32-bit ports should be aligned to addresses which are multiples of four. The processor supports data transfers to unaligned ports, but there is a performance penalty because an extra bus cycle must be used.

The IN and OUT instructions move data between a register and a port in the I/O address space. The instructions INS and OUTS move strings of data between the memory address space and ports in the I/O address space.

I/O port addresses 0F8H through 0FFH are reserved for use by Intel Corporation. Do not assign I/O ports to these addresses.

The exact order of bus cycles used to access ports which require more than one bus cycle is undefined and is not guaranteed to remain the same in future Intel products. If software needs to produce a particular order of bus cycles, this order must be specified explicitly. For example, to load a word-length port at 4H followed by loading a word port at 2H, two word-length instructions must be used, rather than a single doubleword instruction at 2H.

Note that, although the processor automatically masks parity errors for certain types of bus cycles, such as interrupt acknowledge cycles, it does not mask parity for bus cycles to the I/O address space. Programmers may need to be aware of this behavior as a possible source of parity errors.

15.1.2. Memory-Mapped I/O

I/O devices may be placed in the address space for physical memory. This is called memory-mapped I/O. As long as the devices respond like memory components, they can be used with memory-mapped I/O.

Memory-mapped I/O provides additional programming flexibility. Any instruction which references memory may be used to access an I/O port located in the memory space. For example, the MOV instruction can transfer data between any register and a port. The AND, OR, and TEST instructions may be used to manipulate bits in the control and status registers of peripheral devices (see Figure 15-1). Memory-mapped I/O can use the full instruction set and the full complement of addressing modes to address I/O ports.

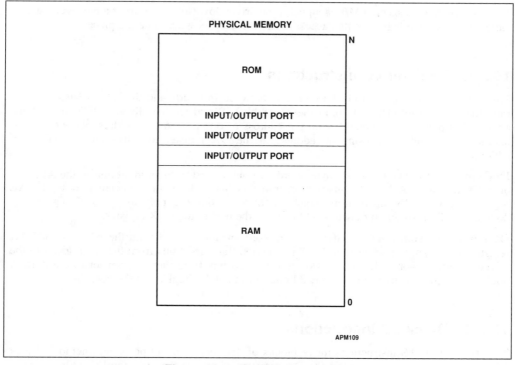

Figure 15-1. Memory-Mapped I/O

Using an I/O instruction for an I/O write can also be advantageous because it guarantees that the write will be completed before the next instruction begins execution. If I/O writes are used to control system hardware, then this sequence of events is desirable, since it guarantees that the next instruction will be executed in the new system hardware state. Refer to Section 15.4 for more information on serialization of I/O operations.

If caching is enabled in real-address mode, designers should consider if it is advantageous to prevent caching of I/O data, whether by using the PCD bit of page table entries or by using the KEN# signal.

15.2. I/O INSTRUCTIONS

The I/O instructions provide access to the processor's I/O ports for the transfer of data. These instructions have the address of a port in the I/O address space as an operand. There are two kinds of I/O instructions:

1. Those which transfer a single item (byte, word, or doubleword) to or from a register.

2. Those which transfer strings of items (strings of bytes, words, or doublewords) located in memory. These are known as "string I/O instructions" or "block I/O instructions."

These instructions cause the M/IO# signal to be driven low (logic 0) during a bus cycle, which indicates to external hardware that access to the I/O address space is taking place.

15.2.1. Register I/O Instructions

The I/O instructions IN and OUT move data between I/O ports and the EAX register (32-bit I/O), the AX register (16-bit I/O), or the AL (8-bit I/O) register. The IN and OUT instructions address I/O ports either directly, with the address of one of 256 port addresses coded in the instruction, or indirectly using an address in the DX register to select one of 64K port addresses.

IN (Input from Port) transfers a byte, word, or doubleword from an input port to the AL, AX, or EAX registers. A byte IN instruction transfers 8 bits from the selected port to the AL register. A word IN instruction transfers 16 bits from the port to the AX register. A doubleword IN instruction transfers 32 bits from the port to the EAX register.

OUT (Output from Port) transfers a byte, word, or doubleword from the AL, AX, or EAX registers to an output port. A byte OUT instruction transfers 8 bits from the AL register to the selected port. A word OUT instruction transfers 16 bits from the AX register to the port. A doubleword OUT instruction transfers 32 bits from the EAX register to the port.

15.2.2. Block I/O Instructions

The INS and OUTS instructions move blocks of data between I/O ports and memory. Block I/O instructions use an address in the DX register to address a port in the I/O address space. These instructions use the DX register to specify:

*   8-bit ports numbered 0 through 65535.
*   16-bit ports numbered 0, 2, 4, . . . , 65532, 65534.
*   32-bit ports numbered 0, 4, 8, . . . , 65528, 65532.

Block I/O instructions use either the (E)SI or (E)DI register to address memory. For each transfer, the (E)SI or (E)DI register is incremented or decremented, as specified by the DF flag.

The INS and OUTS instructions, when used with repeat prefixes, perform block input or output operations. The repeat prefix REP modifies the INS and OUTS instructions to transfer blocks of data between an I/O port and memory. These block I/O instructions are string instructions (see Chapter 3 for more on string instructions). They simplify programming and increase the speed of data transfer by eliminating the need to use a separate LOOP instruction or an intermediate register to hold the data.

The string I/O instructions operate on byte strings, word strings, or doubleword strings. After each transfer, the memory address in the ESI or EDI registers is incremented or decremented by 1 for byte operands, by 2 for word operands, or by 4 for doubleword operands. The DF flag controls whether the register is incremented (the DF flag is clear) or decremented (the DF flag is set).

INS (Input String from Port) transfers a byte, word, or doubleword string element from an input port to memory. The INSB instruction transfers a byte from the selected port to the memory location addressed by the ES and EDI registers. The INSW instruction transfers a word. The INSD instruction transfers a doubleword. A segment override prefix cannot be used to specify an alternate destination segment. Combined with a REP prefix, an INS instruction makes repeated read cycles to the port, and puts the data into consecutive locations in memory.

OUTS (Output String from Port) transfers a byte, word, or doubleword string element from memory to an output port. The OUTSB instruction transfers a byte from the memory location addressed by the DS and ESI registers to the selected port. The OUTSW instruction transfers a word. The OUTSD instruction transfers a doubleword. A segment override prefix can be used to specify an alternate source segment. Combined with a REP prefix, an OUTS instruction reads consecutive locations in memory, and writes the data to an output port.

15.3. PROTECTED-MODE I/O

When the processor is running in protected mode, I/O operates as in real-address mode, but with additional protection features:

- References to memory-mapped I/O ports, like any other memory reference, are subject to access protection and control by both the segmentation and the paging mechanism. Refer to Chapter 12 for a complete discussion of memory protection.

- The execution of I/O instructions is also subject to two protection mechanisms:

  a. The IOPL field in the EFLAGS register controls access to the I/O instructions.

  b. The I/O permission bit map of a TSS segment controls access to individual ports in the I/O address space.

These protection mechanisms are available only when a separate I/O address space is used.

15.3.1. I/O Privilege Level

In systems where I/O protection is used, access to I/O instructions is controlled by the IOPL field in the EFLAGS register. This permits the operating system to adjust the privilege level needed to perform I/O. In a typical protection ring model, privilege levels 0 and 1 have access to the I/O instructions. This lets the operating system and the device drivers perform I/O, but keeps applications and less privileged device drivers from accessing the I/O address space. Applications access I/O through the operating system.

The following instructions can be executed only if CPL ≤ IOPL:

IN	— Input
INS	— Input String
OUT	— Output
OUTS	— Output String
CLI	— Clear Interrupt-Enable Flag
STI	— Set Interrupt-Enable Flag

These instructions are called "sensitive" instructions, because they are sensitive to the IOPL field. In virtual-8086 mode, the I/O permission bit map further limits access to I/O ports (see Chapter 23).

To use sensitive instructions, a procedure must run at a privilege level at least as privileged as that specified by the IOPL field. Any attempt by a less privileged procedure to use a sensitive instruction results in a general-protection exception. Because each task has its own copy of the EFLAGS register, each task can have a different IOPL.

A task can change IOPL only with the POPF and IRET instructions; however, such changes are privileged. No procedure may change its IOPL unless it is running at privilege level 0. An attempt by a less privileged procedure to change the IOPL does not result in an exception; the IOPL simply remains unchanged.

The POPF instruction also may be used to change the state of the IF flag (as can the CLI and STI instructions); however, changes to the IF flag using the POPF instruction are IOPL-sensitive. A procedure may change the setting of the IF flag with a POPF instruction only if it runs with a CPL at least as privileged as the IOPL. An attempt by a less privileged procedure to change the IF flag does not result in an exception; the IF flag simply remains unchanged.

15.3.2. I/O Permission Bit Map

The processor can generate exceptions for references to specific I/O addresses. These addresses are specified in the I/O permission bit map in the TSS (see Figure 15-2). The size of the map and its location in the TSS are variable. The processor finds the I/O permission bit map with the I/O map base address in the TSS. The base address is a 16-bit offset into the TSS. This is an offset to the beginning of the bit map. The limit of the TSS is the limit on the size of the I/O permission bit map.

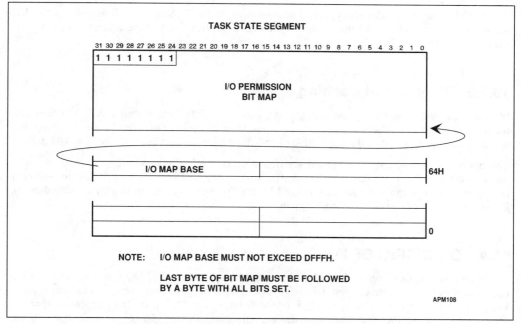

Figure 15-2. I/O Permission Bit Map

Because each task has its own TSS, each task has its own I/O permission bit map. Access to individual I/O ports can be granted to individual tasks.

If CPL ≤ IOPL in protected mode, then the processor allows I/O operations to proceed. If CPL > IOPL, or if the processor is operating in virtual 8086 mode, then the processor checks the I/O permission map. Each bit in the map corresponds to an I/O port byte address; for example, the control bit for address 41 (decimal) in the I/O address space is found at bit position 1 of the sixth byte in the bit map. The processor tests all the bits corresponding to the I/O port being addressed; for example, a doubleword operation tests four bits corresponding to four adjacent byte addresses. If any tested bit is set, a general-protection exception is generated. If all tested bits are clear, the I/O operation proceeds.

Because I/O port addresses are not necessarily aligned to word and doubleword boundaries, it is possible that the processor may need to access two bytes in the bit map when I/O permission is checked. For maximum speed, the processor has been designed to read two bytes for every access to an I/O port. To prevent exceptions from being generated when the ports with the highest addresses are accessed, an extra byte needs to come after the table. This byte must have all of its bits set, and it must be within the segment limit.

It is not necessary for the I/O permission bit map to represent all the I/O addresses. I/O addresses not spanned by the map are treated as if they had set bits in the map. For example, if the TSS segment limit is 10 bytes past the bit map base address, the map has 11 bytes and the first 80 I/O ports are mapped. Higher addresses in the I/O address space generate exceptions.

If the I/O bit map base address is greater than or equal to the TSS segment limit, there is no I/O permission map, and all I/O instructions generate exceptions. The base address must be less than or equal to 0DFFFH.

15.3.3. Paging and Caching

In protected mode, the paging mechanism can also help control cacheability of I/O buffers and memory-mapped I/O addresses. If caching is enabled, either external hardware or the paging mechanism (the PCD bit in the page table entry) must be used to prevent caching of I/O data.

The operating system can also use the segmentation or paging mechanism to manage the data space used by the operands of I/O instructions. The AVL (available) fields in segment descriptors or page table entries can be used by the operating system to mark pages containing I/O buffers as unrelocatable and unswappable.

15.4. ORDERING OF I/O

When controlling I/O devices it is often important that memory and I/O operations be carried out in precisely the order programmed. For example, a program may write a command to an I/O port, then read the status of the I/O device from another I/O port. It is important that the status returned be the status of the device *after* it receives the command, not *before*. Programmers should take care, because there are situations in which the programmed order is not preserved by the processor.

To optimize performance, the Pentium CPU allows memory reads to be reordered ahead of buffered writes in most situations. The Intel486 CPU allows memory reads to be reordered ahead of buffered writes in certain precisely-defined circumstances. (See the *Intel486™ Microprocessor Hardware Reference Manual* for further details about the operation of the write buffer.) Using memory-mapped I/O, therefore, creates the possibility that an I/O read might be performed before the memory write of a previous instruction. To eliminate this possibility on the Intel486 CPU, use an I/O instruction for the read. To eliminate this possibility on the Pentium CPU, insert one of the serializing instructions, such as CPUID, between operations.

When I/O instructions are used instead of memory-mapped I/O, the situation is different in two respects:

1. Some I/O writes are never buffered. The only I/O writes that the Intel486 CPU buffers are those from the OUTS instruction. The Pentium CPU does not buffer any I/O writes. Therefore, strict ordering of I/O operations is enforced by the processor.

2. The processor synchronizes I/O instruction execution with external bus activity. Refer to Table 15-1.

Table 15-1. I/O Serialization

Current Instruction	Processor Holds Execution of ...		Awaiting for Completion of ...	
	Current Instruction?	Next Instruction?	Pending Stores?	Current Store?
IN	YES		YES	
INS	YES		YES	
REP INS	YES		YES	
OUT		YES	YES	YES
OUTS		YES	YES	YES
REP OUTS		YES	YES	YES

Refer to Chapter 13 for more general information on memory access ordering and to Chapter 18 for information about other serializing instructions.

intel®

16

Initialization and Mode Switching

CHAPTER 16
INITIALIZATION AND MODE SWITCHING

The processor is initialized to a known state following hardware reset in order for software execution to begin. When initialized, the processor provides model and stepping information to determine what features are available to software. For feature determination by applications at run-time, a code example and discussion is provided in Chapter 5. This chapter provides processor initialization state information and configuration requirements for both real-address and protected mode. This chapter also discusses the process of switching between real-address and protected modes which is normally part of the initialization process. A program example for switching to protected mode is provided.

The floating-point units (FPU's) of the Intel x86 architectures (except the Intel 287 NPX) operate the same regardless of whether the processor is operating in real-address mode, in protected mode, or in virtual 8086 mode.

To the numerics programmer, the operating mode affects only the manner in which the FPU instruction and data pointers are represented in memory following an FSAVE or FSTENV instruction. Each of these instructions produces one of four formats depending on both the operating mode and on the operand-size attribute in effect for the instruction. The differences are detailed in the discussion of the FSAVE and FSTENV instructions in Chapter 25.

16.1. PROCESSOR INITIALIZATION

The processor has an input, called the RESET pin, which invokes reset initialization. After RESET is asserted, some registers of the processor are set to known states. These known states, such as the contents of the EIP register, are sufficient to allow software to begin execution. Software then can build the data structures in memory, such as the GDT and IDT tables, which are used by system and application software. The internal caches, translation lookaside buffers (TLB's) and the branch target buffers (BTB's) are invalidated when RESET is asserted.

Hardware asserts the RESET signal at power-up. Hardware may assert this signal at other times. For example, a button may be provided for manually invoking reset initialization. Reset also may be the response of hardware to receiving a halt or shutdown indication.

The Pentium processor also has an INIT input, which is similar to RESET except it does not disturb the internal caches, model specific registers, or floating point state. INIT provides a method for switching from protected to real-address mode while maintaining the contents of the internal caches. The TLB's and BTB are invalidated by INIT being asserted.

16.1.1. Processor State After Reset

A self test may be requested at power-up. It is the responsibility of the hardware designer to provide the request for self test, if desired. If the self test is selected, it takes about 2^{19} clock periods to complete. (This clock count is model-specific and Intel reserves the right to change the exact number of periods without notification.)

The EAX register is clear (zero) if the processor passed the test. A non-zero value in the EAX register after self test indicates the processor is faulty. If the self test is not requested, the contents of the EAX register after reset initialization is zero.

The EDX register holds a component identifier and revision number after reset initialization, as shown in Figure 16-1. The DH register contains the value 3, 4, or 5 to indicate an Intel386 CPU, Intel486 CPU, or Pentium CPU, respectively. Different values may be returned for the various proliferations of these families, for example the Intel386 SX CPU contains 23H. Binary object code can be made compatible with other Intel processors by using this number to select the correct initialization software. The DL register contains a unique identifier of the revision level. The upper word of EDX is reserved following reset.

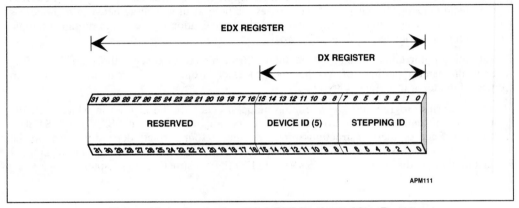

Figure 16-1. Contents of the EDX Register After Reset

The state of the CR0 register for the Pentium processor following power-up is shown in Figure 16-2 (60000010H). This state puts the processor into real-address mode with paging disabled. The state of the flags and other registers following power-up is shown in Table 16-1.

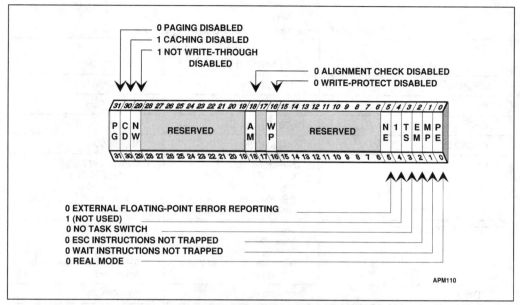

Figure 16-2. Contents of CR0 Register After Reset

Table 16-1. Processor State Following Reset

Register	RESET Without BIST	INIT
EFLAGS[1]	00000002H	00000002H
EIP	0000FFF0H	0000FFF0H
CR0	60000010H	Note 2
CR2/CR3/CR4	00000000H	00000000H
CS	selector=0F000H base=0FFFF0000H limit=0FFFFH AR=Present, Read/Write,Accessed	selector=0F000H base=0FFFF000H limit=0FFFFH AR=Present, Read/Write, Accessed
SS, DS, ES, FS, GS	selector=0000 base=0000H limit=0FFFFH AR=Present, Read/Write, Accessed	selector=0000 base=0000H limit=0FFFFH AR=Present, Read/Write, Accessed
EDX	000005xxH	000005xxH
EAX	0[3]	0
EBX, ECX, ESI, EDI, EBP, ESP	00000000H	00000000H
LDTR	selector=0000H base=00000000H limit=0FFFFH AR=Present,Read/Write	selector=0000H base=00000000H limit=0FFFFH AR=Present,Read/Write
GDTR,IDTR	base=00000000H limit=0FFFFH AR=Present,Read/Write	base=00000000H limit=0FFFFH AR=Present,Read/Write
DR0, DR1, DR2, DR3	00000000H	00000000H
DR6	FFFF0FF0H	FFFF0FF0H
DR7	00000400H	00000400H
Time Stamp Counter	0	Unchanged
Control and Event Select	0	Unchanged
TR12	0	Unchanged
All Other Model Specific Registers (MSR's)	Undefined	Unchanged
Data and Code Cache, TLB's	Invalid	Invalid

NOTES:

1. The high ten bits of the EFLAGS register are undefined following power-up. Undefined bits are reserved. Software should not depend on the states of any of these bits.
2. CD and NW are unchanged, bit 4 is set to 1, all other bits are cleared.
3. If Built-In Self Test is invoked, EAX is 0 only if all tests passed.

16.1.2. First Instruction Executed

To generate an address, the base part of a segment register is added to the effective address to form the linear address. This is true for all modes of operation, although the base address is calculated differently in protected and real-address modes. To fetch an instruction, the base portion of the CS register is added to EIP to form a linear address (see Chapter 9 and Chapter 11 for details on calculating addresses).

In real-address mode, when the value of the segment register selector is changed, the base portion will automatically be changed to this value multiplied by 16. However, immediately after reset, the base portion of the CS register behaves differently: It is not 16 times the selector value. Instead, the CS selector is 0F000H and the CS base is 0FFFF0000H. The first time the CS selector value is changed after reset, it will follow the above rule (base = selector * 16). As a result, after reset, the first instruction that is being fetched and executed is at physical address: CS.base + EIP = 0FFFFFFF0H. This is the address to locate the EPROM with the initialization code. This address is located 16 bytes below the uppermost address of the physical memory of the Pentium processor.

Ensure that no far jump or far call is executed until the initialization is completed. If the first far jump/call is made during real mode, a new value enters the CS selector (16 bits) and sets the value of the CS base to 20 bits only, i.e. the destination address would be in the address space 0 to 1M. You might want to be sure that you have valid memory and code in this area.

The base address for the data segments are set to the bottom of the physical address space (address 0), where RAM is expected to be.

16.2. FPU INITIALIZATION

During system initialization, systems software can determine the absence or presence of a numeric processor extension. Systems software must then initialize the FPU or NPX and set flags in CR0 to reflect the state of the numeric environment. These activities can be quickly and easily performed as part of the overall system initialization. See Chapter 5 for determining the processor type and feature recognition.

A hardware reset leaves the Pentium FPU in a state that is different from the state that is obtained by executing the FNINIT instruction as shown in Table 16-2. See Chapter 23 for a complete list of initialization differences between these processors following RESET.

The state of the FPU registers following RESET or INIT is shown in Table 16-2. Following RESET, the Pentium FPU contains 0 in ST0-ST7 stack registers with the tags set to zero (01). However, the tags are only visible to the programmer by using the FSAVE/FSTENV instructions. When these instructions are used, they interpret the stack locations as zero, returning tag values of 01. The Pentium processor, in addition, has an INIT pin which, when asserted, causes the processor to reset without altering the FPU state. An FNINIT instruction should be executed after reset.

Initializing the FPU simply means placing the FPU in a known state unaffected by any activity performed earlier. A single FNINIT instruction performs this initialization. All the error masks are set, all registers are tagged empty, TOP is set to zero, and default rounding and precision controls are set. Table 16-2 shows the state of the FPU following FINIT or FNINIT.

Table 16-2. FPU State Following FINIT or FNINIT

Field	Value	Interpretation
Control Word	037FH	
(Infinity Control)*	0	Affine
Rounding Control	00	Round to nearest
Precision Control	00	Extended
Exception Masks	111111	Exceptions masked
Status Word	0000H	
(Busy)	0	—
Condition Code	0000	—
Stack Top	000	Register 0 is stack top
Exception Summary	0	No exceptions
Stack Flag	0	—
Exception Flags	000000	No exceptions
Tag Word	FFFFH	
Tags	11	Empty
Registers	Not changed	Not changed
Exception Pointers		
Instruction Code	0	Cleared
Instruction Address	0	Cleared
Operand Address	0	Cleared

NOTES:

*The Pentium™, Intel486™, and Intel386™ processors do not have infinity control. This value is listed to emphasize that programs written for the Intel287 math coprocessor may not behave the same on the 32-bit processors if they depend on this bit.

16.2.1. Configuring the Numerics Environment

System software must load the appropriate values into the MP, EM, and NE bits of the control register 0 (CR0) to control emulation of floating point instructions by software, synchronization between the FPU and CPU context, and software or external interrupt handling of floating-point exceptions. These bits are clear on hardware reset of the Pentium processor.

The MP (Monitor coProcessor) bit determines whether WAIT instructions trap when the context of the FPU is different from that of the currently executing task. If MP = 1 and TS = 1, then a WAIT instruction will cause a Device Not Available fault (interrupt vector 7). The MP bit is used on the Intel 286, Intel386 DX, Intel386 SX and Intel486 SX microprocessors to support the use of a WAIT instruction to wait on a device other than a numeric coprocessor. The device reports its status through the BUSY# pin. Generally, the MP bit should be set for processors with integrated FPU and clear in processors without an integrated FPU or numeric processor extension. However, an operating system can choose to save the floating-point context at every context switch, in which case there would be no need to set the MP bit.

The EM (EMulate coprocessor) bit determines whether ESC instructions are executed by the FPU (EM = 0) or trap via interrupt vector 7 to be handled by software (EM = 1). The EM bit is used on CPU/NPX systems so that numeric applications can be run in the absence of an NPX with a software emulator. For normal operation of Intel processors with an integrated FPU, the EM bit should be cleared to 0. The EM bit must be set in the Intel386 DX, Intel386 SX, or Intel486 SX CPUs if there is no NPX present. If the EM bit is set and no coprocessor or emulator is present, the system will hang.

The interpretation of different combinations of the EM and MP bits are shown in Table 16-3. Recommendations for the different processors is shown in Table 16-4.

Table 16-3. EM and MP Bits Interpretations

EM	MP	Interpretation
0	0	Numeric instructions are passed to FPU; WAIT ignores TS
0	1	Numeric instructions are passed to FPU; WAIT tests TS
1	0	Numeric instructions trap to emulator; WAIT ignores TS
1	1	Numeric instructions trap to emulator, WAIT tests TS

Table 16-4. Recommended Values by Processor

EM	MP	Interpretation
1	0	Intel386™ DX, Intel386 SX, and Intel486™ SX CPU's
0	1	Intel386 DX and Intel387™ DX, Intel386 SX and Intel387 SX , Intel487™ SX, Intel486 DX, Pentium™ CPU's

The action taken for floating-point and wait instructions based on the value of these bits is shown in Table 16-5.

Table 16-5. Action Taken for Different Combinations of EM, MP, and TS

CR0 Bits			Instruction Type	
EM	TS	MP	Floating Point	Wait
0	0	0	Execute	Execute
0	0	1	Execute	Execute
0	1	0	Exception 7	Execute
0	1	1	Exception 7	Exception 7
1	0	0	Exception 7	Execute
1	0	1	Exception 7	Execute
1	1	0	Exception 7	Execute
1	1	1	Exception 7	Exception 7

The NE (Numeric Exception) bit determines whether unmasked floating-point exceptions are handled through interrupt vector 16 (NE = 1) or through external interrupt (NE = 0). In systems using an external interrupt controller to invoke numeric exception handlers, the NE bit should be cleared to 0. This option is used for compatibility with the error reporting scheme used in DOS based systems. Other systems can make use of the automatic error reporting through interrupt 16, and should set the NE bit to 1. Numeric exception handling is discussed in a later section.

16.2.2. FPU Software Emulation

Setting the EM bit to 1 causes the processor to trap via interrupt vector 7 (Device Not Available) to a software exception handler whenever it encounters an ESC instruction. Setting this bit has two uses:

1. The EM bit is used to run numeric applications on an Intel processor without an integrated FPU or NPX using a software Intel387 emulator.

2. Numeric applications designed to be run with a non-standard Intel387 emulator may not run successfully without the emulator. Setting the EM bit to 1 makes it possible to run such applications, or programs which use non-standard floating-point arithmetic.

If a math coprocessor is not present in the system, floating point instructions can be emulated. The system is set up for software emulation as Table 16-6:

Table 16-6. Software Emulation Settings

CR0 Bit	Value
EM	1
MP	0
NE	1

The EM bit must be set in order for software emulation to function properly. Setting the EM bit to 1 will cause the processor to trap via interrupt vector 7 (Device Not Available) to a software exception handler whenever it encounters an ESC instruction. If the EM bit is set and no coprocessor or emulator is present, the system will hang.

The MP bit can be used during a task switch in protected-mode in conjunction with the TS bit to determine if WAIT instructions should trap when the context of the FPU is different from that of the currently executing task. When no FPU is present, this information may be irrelevent and therefore the bit should be set to 0.

Regardless of the value of the NE bit, the Intel486 SX processor generates an interrupt vector 7 (Device Not Available) upon encountering any floating point instruction. It is recommended that NE be set to 1 for normal operation. If a Floating Point Unit is present, this bit follows the description described in Table 16-3.

16.3. CACHE ENABLING

The cache is enabled by clearing the CD and NW bits in the CR0 register (they are set upon hardware reset as indicated above). This enables caching (write-through for the Intel486 processor and write-back for the Pentium processor) and cache invalidation cycles. Because all cache lines are invalid following reset initialization, it is unnecessary to invalidate the cache before enabling caching. See Chapter 18 for complete details of cache handling, including implementation of a write-through cache on the Pentium processor using the PWT bit in the page table entry.

Under circumstances where cache lines may be marked as valid, the cache may need to be flushed or invalidated before the cache is enabled. This may occur as a result of using the test registers to run test patterns through the cache memory as part of confidence testing during software initialization. See the *Pentium™ Processor Data Book* for model-specific details on cache testing.

16.4. SOFTWARE INITIALIZATION IN REAL-ADDRESS MODE

Note that the processor has several processing modes. It begins execution in a mode compatible with an 8086 processor, called real-address mode. After reset initialization, software must set up data structures needed for the processor to perform basic system functions, such as handling interrupts. If the processor remains in real-address mode, software must set up data structures in the form used by the 8086 processor. If the processor is going to operate in protected mode, software must set up data structures in the form used by protected mode and then switch modes (see Section 16.6.).

16.4.1. System Tables

In real-address mode, no descriptor tables are used. The interrupt descriptor table (IDT), which starts at address 0 (unless the IDTR is changed), needs to be loaded with pointers to exception and interrupt handlers before interrupts can be enabled.

16.4.2. NMI Interrupt

The NMI interrupt is always enabled (except on nested NMI's). If the interrupt vector table and the NMI interrupt handler need to be loaded into RAM, there will be a period of time following reset initialization when an NMI interrupt cannot be handled. Hardware must provide a mechanism to prevent an NMI interrupt from being generated while software is unable to handle it.   For example, the IDT and NMI interrupt handler can be provided in ROM. This allows an NMI interrupt to be handled immediately after reset initialization. Most systems enable/disable NMI by passing the NMI signal through an AND gate controlled by a bit in an I/O port. Hardware can clear the bit when the processor is reset, and software can set the bit when it is ready to handle NMI interrupts. System software designers should be aware of the mechanism used by hardware to protect software from NMI interrupts following reset.

16.5. SOFTWARE INITIALIZATION IN PROTECTED MODE

The data structures needed in protected mode are determined by the memory management features which are used. The processor supports segmentation models which range from a single, uniform address space (flat model) to a highly structured model with several independent, protected address spaces for each task (multisegmented model). Paging can be enabled for allowing access to large data structures which are partly in memory and partly on disk. Both of these forms of address translation require data structures which are set up by the operating system and used by the memory management hardware.

16.5.1. System Tables

A flat model without paging minimally requires a GDT with one code and one data segment descriptor. A null descriptor in the first GDT entry is also required. A flat model with paging may provide code and data descriptors for supervisor mode and another set of code and data descriptors for user mode. In addition, it requires a page directory and at least one second-level page table. (Note: the second-level page table can be eliminated if the page directory contains a directory entry pointing to itself, in which case the page directory and page table reside in the same page). The stack can be placed in a normal read/write data segment, so no descriptor for the stack is required. Before the GDT can be used, the base address and limit for the GDT must be loaded into the GDTR register using an LGDT instruction.

A multi-segmented model may require additional segments for the operating system, as well as segments and LDTs for each application program. LDTs require segment descriptors in the GDT. Some operating systems allocate new segments and LDTs as they are needed. This provides maximum flexibility for handling a dynamic programming environment, such as an engineering workstation. However, many operating systems use a single LDT for all processes, allocating GDT entries in advance. An embedded system, such as a process controller, might pre-allocate a fixed number of segments and LDTs for a fixed number of application programs. This would be a simple and efficient way to structure the software environment of a system which requires real-time performance.

16.5.2. Interrupts

If hardware allows interrupts to be generated, the IDT and a gate for the interrupt handler need to be created. Before the IDT can be used, the base address and limit for the IDT must be loaded into the IDTR register using an LIDT instruction. See Chapter 14 for detailed information on this topic.

16.5.3. Paging

Unlike segmentation, paging is controlled by a mode bit. If the PG bit in the CR0 register is clear (its state following reset initialization), the paging mechanism is completely absent from the processor architecture seen by programmers.

If the PG bit is set, paging is enabled. The bit may be set using a MOV CR0 instruction. Before setting the PG bit, the following conditions must be true:

- Software has created at least two page tables, the page directory and at least one second-level page table if 4K pages are used. For information on 4M pages, see Appendix H.

- The PDBR register (same as the CR3 register) is loaded with the physical base address of the page directory.

- The processor is in protected mode (paging is not available in real-address mode). If all other restrictions are met, the PG and PE bits can be set at the same time.

The following guidelines for setting the PG bit (as with the PE bit) should be adhered to maintain both upwards and downwards compatibility:

1. The instruction setting the PG bit should be followed immediately with a JMP instruction. A JMP instruction immediately after the MOV CR0 instruction changes the flow of execution, so it has the effect of emptying the Intel386 and Intel486 processor of instructions which have been fetched or decoded. The Pentium processor, however, uses a branch target buffer (BTB) for branch prediction, eliminating the need for branch instructions to flush the prefetch queue. For more information on the BTB, see Appendix H.

2. The code from the instruction which sets the PG bit through the JMP instruction must come from a page which is identity mapped (i.e., the linear address before the jump is the same as the physical address after paging is enabled).

The 32-bit Intel x86 architectures have different requirements for enabling paging and switching to protected mode. The Intel386 processor requires following steps 1 *or* 2 above. The Intel486 processor requires following both steps 1 *and* 2 above. The Pentium processor requires only step 2 but for upwards and downwards code compatibility with the Intel386 and

Intel486 processors, it is recommended both steps 1 and 2 be taken.

See Chapter 11 for complete information on the paging mechanism.

16.5.4. Tasks

If the multitasking mechanism is not used and changes to more privileged segments are not allowed, it is unnecessary to initialize the TR register.

If the multitasking mechanism is used or changes to more privileged segments are allowed (values for more privileged SS and ESP are obtained from the TSS), a TSS and a TSS descriptor for the initialization software must be created. TSS descriptors must not be marked as busy when they are created; TSS descriptors should be marked as busy by the CPU only as a side-effect of performing a task switch. As with descriptors for LDTs, TSS descriptors reside in the GDT. The LTR instruction is used to load a selector for the TSS descriptor of the initialization software into the TR register. This instruction marks the TSS descriptor as busy, but does not perform a task switch. The selector must be loaded before the software performs the first task switch, because a task switch copies the current task state into the TSS. After the LTR instruction has been used, further operations on the TR register are performed by task switching. As with segments and LDTs, TSSs and TSS descriptors can be either pre-allocated or allocated as needed.

If changes to more privileged segments are allowed, a TSS and TSS descriptor need to be created. The processor uses the TSS to obtain the values for the more privileged stack segment selector and stack pointer values when transferring control to more privileged segments.

16.5.5. TLB, BTB and Cache Testing

As part of the process of switching into protected mode, system programmers may wish to perform TLB, BTB, and cache testing. For more information on testing, see Appendix H.

16.6. MODE SWITCHING

In order to take full advantage of the 32-bit address space and instruction set, the processor must switch from its native real-address mode to protected mode. A system may also find it necessary to switch back into real-address mode for system operations. This section identifies the steps necessary for software to switch the processor from real-address mode to protected mode and from protected mode back into real-address mode.

16.6.1. Switching to Protected Mode

Before switching to protected mode, a minimum set of system data structures must be created, and the GDT, IDT, and TR registers must be initialized, as discussed in the previous section. Once these tables are created, system software can perform the steps to switch into protected mode.

Protected mode is entered by setting the PE bit in the CR0 register. The MOV CR0 instruction may be used to set this bit. The same two guidelines for setting the PG bit to enable paging in Section 16.5.3. apply for setting the PE bit to enable protected mode.

After entering protected mode, the segment registers continue to hold the contents they had in real address mode. Software should reload all the segment registers. Execution in protected mode begins with a CPL of 0.

16.6.2. Switching Back to Real-Address Mode

The processor re-enters real-address mode if software clears the PE bit in the CR0 register with a MOV CR0 instruction. A procedure which re-enters real-address mode should proceed as follows:

1. If paging is enabled, perform the following sequence:
    — Transfer control to linear addresses which have an identity mapping (i.e., linear addresses equal physical addresses). Ensure the GDT and IDT are identity mapped.
    — Clear the PG bit in the CR0 register.
    — Move zero into the CR3 register to flush the TLB.

2. Transfer control to a segment which has a limit of 64K (0FFFFH). This loads the CS register with the segment limit it needs to have in real mode. Ensure the GDT and IDT are in real-address memory (0-1Meg).

3. Load segment registers SS, DS, ES, FS, and GS with a selector for a descriptor containing the following values, which are appropriate for real mode:
    — Limit = 64K   (0FFFFH)
    — Byte granular   (G =0)
    — Expand up   (E = 0)
    — Writable   (W = 1)
    — Present   (P =1)
    — Base = any value

    Note that if the segment registers are not reloaded, execution continues using the descriptors loaded during protected mode.

4. Disable interrupts. A CLI instruction disables INTR interrupts. NMI interrupts can be disabled with external circuitry.

5. Clear the PE bit in the CR0 register.

6. Jump to the real mode program using a far JMP instruction. This flushes the instruction queue (of the Intel386 and Intel486 processors) and puts appropriate values in the access rights of the CS register. This step is not required on the Pentium processor, however, for downwards compatibility, a far JMP should be included as part of the switching back to real-address mode process.

7. Use the LIDT instruction to load the base and limit of the real-mode interrupt vector table.

8. Enable interrupts.

9. Load the segment registers as needed by the real-mode code.

16.7. INITIALIZATION AND MODE SWITCHING EXAMPLE

This section provides an initialization and mode switching example that can be incorporated into your application. Also provided are some assumptions about the Intel development tools that are used which include the ASM386/486 assembler and BLD386 builder.

16.7.1. Goal of this Example

The goal of this example is to move the CPU into protected mode right after reset using initialization code that resides in EPROM/Flash and run a simple application.

16.7.2. Memory Layout Following Reset

Based on the discussion in Section 16.1. and the values shown in Table 16-1, Figure 16-3 shows the memory layout following processor reset and the starting point of this example.

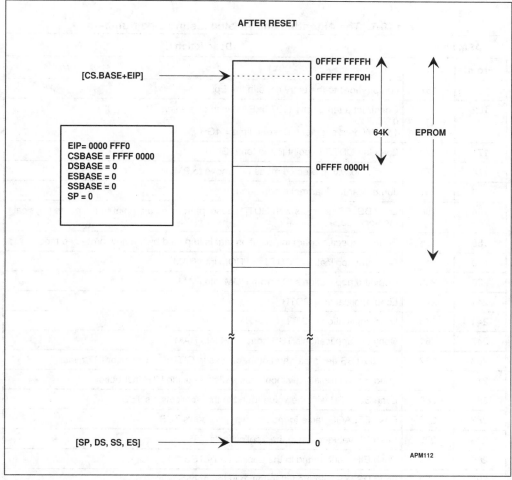

Figure 16-3. Processor State After Reset

16.7.3. The Algorithm

The main steps of this example are shown in Table 16-7 along with the line numbers from the source listing of STARTUP.ASM given in Example 16-1.

Table 16-7. The Algorithm and Related Listing Line Numbers

ASM Lines		Description
From	**To**	
157	157	Jump (short) to the entry code in the Eprom
162	169	Construct a temporary GDT in RAM with one entry: 0 - null 1 - R/W data segment, Base=0 limit = 4GB
171	172	Load the GDTR to point to the temp GDT
174	177	Load CR0 with protected mode bit - move to PM
179	181	Jump near to clear real mode queue
184	186	Load DS, ES registers with GDT[1] descriptor; now both point to the entire physical memory space.
188	195	Perform specific board initialization that is imposed by the new protected mode
196	218	Copy the application's GDT from ROM into RAM
220	238	Copy the application's IDT from ROM into RAM
241	243	Load application's GDTR
244	245	Load application's IDTR
247	261	Copy the application's TSS from ROM into RAM
263	267	Update TSS descriptor and other aliases in GDT (GDT alias or IDT alias)
277	277	Load the TR register (without task switch — using LTR instruction)
282	286	Load SS, ESP with the value found in the application's TSS
287	287	Push EFLAGS value found in the application's TSS
288	288	Push CS value found in the application's TSS
289	289	Push EIP value found in the application's TSS
290	293	Load DS, ES with the value found in the application's TSS
296	296	Perform IRET; pop the above values and enter the application code

NOTES:

If a switch into protected mode is made the CS selector is not changed (by far jump or far call) the original base value is retained (if there is no far jump after reset the base will stay 0FFFF0000H; which is the location space of the EPROM).

Interrupts are disabled after reset and should stay that way, otherwise may impose far jump. NMI is not disabled and must not be active until the initialization is done.

The use of TEMP_GDT allows simple transfer of tables from the Eprom to anywhere in the RAM area. A GDT entry is constructed with its base pointing to address 0 and a limit of 4GB. When the DS and ES registers are loaded with this descriptor, the TEMP_GDT is no longer needed and can be replaced by the application GDT.

The assumption for this code is one TSS no LDTs. If more TSSs exist in the application, they must be copied into RAM. If there are LDTs they may be copied as well.

In some implementations, decoding of the address lines A20 - A31 is not done after reset to simulate the early 8086 chip behaviour. In the process of moving into protected mode it may be desirable to set these decoders to decode the complete address lines.

16.7.4. Tool Usage

In this example, Intel software tools (ASM386 and BLD386) are used.

The following are assumptions that are used when using the Intel ASM386 and BLD386 to generate the initialization code.

- The ASM386 will generate the right operand size opcodes according to the code segment attribute. The attribute is assigned either by the ASM386 invocation controls or in the code segment definition.

- If a code segment that is going to run in real-address mode is defined, it must be set to a USE 16 attribute. If 32-bit operands (MOV EAX, EBX) are used in the segment, an operand prefix will automatically be generated which will force the CPU to execute a 32-bit operation for this instruction although its default code segment attribute is 16-bit.

- Intel's ASM386 assembler allows specific use of the 16- or 32-bit instructions, for example, LGDTW, LGDTD, IRETD. If you are using the generic instruction (LGDT) the default segment attribute will be used to generate the right opcode.

Table 16-8. Relationship Between BLD Item and ASM Source File

Item	ASM386 and Startup.A58	BLD386 Controls and BLD file	Effect
Bootstrap	public startup startup:	bootstrap start(startup)	Near jump at 0FFFFFFF0H to start
GDT location	public GDT_EPROM GDT_EPROM TABLE_REG <>	TABLE GDT(location = GDT_EPROM)	The location of the GDT will be programmed into the GDT_EPROM location
IDT location	public IDT_EPROM IDT_EPROM TABLE_REG <>	TABLE IDT(location = IDT_EPROM	The location of the IDT will be programmed into the IDT_EPROM location
RAM start	RAM_START equ 400H	memory(reserve = (0..3FFFH))	RAM_START is used as the ram destination for moving the tables. It must be excluded from the application's segment area.
Location of the application TSS in the GDT	TSS_INDEX EQU 10	TABLE GDT(ENTRY=(10: PROTECTED_MODE_T ASK))	Put the descriptor of the application TSS in GDT entry 10
EPROM size and location	size and location of the initialization code	SEGMENT startup.code (base= 0FFFF0000H) ...memory (RANGE(ROM_AREA = ROM(x..y))	Initialization code size must be less than 64K and resides at upper most 64K of the 4GB memory space.

16.7.5. STARTUP.ASM Listing

The source code listing to move the CPU into protected mode is provided in Example 16-1. This listing does not include any opcode and offset information.

Example 16-1. STARTUP.ASM

```
DOS 5.0 (045-N) 386(TM) MACRO ASSEMBLER STARTUP
                    09:44:51    08/19/92    PAGE    1


DOS 5.0 (045-N) 386(TM) MACRO ASSEMBLER V4.0, ASSEMBLY OF MODULE
                    STARTUP
OBJECT MODULE PLACED IN startup.obj
ASSEMBLER INVOKED BY: f:\386tools\ASM386.EXE startup.a58 pw (132 )

LINE    SOURCE

    1    NAME    STARTUP
```

```
 2
 3                    ;;;;;;;;;;;;;;;;;;;;;;;;;;;;;;;;;;;;;;;;;;;;;
                      ;;;;;;;;;;;;;;;;;;;;;;;;;;;;;;;;;;
 4   ;
 5   ;    ASSUMPTIONS:
 6   ;
 7   ;       1.   The bottom 64K of memory is ram, and can be used for
 8   ;            scratch space by this module.
 9   ;
10   ;       2.   The system has sufficient free usable ram to copy the
11   ;            initial GDT, IDT, and TSS
12   ;
13   ;;;;;;;;;;;;;;;;;;;;;;;;;;;;;;;;;;;;;;;;;;;;;;;;;;;;;;;;;;;;;;;;;;;
14
15   ; configuration data - must match with build definition
16
17   CS_BASE        EQU     0FFFF0000H
18
19    ; CS_BASE is the linear address of the segment STARTUP_CODE
20    ; - this is specified in the build language file
21
22   RAM_START      EQU     400H
23
24   ; RAM_START  is the start of free, usable ram in the linear
25   ; memory  space.   The GDT,  IDT, and  initial TSS  will be
26   ; copied above this space, and a small data segment will be
27   ; discarded at  this linear  address.   The 32-bit  word at
28   ; RAM_START will contain  the linear  address of  the first
29   ; free byte above the copied tables - this may be useful if
30   ; a memory manager is used.
31
32   TSS_INDEX      EQU      10
33
34   ; TSS_INDEX is the  index of the  TSS of the  first task to
35   ; run after startup
36
37
38    ;;;;;;;;;;;;;;;;;;;;;;;;;;;;;;;;;;;;;;;;;;;;;;;;;;;;;;;;;;;;;;;;
39
40   ; ------------------------ STRUCTURES and EQU ---------------
41   ; structures for system data
42
43   ; TSS structure
44   TASK_STATE  STRUC
45       link          DW ?
46       link_h        DW ?
47       ESP0          DD ?
48       SS0           DW ?
49       SS0_h         DW ?
50       ESP1          DD ?
```

```
51        SS1             DW  ?
52        SS1_h           DW  ?
53        ESP2            DD  ?
54        SS2             DW  ?
55        SS2_h           DW  ?
56        CR3_reg         DD  ?
57        EIP_reg         DD  ?
58        EFLAGS_reg      DD  ?
59        EAX_reg         DD  ?
60        ECX_reg         DD  ?
61        EDX_reg         DD  ?
62        EBX_reg         DD  ?
63        ESP_reg         DD  ?
64        EBP_reg         DD  ?
65        ESI_reg         DD  ?
66        EDI_reg         DD  ?
67        ES_reg          DW  ?
68        ES_h            DW  ?
69        CS_reg          DW  ?
70        CS_h            DW  ?
71        SS_reg          DW  ?
72        SS_h            DW  ?
73        DS_reg          DW  ?
74        DS_h            DW  ?
75        FS_reg          DW  ?
76        FS_h            DW  ?
77        GS_reg          DW  ?
78        GS_h            DW  ?
79        LDT_reg         DW  ?
80        LDT_h           DW  ?
81        TRAP_reg        DW  ?
82        IO_map_base     DW  ?
83    TASK_STATE  ENDS
84
85    ; basic structure of a descriptor
86    DESC     STRUC
87        lim_0_15        DW  ?
88        bas_0_15        DW  ?
89        bas_16_23       DB  ?
90        access          DB  ?
91        gran            DB  ?
92        bas_24_31       DB  ?
93    DESC     ENDS
94
95    ; structure for use with LGDT and LIDT instructions
96    TABLE_REG    STRUC
97        table_lim       DW  ?
98        table_linear    DD  ?
99    TABLE_REG    ENDS
100
```

```
101    ; offset of GDT and IDT descriptors in builder generated GDT
102    GDT_DESC_OFF      EQU 1*SIZE(DESC)
103    IDT_DESC_OFF      EQU 2*SIZE(DESC)
104
105    ; equates for building temp GDT in ram
106    LINEAR_SEL          EQU     2*SIZE (DESC)
107    LINEAR_PROTO_LO     EQU     00000FFFFH  ; LINEAR_ALIAS
108    LINEAR_PROTO_HI     EQU     000CF9200H
109
110    ; Protection Enable Bit in CR0
111    PE_BIT   EQU 1B
112
113    ; ------------------------------------------------------------
114
115    ; ---------------------- DATA SEGMENT----------------------
116
117    ; Initially, this  data segment starts at  linear 0, due to
118    ; CPU powerup state.
119
120    STARTUP_DATA      SEGMENT RW
121
122    free_mem_linear_base    LABEL    DWORD
123    TEMP_GDT                LABEL    BYTE     ; must be first in
segment
124    TEMP_GDT_NULL_DESC   DESC     <>
125    TEMP_GDT_LINEAR_DESC DESC     <>
126
127    ; scratch areas for LGDT and LIDT instructions
128    TEMP_GDT_SCRATCH TABLE_REG    <>
129    APP_GDT_RAM      TABLE_REG    <>
130    APP_IDT_RAM      TABLE_REG    <>
131         ; align end_data
132    fill    DW       ?
133
134    ; last thing in this segment - should be on a dword boundary
135    end_data    LABEL    BYTE
136
137    STARTUP_DATA      ENDS
138    ; ------------------------------------------------------------
139
140
141    ; ---------------------- CODE SEGMENT----------------------
142    STARTUP_CODE SEGMENT ER PUBLIC USE16
143
144    ; filled in by builder
145        PUBLIC   GDT_EPROM
146    GDT_EPROM    TABLE_REG    <>
147
148    ; filled in by builder
149        PUBLIC   IDT_EPROM
```

```
150   IDT_EPROM    TABLE_REG    <>
151
152   ; entry point into startup code - the bootstrap will vector
153   ; here  with a  near JMP  generated by  the builder.   This
154   ; label must be in the top 64K of linear memory.
155
156         PUBLIC   STARTUP
157   STARTUP:
158
159   ; DS,ES address the bottom 64K of flat linear memory
160         ASSUME   DS:STARTUP_DATA, ES:STARTUP_DATA
161   ; See Figure 16-4
162   ; load GDTR with temporary GDT
163         LEA      EBX,TEMP_GDT   ; build the TEMP_GDT in low ram,
164         MOV      DWORD PTR [EBX],0   ; where we can address
165         MOV      DWORD PTR [EBX]+4,0
166         MOV      DWORD PTR [EBX]+8, LINEAR_PROTO_LO
167         MOV      DWORD PTR [EBX]+12, LINEAR_PROTO_HI
168         MOV      TEMP_GDT_scratch.table_linear,EBX
169         MOV      TEMP_GDT_scratch.table_lim,15
170
171              DB       66H          ; execute a 32 bit LGDT
172         LGDT     TEMP_GDT_scratch
173
174   ; enter protected mode
175         MOV      EBX,CR0
176         OR       EBX,PE_BIT
177         MOV      CR0,EBX
178
179    ; clear prefetch queue
180         JMP      CLEAR_LABEL
181   CLEAR_LABEL:
182
183    ; make DS and ES address 4G of linear memory
184         MOV      CX,LINEAR_SEL
185         MOV      DS,CX
186         MOV      ES,CX
187
188     ; do board specific initialization
189     ;
190               ;
191               ; ......
192               ;
193
194
195           ; See Figure 16-5
196           ; copy EPROM GDT to ram at:
197           ;            RAM_START + size (STARTUP_DATA)
198         MOV      EAX,RAM_START
199         ADD      EAX,OFFSET (end_data)
```

```
200            MOV        EBX,RAM_START
201            MOV        ECX, CS_BASE
202            ADD        ECX, OFFSET (GDT_EPROM)
203            MOV        ESI, [ECX].table_linear
204            MOV        EDI,EAX
205            MOVZX      ECX, [ECX].table_lim
206            MOV        APP_GDT_ram[EBX].table_lim,CX
207            INC        ECX
208            MOV        EDX,EAX
209            MOV        APP_GDT_ram[EBX].table_linear,EAX
210            ADD        EAX,ECX
211     REP MOVS       BYTE PTR ES:[EDI],BYTE PTR DS:[ESI]
212
213            ; fixup GDT base in descriptor
214            MOV        ECX,EDX
215            MOV        [EDX].bas_0_15+GDT_DESC_OFF,CX
216            ROR        ECX,16
217            MOV        [EDX].bas_16_23+GDT_DESC_OFF,CL
218            MOV        [EDX].bas_24_31+GDT_DESC_OFF,CH
219
220            ; copy EPROM IDT to ram at:
221            ; RAM_START+size(STARTUP_DATA)+SIZE (EPROM GDT)
222            MOV        ECX, CS_BASE
223            ADD        ECX, OFFSET (IDT_EPROM)
224            MOV        ESI, [ECX].table_linear
225            MOV        EDI,EAX
226            MOVZX      ECX, [ECX].table_lim
227            MOV        APP_IDT_ram[EBX].table_lim,CX
228            INC        ECX
229            MOV        APP_IDT_ram[EBX].table_linear,EAX
230            MOV        EBX,EAX
231            ADD        EAX,ECX
232     REP MOVS       BYTE PTR ES:[EDI],BYTE PTR DS:[ESI]
233
234            ; fixup IDT pointer in GDT
235            MOV        [EDX].bas_0_15+IDT_DESC_OFF,BX
236            ROR        EBX,16
237            MOV        [EDX].bas_16_23+IDT_DESC_OFF,BL
238            MOV        [EDX].bas_24_31+IDT_DESC_OFF,BH
239
240            ; load GDTR and IDTR
241            MOV        EBX,RAM_START
242            DB         66H              ; execute a 32 bit LGDT
243            LGDT       APP_GDT_ram[EBX]
244            DB         66H              ; execute a 32 bit LIDT
245            LIDT       APP_IDT_ram[EBX]
246
247            ; move the TSS
248            MOV        EDI,EAX
249            MOV        EBX,TSS_INDEX*SIZE(DESC)
```

```
250          MOV      ECX,GDT_DESC_OFF ;build linear address for TSS
251          MOV      GS,CX
252          MOV      DH,GS:[EBX].bas_24_31
253          MOV      DL,GS:[EBX].bas_16_23
254          ROL      EDX,16
255          MOV      DX,GS:[EBX].bas_0_15
256          MOV      ESI,EDX
257          LSL      ECX,EBX
258          INC      ECX
259          MOV      EDX,EAX
260          ADD      EAX,ECX
261    REP MOVS      BYTE PTR ES:[EDI],BYTE PTR DS:[ESI]
262
263                  ; fixup TSS pointer
264          MOV      GS:[EBX].bas_0_15,DX
265          ROL      EDX,16
266          MOV      GS:[EBX].bas_24_31,DH
267          MOV      GS:[EBX].bas_16_23,DL
268          ROL      EDX,16
269    ;save start of free ram at linear location RAMSTART
270          MOV      free_mem_linear_base+RAM_START,EAX
271
272    ;assume no  LDT used in  the initial task  - if necessary,
273    ;code  to move the LDT could be added, and should resemble
274    ;that used to move the TSS
275
276    ; load TR
277          LTR      BX   ; No task switch, only descriptor loading
278    ; See Figure 16-6
279    ; load minimal set of registers necessary to simulate task
280    ; switch
281
282
283          MOV      AX,[EDX].SS_reg       ; start loading registers
284          MOV      EDI,[EDX].ESP_reg
285          MOV      SS,AX
286          MOV      ESP,EDI               ; stack now valid
287          PUSH     DWORD PTR [EDX].EFLAGS_reg
288          PUSH     DWORD PTR [EDX].CS_reg
289          PUSH     DWORD PTR [EDX].EIP_reg
290          MOV      AX,[EDX].DS_reg
291          MOV      BX,[EDX].ES_reg
292          MOV      DS,AX      ; DS and ES no longer linear memory
293          MOV      ES,BX
294
295                  ; simulate far jump to initial task
296          IRETD
297
298    STARTUP_CODE   ENDS
*** WARNING #377 IN 298, (PASS 2) SEGMENT CONTAINS PRIVILEGED
```

```
INSTRUCTION(S)
 299
 300   END STARTUP,  DS:STARTUP_DATA,  SS:STARTUP_DATA
 301
 302
```

ASSEMBLY COMPLETE,   1 WARNING,   NO ERRORS.

16.7.6. MAIN.ASM Source Code

The file MAIN.ASM shown in Example 16-2 defines the data and stack segments for this application and can be substituted with the main module task written in a high-level language that is invoked by the IRET instruction executed by STARTUP.ASM.

Example 16-2. MAIN.ASM

```
     NAME      main_module
data     SEGMENT RW
     dw 1000 dup(?)
DATA     ENDS

stack stackseg 800

CODE SEGMENT ER   use32 PUBLIC
main_start:
     nop
     nop
     nop

CODE   ENDS

END main_start, ds:data, ss:stack
```

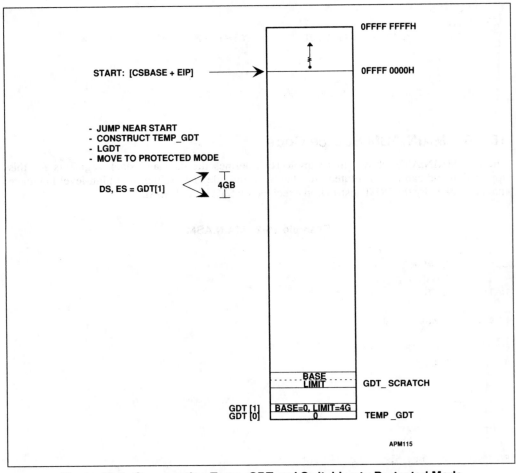

**Figure 16-4. Constructing Temp_GDT and Switching to Protected Mode
(Lines 162-172 of List File)**

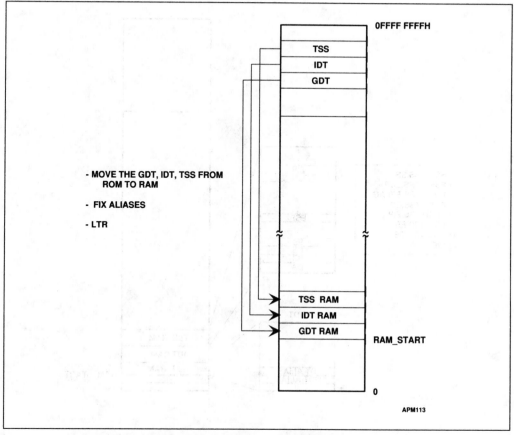

Figure 16-5. Moving The GDT, IDT, and TSS from ROM to RAM
(Lines 196-261 of List File)

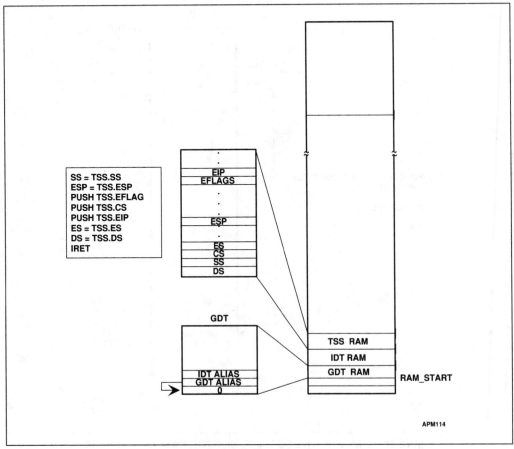

Figure 16-6. Task Switching
(Lines 282-296 of List File)

16.7.7. Supporting Files

The batch file shown in Example 16-3 can be used to assemble the source code files
STARTUP.ASM and MAIN.ASM and build the final application.

Example 16-3. Batch File to Assemble, Compile and Build the Application

```
ASM386 STARTUP.ASM
ASM386 MAIN.ASM
BLD386 STARTUP.OBJ, MAIN.OBJ buildfile(EPROM.BLD) bootstrap(STARTUP)
Bootload
```

The BLD386 has several functions in this example:

- It allocates physical memory location to segments and tables.
- It generates tables using the build file and the input files.
- It links object files and resolves references.
- It generates bootloadable file to be programmed into the EPROM.

Example 16-4 shows the build file used as input to BLD386 to perform the above functions.

Example 16-4. Build File

```
INIT_BLD_EXAMPLE;

SEGMENT
        *SEGMENTS                  (DPL = 0)
      , startup.startup_code      (BASE = 0FFFF0000H)
      ;

TASK
        BOOT_TASK                  (OBJECT = startup, INITIAL,DPL = 0,
                                   NOT INTENABLED)
      , PROTECTED_MODE_TASK        (OBJECT = main_module,DPL = 0,
                                   NOT INTENABLED)
      ;

TABLE
    GDT (
        LOCATION = GDT_EPROM
      , ENTRY = (
          10:              PROTECTED_MODE_TASK
      ,                    startup.startup_code
      ,                    startup.startup_data
      ,                    main_module.data
      ,                    main_module.code
      ,                    main_module.stack
            )
        ),

    IDT (
        LOCATION = IDT_EPROM
        );
```

```
MEMORY
    (
        RESERVE = (0..3FFFH
                            -- Area for the GDT, IDT, TSS copied from
ROM
                    60000H..0FFFEFFFFH)
    ,   RANGE = (ROM_AREA = ROM (0FFFF0000H..0FFFFFFFFH))
                            -- Eprom size 64K
    ,   RANGE = (RAM_AREA = RAM (4000H..05FFFFH))
    );

END
```

intel®

17

Debugging

The Pentium processor has advanced debugging facilities which are particularly important for sophisticated software systems, such as multitasking operating systems. The failure conditions for these software systems can be very complex and time-dependent. The debugging features of the Pentium processor give the system programmer valuable tools for looking at the dynamic state of the processor.

The debugging support is accessed through the debug registers. The debug registers of the Pentium processor hold the addresses of memory and I/O locations, called breakpoints, which invoke debugging software (unlike the Intel386 and Intel486 processors which allowed debugging of memory accesses only). An exception is generated when a memory or I/O operation is made to one of these addresses. A breakpoint is specified for a particular form of memory or I/O access, such as an instruction fetch, doubleword memory write operation or a word I/O read operation. The debug registers support both instruction breakpoints and data breakpoints.

With other processors, instruction breakpoints are set by replacing normal instructions with breakpoint instructions. When the breakpoint instruction is executed, the debugger is called. But with the debug registers of the Pentium processor, this is not necessary. By eliminating the need to write into the code space, the debugging process is simplified (there is no need shadow the ROM code space in RAM) and breakpoints can be set in ROM-based software. In addition, breakpoints can be set on reads and writes to data which allows real-time monitoring of variables.

17.1. DEBUGGING SUPPORT

The features of the architecture which support debugging include:

- **Reserved debug interrupt vector**—Specifies a procedure or task to be called when an event for the debugger occurs.
- **Debug address registers**—Specifies the addresses of up to four breakpoints.
- **Debug control register**—Specifies the forms of memory or I/O access for the breakpoints.
- **Debug status register**—Reports conditions which were in effect at the time of the exception.
- **Trap bit of TSS (T-bit)**—Generates a debug exception when an attempt is made to perform a task switch to a task with this bit set in its TSS.
- **Resume flag (RF)**— Suppresses multiple exceptions to the same instruction.
- **Trap flag (TF)**—Generates a debug exception after every execution of an instruction.
- **Breakpoint instruction**—Calls the debugger (generates a debug exception). This instruction is an alternative way to set code breakpoints. It is especially useful when more

than four breakpoints are desired, or when breakpoints are being placed in the source code.

- **Reserved interrupt vector for breakpoint exception**—Calls a procedure or task when a breakpoint instruction is executed.

These features allow a debugger to be called either as a separate task or as a procedure in the context of the current task. The following conditions can be used to call the debugger:

- Task switch to a specific task.
- Execution of the breakpoint instruction.
- Execution of any instruction.
- Execution of an instruction at a specified address.
- Read or write of a byte, word, or doubleword at a specified memory address.
- Write to a byte, word, or doubleword at a specified memory address.
- Input of a byte or word at a specified I/O address.
- Output of a byte, word, or doubleword at a specified I/O address.
- Attempt to change the contents of a debug register.

17.2. DEBUG REGISTERS

Six registers control debugging. These registers are accessed by forms of the MOV instruction. A debug register may be the source or destination operand for one of these instructions. The debug registers are privileged resources; the MOV instructions which access them may be executed only at privilege level 0. An attempt to read or write the debug registers from any other privilege level generates a general-protection exception. Figure 17-1 shows the format of the debug registers.

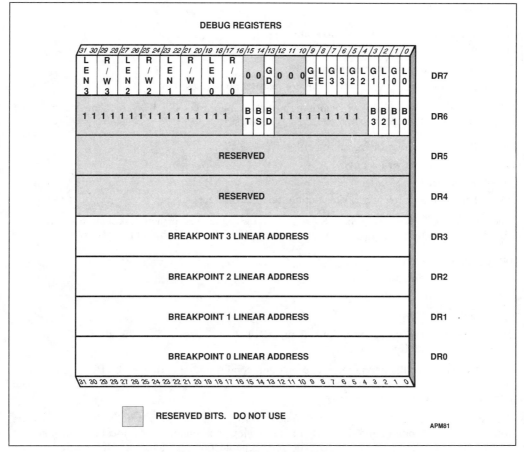

Figure 17-1. Debug Registers

17.2.1. Debug Address Registers (DR0-DR3)

Each of these registers holds the linear address for one of the four breakpoints. That is, breakpoint comparisons are made before physical address translation occurs. Each breakpoint condition is specified further by the contents of the DR7 register.

17.2.2. Debug Control Register (DR7)

The debug control register shown in Figure 17-1 specifies the type of memory or I/O access associated with each breakpoint. Each address in registers DR0 to DR3 corresponds to a field R/W0 to R/W3 in the DR7 register. The DE (Debug Extensions) bit in the CR4 register determines how the R/W bits are interpreted. When the DE bit is set, the processor interprets these bits as follows:

00 — Break on instruction execution only

01 — Break on data writes only

10 — Break on I/O reads or writes

11 — Break on data reads or writes but not instruction fetches

When the DE bit is clear, the Pentium processor interprets the R/W bits the same as the Intel486 and Intel386 processors, which is as follows:

00 — Break on instruction execution only

01 — Break on data writes only

10 — undefined

11 — Break on data reads or writes but not instruction fetches

The LEN0 to LEN3 fields in the DR7 register specify the size of the breakpointed location. A size of 1, 2, or 4 bytes may be specified. The length fields are interpreted as follows:

00 — one-byte length

01 — two-byte length

10 — undefined

11 — four-byte length

If RWn is 00 (instruction execution), then LENn should also be 00. The effect of using any other length is undefined.

The GD bit enables the debug register protection condition that is flagged by BD of DR6. Note that GD is cleared at entry to the debug exception handler by the processor. This allows the handler free access to the debug registers.

The low eight bits of the DR7 register (fields L0 to L3 and G0 to G3) individually enable the four address breakpoint conditions. There are two levels of enabling: the local (L0 through L3) and global (G0 through G3) levels. The local enable bits are automatically cleared by the processor with every task switch to avoid unwanted breakpoint conditions in the new task. They are used to set breakpoint conditions in a single task. The global enable bits are not cleared by a task switch. They are used to enable breakpoint conditions which apply to all tasks.

17.2.3. Debug Status Register (DR6)

The debug status register shown in Figure 11-1 reports conditions sampled at the time the debug exception was generated. Among other information, it reports which breakpoint triggered the exception. Update only occurs if the exception is taken, then all bits are updated.

When an enabled breakpoint generates a debug exception, it loads the low four bits of this register (B0 through B3) before entering the debug exception handler. The B bit is set if the condition described by the DR, LEN, and R/W bits is true, even if the breakpoint is not enabled by the L and G bits. The processor sets the B bits for all breakpoints which match the conditions present at the time the debug exception is generated, whether or not they are enabled.

The BT bit is associated with the T bit (debug trap bit) of the TSS (see Chapter 10 for the format of a TSS). The processor sets the BT bit before entering the debug handler if a task switch has occurred to a task with a set T bit in its TSS. There is no bit in the DR7 register to enable or disable this exception; the T bit of the TSS is the only enabling bit.

The BS bit is associated with the TF flag. The BS bit is set if the debug exception was triggered by the single-step execution mode (TF flag set). The single-step mode is the highest-priority debug exception; when the BS bit is set, any of the other debug status bits also may be set.

The BD bit is set if the next instruction will read or write one of the eight debug registers while they are being used by in-circuit emulation if the GD bit in DR7 is set to one.

Note that the contents of the DR6 register are never cleared by the processor. To avoid any confusion in identifying debug exceptions, the debug handler should clear the register before returning.

17.2.4. Debug Registers DR4 and DR5

Although debug registers 4 and 5 have been documented as *reserved,* previous generations of processors aliased these registers to debug registers 6 and 7, respectively. When debug extensions are not enabled (CR4.DE=0), the Pentium processor remains compatible with existing software by aliasing these references. However, when debug extensions are enabled (CR4.DE=1), attempts to reference debug registers 4 or 5 will result in an Undefined Opcode Exception (#UD).

17.2.5. Breakpoint Field Recognition

The address and LEN bits for each of the four breakpoint conditions define a range of sequential byte addresses for a data or I/O breakpoint. The LEN bits permit specification of a one-, two-, or four-byte range. Two-byte ranges must be aligned on word boundaries (addresses which are multiples of two) and four-byte ranges must be aligned on doubleword boundaries (addresses which are multiples of four). I/O breakpoints must be aligned on doubleword boundaries and may only be one or two bytes. I/O breakpoint addresses are zero extended from 16 to 32 bits for purposes of comparison with the breakpoint address in the selected debug register. These requirements are enforced by the processor; it uses the LEN bits to mask the lower address bits in the debug registers. Unaligned data or I/O breakpoint addresses do not yield the expected results.

A data breakpoint for reading or writing is triggered if any of the bytes participating in an access is within the range defined by a breakpoint address register and its LEN bits. Table 17-1 gives some examples of combinations of addresses and fields with references which do and do not cause traps.

Table 17-1. Breakpointing Examples

Operation		Address (hex)	Length (in bytes)
Register Contents	DR0	A0001	1 (LEN0 = 00)
Register Contents	DR1	A0002	1 (LEN1 = 00)
Register Contents	DR2	B0002	2 (LEN2 = 01)
Register Contents	DR3	C0000	4 (LEN3 = 11)
Data Operations Which Trap		A0001	1
		A0002	1
		A0001	2
		A0002	2
		B0002	2
		B0001	4
		C0000	4
		C0001	2
		C0003	1
Data Operations Which Do Not Trap		A0000	1
		A0003	4
		B0000	2
		C0004	4

A data breakpoint for an unaligned operand can be made from two sets of entries in the breakpoint registers where each entry is byte-aligned, and the two entries together cover the operand. This breakpoint generates exceptions only for the operand, not for any neighboring bytes.

Instruction breakpoint addresses must have a length specification of one byte (LEN = 00); the behavior of code breakpoints for other operand sizes is undefined. The processor recognizes an instruction breakpoint address only when it points to the first byte of an instruction. If the instruction has any prefixes, the breakpoint address must point to the first prefix.

It is recommended that debuggers execute the LGDT instruction before returning to the program being debugged to ensure that breakpoints are detected.

17.3. DEBUG EXCEPTIONS

Two of the interrupt vectors of the Pentium processor are reserved for debug exceptions. The debug exception is the usual way to invoke debuggers designed for the Pentium processor.

17.3.1. Interrupt 1—Debug Exceptions

The handler for this exception usually is a debugger or part of a debugging system. The processor generates a debug exception for any of several conditions. The debugger can check flags in the DR6 and DR7 registers to determine which condition caused the exception and which other conditions also might apply. Table 17-2 shows the states of these bits for each kind of breakpoint condition.

Instruction breakpoints are faults; other debug exceptions are traps. The debug exception may report either or both at one time. The following sections present details for each class of debug exception.

Table 17-2. Debug Exception Conditions

Flags Tested	Description
BS = 1	Single-step trap
B0 = 1 and (GE0 = 1 or LE0 = 1)	Breakpoint defined by DR0, LEN0, and R/W0
B1 = 1 and (GE1 = 1 or LE1 = 1)	Breakpoint defined by DR1, LEN1, and R/W1
B2 = 1 and (GE2 = 1 or LE2 = 1)	Breakpoint defined by DR2, LEN2, and R/W2
B3 = 1 and (GE3 = 1 or LE3 = 1)	Breakpoint defined by DR3, LEN3, and R/W3
BD = 1	Debug registers in use for in-circuit emulation
BT = 1	Task switch

17.3.1.1. INSTRUCTION-BREAKPOINT FAULT

The processor reports an instruction breakpoint before it executes the breakpointed instruction (i.e., a debug exception caused by an instruction breakpoint is a fault).

The RF flag permits the debug exception handler to restart instructions which cause faults other than debug faults. When a debug fault occurs, the system software must set the RF bit in the copy of the EFLAGS register which is pushed on the stack in the debug exception handler routine. This bit is set in preparation for resuming the program's execution at the breakpoint address without generating another breakpoint fault on the same instruction. (Note: The RF bit does not cause breakpoint traps to be ignored, nor other kinds of faults.) The RF flag is set by the IRETD instruction (but not by POPF or POPFD) to the value specified by the saved copy of the EFLAGS register in order to disable the generation of a code breakpoint exception on the instruction immediately following the IRETD.

The processor clears the RF flag at the successful completion of every instruction except after the IRET instruction and JMP, CALL, or INT instructions which cause a task switch.

The processor does not set the RF flag in the copy of the EFLAGS register pushed on the stack before entry into any fault handler. When the fault handler is entered for instruction breakpoints, for example, the debug handler should set the RF flag in the copy of the EFLAGS register pushed on the stack; so that when the IRET instruction is executed, returning control from the exception handler, the RF flag in the EFLAGS register will be set, and execution will resume at the breakpointed instruction without generating another breakpoint for the same instruction.

Code breakpoints are the highest priority faults and are therefore guaranteed to be serviced before any other faults which may be detected during the decoding or execution of an instruction. If after a debug fault, the RF flag is set and the debug handler retries the faulting instruction, it is possible that retrying the instruction will generate other faults. The restart of the instruction after these faults also occurs with the RF flag set, so repeated debug faults continue to be suppressed. The processor clears the RF flag only after *successful* completion of the instruction.

17.3.1.2. DATA MEMORY AND I/O BREAKPOINTS

Data memory and I/O breakpoint exceptions are traps; i.e., the processor generates an exception for a breakpoint after executing the instruction which accesses the breakpointed memory or I/O location.

Because data breakpoints are traps, the original data is overwritten before the trap exception is generated. If a debugger needs to save the contents of a write breakpoint location, it should save the original contents before setting the breakpoint. The handler can report the saved value after the breakpoint is triggered. The data in the debug registers can be used to address the new value stored by the instruction which triggered the breakpoint.

The Pentium processor, like the Intel486 processor, ignores the GE and LE bits in DR7. If any of the Ln/Gn bits is set (or single stepping is enabled), instruction pairing is inhibited and the Pentium processor slows execution so that most breakpoints are reported exactly on the instruction that generated them. In the Intel386 DX processor, exact data breakpoint matching does not occur unless it is enabled by setting either the LE or the GE bit.

The Pentium processor, however, is unable to report data breakpoints exactly for the REP MOVS and REP STOS instructions until the completion of the iteration after the one in which the breakpoint occurs in order to be able to execute the load, store, updates to ESI, EDI and ECX and the check for completion on each iteration of these REPeated instructions in a single clock.

Repeated INS and OUTS instructions that generate an I/O breakpoint debug exception, trap after the completion of the first iteration. Repeated INS and OUTS instructions that generate a memory breakpoint debug exception trap after the iteration in which the memory address breakpoint location is accessed.

17.3.1.3. GENERAL-DETECT FAULT

The general-detect fault occurs when an attempt is made to use the debug registers at the same time they are being used by in-circuit emulation when the GD bit in DR7 is set to one. This additional protection feature guarantees that emulators can have full control over the debug registers when required. The exception handler can detect this condition by checking the state of the BD bit of the DR6 register.

17.3.1.4. SINGLE-STEP TRAP

This trap occurs if the TF flag was set before the instruction was executed. Note that the exception does not occur after an instruction which sets the TF flag. For example, if the POPF instruction is used to set the TF flag, a single-step trap does not occur until after the instruction following the POPF instruction.

The processor clears the TF flag before calling the exception handler. If the TF flag was set in a TSS at the time of a task switch, the exception occurs after the first instruction is executed in the new task.

The single-step flag normally is not cleared by privilege changes inside a task. The INT instructions, however, do clear the TF flag. Therefore, software debuggers which single-step code must recognize and emulate INT n or INTO instructions rather than executing them directly. To maintain protection, the operating system should check the current execution privilege level after any single-step trap to see if single stepping should continue at the current privilege level.

The interrupt priorities guarantee that, if an external interrupt occurs, single stepping stops. When both an external interrupt and a single step interrupt occur together, the single step interrupt is processed first. This clears the TF flag. After saving the return address or switching tasks, the external interrupt input is examined before the first instruction of the single step handler executes. If the external interrupt is still pending, then it is serviced. The external interrupt handler does not run in single-step mode. To single step an interrupt handler, single step an INTn instruction which calls the interrupt handler.

17.3.1.5.   TASK-SWITCH TRAP

The debug exception also occurs after a task switch if the T bit of the new task's TSS is set. The exception occurs after control has passed to the new task, but before the first instruction of that task is executed. The exception handler can detect this condition by examining the BT bit of the DR6 register.

Note that, if the debug exception handler is a task, the T bit of its TSS should not be set. Failure to observe this rule will put the processor in a loop.

17.3.2. Interrupt 3—Breakpoint Instruction

The breakpoint trap is caused by execution of the INT 3 instruction. Typically, a debugger prepares a breakpoint by replacing the first opcode byte of an instruction with the opcode for the breakpoint instruction. When execution of the INT 3 instruction calls the exception handler, the return address points to the first byte of the instruction following the INT 3 instruction.

With older processors, this feature is used extensively for setting instruction breakpoints. With the Pentium, Intel486, and Intel386 processors, this use is more easily handled using the debug registers. However, the breakpoint exception still is useful for breakpointing debuggers, because the breakpoint exception can call another exception handler. The breakpoint exception also can be useful when it is necessary to set a greater number of breakpoints than permitted by the debug registers, or when breakpoints are being placed in the source code of a program under development.

intel®

18

Caching, Pipelining and Buffering

CHAPTER 18
CACHING, PIPELINING AND BUFFERING

The Pentium processor has many features that work together to yield extremely high performance — features such as caches, buffers, and pipelining. In general, these features work behind the scenes; that is, programs automatically run faster without having to explicitly take these performance features into account. In spite of this transparent implementation, some programmers may wish to take maximum advantage of these features. This chapter provides the information necessary to do so. It also documents the few cases in which systems programmers must explicitly take these performance features into account. The features discussed are:

- Internal instruction and data caches.
- Address translation caches.
- Prefetch queues.
- Write buffers.
- Execution pipelining.

18.1. INTERNAL INSTRUCTION AND DATA CACHES

The Pentium microprocessor has separate data and instruction caches on-chip. Caches raise system performance by satisfying an internal read request more quickly than a bus cycle to memory. They also reduce the processor's use of the external bus when the same locations are accessed multiple times. Having separate caches for instructions and data allows simultaneous cache look-up. Up to two data references and up to 32 bytes of raw opcodes can be accessed in one clock. The caches are fully transparent to applications software.

Caching is available in all execution modes: real mode, protected mode, and virtual-8086 mode. For a properly designed, single-processor system, the caching does not require further control once it is enabled during system initialization.

The data and instruction caches hold 8K bytes each. The cache line width of the Pentium CPU is 256 bits or 32 bytes. A line can be filled from memory with a four-transfer burst cycle. External caches are not likely to use cache lines smaller than those of the internal cache.

Cache lines can only be mapped to 32-byte aligned blocks of main memory. (A 32-byte aligned block begins at an address which is clear in its low-order five bits.) The caches do not support partially-filled cache lines, so caching even a single doubleword requires caching an entire line.

The processor allows any area of memory to be cached, although both software and hardware can disallow certain areas from being cached — software by setting the PCD bit in the respective page table entries; hardware by deasserting the KEN# signal for bus cycles with addresses that fall within those areas. When both software and hardware agree that a requested datum is cacheable, the processor reads an entire 32-byte line into the appropriate cache. This operation is called a *cache line fill*. Cache line fills are generated only for read misses, not for write misses. A store that misses the cache does not copy the missed line into cache from memory, but rather posts the datum in a write buffer, then sends it to the external bus when the bus is available.

The CPU can use an external second-level cache outside of the processor chip. An external cache can improve performance by providing a larger cache or wider line, or by allowing the processor bus to run faster than the memory bus.

Caches require special consideration in multiprocessor systems. When one processor accesses data cached in another processor, it must not receive incorrect data. If it modifies data, all other processors which access that data must receive the modified data. This property is called *cache consistency*. The CPU provides mechanisms which maintain cache consistency in the presence of multiple processors and external caches.

The operation of internal and external caches is transparent to application software, but knowledge of the behavior of these caches may be useful in optimizing software performance. For example, knowledge of cache dimensions and replacement algorithms are an indication of how large of a data structure can be operated on at once without causing cache thrashing. In multiprocessor systems, maintenance of cache consistency may, in rare circumstances, require intervention by system software. For these rare cases, the Pentium microprocessor provides privileged cache control operations.

18.1.1. Data Cache

In the data cache, a cache protocol known as MESI maintains consistency with caches of other processors and with an external cache. The data cache has two status bits per tag; so, each line can be in one of the states defined in Table 18-1. The state of a cache line can change as the result of either internal or external activity related to that line. In general, the operation of the MESI protocol is transparent to programs.

Table 18-1. MESI Cache Line States

Cache Line State:	M Modified	E Exclusive	S Shared	I Invalid
This cache line is valid?	Yes	Yes	Yes	No
The memory copy is...	...out of date	...valid	...valid	—
Copies exist in caches of other processors?	No	No	Maybe	Maybe
A write to this line ...	...does not go to bus	...does not go to bus	...goes to bus and updates cache	...goes directly to bus

18.1.2. Data Cache Update Policies

A cache adheres to an *update policy* to determine when a write operation must update main memory. (The update policy does not affect read operations.) The update policies supported by the Pentium microprocessor data cache are:

- *Write-through* — a write request to a line in the cache triggers updates to both cache memory and main memory. Write-through is useful for applications such as a graphics frame buffer, where writes must update memory so that they can be seen on the graphics display.

- *Write-back* — a write request to a line in the cache updates only the cache memory. The write-back policy reduces bus traffic by eliminating many unnecessary writes to memory. Writes to a line in the cache are not immediately forwarded to main memory; instead, they are accumulated in the cache. The modified cache line is written to main memory later, when a write-back operation is performed. Write-back operations are triggered when cache lines need to be deallocated, such as when new cache lines are being allocated in a cache which is already full. Write-back operations also are triggered by the mechanisms used to maintain cache consistency.

The processor allows any area of memory to be subject to either policy. Both software and hardware have control over which policy is employed — software through the PWT bit of page table entries; hardware through the WB/WT# signal.

The internal caches of the Pentium microprocessor can be used with external caches which are write-through, write-back, or a mixture of both.

18.1.3. Instruction Cache

The instruction cache implements only the "SI" part of the MESI protocol, because the instruction cache is not writable.

The instruction cache monitors changes in the data cache to maintain consistency between the caches when instructions are modified. For more information, refer to Section 18.2.3.

18.2. OPERATION OF THE INTERNAL CACHES

Software controls the operating mode of the caches by setting or clearing the CD and NW bits of CR0. These bits after RESET are set to one (cache disabled). Software can leave caching disabled, or software can enable caching by updating the CD bit and NW bits of CR0.

18.2.1. Cache Control Bits

Table 18-2 summarizes the modes controlled by the CD and NW bits of CR0. For normal operation and highest performance, these bits should be set to zero. To completely disable the cache, the following two steps must be performed:

1. CD and NW must be set to 1.
2. The caches must be flushed

If the cache is not flushed, cache hits on reads will still occur and data will be read from the cache. In addition, the cache must be flushed after being disabled to prevent any inconsistencies with main memory.

Table 18-2. Cache Operating Modes

CD	NW	Purpose/Description
0	0	**Normal highest performance cache operation.** Read hits access the cache. Read misses may cause replacement. Write hits update the cache. Only writes to shared lines and write misses appear externally. Write hits can change shared lines to exclusive under control of WB/WT#. Invalidation is allowed.
0	1	**Invalid setting.** A general-protection exception with an error code of zero is generated.
1	0	**Cache disabled. Memory consistency maintained. Existing contents locked in cache.** Read hits access the cache. Read misses do not cause replacement. Write hits update cache. Only write hits to shared lines and write misses update memory. Write hits can change shared lines to exclusive under control of WB/WT#. Invalidation is allowed.
1	1	**Cache disabled. Memory consistency not maintained.** Read hits access the cache. Read misses do not cause replacement. Write hits update cache but not memory. Write hits change exclusive lines to modified. Shared lines remain shared after write hit. Write misses access memory. Invalidation is inhibited.

18.2.2. Cache Management Instructions

The INVD and WBINVD instructions are used to invalidate the contents of the internal and external caches. The INVD instruction invalidates all internal (data and instruction) cache entries and generates a special bus cycle which indicates that external caches also should be invalidated. (The response of external hardware to receiving a cache invalidation bus cycle is dependent on system implementation.) INVD should be used with care. It does not write back modified cache lines; therefore, it can cause the data cache to become inconsistent with other memories in the system. Unless there is a specific requirement or benefit to invalidate a cache without writing back the modified lines (i.e., testing or fault recovery where cache coherency with main memory is not a concern), software should use the WBINVD instruction.

The WBINVD instruction first writes back any modified lines in the data cache, then invalidates the contents of its instruction and data caches. It ensures that cache coherency with main memory will be maintained regardless of system configuration (i.e., write-through or write-back). Following this, it generates special bus cycles to indicate that external caches should also write back modified data and invalidate their contents.

18.2.3. Self-Modifying Code

Unlike the Intel486 microprocessor, the Pentium microprocessor has separate caches for data and instructions. In spite of this difference in implementation, the Pentium microprocessor supports updates to instructions in a manner that is completely compatible with the Intel486 microprocessor.

A write to an instruction that is in the instruction cache causes the instruction to be invalidated in the instruction cache. This check is based on the physical address of the instruction. In addition, the Pentium microprocessor checks whether a write may modify an instruction that has been prefetched for execution; if so, it invalidates the prefetch queue. This check is based on the linear address of the instruction.

Because the linear address of the write is checked against the linear address of the instructions that have been prefetched, special care must be taken for self-modifying code to work correctly when the physical addresses of the instruction and the written data are the same, but the linear addresses differ. In such cases, it is necessary to execute a serializing operation after the write and before executing the modified instruction. See the section on serializing operations below for more information. (Note that the check on linear addresses described above is not in practice a concern for compatibility. Applications that include self-modifying code use the same linear address for modifying and fetching the instruction. Systems software, such as a debugger, that might possibly modify an instruction using a different linear address than that used to fetch the instruction, will execute a serializing operation, such as IRET, before the modified instruction is executed.)

18.3. PAGE-LEVEL CACHE MANAGEMENT

When paging is enabled, two bits in entries of the page directory and second-level page tables are used to manage the caching of pages and to drive processor output pins. (These bits are reserved on Intel386 processors.)

The PCD and PWT bits control caching on a page-by-page basis. The PCD bit (page-level cache disable) affects the operation of the internal cache. Both the PCD bit and the PWT bit (page-level write-through) drive processor output pins (called PCD and PWT) for controlling external caches. The treatment of these signals by external hardware depends on system design; for example, some hardware systems may control the caching of pages by decoding some of the high address bits.

There are three potential sources of the bits used to drive the PCD and PWT outputs of the processor: the CR3 register, the page directory, and the second-level page tables. The processor outputs are driven by the CR3 register for bus cycles where paging is not used to generate the address, such as the loading of an entry in the page directory. The outputs are driven by a page directory entry when an entry from a second-level page table is accessed. The outputs are driven by a second-level page table entry when instructions or data in memory are accessed. When paging is disabled, these bits are ignored (that is, the CPU assumes PCD=1 and PWT=1). See Chapter 9 for descriptions of the PCD and PWT bits in CR3.

18.3.1. PCD Bit

When the PCD bit of a page table entry is set, caching of data from the page is disabled, even if hardware requests caching by asserting the KEN# input. When the PCD bit is clear, caching may be requested by hardware on a cycle-by-cycle basis.

The ability to disable caching is useful for pages which contain memory-mapped I/O ports and for pages which do not provide a performance benefit when cached, such as initialization software.

Regardless of the page-table entries, the processor ignores the PCD output (i.e. assumes PCD=1) whenever the CD (Cache Disable) bit in CR0 is set.

18.3.2. PWT Bit

When a page table entry has a set PWT bit (bit position 3), a write-through caching policy is specified for data in the corresponding page. Clearing the PWT bit on the Pentium microprocessor enables a write-back policy for the page. External caches can also use the output signal driven by the PWT bit to control update policy on a page-by-page basis.

18.4. ADDRESS TRANSLATION CACHES

Refer to Chapter 11 for information on the address translation caches (TLBs).

18.5. CACHE REPLACEMENT ALGORITHM

The data, instruction caches use a least-recently-used (LRU) algorithm to choose which line of a set is overwritten when a miss causes a line fill and all lines in the set contain valid data. The address-translation cache uses a psuedo-LRU algorithm. These algorithms are controlled by LRU bits in the tags of each cache. The states of the valid bits take precedence over the LRU bits. If any of the lines in the set is invalid, an invalid line is used for the line fill, and the LRU bits are not used. RESET initializes the valid bits so that two Pentium CPUs executing the same code on identical boards have exactly the same series of cache hits, misses, and replacements.

18.6. EXECUTION PIPELINING AND PAIRING

The Pentium processor achieves approximately two times the integer execution speed of the Intel486 microprocessor through a superscalar architecture capable of executing two instructions in parallel. Two pipelines operate in parallel allowing integer instructions to execute in a single clock in each pipeline. The allocation of instructions to a pipeline is performed automatically by the processor. The processor preserves the appearance of strict sequential execution even in the presence of interrupts and exceptions.

Refer to Appendix H for information about how to optimize programs to exploit the performance potential of the Pentium processor.

18.7. WRITE BUFFERS

The Pentium processor utilizes write buffers for memory operands and for each pipeline. Write buffers improve performance by allowing the processor to proceed with the next pair of instructions even though one of the current instructions writes to memory when the bus is busy. The write buffers can be filled in parallel when intructions in both pipes write to memory during the same clock; however, they are always emptied in the same sequence in which the write requests were generated by software.

In general, the existence of these buffers is transparent to programmers. The Pentium processor ensures that memory read operations are never reordered ahead of prior pending write operations; however, for compatibility with future processors, programmers should follow the ordering guidelines presented in Chapter 19. Refer also to Chapter 15 for information about the interaction of I/O instructions with the memory write buffers.

18.8. SERIALIZING INSTRUCTIONS

After executing certain instructions the Pentium processor serializes instruction execution. This means that any modifications to flags, registers, and memory for previous instructions are completed before the next instruction is fetched and executed. For example, when a new value is loaded into CR0 to enable protected mode, the processor always fetches the next instruction with protection enabled.

When the processor serializes instruction execution, it ensures that it has completed any modifications to memory, including flushing any internally buffered stores; it then waits for the EWBE# pin to go active before fetching and executing the next instruction. Pentium processor systems can use the EWBE# pin to indicate that a store is pending externally. In this manner, a system designer can ensure that all externally pending stores are complete before the processor begins to fetch and execute the next instruction.

The processor serializes instruction execution after executing any of the following instructions:

CPUID	LGDT	MOV to Debug Register
INVD	LIDT	MOV to Control Register
INVLPG	LLDT	RSM
IRET	LTR	WBINVD
IRETD		WRMSR

The CPUID instruction can be executed at any privilege level to serialize instruction execution.

With regard to serialization, note that:

1. The Pentium processor does not generally write back the contents of modified data in its data cache to external memory when it serializes instruction execution. Software can force modified data to be written back by executing the instruction WBINVD.

2. Whenever an instruction is executed to enable/disable paging (that is, change the PG bit of CR0), this instruction must be followed with a jump. The instruction at the target of the branch is fetched with the new value of PG (i.e., paging enabled/disabled), however, the jump instruction itself is fetched with the previous value of PG. Intel386, Intel486 and Pentium processors have slightly different requirements in this regard. See Chapter 23 for more information. In all other respects a MOV to CR0 that changes PG is serializing. Any MOV to CR0 that does not change PG is completely serializing.

3. Whenever an instruction is executed to change the contents of CR3 while paging is enabled, the next instruction is fetched using the translation tables that correspond to the new value of CR3. Therefore the MOV to CR3 instruction and the sequentially following instructions should be located on a page whose linear address is mapped to the same physical address by both the old and new values of CR3.

4. The Pentium processor implements branch-prediction techniques to improve performance by prefetching the destination of a branch instruction before the branch instruction is executed. Consequently, instruction execution is not generally serialized when a branch instruction is executed.

5. The I/O instructions are not completely serializing; the processor does not wait for these instructions to complete before it prefetches the next instruction. However, they do have some serializing properties that cause them to function in a manner that is compatible with processor generations prior to the Pentium processor. Refer to Chapter 15 for more information.

intel®

19

Multiprocessing

CHAPTER 19
MULTIPROCESSING

The Pentium processor supports multiprocessing both on the processor bus and on a memory bus via secondary cache units. Due to the high bandwidth demands of multiprocessor systems Intel recommends the use of secondary cache.

Multiprocessors can increase particular aspects of system performance. For example, a computer graphics system may use an i860 CPU for fast rendering of raster images, while a Pentium processor is used to support a standard operating system, such as UNIX, IBM OS/2, or Microsoft Windows. Or alternatively, multiple Pentium microprocessors can be used in a symmetric system architecture with an operating system such as multiprocessor UNIX. Multiprocessing systems are sensitive to the following design issues:

- *Maintaining cache consistency*—When one processor accesses data cached in another processor, it must not receive incorrect data. If it modifies data, all other processors which access that data must receive the modified data.

- *Reliable communication*—Processors need to be able to communicate with each other in a way which eliminates interference when more than one processor simultaneously accesses the same area in memory.

- *Write ordering*—In some circumstances, it is important that memory writes be observed externally in precisely the same order as programmed.

Cache consistency is discussed in Chapter 18. Reliable communication and write ordering are discussed in the following sections.

19.1. LOCKED BUS CYCLES

While the system architecture of multiprocessor systems varies greatly, they generally have a need for reliable communication with memory. A processor in the act of updating the Accessed bit of a segment descriptor, for example, should reject other attempts to update the descriptor until the operation is complete.

It also is necessary to have reliable communication with other processors. Bus masters need to exchange data in a reliable way. For example, a bit in memory may be shared by several bus masters for use as a signal that some resource, such as a peripheral device, is idle. A bus master may test this bit, see that the resource is free, and change the state of the bit. The state would indicate to other potential bus masters that the resource is in use. A problem could arise if another bus master reads the bit between the time the first bus master reads the bit and the time the state of the bit is changed. This condition would indicate to both potential bus masters that the resource is free. They may interfere with each other as they both attempt to use the resource. The processor prevents this problem through support of locked bus cycles; requests for control of the bus are ignored during locked cycles.

The Pentium processor protects the integrity of certain critical memory operations by asserting an output signal called LOCK#. It is the responsibility of the hardware designer to use these signals to control memory access among processors.

The processor automatically asserts one of these signals during certain critical memory operations. Software can specify which other memory operations need to have LOCK# asserted.

The features of the general-purpose multiprocessing interface include:

- The LOCK# signal, which appears on a pin of the processor.
- The LOCK instruction prefix, which allows software to assert LOCK#.
- Automatic assertion of LOCK# for some kinds of memory operations.

19.1.1. LOCK Prefix and the LOCK# Signal

The LOCK prefix and its bus signal only should be used to prevent other bus masters from interrupting a data movement operation. The LOCK prefix can be used with the following Pentium CPU instructions when they modify memory. An invalid-opcode exception results from using the LOCK prefix before any other instruction, or with these instructions when no write operation is made to memory (i.e., when the destination operand is in a register).

- Bit test and change: the BTS, BTR, and BTC instructions.
- Exchange: the XCHG, XADD, CMPXCHG, and CMPXCHG8B instructions (no LOCK prefix is needed for the XCHG instruction).
- One-operand arithmetic and logical: the INC, DEC, NOT, NEG instructions.
- Two-operand arithmetic and logical: the ADD, ADC, SUB, SBB, AND, OR, and XOR instructions.

A locked instruction is *guaranteed* to lock only the area of memory defined by the destination operand, but may lock a larger memory area. For example, typical 8086 and 80286 configurations lock the entire physical memory space.

Semaphores (shared memory used for signalling between multiple processors) should be accessed using identical address and length. For example, if one processor accesses a semaphore using word access, other processors should not access the semaphore using byte access.

The integrity of the lock is not affected by the alignment of the memory field. The LOCK# signal is asserted for as many bus cycles as necessary to update the entire operand.

19.1.2. Automatic Locking

There are some critical memory operations for which the processor automatically asserts the LOCK# signal. These operations are:

- Acknowledging interrupts. After an interrupt request, the interrupt controller uses the data bus to send the interrupt vector of the source of the interrupt to the processor. The processor asserts LOCK# to ensure no other data appears on the data bus during this time.
- Setting the Busy bit of a TSS descriptor. The processor tests and sets the Busy bit in the

Type field of the TSS descriptor when switching to a task. To ensure that two different processors do not switch to the same task simultaneously, the processor asserts the LOCK# signal while testing and setting this bit.

- Updating segment descriptors. When loading a segment descriptor, the processor will set the Accessed bit if the bit is clear. During this operation, the processor asserts LOCK# so the descriptor will not be modified by another processor while it is being updated. For this action to be effective, operating-system procedures which update descriptors should use the following steps:

  — Use a locked operation when updating the access-rights byte to mark the descriptor not-present, and specify a value for the Type field which indicates the descriptor is being updated.

  — Update the fields of the descriptor. (This may require several memory accesses; therefore, LOCK cannot be used.)

  — Use a locked operation when updating the access-rights byte to mark the descriptor as valid and present.

  Note that the Intel386 DX processor always updates the Accessed bit, whether it is clear or not. The Intel486 and Pentium processors only update the Accessed bit if it is not already set.

- Updating page-directory and page-table entries. When updating page-directory and page-table entries, the processor uses locked cycles to set the Accessed and Dirty bits.

- Executing an XCHG instruction. The Pentium processor always asserts LOCK# during an XCHG instruction which references memory (even if the LOCK prefix is not used).

19.2. MEMORY ACCESS ORDERING

The Pentium microprocessor is a strongly ordered machine. "Strongly ordered" means that, in spite of parallel instruction execution, internal and external cache inquiry write-backs, and write buffering, the order in which writes are programmed is the order in which they are observed externally. In the case of I/O operations, both reads and writes always appear in programmed order. However, to optimize performance, the Pentium CPU allows memory reads to be reordered ahead of buffered writes in most situations.

Strong ordering helps software designed for execution by a uniprocessor system work correctly in a multiprocessor or multimaster environment. Such software does not necessarily consider the possible effect of the reordering of memory writes. Strong ordering, however, exacts a performance penalty and therefore may not be implemented in future processors.

Software intended to operate correctly in future, high-performance, weakly-ordered systems should not depend on the strongly ordered properties of the Pentium microprocessor. Instead, it should ensure that those accesses to shared variables which are intended to control concurrent execution among processors are explicitly ordered through the use of appropriate ordering operations. The ordering operations available on the Pentium microprocessor include the locking operations discussed in Section 19.1. and the serializing operations discussed in Chapter 18.

intel ®

20

System Management Mode

CHAPTER 20
SYSTEM MANAGEMENT MODE

System Management Mode (SMM) helps systems developers provide very high level systems functions, such as power management or security, in a manner that is transparent not only to application software but also to operating systems.

SMM is one of the major operating modes, on a level with protected mode, real-address mode, or virtual-86 mode. SMM, however, is intended for use only by firmware, not by applications software or general-purpose systems software. Figure 20-1 shows how the processor can enter SMM from any of the other modes, then return. The external signal SMI# causes the processor to switch to SMM. The instruction RSM exits SMM. The SMI# signal might be generated, for example, by closing the lid of a portable computer.

SMM is transparent to applications programs and operating systems because:

- The only way to enter SMM is via a type of non-maskable interrupt triggered by an external signal.

- The processor begins executing SMM code from a separate address space, referred to as system management RAM (SMRAM).

- Upon entry into SMM, the processor saves the register state of the interrupted program in a part of SMRAM called the SMM state dump record.

- All interrupts normally handled by the operating system or by applications are disabled upon entry into SMM.

- A special instruction RSM restores processor registers from the SMM state dump record and returns control to the interrupted program.

SMM is similar to real-address mode in that there are no privilege levels or address mapping. An SMM program can execute I/O and other system instructions and can address four gigabytes of memory.

20.1. THE SMI INTERRUPT

When an SMI# signal is recognized on an instruction execution boundary, the processor waits for all stores to complete (including those pending externally). The processor then saves its register state to SMRAM space and begins to execute the SMM handler.

SMI# has greater priority than debug exceptions and external interrupts. This means that if more than one of these conditions occur at an instruction boundary, only the SMI# processing occurs, not a debug exception or external interrupt.

Subsequent SMI# and NMI requests are not acknowledged while the processor is in SMM. The machine check enable bit in CR4 is cleared as well. SMI# and NMI interrupt requests that occur in SMM are latched and executed when the processor exits SMM with the RSM instruction.

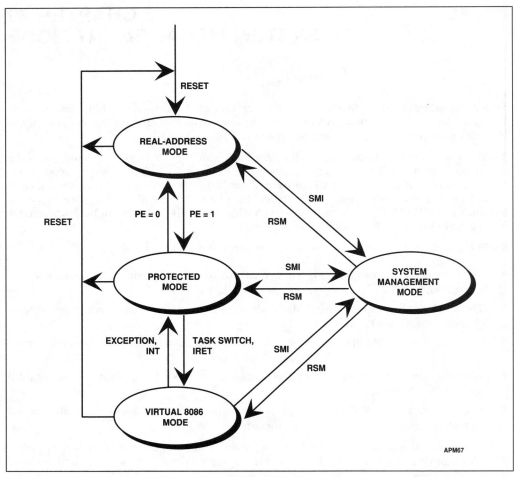

Figure 20-1. Mode State Transitions

Upon entry into SMM, external interrupts that require handlers are disabled (the IF bit in EFLAGS is cleared). This is necessary, because, while the processor is in SMM, it is running in a separate memory space. Consequently, the vectors stored in the interrupt descriptor table (IDT) for the prior mode are not applicable. To enable exception handling, the SMM program must set up new interrupt and exception vectors. The interrupt vector table for SMM has the same format as for real-address mode. Refer to Chapter 9 for information on the real-mode interrupt vector and changing the IDT register. Until it correctly sets up the interrupt vector table, the SMM handler program must not generate an exception. Even though interrupts are disabled, exceptions can still occur. Only correctly written software can prevent internal exceptions. When new exception vectors are set up, internal exceptions can be serviced.

Also upon entry into SMM, single-step exceptions are disabled (the TF bit of EFLAGS is zero) and address breakpoint exceptions are disabled (DR7 is cleared). To use the debugging features of the processor to debug the SMM handler itself, the SMM handler must ensure that an appropriate handler is available and installed in the IDT, then load the appropriate values into the debug registers or EFLAGS.

20.2. SMM INITIAL STATE

After the processor recognizes SMI# and saves the register state, it changes its state to the values shown in Table 20-1.

Table 20-1. SMM Initial State

Register	Content
General Purpose Registers	Undefined
EFLAGS	00000002H
EIP	00008000H
CS Selector	3000H. This value gives an initial instruction base address of 30000H; subsequently the instruction base address is the value of the prior State Dump Base field, even though CS remains 3000H.
DS,ES,FS,GS,SS Selectors	0000H (giving base addresses of 00000000H)
CS,DS,ES,FS,GS,SS Limit	FFFFFFFFH (4 gigabytes)
CS,DS,ES,FS,GS,SS Attributes	16-bit, expand up
CR0	Bits 0,2,3, & 31 cleared (PE,EM,TS & PG); rest unchanged
CR4	00000000H
DR6	Undefined
DR7	00000400H
GDTR, LDTR, IDTR, TSSR	Undefined
Model Specific Registers	Unmodified

External hardware is responsible for flushing the data cache, invalidating both the data and instruction caches, and keeping them disabled during SMM.

20.2.1. System Management Mode Execution

The processor begins executing the SMM handler at offset 8000H in the CS segment. The code segment base address is initially 30000H. This base address can be changed, however.

When the System Management Mode handler is invoked, the processor's PE (protection) and PG (paging) bits in CR0 are cleared to zero, putting the processor in an environment similar to real-address mode. Because the segment bases (other than CS) are cleared to zero and the segment limits are set to FFFFFFFFH, the address space can be treated as a single flat 4GB linear space that is unsegmented. The processor, however, still generates addresses as in real mode. When a segment selector is loaded with a 16-bit value, that value is still shifted 4 bits to the left and loaded into the segment base. Loading a segment register in SMM does not modify the limit and attributes in the hidden parts of descriptor registers.

The default operand size and the default address size are 16-bits; however, operand-size override and address-size override prefixes can be used as needed to directly access data anywhere within the four-gigabyte logical address space.

With operand-size override prefixes, the SMM handler can use jumps, calls, and returns, to transfer control to any location within the four-gigabyte space. Note, however, the following restrictions:

- Any control transfer that does not have an operand-size override prefix truncates EIP to 16 low-order bits.

- Due to the real-mode style of base-address formation, a long jump, call, interrupt, or exception cannot transfer control to a segment with a base address of more than 20 bits (one megabyte).

- An interrupt or exception cannot transfer control to a segment offset of more than 16 bits (64 kilobytes).

- If exceptions or interrupts are allowed to occur, only the low-order 16 bits of the return address are pushed onto the stack. If the offset of the interrupted procedure is greater than 64 Kbyte, it is not possible for the interrupt handler to return control to that procedure without some software adjustment of the return address on the stack.

20.3. SMRAM PROCESSOR STATE DUMP FORMAT

Table 20-2 shows the organization of the state dump record in the SMRAM area . The physical locations of the registers are relative to the value loaded into the CS Base, which is initially 30000H but which can be changed. The absolute location of the registers is: (CS Base + Register Offset).

The fields at offsets FFA8H–FFFFH hold the register state of the processor at the time of the SMI# interrupt. The remaining fields are explained in the following sections.

Table 20-2. State Dump Format

Register Offset (Hexadecimal)	Register
FFFC	CR0
FFF8	CR3
FFF4	EFLAGS
FFF0	EIP
FFEC	EDI
FFE8	ESI
FFE4	EBP
FFE0	ESP
FFDC	EBX
FFD8	EDX
FFD4	ECX
FFD0	EAX
FFCC	DR6
FFC8	DR7
FFC4	TR*
FFC0	LDTR*
FFBC	GS*
FFB8	FS*
FFB4	DS*
FFB0	SS*
FFAC	CS*
FFA8	ES*
FFA7–FF04	RESERVED
FF02	Halt Auto Restart
FF00	I/O Trap Restart
FEFC	SMM Revision Identifier
FEF8	State Dump Base
FEF7–FE00	RESERVED

NOTES:

Areas marked RESERVED should not be used by the SMM handler. Writing to these areas may cause the processor to malfunction. Software that depends on the contents of these areas will not be compatible with future processor generations.

*Upper 2 bytes are RESERVED.

The registers named in Table 20-2 are visible; that is, the SMM handler can read their values from the state dump record. Some (but not all) of these items can be changed by the SMM handler and the changed values will be restored to the processor registers by the RSM instruction. Table 20-3 shows which items can be changed and which cannot. Table 20-3 also indicates that some processor registers are saved in the state dump record but are not visible. These items are stored in RESERVED areas, but their locations and formats may be different in different processor versions. The last row of Table 20-3 shows the processor registers that are not automatically saved and restored by SMI# and RSM. If the SMM handler changes these registers, it must also save and restore them.

Table 20-3. State Disposition

State Item	Saved and Restored?	Readable?	Writeable?
EDI, ESI, EBP, ESP, EBX, EDX, ECS, EAX, EFLAGS, EIP	YES	YES	YES
CR0, CR3, DR6, DR7, TR, LDTR, GS, FS, DS, SS, CS, ES	YES	YES	NO
CR1, CR2, CR4, hidden descriptor registers for GDT, LDT, IDT, CS, DS, ES, FS, GS	YES	NO	NO
DR0–DR7, FP registers STn, FCS, FSW, tag word, FP instruction pointer, FP opcode and operand pointer	NO	NO	NO

20.3.1. System Management Mode Revision Identifier (Offset FEFCH)

The 32-bit SMM Revision Identifier specifies the version of SMM and the extensions that are available on the processor. Figure 20-2 shows the format of the SMM Revision Identifier.

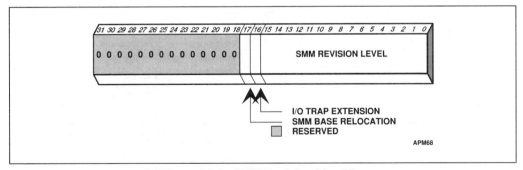

Figure 20-2. SMM Revision Identifier

The fields of the SMM Revision Identifier are shown in Table 20-4. A one in bits 16 or 17 indicate the processor supports those features.

Table 20-4. SMM Revision Identifier

Bits	Comments
0..15	Base SMM version identifier
16	The processor supports I/O Trap Restart
17	The processor supports SMRAM relocation

NOTE: All other bits are RESERVED.

20.3.2. I/O Trap Restart (Offset FF00H)

The I/O Trap Restart slot gives the SMM handler the option of causing the RSM instruction to automatically re-execute an interrupted I/O instruction. If, when the RSM instruction is executed, the I/O Trap Restart slot contains the value FFH, the CPU automatically re-executes the I/O instruction that SMI# has trapped. If the I/O Trap Restart slot contains the value 00H when the RSM instruction is executed, the CPU does not re-execute the I/O instruction. The CPU automatically initializes the I/O Trap Restart slot to zero during SMI# processing. The SMM handler should set the I/O Trap Restart slot to FFH only when an SMI# traps at an I/O-instruction boundary. Operation is unpredictable if the processor executes an RSM instruction and finds that the I/O Trap Restart slot is set to FFH but the interrupted instruction is not an I/O instruction.

20.3.3. Halt Auto Restart (Offset FF02H)

If SMI# is recognized while the processor is halted, the processor sets the value of the Halt Auto Restart slot to 1, otherwise the processor clears this value to 0. If this field is 1, the SMM handler can change its value to control whether the processor resumes the HLT instruction upon returning from the handler with the RSM instruction. Table 20-5 shows the possibilities.

Table 20-5. Halt Auto Restart

Value at Entry	Value at Exit	Processor Action on Exit
0	0	Returns to next instruction in interrupted program
0	1	Unpredictable
1	0	Returns to instruction after HLT
1	1	Returns to interrupted HLT instruction

20.3.4. State Dump Base (Offset FEF8H)

The processor contains an invisible internal register that specifies the physical base address for the state dump record and for the first instruction of the SMM handler. Processors that support SMRAM relocation (including the Pentium microprocessor) save the value of this register in the State Dump Base slot during SMI# processing.

The Pentium processor reloads the internal registers from the State Dump Base when executing the RSM instruction, which makes it possible to change the value of this register. The initial value for the State Dump Base and the value stored in the reserved internal register in the processor is 030000H.

This is for compatibility with existing SMM systems where the default SMRAM area is minimally defined to be the 32-Kbyte region starting at 38000H. Now that the SMRAM location is variable, the SMRAM area is minimally defined to be the 32-Kbyte region starting at [8000H + CS Base].

20.4. RELOCATING SMRAM

The SMM Revision Identifier indicates whether the processor supports the relocation of SMRAM. Relocating SMRAM to noncacheable addresses can prevent SMI# processing from disturbing cache contents.

SMRAM relocation is implemented through the use of a location in the SMRAM state dump (State Dump Base slot) and an invisible internal register. The 4-byte State Dump Base field corresponds to the invisible internal register that the processor uses upon entering SMM to determine the location of the SMM state dump and the location of the first instruction of the SMM handler.

When an SMI# is serviced, the value in the invisible register on the processor is stored to the State Dump Base field. Upon executing the RSM instruction, the processor reloads the invisible register from the State Dump Base slot.

The SMM handler can modify the value of the State Dump Base slot in the state dump record. Then, when subsequent SMI#'s are generated, the processor uses the new value to generate the location used for the SMM state dump and for the code-segment base. The state dump location must be aligned on a 32-Kbyte boundary.

Note that assertion of the INIT signal does not change the value of the internal state dump base register.

Note also that when the processor loads a new state dump base, the CS selector is not affected by the change.

20.5. RETURNING FROM SMM

The RSM instruction leaves SMM and returns control to the interrupted program. The RSM instruction can be executed only in SMM; an attempt to execute this instruction outside of SMM generates an invalid opcode exception.

When the RSM instruction is executed, the processor state that was previously stored upon entrance to SMM is restored, and control returns to the interrupted application. If the processor detects invalid state information, it enters the shutdown state; this happens only in the following situations:

- The value stored in the State Dump Base field is not a 32-Kbyte aligned address.
- A reserved bit of CR4 is set to 1.

- A combination of bits in CR0 is illegal; namely, (PG=1 and PE=0) or (NW=1 and CD=0).

In shutdown mode, the processor stops executing instructions until an NMI interrupt is received or reset initialization is invoked. The processor generates a special bus cycle to indicate it has entered shutdown mode. Hardware designers may choose from a variety of responses to the shutdown signal; for example, turning on an indicator light on the front panel, generating an NMI interrupt to record diagnostic information, or invoking reset initialization.

If the SMM handler has modified any system state that is not restored by RSM (such as the floating-point registers), then it should restore that state before executing RSM.

Part III

Compatibility

intel®

21

Mixing 16-Bit and 32-Bit Code

The Pentium processor running in protected mode, like the Intel486 and Intel386 processors, is a complete 32-bit architecture, but it supports programs written for the 16-bit architecture of earlier Intel processors. There are three levels of this support:

1. Running 8086 and 80286 code with complete compatibility.
2. Mixing 16-bit modules with 32-bit modules.
3. Mixing 16-bit and 32-bit addresses and data within one module.

The first level is discussed in Chapter 9, Chapter 22, and Chapter 23. Chapter 18 shows how 16-bit and 32-bit modules can cooperate with one another, and how one module can use both 16-bit and 32-bit operands and addressing.

The Pentium processor functions most efficiently when the processor can distinguish between pure 16-bit modules and pure 32-bit modules. A pure 16-bit module has these characteristics:

- All segments occupy 64 Kbytes or less.
- Data items are primarily 8 bits or 16 bits wide.
- Pointers to code and data have 16-bit offsets.
- Control is transferred only among 16-bit segments.

A pure 32-bit module has these characteristics:

- Segments may occupy more than 64 Kbytes (0 bytes to 4 gigabytes).
- Data items are primarily 8 bits or 32 bits wide.
- Pointers to code and data have 32-bit offsets.
- Control is transferred only among 32-bit segments.

A program written for 16-bit processor would be pure 16-bit code. A new program written for the protected mode of the Pentium processor would be pure 32-bit code.

21.1. USING 16-BIT AND 32-BIT ENVIRONMENTS

The features of the architecture which permit the Pentium processor to mix 16-bit and 32-bit address and operand size include:

- The D-bit (default bit) of code-segment descriptors, which determines the default choice of operand-size and address-size for the instructions of a code segment. (In real-address mode and virtual-8086 mode, which do not use descriptors, the default is 16 bits.) A code segment whose D-bit is set is a 32-bit segment; a code segment whose D-bit is clear is a 16-bit segment. The D-bit eliminates the need to put the operand size and address size in instructions when all instructions use operands and effective addresses of the same size.

- Instruction prefixes to override the default choice of operand size and address size (available in protected mode as well as in real-address mode and virtual-8086 mode).

- Separate 32-bit and 16-bit gates for intersegment control transfers (including call gates, interrupt gates, and trap gates). The operand size for the control transfer is determined by the type of gate, not by the D-bit or prefix of the transfer instruction.

- Registers which can be used both for 16-bit and 32-bit operands and effective-address calculations.

- The B bit (Big bit) of the stack segment descriptor, which specifies the size of stack pointer (the 32-bit ESP register or the 16-bit SP register) used by the processor for implicit stack references. The B bit for all data descriptors also controls upper address range for expand down segments.

21.2. MIXING 16-BIT AND 32-BIT OPERATIONS

The Pentium processor has two instruction prefixes which allow mixing of 32-bit and 16-bit operations within one segment:

- The operand-size prefix (66H)
- The address-size prefix (67H)

These prefixes *reverse* the default size selected by the Default bit. For example, the processor can interpret the MOV mem, reg instruction in any of four ways:

- In a 32-bit segment:
  1. Moves 32 bits from a 32-bit register to memory using a 32-bit effective address.
  2. If preceded by an operand-size prefix, moves 16 bits from a 16-bit register to memory using a 32-bit effective address.
  3. If preceded by an address-size prefix, moves 32 bits from a 32-bit register to memory using a 16-bit effective address.
  4. If preceded by both an address-size prefix and an operand-size prefix, moves 16 bits from a 16-bit register to memory using a 16-bit effective address.

- In a 16-bit segment:
  1. Moves 16 bits from a 16-bit register to memory using a 16-bit effective address.
  2. If preceded by an operand-size prefix, moves 32 bits from a 32-bit register to memory using a 16-bit effective address.
  3. If preceded by an address-size prefix, moves 16 bits from a 16-bit register to memory using a 32-bit effective address.
  4. If preceded by both an address-size prefix and an operand-size prefix, moves 32 bits from a 32-bit register to memory using a 32-bit effective address.

These examples show that any instruction can generate any combination of operand size and address size regardless of whether the instruction is in a 16- or 32-bit segment. The choice of the 16- or 32-bit default for a code segment is based upon these criteria:

1. The need to address instructions or data in segments which are larger than 64 Kbytes.

2. The predominant size of operands.

3. The addressing modes desired.

The Default bit should be given a setting which allows the predominant size of operands to be accessed without operand-size prefixes.

21.3. SHARING DATA AMONG MIXED-SIZE CODE SEGMENTS

Because the choice of operand size and address size is specified in code segments and their descriptors, data segments can be shared freely among both 16-bit and 32-bit code segments. The only limitation is imposed by pointers with 16-bit offsets, which only can point to the first 64 Kbytes of a segment. When a data segment with more than 64 Kbytes is to be shared among 16- and 32-bit segments, the data which is to be accessed by the 16-bit segments must be located within the first 64 Kbytes.

A stack which spans less than 64 Kbytes can be shared by both 16- and 32-bit code segments. This class of stacks includes:

- Stacks in expand-up segments with the Granularity and Big bits clear.

- Stacks in expand-down segments with the Granularity and Big bits clear.

- Stacks in expand-up segments with the Granularity bit set and the Big bit clear, in which the stack is contained completely within the lower 64 Kbytes. (Offsets greater than 0FFFFH can be used for data, other than the stack, which is not shared.)

The B-bit of a stack segment cannot, in general, be used to change the size of stack used by a 16-bit code segment. The size of stack pointer used by the processor for implicit stack references is controlled by the B-bit of the data-segment descriptor for the stack. Implicit references are those caused by interrupts, exceptions, and instructions such as the PUSH, POP, CALL, and RET instructions. Although it seems like the B bit could be used to increase the stack segment for 16-bit programs beyond 64 Kbytes, this may not be done. The B-bit does not control *explicit* stack references, such as accesses to parameters or local variables. A 16-bit code segment can use a "big" stack only if the code is modified so that all explicit references to the stack are preceded by the address-size prefix, causing those references to use 32-bit addressing and explicit writes to the stack pointer are preceded by an operand-size prefix.

In big, expand-down segments (the Big, and Expand-down bits set), all offsets may be greater than 64K, therefore 16-bit code cannot use this kind of stack segment unless the code segment is modified to use 32-bit addressing. (See Chapter 12 for more information about the B and E bits.)

21.4. TRANSFERRING CONTROL AMONG MIXED-SIZE CODE SEGMENTS

When transferring control among procedures in 16-bit and 32-bit code segments, programmers must be aware of three points:

- Addressing limitations imposed by pointers with 16-bit offsets.

- Matching of operand-size attribute in effect for the CALL/RET instruction pair and the Interrupt/IRET pair for managing the stack correctly.

- Translation of parameters, especially pointer parameters.

- The validity of the SP register must be noted when using 16-bit gates (see Section 21.4.2.).

Clearly, 16-bit effective addresses cannot be used to address data or code located beyond 0FFFFH in a 32-bit segment, nor can large 32-bit parameters be squeezed into a 16-bit word; however, except for these obvious limits, most interface problems between 16-bit and 32-bit modules can be solved. Some solutions involve inserting interface code between modules.

21.4.1. Size of Code-Segment Pointer

For control-transfer instructions which use a pointer to identify the next instruction (i.e., those which do not use gates), the size of the offset portion of the pointer is determined by the operand-size attribute. The implications of the use of two different sizes of code-segment pointer are:

- A JMP, CALL, or RET instruction from a 32-bit segment to a 16-bit segment is always possible using a 32-bit operand size.

- A JMP, CALL, or RET instruction from a 16-bit segment using a 16-bit operand size cannot address a destination in a 32-bit segment if the address of the destination is greater than 0FFFFH.

An interface procedure can provide a mechanism for transfers from 16-bit segments to destinations in 32-bit segments beyond 64K. The requirements for this kind of interface procedure are discussed later in this chapter.

21.4.2. Stack Management for Control Transfer

Because stack management is different for 16-bit CALL and RET instructions than for 32-bit CALL and RET instructions, the operand size of the RET instruction must match the CALL instruction. (See Figure 21-1. A 16-bit CALL instruction pushes the contents of the 16-bit IP register and (for calls between privilege levels) the 16-bit SP register. The matching RET instruction also must use a 16-bit operand size to pop these 16-bit values from the stack into the 16-bit registers. A 32-bit CALL instruction pushes the contents of the 32-bit EIP register and (for interlevel calls) the 32-bit ESP register. The matching RET instruction also must use a 32-bit operand size to pop these 32-bit values from the stack into the 32-bit registers. If the two parts of a CALL/RET instruction pair do not have matching operand sizes, the stack will not be managed correctly and the values of the instruction pointer and stack pointer will not be restored to correct values.

While executing 32-bit code, if a call to 16-bit code at a higher or equal privilege level (i.e., DPL≤CPL) is made via a 16-bit call gate, then the upper 16-bits of the ESP register may be unreliable upon returning to the 32-bit code (i.e., after executing a RET in the 16-bit code segment).

When the CALL instruction and its matching RET instruction are in segments which have D bits with the same values (i.e., both have 32-bit defaults or both have 16-bit defaults), the default settings may be used. When the CALL instruction and its matching RET instruction are in segments which have different D-bit values, an operand size prefix must be used.

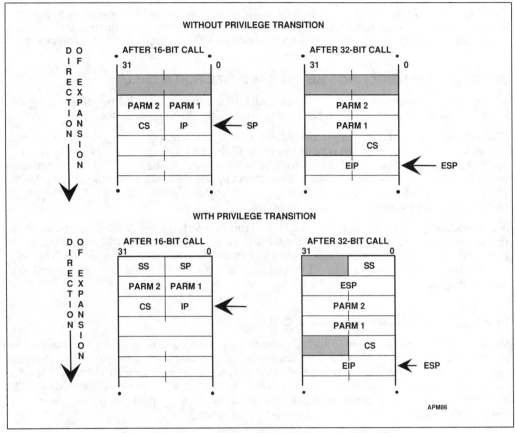

Figure 21-1. Stack After Far 16- and 32-Bit Calls

There are three ways for a 16-bit procedure to make a 32-bit call:

1. Use a 16-bit call to a 32-bit interface procedure. The interface procedure uses a 32-bit call to the intended destination.

2. Make the call through a 32-bit call gate.

3. Modify the 16-bit procedure, inserting an operand-size prefix before the call, to change it to a 32-bit call.

Likewise, there are three ways to cause a 32-bit procedure to make a 16-bit call:

1. Use a 32-bit call to a 32-bit interface procedure. The interface procedure uses a 16-bit call to the intended destination.

2. Make the call through a 16-bit call gate (the offset cannot exceed 0FFFFH).

3. Modify the 32-bit procedure, inserting an operand-size prefix before the call, thereby changing it to a 16-bit call. (Be certain that the return offset does not exceed 0FFFFH.)

Programmers can use any of the preceding methods to make a CALL instruction in a 16-bit segment match the corresponding RET instruction in a 32-bit segment, or to make a CALL instruction in a 32-bit segment match the corresponding RET instruction in a 16-bit segment.

21.4.2.1. CONTROLLING THE OPERAND SIZE FOR A CALL

The operand-size attribute in effect for the CALL instruction is specified by the D bit for the segment containing the destination and by any operand-size instruction prefix.

When the selector of the pointer referenced by a CALL instruction selects a gate descriptor, the type of call is determined by the type of call gate. Calls gates with descriptor type 4 have a 16-bit operand-size attribute; call gates with descriptor type 12 have a 32-bit operand-size attribute. The offset to the destination is taken from the gate descriptor; therefore, even a 16-bit procedure can call a procedure located more than 64 Kbytes from the base of a 32-bit segment, because a 32-bit call gate contains a 32-bit offset.

An unmodified 16-bit code segment which has run successfully on an 8086 processor or in real-mode on an Intel 286 processor will have a D-bit which is clear and will not use operand-size override prefixes; therefore, it will use 16-bit versions of the CALL instruction. The only modification needed to make a 16-bit procedure produce a 32-bit call is to relink the call to a 32-bit call gate.

21.4.2.2. CHANGING SIZE OF A CALL

When adding 32-bit gates to 16-bit procedures, it is important to consider the number of parameters. The count field of the gate descriptor specifies the size of the parameter string to copy from the current stack to the stack of the more privileged procedure. The count field of a 16-bit gate specifies the number of 16-bit words to be copied, whereas the count field of a 32-bit gate specifies the number of 32-bit doublewords to be copied; therefore, the 16-bit procedure must use an even number of words as parameters.

21.4.3. Interrupt Control Transfers

With a control transfer caused by an exception or interrupt, a gate is used. The operand-size attribute for the interrupt is determined by the gate descriptor in the interrupt descriptor table (IDT).

A 32-bit interrupt or trap gate (descriptor type 14 or 15) to a 32-bit interrupt handler can be used to interrupt either 32-bit or 16-bit procedures. However, sometimes it is not practical to permit an interrupt or exception to call a 16-bit handler when 32-bit code is running, because a 16-bit interrupt procedure has a return offset of only 16 bits saved on its stack. If the 32-bit procedure is running at an address beyond 0FFFFH, the 16-bit interrupt procedure cannot provide the return address.

21.4.4. Parameter Translation

When segment offsets or pointers (which contain segment offsets) are passed as parameters between 16-bit and 32-bit procedures, some translation is required. If a 32-bit procedure passes a pointer to data located beyond 64K to a 16-bit procedure, the 16-bit procedure cannot use it. Except for this limitation, interface code can perform any format conversion between 32-bit and 16-bit pointers which may be needed.

Parameters passed by value between 32-bit and 16-bit code also may require translation between 32-bit and 16-bit formats. The form of the translation is application-dependent.

21.4.5. The Interface Procedure

Placing interface code between 32-bit and 16-bit procedures can be the solution to several interface problems:

- Allowing procedures in 16-bit segments to call procedures with offsets greater than 0FFFFH in 32-bit segments.
- Matching operand size between CALL and RET instructions.
- Translating parameters (data).
- Possible invalidation of the upper bits of the ESP register.

The interface code is simplified where these restrictions are followed.

- Interface code resides in a code segment whose D-bit is set, which indicates a default operand size of 32 bits.
- All procedures which may be called by 16-bit procedures have offsets which are not greater than 0FFFFH.
- All return addresses saved by 16-bit procedures also have offsets not greater than 0FFFFH.

The interface code becomes more complex if any of these restrictions are violated. For example, if a 16-bit procedure calls a 32-bit procedure with an entry point beyond 0FFFFH, the interface code will have to provide the offset to the entry point. The mapping between 16- and 32-bit addresses only is performed automatically when a call gate is used, because the descriptor for a call gate contains a 32-bit address. When a call gate is not used, the descriptor must provide the 32-bit address.

The interface code calls procedures in other segments. There may be two kinds of interface:

- Where 16-bit procedures call 32-bit procedures. The interface code is called by 16-bit CALL instructions and uses the operand-size prefix before RET instructions for performing a 16-bit RET instruction. Calls to 32-bit segments are 32-bit CALL instructions (by default, because the D-bit is set), and the 32-bit code returns with 32-bit RET instructions.

- Where 32-bit procedures call 16-bit procedures. The interface code is called by 32-bit CALL instructions, and returns with 32-bit RET instructions (by default, because the D-bit is set). CALL instructions to 16-bit procedures use the operand-size prefix; 16-bit procedures return with 16-bit RET instructions.

intel®

22

Virtual-8086 Mode

The Pentium processor supports execution of one or more 8086 or 8088 programs in an Pentium processor protected-mode environment. An 8086 program runs in this environment as part of a virtual-8086 task. Virtual-8086 tasks take advantage of the hardware support for multitasking offered by the protected mode. Not only can there be multiple virtual-8086 tasks, each one running an 8086 program, but virtual-8086 tasks can be multitasked with other Pentium processor tasks.

The purpose of a virtual-8086 task is to form a "virtual machine" for running programs written for the 8086 processor. A complete virtual machine consists of hardware and system software. The emulation of an 8086 processor is the result of software using hardware in the following ways:

- The hardware provides a virtual set of registers (through the TSS), a virtual memory space (the first megabyte of the linear address space of the task), and virtual interrupt support and directly executes all instructions which deal with these registers and with this address space.

- The software controls the external interfaces of the virtual machine (I/O, interrupts, and exceptions) in a manner consistent with the larger environment in which it runs. Software can choose to emulate I/O and interrupt and exception handling or let the hardware execute them directly without software intervention.

Software which supports virtual 8086 machines is called a virtual-8086 monitor. The Pentium processor includes extensions to its virtual-8086 mode of operation that improve the performance of applications by eliminating the overhead of faulting to a virtual-8086 monitor for emulation of certain operations. For more information on the virtual mode extensions on the Pentium processor, see Appendix H.

22.1. EXECUTING 8086 CPU CODE

The processor runs in virtual-8086 mode when the VM (virtual machine) bit in the EFLAGS register is set. The processor tests this flag under two general conditions:

1. When loading segment registers, to know whether to use 8086-style address translation.

2. When decoding instructions, to determine which instructions are sensitive to IOPL and which instructions are not supported (as in real mode).

22.1.1. Registers and Instructions

The register set available in virtual-8086 mode includes all the registers defined for the 8086 processor plus new registers introduced after the 8086 processor (FS and GS). Instructions, which explicitly operate on the segment registers FS and GS, are available. The segment-override prefixes can be used to cause instructions to use the FS and GS registers for address calculations. Instructions can take advantage of 32-bit operands through the use of the operand size prefix.

Programs running as virtual-8086 tasks can take advantage of the new application-oriented instructions added to the architecture by the introduction of the Intel 286, Intel386, Intel486, and Pentium processors:

- New instructions introduced on the Intel 286 processors.
    - PUSH immediate data
    - Push all and pop all (PUSHA and POPA)
    - Multiply immediate data
    - Shift and rotate by immediate count
    - String I/O
    - ENTER and LEAVE instructions
    - BOUND instruction
- New instructions introduced on the Intel386 processors.
    - LSS, LFS, LGS instructions
    - Long-displacement conditional jumps
    - Single-bit instructions
    - Bit scan instructions
    - Double-shift instructions
    - Byte set on condition instruction
    - Move with sign/zero extension
    - Generalized multiply instruction
- New instructions introduced on the Intel486 processor.
    - BSWAP instruction
    - XADD instruction
    - CMPXCHG instruction
- New instructions introduced on the Pentium processor.
    - CMPXCHG8B instruction
    - CPUID instruction

Existing interrupt flag sensitive instructions provide significant performance improvement when using the virtual mode extensions of the Pentium processor. See Appendix H for more information.

22.1.2. Address Translation

In virtual-8086 mode, the Pentium processor does not interpret 8086 selectors by referring to descriptors; instead, it forms linear addresses as an 8086 processor would. It shifts the selector left by four bits to form a 20-bit base address. The effective address is extended with four clear bits in the upper bit positions and added to the base address to create a linear address, as shown in Figure 22-1.

Because of the possibility of a carry, the resulting linear address may have as many as 21 significant bits. An 8086 program may generate linear addresses anywhere in the range 0 to 10FFEFH (1 megabyte plus approximately 64 Kbytes) of the task's linear address space.

Virtual-8086 tasks generate 32-bit linear addresses. While an 8086 program can use only the lowest 21 bits of a linear address, the linear address can be mapped using paging to any 32-bit physical address.

Unlike the 8086 and 80286 processors, but like the Intel386 and Intel486 processors, the Pentium processor can generate 32-bit effective addresses using an address override prefix. However in virtual-8086 mode, the value of a 32-bit address may not exceed 65,535 without causing an exception. Protection faults (interrupt 12 or 13 with no error code) occur if an effective address is generated outside the range 0 through 65,535.

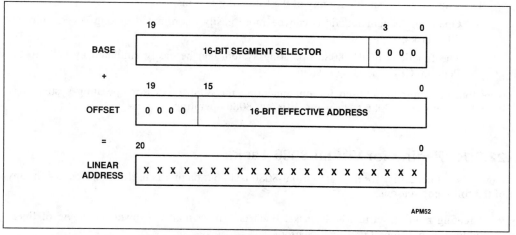

Figure 22-1. 8086 Address Translation

22.2. STRUCTURE OF A VIRTUAL-8086 TASK

A virtual-8086 task consists of the 8086 program to be run and the 32-bit "native mode" code which serves as the virtual-machine monitor. The task must be represented by a 32-bit TSS (not a 16-bit TSS). The processor enters virtual-8086 mode to run the 8086 program and returns to protected mode to run the monitor or other 32-bit protected mode tasks.

To run in virtual-8086 mode, an existing 8086 processor program needs the following:

- A virtual-8086 monitor.
- Operating-system services.

The virtual-8086 monitor is 32-bit protected-mode code which runs at privilege-level 0 (most privileged). The monitor mostly consists of initialization, exception-handling procedures, and I/O emulation in order to virtualize the PC platform. As with any other Pentium CPU program, code-segment descriptors for the monitor must exist in the GDT or in the task's LDT. The linear addresses above 10FFEFH are available for the virtual-8086 monitor, the operating system, and other system software. The monitor also may need data-segment descriptors so it can examine the interrupt vector table or other parts of the 8086 program in the first megabyte of the address space.

In general, there are two options for implementing the 8086 operating system:

1. The 8086 operating system may run as part of the 8086 program. This approach is desirable for either of the following reasons:

    — The 8086 application code modifies the operating system.

    — There is not sufficient development time to reimplement the 8086 operating system as a Pentium CPU operating system.

2. The 8086 operating system may be implemented or emulated in the virtual-8086 monitor. This approach is desirable for any of the following reasons:

    — Operating system functions can be more easily coordinated among several virtual-8086 tasks.

    — The functions of the 8086 operating system can be easily emulated by calls to the Pentium CPU operating system.

Note that the approach chosen for implementing the 8086 processor operating system may have different virtual-8086 tasks using different 8086 operating systems.

22.2.1. Paging for Virtual-8086 Tasks

Paging is not necessary for a single virtual-8086 task, but paging is useful or necessary for any of the following reasons:

- Creating multiple virtual-8086 tasks. Each task must map the lower megabyte of linear addresses to different physical locations.

- Emulating the address wraparound which occurs at 1 megabyte. With members of the 8086 family, it is possible to specify addresses larger than 1 megabyte. For example, with a selector value of 0FFFFH and an offset of 0FFFFH, the effective address would be 10FFEFH (1 megabyte plus 65519 bytes). The 8086 processor, which can form addresses only up to 20 bits long, truncates the high-order bit, thereby "wrapping" this address to 0FFEFH. The Pentium processor, however, does not truncate such an address. If any 8086 processor programs depend on address wraparound, the same effect can be achieved in a virtual-8086 task by mapping linear addresses between 100000H and 110000H and linear addresses between 0 and 10000H to the same physical addresses.

- Creating a virtual address space larger than the physical address space.

- Sharing 8086 operating system or ROM code which is common to several 8086 programs running in multitasking.

- Redirecting or trapping references to memory-mapped I/O devices.

22.2.2. Protection within a Virtual-8086 Task

Protection is not enforced between the segments of an 8086 program. To protect the system software running in a virtual-8086 task from the 8086 application program, software designers may follow either of these approaches:

- Reserve the first megabyte (plus 64 Kbytes) of each task's linear address space for the 8086 processor program. An 8086 processor task cannot generate addresses outside this range.

- Use the U/S bit of page-table entries to protect the virtual-machine monitor and other system software in each virtual-8086 task's space. When the processor is in virtual-8086 mode, the CPL is 3 (least privileged). Therefore, an 8086 processor program has only user privileges. If the pages of the virtual-machine monitor have supervisor privilege, they cannot be accessed by the 8086 program.

22.3. ENTERING AND LEAVING VIRTUAL-8086 MODE

Figure 22-2 summarizes the ways to enter and leave an 8086 program. Virtual-8086 mode is entered when the VM flag is set. There are two ways to do this:

1. A switch to a task loads the image of the EFLAGS register from the new TSS. The TSS of the new task must be a 32-bit TSS, not a 16-bit TSS, because the 16-bit TSS does not load the high word of the EFLAGS register, which contains the VM flag. A set VM flag in the new contents of the EFLAGS register indicates that the new task is executing 8086 instructions; therefore, while loading the segment registers from the TSS, the processor forms base addresses in the 8086 style.

2. An IRET instruction from a procedure of a task loads the EFLAGS register from the stack. A set VM flag indicates the procedure to which control is being returned to be an 8086 procedure. The CPL at the time the IRET instruction is executed must be 0, otherwise the processor does not change the state of the VM flag.

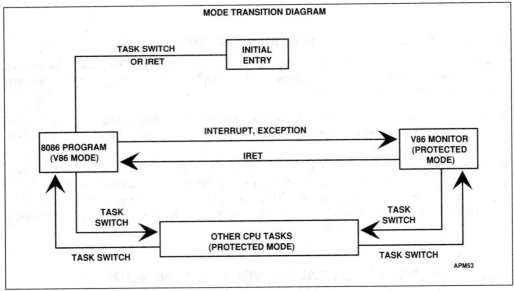

Figure 22-2. Entering and Leaving Virtual-8086 Mode

When a task switch is used to enter virtual-8086 mode, the segment registers are loaded from a TSS. When an IRET instruction is used to set the VM flag, however, the segment registers are loaded from the segment registers on the PL0 stack (see Figure 22-3).

The processor leaves virtual-8086 mode when an interrupt or exception occurs. There are two cases:

1. The interrupt or exception causes a task switch. A task switch from a virtual-8086 task to any other task loads the EFLAGS register from the TSS of the new task. If the new TSS is a 32-bit TSS and the VM flag in the new contents of the EFLAGS register is clear or if the new TSS is a 16-bit TSS, the processor clears the VM flag of the EFLAGS register, loads the segment registers from the new TSS using protected mode address formation, and begins executing the instructions of the new task in 32-bit protected mode.

2. The interrupt or exception calls a privilege-level 0 procedure (most privileged). The processor stores the current contents of the EFLAGS register on the stack, then clears the VM flag. The interrupt or exception handler, therefore, runs as "native" 32-bit protected-mode code. If an interrupt or exception calls a procedure in a conforming segment or in a segment at a privilege level other than 0 (most privileged), the processor generates a general-protection exception; the error code is the selector of the code segment to which a call was attempted.

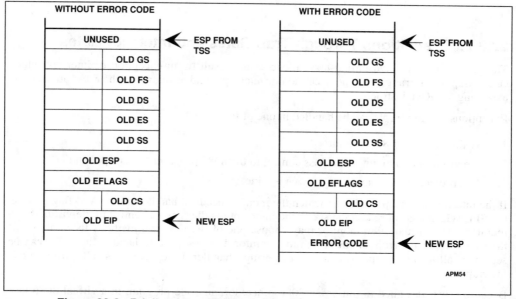

Figure 22-3. Privilege Level 0 Stack After Interrupt in Virtual-8086 Mode

System software does not change the state of the VM flag directly, but instead changes states in the image of the EFLAGS register stored on the stack or in the TSS. The virtual-8086 monitor sets the VM flag in the EFLAGS image on the stack or in the TSS when first creating a virtual-8086 task. Exception and interrupt handlers can examine the VM flag on the stack. If the interrupted procedure was running in virtual-8086 mode, the handler may need to call the virtual-8086 monitor.

22.3.1. Transitions Through Task Switches

A task switch to or from a virtual-8086 task may have any of three causes:

1. An interrupt which calls a task gate.
2. An action of the scheduler of the 32-bit operating system.
3. Executing an IRET instruction when the NT flag is set.

In any of these cases, the processor changes the VM flag in the EFLAGS register according to the image in the new TSS. If the new TSS is a 16-bit TSS, the upper word of the EFLAGS register is not in the TSS; the processor clears the VM flag in this case. The processor updates the VM flag prior to loading the segment registers from their images in the new TSS. The new setting of the VM flag determines whether the processor interprets the new segment-register images as 8086 selectors, 80286 selectors or 32-bit selectors.

22.3.2. Transitions Through Trap Gates and Interrupt Gates

The processor may leave virtual-8086 mode as the result of an exception or interrupt which calls a trap or interrupt gate. The exception or interrupt handler returns to the 8086 program by executing an IRET instruction.

Exceptions and interrupts can be handled in one of three ways:

1.   By the the virtual-8086 monitor.
2.   The virtual-8086 monitor can pass control to the 8086 program's interrupt handler.
3.   By a protected-mode interrupt service routine.

If the interrupt or exception is one which the monitor needs to handle and the VM flag is set in the EFLAGS image stored on the stack, the interrupt handler passes control to the virtual-8086 monitor. The virtual-8086 monitor may choose one of the first two methods listed above. If the exception or interrupt is one which the monitor does not need to handle, the IOPL can be set to 3 allowing the protected-mode interrupt handler to execute for all virtual-mode interrupts.

Because it was designed to run on an 8086 processor, an 8086 program in a virtual-8086 task has an 8086-style interrupt table, which starts at linear address 0. However, for exceptions and interrupts requiring virtual-8086 monitor intervention and a transition into protected mode, the processor does not use this table directly. Instead, the processor calls handlers through the IDT. The IDT entry for an interrupt or exception in a virtual-8086 task must contain either:

•   A task gate.
•   A 32-bit trap gate (descriptor type 14) or 32-bit interrupt gate (descriptor type 15), which must point to a nonconforming, privilege-level 0 (most privileged), code segment.

Interrupts and exceptions which call 32-bit trap or interrupt gates use privilege-level 0. The contents of the segment registers are stored on the stack for this privilege level. Figure 22-3 shows the format of this stack after an exception or interrupt which occurs while a virtual-8086 task is running an 8086 program.

After the processor saves the 8086 segment registers on the stack for privilege level 0, it clears the segment registers before running the handler procedure. This lets the interrupt handler safely save and restore the DS, ES, FS, and GS registers as though they were Pentium CPU selectors. Interrupt handlers, which may be called in the context of either a regular task or a virtual-8086 task, can use the same code sequences for saving and restoring the registers for any task. Clearing these registers before execution of the IRET instruction does not cause a trap in the interrupt handler. Interrupt procedures which expect values in the segment registers or which return values in the segment registers must use the register images saved on the stack for privilege level 0. Interrupt handlers which need to know whether the interrupt occurred in virtual-8086 mode can examine the VM flag in the stored contents of the EFLAGS register.

Sending an interrupt or exception back to the 8086 program involves the following steps:

1.   Use the 8086 interrupt vector to locate the appropriate handler procedure.

2. Store the FLAGS, CS and IP values of the 8086 program on the privilege-level 3 stack (least privileged).

3. Change the return link on the privilege-level 0 stack to point to the privilege-level 3 handler procedure.

4. Execute an IRET instruction to pass control to the handler.

5. When the IRET instruction from the privilege-level 3 handler again calls the virtual-8086 monitor, restore the return link on the privilege-level 0 stack to point to the original, interrupted, privilege-level 3 procedure.

6. Execute an IRET instruction to pass control back to the interrupted procedure.

If the IOPL is set to three and the DPL of the interrupt gate is set to three, INT n instructions will trap with the given vector number n. Interrupt vectors that must have their IDT gates set to three can examine the VM bit in the EFLAGS image on the stack to determine if the interrupt needs to be redirected to the virtual-8086 monitor or passed to the 8086 program's interrupt handler.

22.4. SENSITIVE INSTRUCTIONS

When the Pentium processor is running in virtual-8086 mode, the CLI, STI, PUSHF, POPF, INT n, and IRET instructions are sensitive to IOPL. The IN, INS, OUT, and OUTS instructions, which are sensitive to IOPL in protected mode, are not sensitive in virtual-8086 mode. Following is a complete list of instructions which are sensitive in virtual-8086 mode:

CLI   — Clear Interrupt-Enable Flag
STI   — Set Interrupt-Enable Flag
PUSHF   — Push Flags
POPF   — Pop Flags
INT n   — Software Interrupt
IRET   — Interrupt Return

The CPL is always 3 while running in virtual-8086 mode; if the IOPL is less than 3, an attempt to use the instructions listed above triggers a general-protection exception. These instructions are sensitive to IOPL in order to give the virtual-8086 monitor a chance to emulate the facilities they affect. For information on the behavior of these instructions using the virtual mode extensions, see Appendix H.

22.5. VIRTUAL INTERRUPT SUPPORT

Many 8086 programs written for non-multitasking systems set and clear the IF flag to control interrupts. This may cause problems in a multitasking environment. As a result, virtual monitors running on the Intel386 and Intel486 processors require maintaining a virtual interrupt flag in software. All instructions affecting the IF flag trap to the virtual-8086 monitor for emulation on these processors. For more information on Pentium processor support of a virtual interrupt flag, see Appendix H.

22.6. EMULATING 8086 OPERATING SYSTEM CALLS

Many 8086 operating systems are called by pushing parameters onto the stack, then executing an INT n instruction. The INT n instruction is sensitive to IOPL to allow the virtual-8086 monitor to emulate the function of the 8086 operating system or send the interrupt back to the 8086 operating system.

When the IOPL<3, INT n instructions are intercepted by the virtual-8086 monitor. When the IOPL=3, interrupts are serviced by the protected-mode interrupt service routine in a manner compatible with the Intel486 processor. On the Intel386 and Intel486 processors, all INT n instructions running in virtual-8086 mode require interception by the virtual-8086 monitor when the IOPL is less than 3. For information on Pentium processor virtual mode extension support of interrupt handling, see Appendix H.

Table 22-1 determines what action the Pentium processor takes in virtual-8086 mode for a software interrupt based on the IOPL.

Table 22-1. Software Interrupt Operation

IOPL	Processor Action
=3	**Interrupt from Virtual-8086 Mode to Protected Mode:**
	Clears VM and TF flags
	If service through interrupt gate, clears IF flag
	Changes to PL0 stack using TSS values
	Pushes GS, FS, DS and ES onto PL0 stack
	Clears GS, FS, DS and ES to 0
	Pushes SS, ESP, EFLAGS, CS and EIP of interrupted task onto PL0 stack
	Sets CS and EIP from interrupt gate
<3	**General protection exception**

22.7. VIRTUAL I/O

Many 8086 programs written for non-multitasking systems directly access I/O ports. This may cause problems in a multitasking environment. If more than one program accesses the same port, they may interfere with each other. Most multitasking systems require application programs to access I/O ports through the operating system. This results in simplified, centralized control.

The processor provides I/O protection for creating I/O which is compatible with the environment and transparent to 8086 programs. Designers may take any of several possible approaches to protecting I/O ports:

- Protect the I/O address space and generate exceptions for all attempts to perform I/O directly.

- Let the 8086 processor program perform I/O directly.
- Generate exceptions on attempts to access specific I/O ports.
- Generate exceptions on attempts to access specific memory-mapped I/O ports.

The method of controlling access to I/O ports depends upon whether they are I/O-mapped or memory-mapped.

22.7.1. I/O-Mapped I/O

The I/O permission bit map can be used to generate exceptions on attempts to access specific I/O addresses. The I/O permission bit map of each virtual-8086 task determines which I/O addresses generate exceptions for that task. Because each task may have a different I/O permission bit map, the addresses which generate exceptions for one task may be different from the addresses for another task. This differs from protected mode because the IOPL is not checked. See Chapter 8 for more information about the I/O permission bit map.

22.7.2. Memory-Mapped I/O

In systems which use memory-mapped I/O, the paging facilities of the processor can be used to generate exceptions for attempts to access I/O ports. The virtual-8086 monitor may use paging to control memory-mapped I/O in these ways:

- Map part of the linear address space of each task which needs to perform I/O to the physical address space where I/O ports are placed. By putting the I/O ports at different addresses (in different pages), the paging mechanism can enforce isolation between tasks.
- Map part of the linear address space to pages which are not-present. This generates an exception whenever a task attempts to perform I/O to those pages. System software then can interpret the I/O operation being attempted.

Software emulation of the I/O space may require too much operating system intervention under some conditions. In these cases, it may be possible to generate an exception for only the first attempt to access I/O. The system software then may determine whether a program can be given exclusive control of I/O temporarily, the protection of the I/O space may be lifted, and the program allowed to run at full speed.

22.7.3. Special I/O Buffers

Buffers of intelligent controllers (for example, a bit-mapped frame buffer) also can be emulated using page mapping. The linear space for the buffer can be mapped to a different physical space for each virtual-8086 task. The virtual-8086 monitor then can control which virtual buffer to copy onto the real buffer in the physical address space.

22.8. DIFFERENCES FROM 8086 CPU

In general, virtual-8086 mode will run software written for the 8086 and 8088 processors. The following list shows the minor differences between the 8086 processor and the virtual-8086 mode of the Pentium processor and other 32-bit processors.

1. Instruction clock counts.

    The 32-bit processors takes fewer clocks for most instructions than the 8086 processor. The areas most likely to be affected include:

    — Delays required by I/O devices between I/O operations.

    — Assumed delays with 8086 processor operating in parallel with an 8087.

2. Divide exceptions point to the DIV instruction.

    Divide exceptions on the Pentium processor always leave the saved CS:IP value pointing to the instruction which failed. On the 8086 processor, the CS:IP value points to the next instruction.

3. Undefined 8086 processor opcodes.

    Opcodes which were not defined for the 8086 processor generate an invalid-opcode or execute as one of the new instructions defined for the Pentium processor.

4. Value written by PUSH SP.

    The Pentium processor pushes a different value on the stack for PUSH SP than the 8086 processor. The Pentium processor pushes the value in the SP register before it is decremented as part of the push operation; the 8086 processor pushes the value of the SP register after it is decremented. If the pushed value is important, replace PUSH SP instructions with the following three instructions:

    ```
    PUSH      BP
    MOV BP,   SP
    XCHG      BP, [BP]
    ```

    This code functions as the 8086 PUSH SP instruction on the Pentium processor.

5. Shift or rotate by more than 31 bits.

    The Pentium processor masks all shift and rotate counts to the lowest five bits. This limits the count to a maximum of 31 bit positions.

6. Redundant prefixes.

    The Pentium processor limits instructions to 15 bytes. The only way to violate this limit is with redundant prefixes before an instruction. A general-protection exception is generated if the limit on instruction length is violated. The 8086 processor has no instruction length limit.

7. Operand crossing offset 0 or 65,535.

    On the 8086 processor, an attempt to access a memory operand which crosses offset 65,535 (e.g., MOV a word to offset 65,535) or offset 0 (e.g., PUSH a word when the contents of the SP register are 1) causes the offset to wrap around modulo 65,536. The Pentium processor generates an exception in these cases, a general-protection exception if the segment is a data segment (i.e., if the CS, DS, ES, FS, or GS register is being used to address the segment), or a stack exception if the segment is a stack segment (i.e., if the SS register is being used).

8. Sequential execution across offset 65,535.

    On the 8086 processor, if sequential execution of instructions proceeds past offset 65,535, the processor fetches the next instruction byte from offset 0 of the same segment. On the Pentium processor, the processor generates a general-protection exception.

9. LOCK is restricted to certain instructions.

    The LOCK prefix and its output signal should only be used to prevent other bus masters from interrupting a data movement operation. The LOCK prefix only may be used with the following Pentium CPU instructions when they modify memory. An invalid-opcode exception results from using LOCK before any other instruction, or with these instructions when no write operation is made to memory.

    — Bit test and change: the BTS, BTR, and BTC instructions.

    — Exchange: the XCHG, XADD, CMPXCHG, and CMPXCH8B instructions (no LOCK prefix is needed for the XCHG instruction).

    — One-operand arithmetic and logical: the INC, DEC, NOT, NEG instructions

    — Two-operand arithmetic and logical: the ADD, ADC, SUB, SBB, AND, OR, and XOR instructions.

10. Single-stepping external interrupt handlers.

    The priority of the Pentium processor single-step exception is different from that of the 8086 processor. This change prevents an external interrupt handler from being single-stepped if the interrupt occurs while a program is being single-stepped. The Pentium processor single-step exception has higher priority than any external interrupt. The Pentium processor will still single-step through an interrupt handler called by the INT instruction or by an exception.

11. IDIV exceptions for quotients of 80H or 8000H.

    The Pentium processor can generate the largest negative number as a quotient from the IDIV instruction. The 8086 processor generates a divide-error exception instead.

12. Flags in stack.

    The contents of the EFLAGS register stored by the PUSHF instruction, by interrupts, and by exceptions is different from that stored by the 8086 processor in bit positions 12 through 15. On the 8086 processor these bits are stored as though they were set, but in virtual-8086 mode bit 15 is always clear, and bits 14 through 12 have the last value loaded into them.

13. NMI interrupting NMI handlers.

    After an NMI interrupt is accepted by the Pentium processor, the NMI interrupt is masked until an IRET instruction is executed.

14. Floating-point errors call the floating-point-error exception.

    Floating-point exceptions on the Pentium processor call the floating-point error exception handler. If an 8086 processor uses another exception for the 8087 interrupt, both exception vectors should call the floating-point error exception handler. The Pentium processor has signals which, with the addition of external logic, support user-defined error reporting for emulation of the interrupt mechanism used in many personal computers.

15. Numeric exception handlers should allow prefixes.

    On the Pentium processor, the value of the CS and IP registers saved for floating-point exceptions points at any prefixes which come before the ESC instruction. On the 8086 processor, the saved CS:IP points to the ESC instruction.

16. Floating-Point Unit does not use interrupt controller.

The floating-point error signal to the Pentium processor does not pass through an interrupt controller (an INT signal from 8087 coprocessor does). Some instructions in a coprocessor-error exception handler may need to be deleted if they use the interrupt controller. The Pentium processor has signals which, with the addition of external logic, support user-defined error reporting for emulation of the interrupt mechanism used in many personal computers.

17. Response to bus hold.

Unlike the 8086 and Intel 286 processors, the Pentium processor responds to requests for control of the bus from other potential bus masters, such as DMA controllers, between transfers of parts of an unaligned operand, such as two words which form a doubleword.

18. CPL is 3 in virtual-8086 mode.

The 8086 processor does not support protection, so it has no CPL. Virtual-8086 mode uses a CPL of 3, which prevents the execution of privileged instructions. These are:

— LIDT instruction

— LGDT instruction

— LMSW instruction

— Special forms of the MOV instruction for loading and storing the control registers

— CLTS instruction

— HLT instruction

— INVD instruction

— WBINVD instruction

— INVLPG instruction

— RDMSR instruction

— WRMSR instruction

— RSM instruction

These instructions may be executed while the processor is in real-address mode following reset initialization. They allow system data structures, such as descriptor tables, to be set up before entering protected mode. Since virtual-8086 mode is entered from protected mode, these structures will already be set up.

19. Denormal exception handling is different. See Chapter 23 for details on exception handling differences.

22.9. DIFFERENCES FROM Intel 286 CPU

The differences between virtual-8086 mode and Intel 286 real-address mode affect the interface between applications and the operating system. The application runs at privilege level 3 (user mode), so all attempts to use privilege-protected instructions and architectural features generate calls to the virtual-machine monitor. The monitor examines these calls and emulates them.

22.9.1. Privilege Level

Programs running in virtual-8086 mode have a privilege level of 3 (user mode), which prevents the execution of privileged instructions. These are:

- LIDT instruction
- LGDT instruction
- LMSW instruction
- Special forms of the MOV instruction for loading and storing the control and debug registers
- CLTS instruction
- HLT instruction
- INVD instruction
- WBINVD instruction
- INVLPG instruction
- RDMSR instruction
- WRMSR instruction
- RSM instruction

Virtual-8086 mode is entered from protected mode, so it should have no need for these instructions. These instructions, while not executable in virtual-8086 mode, can be executed in real-address mode.

22.9.2. Bus Lock

The Intel 286 processor implements the bus lock function differently than the Intel386, Intel486, and Pentium processors. This fact may or may not be apparent to 8086 programs, depending on how the virtual-8086 monitor handles the LOCK prefix. Instructions with the LOCK prefix are sensitive to the IOPL; software designers can choose to emulate its function. If, however, 8086 programs are allowed to execute LOCK directly, programs which use forms of memory locking specific to the 8086 processor may not run properly when run on the Pentium and other 32-bit processors.

The LOCK prefix and its bus signal only should be used to prevent other bus masters from interrupting a data movement operation. The LOCK prefix only may be used with the following Pentium CPU instructions when they modify memory. An invalid-opcode exception results from using the LOCK prefix before any other instruction, or with these instructions when no write operation is made to memory (i.e., when the destination operand is in a register).

- Bit test and change: the BTS, BTR, and BTC instructions.
- Exchange: the XCHG, XADD, and CMPXCHG instructions (no LOCK prefix is needed for the XCHG instruction).

- One-operand arithmetic and logical: the INC, DEC, NOT, NEG instructions.

- Two-operand arithmetic and logical: the ADD, ADC, SUB, SBB, AND, OR, and XOR instructions.

A locked instruction is guaranteed to lock only the area of memory defined by the destination operand, but may lock a larger memory area. For example, typical 8086 and Intel 286 configurations lock the entire physical memory space.

Unlike the 8086 and Intel 286 processors, the Intel386, Intel486 and Pentium processors respond to requests for control of the bus from other potential bus masters, such as DMA controllers, between transfers of parts of an unaligned operand, such as two words which form a doubleword.

22.10. DIFFERENCES FROM Intel386 AND Intel486 CPU'S

Real-address mode behavior is the same on the Intel386, Intel486, and Pentium processors. When the virtual mode extensions are disabled (VME bit in CR4 is set to zero), the virtual-8086 mode behavior of the Pentium processor is the same as on the Intel386 and Intel486 processors. By enabling the virtual mode extensions (VME bit in CR4 is set to one), however, the virtual-8086 mode performance of the Pentium processor is significantly improved. See Appendix H for obtaining information on these extensions. For maximum performance, programs ported to the Pentium processor should be run with the cache enabled.

intel®

23

Compatibility

The Pentium CPU is fully binary compatible with the Intel486 DX and SX CPU's, the Intel386 DX and SX CPU's, the Intel 286 CPU and the 8086/8088 CPU's. Compatibility means that, within certain limited constraints, programs that execute on any previous generations of compatible microprocessors will produce identical results when executed on the Pentium CPU. There are, however, slightly different implementations of architectural features. These limitations and any implementation differences are listed in this chapter.

The Pentium processor also includes extensions to the registers, instruction set, and control functions of the Intel486 architecture just as the Intel486 CPU included extensions to the Intel386 CPU. Those extensions have been defined with consideration for compatibility with previous and future microprocessors. This section also summarizes the compatibility considerations for those extensions.

23.1. RESERVED BITS

Throughout this manual, certain bits are marked as reserved in many register and memory layout descriptions. When bits are marked as undefined or reserved, it is essential for compatibility with future processors that software treat these bits as having a future, though unknown effect. Software should follow these guidelines in dealing with reserved bits:

- Do not depend on the states of any reserved bits when testing the values of registers or memory locations which contain such bits. Mask out the reserved bits before testing.

- Do not depend on the states of any reserved bits when storing to memory or to a register.

- Do not depend on the ability to retain information written into any reserved bits.

- When loading a register, always load the reserved bits with the values indicated in the documentation, if any, or reload them with values previously stored from the same register.

Depending on the values of reserved register bits will make software dependent upon the unspecified manner in which the Pentium processor handles these bits. Depending upon reserved values risks incompatibility with future processors. AVOID ANY SOFTWARE DEPENDENCE UPON THE STATE OF RESERVED PENTIUM PROCESSOR REGISTER BITS.

Software written for an Intel386 or Intel486 CPU which uses reserved bits correctly will port to the Pentium processor without generating general exceptions.

23.2. INTEGER UNIT

This section identifies the new features and the implementation differences of existing features in the integer unit, which includes added registers and flags, exception handling, memory

23.2.1. New Functions and Modes

New control functions defined for the Pentium processor are enabled by mode bits in newly defined registers, discussed below, that were not present in the Intel486 architecture. The instructions that are executed to read and write these new registers are undefined on the Intel486 processor, and an invalid opcode exception occurs when an attempt is made to execute one of these instructions on the Intel486 processor. Consequently, programs that execute correctly on the Intel486 processor cannot erroneously enable these functions. However, when an instruction is executed to write one of the new registers and an attempt is made to set a reserved bit to a value other than the original value, then a general protection exception occurs on the Pentium processor so programs that execute on the Pentium processor cannot erroneously enable functions that may be implemented in future processors. The Pentium processor does not check for attempts to set reserved bits in model-specific registers. It is the obligation of the software writer to enforce this discipline. These reserved bits may be used in future Intel processors.

23.2.2. Serializing Instructions

Certain instructions have been defined to serialize instruction execution to ensure that modifications to flags, registers and memory are completed before the next instruction is fetched and executed. Because the Pentium processor uses branch-prediction techniques to improve performance, instruction execution is not generally serialized when a branch instruction is executed. As a result, branch instructions do not necessarily flush the prefetch queue on the Pentium processor and serializing instructions should replace branch instructions used for this purpose. Refer to Chapter 18 and the *Pentium™ Processor Data Book* for more information on serializing instructions. For more information on branch prediction, see Appendix H.

23.2.3. Detecting the Presence of New Features

As the Pentium processor provides extensions to the architecture of the Intel486 processor, other models within the processor family have provided both extensions to previous models and features specific to that model (such as testability functions). Consequently, software that wishes to use the extensions or specific features must identify on which model it is executing to determine what features are available. Programmers have developed code sequences that can be executed to distinguish between the 8086, Intel 286, Intel386, and Intel486 microprocessors. The code sequences commonly test which bits in the processor's FLAGS register are implemented. (For an example see Chapter 5.) The CPUID instruction has been defined to provide a straightforward way for software to identify what family, model and stepping of processor it is running on. This can be accomplished as follows:

1. One of the code sequences described in Chapter 5 can be executed to determine that the software is executing on an Intel486 CPU or a later model that implements a superset of the Intel486 architecture. (This is typically done by testing the ability to change the value

of the AC flag.)

2. Having determined that the processor is "at least" an Intel486 processor, a software sequence can test whether it is able to change the value of the ID bit. If software is able to change the value of the ID bit, then the processor supports the CPUID instruction.

3. The sequence can then continue by executing the CPUID instruction. In order to use a particular architecture extension, software should check that the appropriate feature bit returned by this instruction is set. Refer to this instruction in Chapter 25 for more information about its operation.

23.2.4. Undefined Opcodes

All new instructions defined for the Pentium processor use binary encodings for which the invalid opcode exception occurs when an attempt is made to execute these instructions on the Intel486 processor. Consequently, programs that execute correctly on the Intel486 processor cannot erroneously execute these instructions and thereby produce unexpected results.

23.2.5. Clock Counts

Each processor takes fewer clocks for most instructions than earlier processors. The areas most likely to be affected include:

*   Delays required by I/O devices between I/O operations.

*   Assumed delays with 8086 processor operating in parallel with an 8087.

23.2.6. Initialization and Reset

This section identifies the state of the integer and floating-point units for the various microprocessors and numeric processor extensions.

23.2.6.1.   INTEGER UNIT INITIALIZATION AND RESET

Table 23-1 identifies the values of the integer unit registers following hardware reset for the 32-bit Intel x86 microprocessors. These values are the same regardless of whether the Built-In Self Test (BIST) is invoked.

23.2.6.2.   FPU/NPX INITIALIZATION AND RESET

The Pentium and Intel486 processors, following RESET, contain 0 in ST0-ST7 stack registers with the tags set to valid (10) (but visible to the programmer as 01 via FSAVE/FSTENV). The Pentium processor, in addition, has an INIT pin which, when asserted, causes the processor to reset without altering the FPU state. The state of the Intel486 FPU is left unchanged when the Built-In Self Test (BIST) is not requested during RESET.

Table 23-1. Processor State Following Power-Up

Register	Pentium™ CPU	Intel486™ CPU	Intel386™ CPU
EFLAGS[1]	00000002H	00000046H	00000000H
EIP	0000FFF0H	0000FFF0H	0000FFF0H
CR0	60000010H	60000010H	7FFFFFE0H
CR2	00000000H	00000000H	00000000H
CR3	00000000H	00000000H	00000000H
CR4	00000000H	00000000H	00000000H
CS	0F000H base=0FFFF000H limit=0FFFFH AR=00000093H	0F000H base=0FFFF000H limit=0FFFFH AR=0FF3F93FFH	0F000F000H base=0FFFF000H limit=0FFFFH AR=0FF3F93FFH
SS, DS, ES, FS, GS	0000 base=00000000H limit=0FFFFH AR=00000093H	0000 base=00000000H limit=0FFFFH AR=0FF3F93FFH	0000 base=00000000H limit=0FFFFH AR=0FF3F93FFH
EDX	0000x5xxH	0000x4xxH	00000308H
EAX	0[2]	0[2]	0C51BB653H
EBX, ECX, ESI, EDI, EBP, ESP	00000000H	00000000H	00000000H
GDTR,LDTR	00000000 base=00000000H limit=0FFFFH AR=00000082H	xxxx0000 base=00000000H limit=0FFFFH AR=0FFFFFFFFH	00000000 base=00000000H limit=0FFFFH AR=0FFFFFFFFH
IDTR	00000000 base=00000000H limit=0FFFFH AR=00000082H	xxxx0000 base=00000000H limit=0FFFFH AR=0FFFFFFFFH	00000000 base=00000000H limit=0FFFFH AR=0FFFFFFFFH
DR0, DR1, DR2, DR3	00000000H	00000000H	00000000H
DR6	FFFF0FF0H	FFFF1FF0H	FFFF1FF0H
DR7	00000400H	00001400H	00001400H
Time Stamp Counter	0	NA[3]	NA
Control and Event Select	0	NA	NA
TR12	0	NA	NA
All Other MSR's	Undefined	NA	NA
Data and Code Cache	Invalid	Invalid	NA
TLB(s)	Invalid	Invalid	NA

---

NOTES:

1. The high ten (14 for the Intel486 and Intel386 CPU's) bits of the EFLAGS register are undefined following power-up. Undefined bits are reserved. Software should not depend on the states of any of these bits.
2. If Built-In Self Test is invoked, EAX is 0 only if all tests passed.
3. Not Applicable.

Upon hardware RESET on a system with an Intel386 CPU and an Intel387 math coprocessor, the floating-point registers will remain unchanged unless the BIST is requested. When the BIST is requested, hardware RESET has almost the same effect as the FINIT instruction; the only difference is that FINIT leaves the stack registers unchanged, while hardware RESET with BIST resets them to 0. This could show up as a difference in the value of the tag word observed after the FSAVE/FSTENV instructions are executed. The FINIT instruction clears both the data and instruction error pointers.

Following an Intel386 processor reset, the processor identifies the type of its coprocessor (Intel287 or Intel387 DX math coprocessor) by sampling its ERROR# input some time after the falling edge of RESET and before execution of the first ESC instruction. The Intel287 coprocessor keeps its ERROR# output in inactive state after hardware reset; the Intel387 coprocessor keeps its ERROR# output in active state after hardware reset. Upon hardware RESET or FINIT, the Intel387 math coprocessor signals an error condition. The Pentium and Intel486 processors, like the Intel287 coprocessor, do not. Table 23-2 provides a summary of the differences between the Intel386, Intel486, and Pentium FPU's following power-up.

Table 23-2. FPU and NPX State Following Power-Up

Register	Pentium™ FPU	Intel486™ FPU	Intel387™ NPX
Control Word	0040H	037FHH	037FH
Status Word	0000H	0000H	0000H
Tag Word	5555H	0FFFFH	0FFFFH
IP Offset	00000000H	00000000H	00000000H
Data Operand Offset	00000000H	00000000H	00000000H
CS Selector	0000H	0000H	0000H
Operand Selector	0000H	0000H	0000H
FSTACK	All zeroes	All zeroes	All zeroes

NOTES:

The state of the FPU is left unchanged on the Pentium following INIT. The state of the FPU is left unchanged on the Intel486 FPU following RESET w/o BIST.

23.2.6.3. Intel486 SX MICROPROCESSOR AND Intel487 SX MATH COPROCESSOR INITIALIZATION

This interface is designed for two distinct sockets: one for the Intel486 SX CPU and one for end-user/dealer upgrade with Intel487 SX math coprocessor. Refer to the *Intel486™ SX Microprocessor/Intel487™ SX Math CoProcessor Data Book* for more details. The following should be considered when designing an Intel486 SX CPU/Intel487 SX MCP system.

1. The timing loops should be independent of clock speed and clocks per instruction. One way to attain this is to implement these loops in hardware and not in software (e.g., BIOS).

2. The initialization routine should check the presence of a math coprocessor (e.g., Intel487 SX math coprocessor) and should set the floating-point related bits in the CR0 register accordingly (see Chapter 10 for a complete description of these bits). The recommended bit pattern is given in Table 23-3. The FSTCW instruction will give a value of FFFFh for the Intel486 SX microprocessor and 037Fh for the Intel487 SX math coprocessor.

Table 23-3. Recommended Values of the FP Related Bits for Intel486™ SX Microprocessor/Intel487™ SX Math CoProcessor System

CR0 Bit	Intel486™ SX Microprocessor	Intel487™ SX Math CoProcessor
EM	1	0
MP	0	1
NE	1	0, for DOS systems 1, for user-defined exception handler

Following is an example code sequence to initialize the system and check for the presence of Intel486 SX microprocessor/Intel487 SX math coprocessor. Refer to Chapter 5 for complete CPU and coprocessor identification information.

```
fninit
fstcw mem_loc
mov ax, mem_loc
cmp ax, 037fh
jz Intel487_SX_Math_CoProcessor_present        ;ax=037fh
jmp Intel486_SX_microprocessor_present         ;ax=ffffh
```

If the Intel487 SX math coprocessor is not present, the following code can be run to set the CR0 register for the Intel486 SX microprocessor.

```
mov eax, cr0
and eax, fffffffdh              ;make MP=0
or eax, 0024h                   ;make EM=1, NE=1
mov cr0, eax
```

The above initialization will cause any floating-point instruction to generate the interrupt 7. The software emulation will then take control to execute these instructions. This code is not required if an Intel487 SX math coprocessor is present in the system, thereupon the typical intialization routine for the Intel486 SX microprocessor will be adequate.

The interpretation of different combinations of the EM and MP bits is shown in Table 23-4.

Table 23-4. EM and MP Bits Interpretations

EM	MP	Interpretation
0	0	Numeric instructions are passed to FPU; WAIT ignores TS
0	1	Numeric instructions are passed to FPU; WAIT tests TS
1	0	Numeric instructions trap to emulator; WAIT ignores TS
1	1	Numeric instructions trap to emulator, WAIT tests TS

23.2.7. New Instructions

This section identifies the introduction of new instructions for the 32-bit microprocessors.

23.2.7.1. NEW PENTIUM PROCESSOR INSTRUCTIONS

The Pentium processor introduces three new application instructions:

- CMPXCHG8B instruction
- CPUID instruction
- RDTSC instruction — For more information on RDTSC, see Appendix H.

There are four new system instructions, used for reading from and writing to the new control register (CR4) and model specific registers, and resuming from system management mode:

- MOV CR4, r32 and MOV r32, CR4
- RDMSR
- WRMSR
- RSM

The form of the MOV instruction used to access the test registers has been removed on the Pentium processor. New test registers have been defined for the cache, the TLB's and the BTB which are accessed through the model-specific registers on the Pentium processor. For more information on the test registers used with the RDMSR and WRMSR instructions, see Appendix H.

23.2.7.2. NEW Intel486 PROCESSOR INSTRUCTIONS

The Intel486 CPU introduced three new application instructions:

- BSWAP instruction
- XADD instruction
- CMPXCHG instruction

Three new system instructions, used for managing the cache and TLB, were introduced:

- INVD instruction
- WBINVD instruction
- INVLPG instruction

23.2.7.3.   NEW Intel386 PROCESSOR INSTRUCTIONS

New instructions introduced on the Intel386 processor include:

- LSS, LFS, LGS instructions
- Long-displacement conditional jumps
- Single-bit instructions
- Bit scan instructions
- Double-shift instructions
- Byte set on condition instruction
- Move with sign/zero extension
- Generalized multiply instruction
- MOV to and from control registers
- MOV to and from test registers (now obsolete)
- MOV to and from debug registers

23.2.8.   Obsolete Instructions

The following instructions no longer supported include:

- MOV to and from test registers (removed from the Pentium processor)

Execution of these instructions generates an invalid opcode fault.

23.2.9.   Flags

This section discusses the flag bits additions to the EFLAGS register as shown in Figure 23-1.

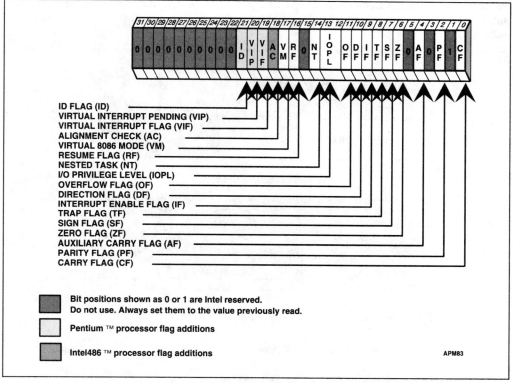

ID FLAG (ID)
VIRTUAL INTERRUPT PENDING (VIP)
VIRTUAL INTERRUPT FLAG (VIF)
ALIGNMENT CHECK (AC)
VIRTUAL 8086 MODE (VM)
RESUME FLAG (RF)
NESTED TASK (NT)
I/O PRIVILEGE LEVEL (IOPL)
OVERFLOW FLAG (OF)
DIRECTION FLAG (DF)
INTERRUPT ENABLE FLAG (IF)
TRAP FLAG (TF)
SIGN FLAG (SF)
ZERO FLAG (ZF)
AUXILIARY CARRY FLAG (AF)
PARITY FLAG (PF)
CARRY FLAG (CF)

Bit positions shown as 0 or 1 are Intel reserved.
Do not use. Always set them to the value previously read.

Pentium ™ processor flag additions

Intel486 ™ processor flag additions

APM83

Figure 23-1. Pentium™ Processor EFLAGS Register

23.2.9.1.   NEW PENTIUM PROCESSOR FLAGS

The Pentium processor includes the following three bits to the EFLAGS register:

- VIF — For more information, see Appendix H.

- VIP — For more information, see Appendix H.

- ID — The ability to set and clear the IDentification Flag indicates that the processor supports the CPUID instruction.

23.2.9.2.   NEW Intel486 PROCESSOR FLAGS

The AC flag (bit position 18), in conjunction with the AM bit in the CR0 register, controls alignment checking.

23.2.10. Control Registers

This section identifies the addition of new control registers and control register bits in the 32-

bit Intel x86 microprocessors. See Figure 23-2 for extensions to the control registers for the Intel486 and Pentium processors. These extensions are discussed further in the following subsections.

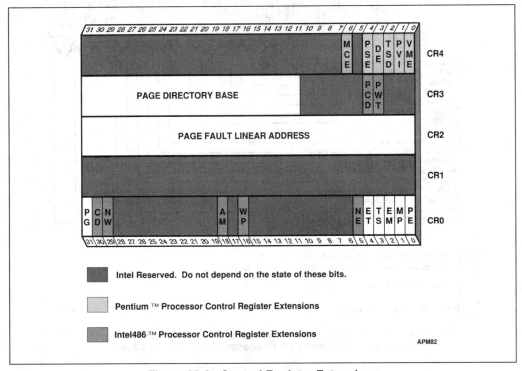

Figure 23-2. Control Register Extensions

23.2.10.1. PENTIUM PROCESSOR CONTROL REGISTERS

The recommended values for the CD and NW bits in CR0 (00) implements a write-back strategy for the data cache of the Pentium processor. On the Intel486 processor, these values implement a write-through strategy. See Table 23-5 for a comparison of these bits on the Intel486 and Pentium processors. For complete information on caching, refer to Chapter 18.

One new Control Register (CR4) is defined. CR4 contains bits that enable certain extensions to the Intel486 architecture provided in the Pentium processor. These include:

- VME — For more information, see Appendix H.
- PVI — For more information, see Appendix H.
- TSD — For more information, see Appendix H.
- DE — While this bit is 1, Debugging Extensions are enabled, providing support for I/O breakpoints. Refer to Chapter 17 for more information.

- PSE — For more information, see Appendix H.

- MCE — While this bit is 1, Machine Check Exceptions are enabled, allowing exception handling for certain hardware error conditions. Refer to the *Pentium™ Processor Data Book* for more information.

The content of CR4 is zero following reset.

23.2.10.2.   Intel486 PROCESSOR CONTROL REGISTERS

Five new bits are defined in the CR0 register for the Intel486 processor:

- NE — The Numeric Error bit enables the standard mechanism for reporting floating-point numeric errors.

- WP — The Write Protect bit write-protects user-level pages against supervisor-mode accesses.

- AM — The Alignment Mask bit, in conjunction with the AC (Alignment Check) flag, controls whether alignment checking is performed.

- NW — The Not Write-through bit enables write-throughs and cache invalidation cycles when clear and disables invalidation cycles and write-throughs which hit in the cache when set.

- CD — The Cache Disable bit enables the internal cache when clear and disables the cache when set.

Two new bits have been defined in the CR3 register:

- PCD — The state of the Page-Level Cache Disable bit is driven on the PCD pin during bus cycles which are not paged, such as interrupt acknowledge cycles, when paging is enabled.   The PCD pin is used to control caching in an external cache on a cycle-by-cycle basis.

Table 23-5. Cache Mode Differences Between the Pentium™ and Intel486™ Processors

CD	NW	Pentium™ CPU Description	Intel486™ CPU Description
0	0	**Normal highest performance cache operation.** Read hits access the cache. Read misses may cause replacements. These lines will enter the Exclusive or Shared state under the control of the WB/WT# pin. Write hits update the cache. Only writes to shared lines and write misses appear externally Writes to Shared lines can be changed to the Exclusive State under the control of the WB/WT# pin. Invalidations are allowed.	**Normal highest performance cache operation** Read hits access the cache. Read misses may cause replacements. Write hits update the cache. All writes appear externally. Invalidations are allowed.
0	1	**Invalid Operation** GP(0)	**Invalid Operation** GP(0)
1	0	**Cache disabled. Memory consistency maintained. Contents locked in cache.** Read hits access the cache. Read misses do not cause replacement. Write hits update the cache. Only writes to Shared lines and write misses update external memory Writes to Shared lines can be changed to the Exclusive State under the control of the WB/WT# pin. Invalidations are allowed.	**Cache disabled. Memory consistency maintained. Contents locked in cache.** Read hits access the cache. Read misses do not cause replacement. Write hits update the cache. All writes update external memory Invalidations are allowed.
1	1	**Cache disabled. Memory consistency not maintained.** Read hits access the cache. Read misses do not cause replacement. Write hits update the cache, but do not access memory. Write hits will cause Exclusive State lines to change to Modified State Shared lines will remain in the Shared state after write hits. Write misses access memory. Inquire and Invalidation Cycles do not effect the cache state or contents. This is the state after reset.	**Cache disabled. Memory consistency not maintained.** Read hits access the cache. Read misses do not cause replacement. Write hits update the cache, but do not access memory. Write misses access memory. Inquire and Invalidation Cycles do not effect the cache state or contents. This is the state after reset.

- PWT — The state of the Page-Level Write Through bit is driven on the PWT pin during bus cycles which are not paged, such as interrupt acknowledge cycles, when paging is enabled. The PWT pin is used to control write-through in an external cache on a cycle-by-cycle basis.

23.2.11. Debug Registers

The Pentium processor includes extensions to the Intel486 processor debugging support for breakpoints on I/O references. To use the new breakpoint features, it is necessary to set CR4.DE to 1.

23.2.11.1. DIFFERENCES IN DR6

It is not possible to write a 1 to reserved bit 12 in DR6 on the Pentium processor. However, on the Intel486 processor, it is possible to write a 1 in bit position 12.

See "Initialization Values" in this chapter for differences of this register at processor reset.

23.2.11.2. DIFFERENCES IN DR7

The Pentium processor determines the type of breakpoint access by the bits R/W0 to R/W3 in DR7 as follows:

00   Break on instruction execution only
01   Break on data writes only
10   undefined if CR4.DE=0, break on I/O reads or writes but not instruction fetches if CR4.DE=1
11   Break on data reads or writes but not instruction fetches

On the Pentium processor, reserved bits 11, 12, 14 and 15 are hard-wired to 0. On the Intel486 CPU, however, bit 12 can be set.

See "Initialization Values" above for differences of this register at processor reset.

23.2.11.3. DEBUG REGISTERS 4 AND 5

Although the DR4 and DR5 registers have been documented as "Reserved", previous generations of processors aliased references to these registers to Debug Registers 6 and 7, respectively. When Debug Extensions are not enabled (CR4.DE=0), the Pentium processor remains compatible with existing software by allowing these aliased references. However, when Debug Extensions are enabled (CR4.DE=1), attempts to reference DR4 or DR5 will result in an invalid opcode exception.

23.2.12. Test Registers

The implementation of test registers on the Intel486 CPU used for testing the cache and TLB has been redesigned using model specific registers (discussed below) on the Pentium processor. The MOV to and from test register instructions generate invalid opcode exceptions on the Pentium processor. For more information on the use of the test registers, see Appendix H.

23.2.13. Model Specific Registers

Certain features of the Pentium processor that are described in the *Pentium™ Processor Data Book* are specific to the Pentium processor and may not be continued in the same way in future processors. Examples are functions for testability, performance monitoring, and machine check errors. These features are accessed through Model Specific Registers. The new instructions RDMSR and WRMSR are used to read and write these registers. In order to use such model-specific features, software should check that the "Family" number reported by the CPUID instruction is equal to 5. Software which uses these registers and functions may be incompatible with future processors. For more information, see Appendix H.

Refer to the *Pentium™ Processor Data Book* for more information.

23.2.14. Exceptions

This section identifies the introduction of new exceptions in the 32-bit microprocessor family and implementation differences in existing exception handling.

23.2.14.1. NEW PENTIUM PROCESSOR EXCEPTIONS

The Pentium processor includes the following extensions and conditions to the Intel486 architecture for exceptions and interrupts:

- Exception #13 — A General-Protection exception occurs when an attempt is made to write 1 to a reserved bit position of a special register.

- Exception #14 — A Page Fault exception occurs when a 1 is detected in any of the reserved bit positions of a page table entry, page directory entry, or page directory pointer during address translation by the Pentium processor.

- Exception #18 — A Machine Check Exception is newly defined for reporting parity errors and other hardware errors. This is a model-specific exception and may not be implemented the same in future processors. For compatibility reasons, the MCE bit in the CR4 register acts as the machine check enable bit. When this bit is clear (which it is at reset), the processor inhibits generation of the machine check abort. In the event that a system is using the machine check interrupt vector for another purpose and the MCE bit in CR4 is set, the interrupt routine must examine the state of the CHK bit in the model-specific Machine Check Type register to determine the cause of the interrupt. See the *Pentium™ Processor Data Book* for more information on the Machine Check Type register and model-specific registers.

See Chapter 14 for details on exceptions and interrupts.

23.2.14.2.   NEW Intel486 PROCESSOR EXCEPTIONS

The Intel486 processor includes the following extensions and conditions to the Intel486 architecture for exceptions and interrupts:

- Exception #17 — An Alignment Check exception reports unaligned memory references when alignment checking is being performed.

23.2.14.3.   NEW Intel386 PROCESSOR EXCEPTIONS

The Intel386 processor introduced new conditions which can occur even in systems designed for the Intel 286 processor.

- Exception #6 — The Invalid Opcode exception can result from improper use of the LOCK instruction prefix.
- Exception #14 — A Page Fault exception can occur in a 16-bit program if the operating system enables paging. Paging can be used in a system with 16-bit tasks if all tasks use the same page directory. Because there is no place in a 16-bit TSS to store the PDBR register, switching to a 16-bit task does not change the value of the PDBR register. Tasks ported from the Intel 286 processor should be given 32-bit TSSs so they can make full use of paging.
- Exception #13 — The Intel386 processor set a limit of 15 bytes on instruction length. The only way to violate this limit is by putting redundant prefixes before an instruction. A general-protection exception is generated if the limit on instruction length is violated. The 8086 processor has no instruction length limit.

23.2.14.4.   INTERRUPT PROPAGATION DELAY

External hardware interrupts on the Pentium processor may be recognized on different instruction boundaries due to the pipelined execution of the Pentium processor and possibly an extra instruction passing through the v-pipe concurrently with an instruction in the u-pipe. When the two instructions complete execution, the interrupt is then serviced. Therefore, the EIP pushed onto the stack when servicing the interrupt on the Pentium processor may be different then that for the Intel486 processor (i.e., it is serviced later).

23.2.14.5.   PRIORITY OF EXCEPTIONS

The priority of exceptions are broken down into several major categories:
- Traps on the previous instruction
- External interrupts
- Faults on fetching the next instruction
- Faults in decoding the next instruction
- Faults on executing an instruction

There are no changes in the priority of these major categories between the different processors, however, exceptions within these categories are implementation dependent and may change from processor to processor. To obtain information on exception priority within these categories, see Appendix H.

23.2.14.6. DIVIDE-ERROR EXCEPTIONS

Divide-error exceptions on the Pentium, Intel486, and Intel386 processors always leave the saved CS:IP value pointing to the instruction which failed. On the 8086 processor, the CS:IP value points to the next instruction.

The Pentium, Intel486, and Intel386 processors can generate the largest negative number as a quotient for the IDIV instruction (80H and 8000H). The 8086 processor generates a divide-error exception instead.

23.2.14.7. WRITES USING THE CS REGISTER PREFIX

Following a switch from protected mode to real-address mode, the Intel486 processor requires the coding of a far jump control flow instruction prior to performing a write using the CS segment register prefix (for example: MOV CS:[0], EAX). The far jump in protected mode on the Intel486 processor reloads the CS access rights to be writable. If this requirement is not met, a general protection exception occurs. This requirement has been eliminated on the Pentium processor which leaves the access rights unchanged and ignores code segment access right protection checks in real-address mode. As a result, the code segment register can be used as a prefix in a write operation in real-address mode without generating an exception. For upwards and downwards compatibility, however, programmers may wish to include the far jump instruction prior to any writes to the code segment in real-address mode.

The code segment can not be written to in protected mode on either the Intel486 or Pentium processor.

23.2.14.8. NMI INTERRUPTS

After an NMI interrupt is recognized by the Intel 286, Intel386, Intel486 and Pentium processors, the NMI interrupt is masked until the first IRET instruction is executed, unlike the 8086 processor.

23.2.14.9. INTERRUPT VECTOR TABLE LIMIT

The LIDT instruction can be used to set a limit on the size of the interrupt vector table. The double fault exception is generated if an interrupt or exception attempts to read a vector beyond the limit. Shutdown then occurs on the 32-bit Intel x86 processors if the double fault handler vector is beyond the limit. (The 8086 processor does not have a shutdown mode nor a limit.)

23.2.15. Descriptor Types and Contents

Operating-system code which manages space in descriptor tables often contains an invalid value in the access-rights field of descriptor-table entries to identify unused entries. Access rights values of 80H and 00H remain invalid for the Intel 286, Intel386, Intel486, and Pentium processors. Other values which were invalid on the Intel 286 processor may be valid on the 32-bit processors because uses for these bits have been defined.

23.2.16. Changes in Segment Descriptor Loads

On the Intel386 processors, loading a segment descriptor always causes a locked read and write to set the accessed bit of the descriptor. On the Pentium and Intel486 processors, the locked read and write occur only if the bit is not already set.

23.2.17. Task Switching and Task State Segments

This section identifies the implementation differences of task switching, additions to the task state segment and the handling of TSS's and TSS selectors.

23.2.17.1.   PENTIUM PROCESSOR TASK STATE SEGMENTS

The Pentium CPU TSS may contain additional information used in virtual-8086 mode by the virtual mode extensions to the Pentium CPU. For more information on virtual mode extensions, see Appendix H.

23.2.17.2.   TSS SELECTOR WRITES

During task state saves, the Intel486 CPU writes two-byte selectors into a 32-bit TSS, leaving the upper 16 bits undefined. For performance reasons, the Pentium CPU writes four-byte selectors into the TSS with the upper two bytes being zero. For compatibility reasons, code should not depend on the value of the upper 16 bits of the selector in the TSS.

23.2.17.3.   ORDER OF READS/WRITES TO THE TSS

The order of reads and writes into the TSS is processor dependent. The Pentium CPU may generate different page fault addresses (CR2) in the same TSS area than the Intel486 CPU, if a TSS crosses a page boundary (which is not recommended).

23.2.17.4.   USING A 16-BIT TSS WITH 32-BIT CONSTRUCTS

Task switches using 16-bit TSS's should be used only for pure 16-bit code. Any new code written using 32-bit constructs (operands, addressing, or the upper word of the EFLAGS register) should use only 32-bit TSSs. This is due to the fact that the 32-bit processors do not save the upper 16 bits of EFLAGS to a 16-bit TSS. A task switch back to a 16-bit task that was executing in virtual mode will never re-enable the virtual mode, as this bit was not saved in the upper half of the EFLAGS value in the TSS. Therefore, it is strongly recommended that any code using 32-bit constructs use a only a 32-bit TSS to ensure correct behavior in a multitasking environment.

23.2.17.4.1. Differences In I/O Map Base Addresses

The Intel486 processor considers the TSS segment to be a 16-bit segment and wraps around the 64K boundary. Any I/O accesses check for permission to access this I/O address at the I/O base address plus the I/O offset. If the I/O map base address exceeds the specified limit of 0DFFFH, an I/O access will wrap around and obtain the permission for the I/O address at an incorrect location within the TSS. A TSS limit violation does not occur in this situation on the Intel486 processor. However, the Pentium processor considers the TSS to be a 32-bit segment and a limit violation occurs when the I/O base address plus the I/O offset is greater than the TSS limit. By following the recommended specification for the I/O base address to be less than 0DFFFH, the Intel486 processor will not wrap around and access incorrect locations within the TSS for I/O port validation and the Pentium processor will not experience general protection faults. Figure 23-3 demonstrates the different areas accessed by the Intel486 and Pentium processors.

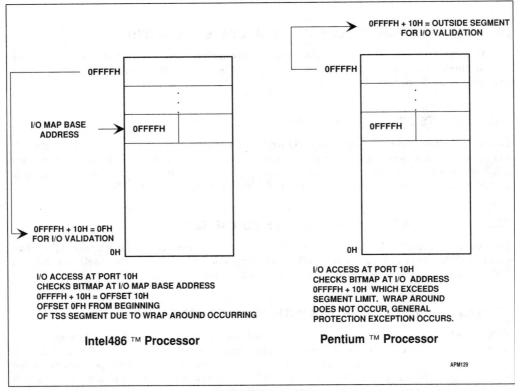

Figure 23-3. I/O Map Base Address Differences

23.2.17.4.2. Caching, Pipelining, Prefetching

The Pentium processor includes separate instruction and data caches. The data cache supports a write-back (or alternatively write-through, on a line by line basis) policy for memory updates. Refer to Chapter 18 and the *Pentium™ Processor Data Book* for more information about the organization and operation of the Pentium processor caches.

The Intel486 processor includes a single internal cache for both instructions and data.

The meaning of bits CD and NW in CR0 have been redefined so the recommended value (00) enables write-back for the data cache of the Pentium processor. In the Intel486 processor the same value for these bits enables write-through for the cache. However, it is possible for external system hardware to force the Pentium processor to disable caching or to use write-through policy should that be required. Refer to Chapter 18 and the *Pentium™ Processor Data Book* for more information about hardware control of the Pentium processor caches.

The Pentium processor supports page-level cache management in the same manner as the Intel486 by using the PCD and PWT bits in CR3, page directory pointers, page directory entries, and page table entries. The Intel486 processor, however, is not affected by the state of the PWT bit since the internal cache of the Intel486 processor is a write-through cache.

23.2.17.5. SELF MODIFYING CODE WITH CACHE ENABLED

On the Intel486 processor, a write to an instruction in the cache will modify it in both cache and memory. If the instruction was prefetched before the write, however, the old version of the instruction could be the one executed. To prevent this, it is necessary to flush the instruction prefetch unit of the Intel486 processor by coding a jump instruction immediately after any write that modifies an instruction. The Pentium processor, however, checks whether a write may modify an instruction that has been prefetched for execution. This check is based on the linear address of the instruction. If the linear address of an instruction is found to be present in the prefetch queue, the Pentium processor flushes the prefetch queue, eliminating the need to code a jump instruction after any writes that modify an instruction.

Because the linear address of the write is checked against the linear address of the instructions that have been prefetched, special care must be taken for self-modifying code to work correctly when the physical addresses of the instruction and the written data are the same, but the linear addresses differ. In such cases, it is necessary to execute a serializing operation to flush the prefetch queue after the write and before executing the modified instruction. See Chapter 18 for more information on serializing instructions.

NOTE

The check on linear addresses described above is not in practice a concern for compatibility. Applications that include self-modifying code use the same linear address for modifying and fetching the instruction. Systems software, such as a debugger, that might possibly modify an instruction using a different linear address than that used to fetch the instruction must execute a serializing operation, such as IRET, before the modified instruction is executed.

23.2.18. Paging

This section identifies enhancements made to the paging unit and implementation differences in the paging mechanism.

23.2.18.1. PENTIUM PROCESSOR PAGING

The Pentium processor provides an extension to the memory management/paging functions of the Intel486 CPU to support larger page sizes. See Appendix H for more information.

23.2.18.2. Intel486 PROCESSOR PAGING

Two bits introduced in the Intel486 processor have been defined in page table entries for controlling caching of pages:

- PCD — The Page-Level Cache Disable bit controls caching on a page-by-page basis.
- PWT — The Page-Level Write Through bit controls the use of a write-through of or write-back policy on a page-by-page basis. Since the internal cache of the Intel486 processor is a write-through cache, it is not affected by the state of the PWT bit.

23.2.18.3. ENABLING AND DISABLING PAGING

Paging is enabled and disabled by a MOV CR0, REG instruction that modifies the PG bit. The Intel386 CPU family, the Intel486 CPU family, and the Pentium CPU have slightly different requirements on the following code used to enable and disable paging:

1. MOV CR0, REG followed immediately by a short JMP instruction.
2. Identity map the entire sequence bounded by the MOV and JMP instructions.

The Intel386 family of CPUs require steps 1 *or* 2 be performed. The Intel486 family of CPUs require that both steps 1 *and* 2 be performed. The Pentium CPU requires *only* step 2. Although a JMP instruction need not follow immediately, it is recommended, for upwards and downwards compatibility, that both requirements be observed. Specifically, the instructions modifying the PG bit should be followed immediately by a JMP instruction and those instructions should reside on a page whose linear and physical addresses are identical.

23.2.19. Stack Operations

This section identifies the differences in stack implementation between the various microprocessors.

23.2.19.1. PUSH SP

The Pentium CPU, Intel486, Intel386, and Intel 286 processors push a different value on the stack for a PUSH SP instruction than the 8086 processor. The 32-bit processors push the value of the SP register before it is decremented as part of the push operation; the 8086 processor pushes the value of the SP register after it is decremented. If the value pushed is important, replace PUSH SP instructions with the following three instructions:

```
PUSH BP
```

```
MOV  BP, SP
XCHG BP, [BP]
```

This code functions as the 8086 processor PUSH SP instruction on the Pentium processor.

23.2.19.2. FLAGS PUSHED ON THE STACK

The setting of the flags stored by the PUSHF instruction, by interrupts, and by exceptions is different on the 32-bit processors than that stored by the 8086 and Intel 286 processors in bits 12 and 13 (IOPL), 14 (NT), and 15 (reserved). The differences are as follows:

- 8086 processor — bits 12 through 15 are always set.
- Intel 286 processor — bits 12 through 15 are always clear in real-address mode.
- 32-bit processors in real-address mode, bit 15 is always clear, and bits 14 through 12 have the last value loaded into them.

Other bits that can be used to differentiate between the 32 bit processors include:

- Bit 18 (AC) can be used to distinguish an Intel386 processor from the Intel486 and Pentium processors. Since it is not implemented on the Intel386 processor, it will always be clear.
- Bit 21 (ID) can be used to determine if an application can execute the CPUID instruction. This instruction supplies information to applications at runtime that identifies the family, model, stepping, vendor and what features are implemented on the processor in a system. The ability to set and clear this bit indicates that the CPUID is supported on a processor.
- Bits 19 and 20 will always be zero on processors that do not support virtual mode extensions. For more information on virtual mode extensions, see Appendix H.

These differences can be used to distinguish what type of processor is present and are used in the CPU identification code example in Chapter 5.

23.2.19.3. SELECTOR PUSHES/POPS

On selector pushes, the Intel486 CPU writes two bytes onto four byte stacks and decrements ESP by 4. The Pentium CPU writes 4 bytes with the upper two bytes being zeros.

On selector pops, the Intel486 CPU reads only 2 bytes. The Pentium CPU reads 4 bytes and discards the upper 2 bytes. This may have an effect if the ESP is close to the stack segment limit. On the Pentium CPU, ESP+4 may be above the stack limit in which case a fault will be generated. On the Intel486 CPU, ESP+2 may be less than the stack limit and no fault is generated.

23.2.19.4. ERROR CODE PUSHES

The Intel486 CPU implements the error code pushed on the stack as a 16-bit value. When pushed onto a 32-bit stack, the Intel486 CPU only pushes 2 bytes and updates ESP by 4. The Pentium CPU error code is a full 32 bits with the upper 16 bits set to zero. The Pentium CPU, therefore, pushes 4 bytes and updates ESP by 4. Any code that relys on the state of the upper 16 bits may produce inconsistent results.

23.2.19.5. FAULT HANDLING EFFECTS ON THE STACK

During the handling of certain instructions, such as CALL and PUSHA, faults may occur in different sequences for the different processors. For example, during far calls, the Intel486 CPU pushes the old CS and EIP before a possible branch fault is resolved. A branch fault is a fault from a branch instruction occurring from a segment limit or access rights violation. If a branch fault is taken, the Intel486 CPU will have corrupted memory below the stack pointer. However, ESP is backed up in order to make the instruction restartable. The Pentium CPU issues the branch before the pushes. Therefore, if a branch fault does occur, the Pentium CPU does not corrupt memory below the stack pointer. This implementation difference, however, does not constitute a compatibility problem, as only values at or above the stack pointer are considered to be valid.

23.2.19.6. INTERLEVEL RET/IRET FROM A 16-BIT INTERRUPT OR CALL GATE

If a call or interrupt is made from a 32-bit stack environment through a 16-bit gate, only 16 bits of the old ESP can be pushed onto the stack. On the subsequent RET/IRET, the 16-bit ESP is popped but the full 32-bit ESP is updated since control is being resumed in a 32-bit stack environment. The Intel486 processor writes the SS selector into the upper 16 bits of ESP. The Pentium CPU writes zeros into the the upper 16 bits.

23.2.20. Mixing 16- and 32-Bit Segments

The features of the 16-bit Intel 286 processor are an object-code compatible subset of those of the Pentium processor. The Default bit in segment descriptors indicates whether the processor is to treat a code, data, or stack segment as a 16-bit or 32-bit segment.

The segment descriptors used by the Intel 286 processor are supported by the 32-bit processors if the Intel-reserved word (highest word) of the descriptor is clear. On the 32-bit Intel x86 processors, this word includes the upper bits of the base address and the segment limit.

The segment descriptors for data segments, code segments, local descriptor tables (there are no descriptors for global descriptor tables), and task gates are the same for the 16- and 32-bit processors. Other 16-bit descriptors (TSS segment, call gate, interrupt gate, and trap gate) are supported by the 32-bit processors. The 32-bit processors also have descriptors for TSS segments, call gates, interrupt gates, and trap gates which support the 32-bit architecture. Both kinds of descriptors can be used in the same system.

For those segment descriptors common to both 16 and 32-bit processors, clear bits in the reserved word cause the 32-bit processors to interpret these descriptors exactly as an Intel 286 processor does; for example:

- Base Address—The upper eight bits of the 32-bit base address are clear, which limits base addresses to 24 bits.

- Limit—The upper four bits of the limit field are clear, restricting the value of the limit field to 64 Kbytes.

- Granularity bit—The Granularity bit is clear, indicating the value of the 16-bit limit is interpreted in units of 1 byte.

- Big bit—In a data-segment descriptor, the B bit is clear in the segment descriptor used by the 32-bit processors, indicating the segment is no larger than 64 Kbytes.

- Default bit—In a code-segment descriptor, the D bit is clear, indicating 16-bit addressing and operands are the default. In a stack-segment descriptor, the D bit is clear, indicating use of the SP register (instead of the ESP register) and a 64 Kbyte maximum segment limit.

For formats of these descriptors and documentation of their use see the *iAPX 286 Programmer's Reference Manual*. For information on mixing 16 and 32-bit code in applications, see Chapter 21.

23.2.21. Segment and Address Wraparound

This section discusses differences in segment and address wraparound between the Pentium, Intel486, Intel386, Intel 286, and 8086 processors.

23.2.21.1.   SEGMENT WRAPAROUND

On the 8086 processor, an attempt to access a memory operand which crosses offset 65,535 or 0FFFFH or offset 0 (e.g., MOV a word to offset 65,535 or PUSH a word when SP = 1) causes the offset to wrap around modulo 65,536 or 010000H. With the Intel 286 processor, any base and offset combination which addresses beyond 16 megabytes wraps around to the first megabyte of the address space. The Pentium, Intel486, and Intel386 processors in real-address mode generate an exception in these cases: a general-protection exception if the segment is a data segment (i.e. if the CS, DS, ES, FS, or GS register is being used to address the segment) or a stack exception if the segment is a stack segment (i.e., if the SS register is being used). An exception to this behavior occurs when a stack access is datum aligned, and the stack pointer is pointing to the last aligned datum of that size at the top of the stack (ESP=0FFFFFFFCH). When this data is popped, no segment limit violation occurs and the stack pointer will wrap around to 0.

The address space of the Pentium and Intel486 processors may wraparound at 1 megabyte in real-address mode. An external pin A20M# forces wraparound if enabled. On members of the 8086 family, it is possible to specify addresses greater than 1 megabyte. For example, with a selector value 0FFFFH and an offset of 0FFFFH, the effective address would be 10FFEFH (1 megabyte + 65519 bytes). The 8086 processor, which can form addresses up to 20 bits long, truncates the uppermost bit, which "wraps" this address to 0FFEFH. However, the Pentium and Intel486 processors do not truncate this bit if A20M# is not enabled.

If a stack operation wraps around the address limit, shutdown occurs. (The 8086 processor does not have a shutdown mode nor a limit.)

23.2.22. Write Buffers and Memory Ordering

The Pentium processor has two write buffers, one corresponding to each of the pipelines, to enhance the performance of consecutive writes to memory. These write buffers can be filled simultaneously in one clock e.g., by two simultaneous write misses in the two pipelines. Writes in these buffers are driven out on the external bus in the order they were generated by the processor core. No reads (as a result of cache miss) are reordered around previously generated writes sitting in the write buffers. The implication of this is that the write buffers will be flushed or emptied before a subsequent bus cycle is run on the external bus.

It should be noted that only memory writes are buffered and I/O writes are not. The Pentium and Intel486 processors do not synchronize the completion of memory writes on the bus and instruction execution after the write. The OUT instruction or a serializing instruction needs to be executed to synchronize writes with the next instruction. Refer to Chapter 18 for information on serializing instructions.

No re-ordering of read cycles occurs on the Pentium processor. Specifically, the write buffers are flushed before the IN instruction is executed.

On the Intel486 CPU, under certain conditions, a memory read will go onto the external bus before the memory writes pending in the buffer even though the writes occurred earlier in the program execution. A memory read will only be reordered in front of all writes pending in the buffers if all writes pending in the buffers are cache hits and the read is a cache miss. Under these conditions, the Intel486 processor will not read from an external memory location that needs to be updated by one of the pending writes.

Locked bus cycles are used for read-modify-write accesses to memory. During a locked bus cycle, the Intel486 processor will always access external memory, it will never look for the location in the on-chip cache. All data pending in the Intel486 processor's write buffers will be written to memory before a locked cycle is allowed to proceed to the external bus. Thus, the locked bus cycle can be used for eliminating the possibility of reordering read cycles on the Intel486 processor. If the line is present in the cache, the Pentium processor will write it back if it was dirty and invalidate the line.

I/O reads are never reordered in front of buffered memory writes on the Intel486 processor. This ensures an update of all memory locations before reading the status from an I/O device.

23.2.23. Bus Locking

The LOCK prefix and its bus signal only should be used to prevent other bus masters from interrupting a data movement operation. The LOCK prefix only may be used with the following Pentium CPU, Intel486 CPU, and Intel386 CPU instructions when they modify memory. An invalid-opcode exception results from using the LOCK prefix before any other instruction, or with these instructions when no write operation is made to memory (i.e., when the destination operand is in a register).

- Bit test and change: the BTS, BTR, and BTC instructions.
- Exchange: the XCHG, XADD, CMPXCHG, and CMPXCHG8B instructions (no LOCK prefix is needed for the XCHG instruction).
- One-operand arithmetic and logical: the INC, DEC, NOT, NEG instructions.
- Two-operand arithmetic and logical: the ADD, ADC, SUB, SBB, AND, OR, and XOR instructions.

The Intel 286 processor performs the bus lock function differently than the Intel486 processor. Programs which use forms of memory locking specific to the Intel 286 processor may not run properly when run on the Intel486 processor.

A locked instruction is guaranteed to lock only the area of memory defined by the destination operand, but may lock a larger memory area. For example, typical 8086 and Intel 286 configurations lock the entire physical memory space. Programmers should not depend on this.

On the Intel 286 processor, the LOCK prefix is sensitive to IOPL; if CPL is less privileged than the IOPL, a general protection exception is generated. On the Intel386 DX, Intel486, and Pentium processors, no check against IOPL is performed.

23.2.24. Bus Hold

Unlike the 8086 and Intel 286 processors, but like the Intel386 and Intel486 processors, the Pentium processor respond to requests for control of the bus from other potential bus masters, such as DMA controllers, between transfers of parts of an unaligned operand, such as two words which form a doubleword. Unlike the Intel386 processor, the Pentium and Intel486 processors respond to bus hold during reset initialization.

23.2.25. Two Ways to Run Intel 286 CPU Tasks

When porting 16-bit programs to the Pentium processor, there are two approaches to consider:

1. Porting an entire 16 software system to a 32-bit processor, complete with the old operating system, loader, and system builder.

   In this case, all tasks will have 16-bit TSSs. The 32-bit processor is being used as if it were a faster version of the 16-bit processor.

2. Porting selected 16-bit applications to run in a 32-bit processor environment with a 32-bit operating system, loader, and system builder.

   In this case, the TSSs used to represent 286 tasks should be changed to 32-bit TSSs. It is possible to mix 16 and 32-bit TSSs, but the benefits are small and the problems are great. All tasks in a 32-bit software system should have 32-bit TSSs. It is not necessary to change the 16-bit object modules themselves; TSSs are usually constructed by the operating system, by the loader, or by the system builder. See Chapter 21 for more discussion of the interface between 16-bit and 32-bit code.

Because the 32-bit processors use the contents of the reserved word of 16-bit segment descriptors, 16-bit programs which place values in this word may not run correctly on the 32-bit processors.

23.3. FLOATING-POINT UNIT

This section addresses the issues that must be faced when transporting numerical software to a Pentium processor with integrated FPU from one of its predecessor systems. To software, the Pentium processor looks very much like an Intel486 DX system, an Intel486 SX and Intel487 SX math coprocessor system, or an Intel386 CPU and Intel387 math coprocessor system. Software which runs on any of these systems will run with at most minor modifications on the Pentium processor. To transport code directly from an Intel 286 CPU with an Intel287 math coprocessor-based system or an 8086 CPU with an 8087 math coprocessor-based system to the

Intel486 processor, certain additional issues must be addressed.

23.3.1. Control Register Bits

This section summarizes the differences in control register bits that may affect numerical software.

23.3.1.1. EXTENSION TYPE (ET) BIT

The ET (Extension Type) bit of the CR0 control register is used in the Intel386 processor to indicate whether the math coprocessor in the system is an Intel287 math coprocessor (ET=0) or an Intel387 DX math coprocessor (ET=1). This bit is not used by Pentium processor or Intel486 processor hardware. The ET bit is hardwired to "1".

23.3.1.2. NUMERIC EXCEPTION (NE) BIT

The NE (Numeric Exception) bit of the CR0 register is used in the Pentium and Intel486 processors to determine whether unmasked floating-point exceptions are reported internally via interrupt vector 16 (NE=1) or through external interrupt (NE=0). On reset, the NE bit is initialized to 0, so software using the automatic internal error-reporting mechanism must set this bit to 1. This bit is nonexistent on the Intel386 processor.

23.3.1.3. MONITOR COPROCESSOR (MP) BIT

As on the Intel 286 and Intel386 processors, the MP (Monitor coProcessor) bit of the CR0 control register determines whether WAIT instructions trap when the context of the FPU is different from that of the currently-executing task. If MP=1 and TS=1, then a WAIT instruction will cause a Device Not Available fault (interrupt vector 7). The MP bit is used on the Intel 286 and Intel386 microprocessors to support the use of a WAIT instruction to wait on a device other than a numeric coprocessor. The device reports its status through the BUSY# pin. Since the Pentium and Intel486 processors do not have such a pin, the MP bit has no relevant use, and should be set to 1 for normal operation.

23.3.1.4. FPU STATUS WORD

This section identifies differences to the FPU status word for the different Intel architecture processors/math coprocessors, as well as the reason for the differences, and their impact on software.

- Bits C3-C0 — After FINIT and hardware reset, these bits are set to zero on the Pentium CPU, Intel486 CPU, and Intel387 math coprocessor. After FINIT and hardware reset, the Intel287 and 8087 math coprocessors leave these bits intact (they contain the prior value). This has no impact on software and provides a consistent state after reset. Transcendental instruction results in the core range of the Pentium processor (as defined in Chapter 7) may differ from the Intel486 DX and Intel487 SX CPU's by around 2 to 3 units in last place (ulps). As a result, C1 may also differ.

- Bits C3, C1, C0 — After an incomplete FPREM/FPREM1, these bits are set on zero on the Pentium processor, Intel486 processor and the Intel387 math coprocessor. On the 8087 and the Intel287 math coprocessor, these bits are left intact following incomplete FPREM/FPREM1 execution.

- Bit C2 — Bit 10 serves as an incomplete bit for FPTAN on the Pentium and Intel486 processors and the Intel387 math coprocessor. This bit is undefined for FPTAN on the Intel287 and 8087 math coprocessors. This change has no impact on software as programs do not check C2 after FPTAN. This upgrade allows fast checking of operand range.

- Status Word Bit 6 for Stack Fault — When an invalid-operation exception occurs on the Pentium CPU, Intel486 CPU, or Intel387 math coprocessor due to stack overflow or underflow, not only is bit 0 (IE) of the status word set, but also bit 6 is set to indicate a stack fault and bit 9 (C1) specifies overflow or underflow. Bit 6 is called SF and serves to distinguish invalid exceptions caused by stack overflow/underflow from those caused by numeric operations. When an invalid-operation exception occurs on the Intel287 or 8087 math coprocessor due to stack overflow or underflow, only bit 0 (IE) of the status word is set. Bit 6 is RESERVED. This has no impact on software. Existing exception handlers need not change, but may be upgraded to take advantage of the additional information. Newly written handlers will be more effective. This upgrade provides performance improvement.

23.3.1.5. CONTROL WORD

Only affine closure is supported for infinity control on the Pentium CPU, Intel486 CPU, and Intel387 NPX. Bit 12 remains programmable but has no effect on operation. On the Intel287 and 8087 math coprocessors, both affine and projective closures are supported. After RESET, the default value in the control word is projective. Software that requires projective infinity arithmetic may give different results. This change was made in order to conform to IEEE Standard 754.

23.3.1.6. TAG WORD

This section describes the differences in the tag word for the difference Intel architectures, the reason for the differences, and their impact on software.

- When loading the tag word of the Pentium CPU, Intel486 CPU, or Intel387 NPX with an FLDENV or FRSTOR instruction, the processor examines the incoming tag and classifies the location only as empty or non-empty. Thus, tag values of 00, 01, and 10 are interpreted by the CPU to indicate a non-empty location. Tag values of 11 are interpreted by the CPU to indicate an empty location. Subsequent operations on a nonempty register always examine the value in the register, not the value in its tag. The FSTENV and FSAVE instructions examine the nonempty registers and put the correct values in the tags before storing the tag word.

  The corresponding tag for the Intel287 and 8087 math coprocessor is checked before each register access to determine the class of operand in the register; the tag is updated after every change to a register so that the tag always reflects the most recent status of the register. Programmers can load a tag with a value that disagrees with the contents of a register (for example, the register contains valid contents, but the tag says *special*; the Intel287 and 8087 math coprocessors, in this case, honor the tag and do not examine the register).

Software may not operate correctly if it uses FLDENV or FRSTOR to change tags to values (other than empty) that are different from actual register contents.

The reason for this change was due to performance improvement.

● The encoding in the tag word for the Pentium CPU/Intel486 CPU/Intel487 NPX for the unsupported data formats is "special data" (type 10). The encoding the Intel287 and 8087 math coprocessors for pseudo-zero and unnormal is "valid" (type 00); the others are "special data" (type 10). Exception handlers may need to be changed if programmers use such data types.

The reason for this difference is IEEE Standard 754 compatibility.

23.3.2. Data Types

This section discusses the differences of data types for the various microprocessors/math coprocessors, the reason for the differences, and their impact on software.

23.3.2.1. NaN'S

The Pentium CPU, Intel486 DX CPU, Intel487 SX NPX, and Intel387 NPX distinguish between signaling NaNs and quiet NaNs. These processors only generate quiet NaNs. An invalid-operation exception is raised only upon encountering a signaling NaN (except for FCOM, FIST, and FBSTP which also raise IE for quiet NaNs).

The Intel287 and 8087 math coprocessors only generate one kind of NaN (the equivalent of a quiet NaN) but raise an invalid-operation exception upon encountering any kind of NaN.

Uninitialized memory locations that contain QNaNs should be changed to SNaNs to cause the Pentium and Intel486 processors and the Intel387 math coprocessor to fault when uninitialized memory locations are referenced.

The reason for the difference is IEEE Standard 754 compatibility.

23.3.2.2. PSEUDOZERO, PSEUDO-NaN, PSEUDEOINFINITY, AND UNNORMAL FORMATS

The Pentium CPU/Intel486 CPU/Intel387 NPX neither generate nor support these formats; they raise an invalid-operation exception whenever they encounter them in an arithmetic operation. The Intel287 and 8087 math coprocessors define and support special handling for these formats.

This difference has no impact on software. The Pentium and Intel486 processors and the Intel387 DX math coprocessor do not generate these formats, and therefore will not encounter them unless a programmer deliberately enters them.

The reason for this difference is to conform to IEEE Standard 754.

23.3.3. Exceptions

This section identifies the implementation differences in exception handling of floating-point instructions.

23.3.3.1. DENORMAL EXCEPTIONS

The denormal exception is not raised in transcendental instructions and FXTRACT on the Intel287 and 8087 math coprocessors. The denormal exception is raised in transcendental instructions and FXTRACT on the Pentium and Intel486 processors and the Intel387 math coprocessor. The exception handler needs to be changed only if it gives special treatment to different opcodes. The reason for this change was performance enhancement for normal cases.

Because the Pentium CPU, Intel486 CPU, and Intel387 NPX automatically normalize denormalized numbers when possible, an 8087 program that uses the denormal exception solely to normalize denormalized operands can run on the 32-bit Intel x86 FPU's by masking the denormal exception. The 8087 denormal exception handler would not be used by the 32-bit Intel x86 FPU's in this case. A numerics program runs faster when the FPU performs normalization of denormalized operands.

23.3.3.2. OVERFLOW EXCEPTIONS

There are differences in overflow exception behavior when it is masked and unmasked.

On the Pentium CPU/Intel486 CPU/Intel487 NPX when the overflow exception is masked, and the rounding mode is set to chop (toward zero), the result is the largest positive or smallest negative number. The Intel287 and 8087 math coprocessors do not signal the overflow exception when the masked response is not infinity; i.e., they signal overflow only when the rounding control is not set to round to zero. If rounding is set to chop (toward zero), the result is positive or negative infinity. Under the most common rounding modes, there is no impact on software.

If rounding is toward zero (chop), a program on the Pentium CPU/Intel486 CPU/Intel387 NPX produces, under overflow conditions, a result that is different in the least significant bit of the significand, compared to the result on the Intel287 math coprocessor. The reason for this difference is IEEE Standard 754 compatibility.

When the overflow exception is not masked, the precision exception is flagged on the Pentium CPU, Intel486 CPU, and Intel387 NPX. When the result is stored in the stack, the significand is rounded according to the precision control (PC) bit of the control word or according to the opcode. On the Intel287 and 8087 math coprocessors, the precision exception is not flagged and the significand is not rounded. The impact on software is that if the result is stored on the stack, a program on the Pentium and Intel486 processors and the Intel387 math coprocessor produce a different result under overflow conditions than on the Intel287 and 8087 math coprocessors. The difference is apparent only to the exception handler. This difference is for IEEE Standard 754 compatibility.

23.3.3.3. UNDERFLOW EXCEPTIONS

Two related events contribute to underflow:

1. The creation of a *tiny* (denormal) result. A tiny number, because it is so small, may cause some other exception later (such as overflow upon division).
2. Loss of accuracy during the denormalization of a tiny number.

    Which of these events triggers the underflow exception depends on whether the underflow exception is masked.

When the underflow exception is masked on the 32-bit FPU's and NPX's, the underflow exception is signaled when both the result is tiny and denormalization results in a loss of accuracy. When the underflow exception is unmasked and the instruction is supposed to store the result on the stack, the significand is rounded to the appropriate precision (according to the precision control (PC) bit of the control word, for those instructions controlled by PC, otherwise to extended precision), after adjusting the exponent.

When the underflow exception is masked on the Intel287 and 8087 math coprocessors and rounding is toward zero, the underflow exception flag is raised on tininess, regardless of loss of accuracy. When the underflow exception is not masked and the destination is the stack, the significand is not rounded but rather is left as is.

When the underflow exception is masked, there is no impact on software. The underflow exception occurs less often when rounding is toward zero.

When the underflow exception not masked. A program on a 32-bit Intel x86 FPU or NPX produces a different result during underflow conditions than on the Intel287 and 8087 math coprocessors if the result is stored on the stack. The difference is only in the least significant bit of the significand and is apparent only to the exception handler.

The reason for these differences are due to EEE Standard 754 compatibility.

23.3.3.4. EXCEPTION PRECEDENCE

There is no difference in the precedence of the denormal exception on the Pentium and Intel487 processors and the Intel387 NPX, whether it be masked or not. When the denormal exception is not masked on the Intel287 and 8087 math coprocessors, it takes precedence over all other exceptions. This difference causes no impact on software, but some unneeded normalization of denormalized operands is prevented on the Intel486 CPU and Intel387 NPX. Operational improvement is the reason for this difference.

23.3.3.5. CS AND IP FOR FPU EXCEPTIONS

On the Intel 32-bit Intel x86 FPU's and NPX's, the value of the CS and IP registers saved for floating-point exceptions points at any prefixes which come before the ESC instruction. On the 8086 processor, the saved CS:IP points to the ESC instruction.

23.3.3.6.   FPU ERROR SIGNALS

The floating-point error signals to the Pentium and Intel486 processors do not pass through an interrupt controller (an INT signal from Intel387, Intel287 or 8087 math coprocessors do). If an 8086 processor uses another exception for the 8087 interrupt, both exception vectors should call the floating-point error exception handler. Some instructions in a floating-point error exception handler may need to be deleted if they use the interrupt controller. The Pentium and Intel486 processors have signals which, with the addition of external logic, support reporting for emulation of the interrupt mechanism used in many personal computers.

On the Pentium and Intel486 processors, an undefined ESC opcode will cause an Invalid Opcode exception (interrupt vector 6). Undefined ESC opcodes, like legal ESC opcodes, cause a Device Not Available exception (interrupt vector 7) when either the TS or the EM bit of CR0 is set. The Pentium and Intel486 processors do not check for floating-point error conditions on encountering an undefined ESC opcode.

23.3.3.7.   INVALID OPERATION ON DENORMALS

No invalid opcode exception is raised on the Pentium CPU/Intel486 CPU/Intel487 NPX upon encountering a denormal in FSQRT, FDIV, or FPREM or upon conversion to BCD or to integer. The operation proceeds by first normalizing the value. On Intel287 and 8087 math coprocessors, upon encountering a denormal in FSQRT, FDIV, or FPREM or upon conversion to BCD or to integer, the invalid-operation exception is raised. This difference has no impact on software. Software on the Pentium CPU/Intel486 CPU/Intel387 NPX continues to execute in cases where Intel287 and 8087 math coprocessors trap. The reason for this change was to eliminate an exception from being raised.

23.3.3.8.   ALIGNMENT EXCEPTIONS

A misaligned data operand on the Pentium and Intel486 processors causes an alignment exception (interrupt vector 17) in level 3 software, except for the stack portion of an FSAVE/FRSTOR operation.

23.3.3.9.   SEGMENT FAULT DURING FLDENV

On the Intel486 processor, when a segment fault occurs in the middle of an FLDENV operation, it can happen that part of the environment is loaded and part not. In such cases, the FPU control word is left with a value of 007FH. The Pentium processor ensures the internal state is correct at all times by attempting to read the first and last bytes of the environment before updating the internal state.

23.3.3.10.   INTERRUPT 7 — DEVICE NOT AVAILABLE

Interrupt 7 will occur in the Pentium and Intel486 processors when executing ESC instructions with either TS (task switched) or EM (emulation) of the MSW set (TS=1 or EM=1). If TS and MP are set, then a WAIT instruction will also cause interrupt 7. An exception handler should be included in the Pentium and Intel486 processor code to handle these situations.

23.3.3.11. INTERRUPT 9 — COPROCESSOR SEGMENT OVERRUN

Interrupt 9 does not occur in the Pentium and Intel486 processors. In cases where the Intel387 math coprocessor would cause interrupt 9, the Pentium and Intel486 processors simply abort the instruction. Some care is necessary, however. Memory faults (especially page faults), if they occur in FLDENV or FRSTOR while the operating system is performing a task switch, can cause the floating-point environment to be lost. Intel strongly recommends that the floating-point save area be the same page as the TSS.

23.3.3.12. INTERRUPT 13 — GENERAL PROTECTION

Interrupt 13 occurs if the starting address of a numeric operand falls outside a segment's size. An exception handler should be included to report these programming errors.

23.3.3.13. INTERRUPT 16 — FLOATING-POINT ERROR

In real mode and protected mode (not including virtual 8086 mode), interrupt vector 16 must point to the numeric exception handling routine. In virtual 8086 mode, the virtual-8086 monitor can be programmed to accommodate a different location of the interrupt vector for numeric exceptions.

23.3.4. Instructions

This section identifies the differences in instructions for the various Intel architectures, the reason for the differences, and their impact on software.

- FDIV, FPREM, FSQRT — Operation on denormalized operands is supported on the Pentium CPU, Intel486 CPU, and Intel387 NPX and an underflow exception can occur. Operation on denormalized operands raise an invalid-operation exception on the Intel287 and 8087 math coprocessors and underflow is not possible. The exception handler for underflow may require change only if it gives different treatment to different opcodes. Possibly fewer invalid-operation exceptions will occur. The reason for this change was for IEEE Standard 754 compatibility.

- FSCALE — The range of the scaling operand on the Pentium CPU, Intel486 CPU, and Intel387 NPX is not restricted. If $0 < |ST(1)| < 1$, the scaling factor is zero; therefore, $ST(0)$ remains unchanged. If the rounded result is not exact or if there was a loss of accuracy (masked underflow), the precision exception is signaled. The range of the scaling operand on the Intel287 and 8087 NPX's is restricted. If $0 < |ST(1)| < 1$, the result is undefined and no exception is signaled. The impact on software is that a different result will occur when $0 < |ST(1)| < 1$. This change was to upgrade the existing range of scaling.

- FPREM1 — The Pentium CPU, Intel486 CPU, and Intel387 NPX perform partial remainder according to the IEEE Standard 754 standard. This instruction does not exist on the Intel287 and 8087 NPX's. There is no impact on software but provides IEEE Standard 754 compatibility and an upgrade to the architecture.

- FPREM — Bits C0, C3, C1 of the status word on the Pentium CPU, Intel486 CPU, and Intel387 NPX correctly reflect the three low-order bits of the quotient. On the Intel287 and 8087 NPX's, the quotient bits are incorrect when performing a reduction of 64^N+M when $N \geq 1$ and M=1 or M=2. This has no impact on software. Software that works around the bug should not be affected.

- FUCOM, FUCOMP, FUCOMPP — The Pentium CPU, Intel486 CPU, and Intel387 NPX perform unordered compare according to IEEE Standard 754 standard. These instructions do not exist on the Intel287 and 8087 NPX's. There is no impact on existing software and provides IEEE Standard 754 compatibility.

- FPTAN — The range of operand is much less restricted ($| ST(0) | < 2^{63}$) on the Pentium CPU, Intel486 CPU, and Intel387 NPX; reduces operand internally using an internal $\pi/4$ constant that is more accurate. The range of operand is restricted ($| ST(0) | < \pi/4$) on the Intel287 and 8087 NPX's; the operand must be reduced to range using FPREM. There is no impact on software due to this difference but provides a performance upgrade.

  After a stack overflow, when the invalid-operation exception is masked on the Pentium CPU, Intel486 CPU, and Intel387 NPX, both ST and ST(1) contain quiet NaNs. After a stack overflow when the invalid-operation exception is masked on the Intel287 and 8087 NPX's, the original operand remains unchanged, but is pushed to ST(1). This has no impact on software and provides IEEE Standard 754 compatibility.

- FSIN, FCOS, FSINCOS — These instructions perform three common trigonometric functions on the Pentium CPU, Intel486 CPU, and Intel387 NPX. They do not exist on the Intel287 and 8087 NPX's and their presence on more recent architectures have no impact on existing software but provide a performance upgrade.

- FPATAN — The range of operands is unrestricted on the Pentium CPU, Intel486 CPU, and Intel387 NPX. $| ST(0) |$ must be smaller than $| ST(1) |$ on the Intel287 and 8087 NPX's. There is no software compatibility impact but serves as a performance upgrade only.

- F2XM1 — The Pentium CPU, Intel486 CPU, and Intel387 NPX support a wider range of operands ($-1 < ST(0) < +1$). The supported operand range on the Intel287 and 8087 NPX's is $0 \leq ST(0) \leq 0.5$. There is no software compatibility impact but serves as a performance upgrade only.

- FLD extended-real — On the Pentium CPU, Intel486 CPU, and Intel387 NPX, this instruction does not report denormal exception because the instruction is not arithmetic. The Intel287 and 8087 NPX's report denormal exception. There is no software compatibility impact but serves as a performance upgrade only.

- FXTRACT — If the operand is zero on the Pentium CPU, Intel486 CPU, or Intel387 NPX, the zero-divide exception is reported and $-\infty$ is delivered to ST(1). If the operand is $+\infty$, no exception is reported. If the operand is zero on the Intel287 and 8087 NPX's, ST(1) is zero and no exception is reported. If the operand is $+\infty$, the invalid-operation exception is reported. There is no impact on software due to these differences. Software usually bypasses zero and ∞. This change is due to the IEEE 754 recommendation to fully support the logb function.

- FLD constant — Rounding control is in effect for the Pentium CPU, Intel486 CPU, and Intel387 NPX. Rounding control is not in effect for the Intel287 and 8087 NPX's. Results for FLDPI, FLDLN2, FLDLG2, and FLDL2E are the same as for the Intel287 and 8087 NPX's when rounding control is set to round to nearest or round to +∞. They are the the the same for FLDL2T when rounding control is set to round to nearest, round to −∞, or round to zero. Results are different from the Intel287 and 8087 NPX's in the leaast significant bit of the mantissa if rounding control is set to round to −∞ or round to 0 for FLDPI, FLDLN2, FLDLG2, and FLDL2E; they are different for FLDL2T if round to +∞ is specified. These changes were implemented due to IEEE 754 recommendations.

- FLD single/double precision — Loading a denormal on the Pentium CPU, Intel486 CPU, or Intel387 NPX causes the number to be converted to extended precision (because it is put on the stack). Loading a denormal on the Intel287 and 8087 NPX causes the number to be converted to an unnormal. If the next instruction is FXTRACT or FXAM, the Pentium CPU, Intel486 CPU, and Intel387 NPX will give a different result than the Intel287 and 8087 NPX's. This change was made for IEEE Standard 754 compatibility.

- FLD single/double precision — When loading a signaling NaN, the Pentium CPU, Intel486 CPU, and Intel387 NPX raises an invalid exception. The Intel287 and 8087 NPX's do not raise an exception when loading a signaling NaN. The exception handler needs to be updated to handle this condition. This change was made for IEEE Standard 754 compatibility.

- FSETPM — This instruction is treated as FNOP (no operation) on the Pentium CPU, Intel486 CPU, and Intel387 NPX. This intruction informs the Intel287 math coprocessor that the system is in protected mode. There is no impact on software as a result of this difference. The Pentium, Intel486, and Intel386 CPU's handle all addressing and exception-pointer information, whether in protected mode or not.

- FXAM — Encountering an empty register on the Pentium CPU, Intel486 CPU, or Intel387 NPX will not generate combinations of C3-C0 equal to 1101 or 1111. The Intel287 and 8087 NPX's may generate these combinations, among others. There is no impact on software but provides a performance upgrade, to provide repeatable results.

- FSAVE, FSTENV — The address of a memory operand pointer stored by FSAVE or FSTENV is undefined if the previous ESC instruction did not refer to memory on the Pentium and Intel486 FPUs and the Intel387 NPX.

23.3.5. Transcendental Instructions

The numeric results of the Pentium processor for transcendental instructions in the core range (as defined in Chapter 7) may differ from the Intel486 processors by about 2 or 3 ulps. The C1 bit may differ as a result. The exact threshold for underflow/overflow will vary by a few ulps. The Pentium processor results will have a worst case error of less than 1 ulp when rounding to the nearest-even and less than 1.5 ulps when rounding in other modes. The transcendental instructions are guaranteed to be monotonic, with respect to the input operands, throughout the domain supported by the instruction. See Appendix G for more information on transcendental accuracy.

On the Intel486 processor but not on the Pentium processor, transcendental instructions can be aborted at certain checkpoints during execution if an INTR is pending. Transcendental instructions should therefore be used only in an environment where INTRs are not expected to come as close as 200 clocks apart.

Transcendental instructions may generate different results in the round-up bit (C1) of status word on the Pentium CPU, Intel486 CPU, and Intel387 NPX. The round-up bit of the status word is undefined for these instructions on the Intel287 and 8087 NPX's. There is no impact on software due to this difference but it serves as an upgrade to signal rounding status.

23.3.6. Obsolete Instructions

The 8087 processor instructions FENI and FDISI and the Intel287 processor instruction FSETPM are treated as NOPS in the Pentium CPU, Intel486 CPU, and Intel387 math coprocessor. If these opcodes are detected in the instruction stream, no specific operation is performed and no internal states are affected.

The *80387 DX User's Manual Programmer's Reference* and the *Intel486™ DX Processor Programmer's Reference Manual* indicate that the Intel287 and 8087 floating-point unit (FPU) opcodes for FENI, FDISI, and FSETPM are treated as FNOP in the Intel387 NPX and the Intel486 and Pentium FPUs. However, FNOP checks for unmasked floating point exceptions and these instructions do not. Thus, these instructions are integer NOP instructions rather than FNOP's in the Intel387 NPX, and in the Intel486 and Pentium FPU's.

23.3.6.1. WAIT PREFIX DIFFERENCES

On the Intel486 processor, when a WAIT prefix precedes a numeric instruction (one which itself automatically synchronizes with the previous numeric instruction), the WAIT is treated as a NOP. Pending numeric exceptions from a previous numeric instruction are processed not on the WAIT but on the numeric instruction following the WAIT. In such a case, the report of a numeric exception may appear one instruction later on the Intel486 processor than on an Intel386 CPU/Intel387 NPX system or Pentium processor.

23.3.6.2. OPERANDS SPLIT ACROSS SEGMENTS/PAGES

On the Pentium and Intel486 processors, when the first half of an operand to be written is inside a page or segment and the second half is outside, a memory fault can cause the first half to be stored without the second. In such cases, Intel386 CPU/Intel387 NPX systems store nothing.

23.3.6.3. FPU INSTRUCTION SYNCHRONIZATION

All of the Pentium CPU, Intel486 CPU, and Intel387 NPX numeric instructions are automatically synchronized—the processor automatically waits until the previous numeric instruction has completed before executing the next ESC instruction. No explicit WAIT instructions are required to assure this synchronization. For the 8087 used with 8086 and 8088 processors, explicit WAITs are required before each numeric instruction to ensure synchronization. Although 8087 programs having explicit WAIT instructions execute perfectly on the 32-bit Intel x86 processors without reassembly, these WAIT instructions are unnecessary.

Since the 32-bit Intel x86 FPU's do not require WAIT instructions before each numeric instruction, the ASM386/486 assembler does not automatically generate these WAIT instructions. The ASM86 assembler, however, automatically precedes every ESC instruction with a WAIT instruction. Although numeric routines generated using the ASM86 assembler will generally execute correctly on the 32-bit Intel x86 FPU's, reassembly using ASM386/486 may result in a more compact code image and faster execution. The control instructions for the 32-bit Intel x86 FPU's can be coded using either a WAIT or No-WAIT form of mnemonic. The WAIT forms of these instructions cause ASM386/486 to precede the ESC instruction with a WAIT instruction, in the identical manner as does ASM86.

Part IV

Optimization

intel®

24

Optimization

This chapter provides some general guidelines for programming Intel's x86 architectures. For Pentium processor specific optimization techniques, see Appendix H.

24.1. ADDRESSING MODES AND REGISTER USAGE

This section identifies instruction examples that result on delays based on addressing modes and register usage.

An Address Generation Interlock (AGI) occurs when a register being used as the base or index component of an effective address calculation was the destination register of a previous instruction. It causes a 1-clock delay.

In the following sequence, the MOV instruction has a one clock stall on both the Intel486 and the Pentium processors.

```
add edx, 4
mov esi, [edx]
```

On the Intel486 processor, only adjacent instructions can cause AGI's. On the Pentium CPU, with its higher degree of concurrent execution, instructions which are up to three instructions away can interact to cause an AGI. Consider the following fabricated worst case sequence:

```
add esi, 4
pop ebx
inc ebx
mov edx, [esi]
```

This sequence executes on the Intel486 processor in four clocks. Due to the pairing of instructions on the Pentium CPU, the MOV needs the value of ESI, which is not available until the ADD completes the execute (EX) stage, the MOV stalls for one clock. Therefore, the above instruction sequence executes in three clocks on the Pentium processor.

Note that some instructions have implicit writes/reads to registers. Instructions that generate addresses implicitly through ESP (PUSH/POP/RET/CALL) also suffer from the AGI penalty (explicit write followed by explicit or implicit read).

Examples:

```
sub esp, 24        / 1 cycle stall
  (sub)
push ebx
```

```
mov esp, ebp       / 1 cycle stall
  (mov)
pop ebp
```

PUSH and POP also implicitly write to ESP. This, however, does not cause an AGI when the next instruction addresses through ESP (implicit write followed by explicit or implicit read through ESP). The following example demonstrates that an implicit write followed by an explicit or implicit read of ESP does not generate an AGI.

Example:

```
push edi                    / no stall
mov  ebx, [esp]
```

On the Intel486 CPU, there is a one clock penalty for decoding an instruction with either an index or an immediate-displacement combination. On the Pentium CPU, there is no one clock penalty. There also is no penalty for an indexed instruction on the Pentium CPU.

Example:

```
mov result, 555             / 555 is immediate, result
                            /   is displacement
mov dword ptr [esp+4], 1    / 1 is immediate, 4 is
                                displacement
```

Unlike the Intel486 CPU, there is no one clock penalty when using a register immediately after its sub-register was written.

Example (Pentium CPU):

```
mov al, 0                   /1
mov [ebp], eax              /2 no delay on Pentium CPU
```

Example (Intel486 CPU):

```
mov al, 0                   /1
   (mov)                    /2 one clock delay on Intel486 CPU
mov [ebp], eax              /3
```

24.2. ALIGNMENT

The effect of data misalignment on the Pentium CPU is similar to its effect on the Intel486 CPU. However, code alignment requirements are not as strict as on the Intel486 CPU.

24.2.1. Code Alignment

Unlike the Intel486 CPU, alignment of code on a cache line boundary (32-byte on Pentium CPU, 16-byte on Intel486 CPU) does not have a substantial effect on Pentium CPU performance. However, labels may be aligned as recommended for the Intel486 CPU because the incremental cost on the Pentium CPU is negligible and it improves the efficiency of the Intel486 CPU.

24.2.2. Data Alignment

A misaligned access in the data cache costs an extra 3 cycles on both the Intel486 and Pentium CPUs.

- **4-byte Data**. The alignment of 4-byte objects should be on a 4-byte boundary.

- **2-byte Data**. A 2-byte object should be fully contained within an aligned 4-byte word (i.e., its binary address should be xxxx00, xxxx01, xxxx10, but not xxxx11). (In the Intel486 CPU, a 2-byte data object has to be aligned on a 2-byte boundary to avoid a penalty).

- **8-byte Data**. The penalty for a misaligned 8-byte data object (64-bit, e.g., double precision reals) access is 3 cycles (as in Intel486 CPU). An 8-byte datum should be aligned on an 8-byte boundary.

24.3. PREFIXED OPCODES

The prefixes lock, segment override, address size, two-byte opcode map (0F), and operand size are decoded in one clock for each prefix. Note that this includes all the 16-bit instructions when executing in 32-bit mode because an operand size prefix is required (e.g., MOV WORD PTR [..], ADD WORD PTR [..], ...). Use 32-bit operands for 32-bit segments and 16-bit operands for 16-bit segments as much as possible to avoid the additional byte for prefixes.

The near conditional jump instructions that have a 0FH prefix are decoded differently. In this case, the processor does not take an extra clock. Other 0F opcodes behave as normal prefixed instructions.

24.4. OPERAND AND REGISTER USAGE

This section discusses some guidelines to follow and delays which can occur based on the type of operand and register selection.

- Use the EAX register when possible. Many instructions are one byte shorter when the EAX register is used, such as loads and stores to memory when absolute addresses are used, transfers to other registers using the XCHG instruction, and operations using immediate operands.

- Use the DS register to access the data segment when possible. Instructions which deal with the DS register are one byte shorter than instructions which use the other data segments, because of the lack of a segment-override prefix.

- Use the ESP register to reference the stack in the deepest level of subroutines.

- When several references are made to a variable addressed with a displacement, load the displacement into a register.

24.5. INTEGER INSTRUCTION SELECTION

This section highlights some instruction sequences to avoid and some sequences to use when generating x86 assembly code.

1. LEA

    The LEA instruction can be advantageous in the following circumstances:

— LEA may be used sometimes as a three/four operand addition instruction. LEA ECX,[EAX+EBX*4+ARRAY_NAME]).

— In many cases an LEA instruction (or a sequence of of LEA, add and shift instructions) may be used to replace constant multiply instructions.

— This can also be used to avoid copying a register when both operands to an ADD are being used after the add, since LEA need not overwrite its operands.

The disadvantage of the LEA instruction is that it increases the possibility of an AGI stall with previous instructions.

2. Complex Instructions

Avoid using complex instructions (ENTER, LEAVE, LOOP, string instructions, etc.). Use sequences of simple instructions instead.

3. Zero-Extension of Short Integers

The MOVZX instruction has a prefix and takes 3 cycles to execute (a total of 4 cycles). As with the Intel486 CPU, it is recommended to use the following sequence instead:

```
xor eax, eax
mov al, mem
```

If this occurs within a loop, it may be possible to pull the XOR out of the loop if the only assignment to EAX is the MOV AL, MEM. This has greater importance for the Pentium CPU due to its concurrency of instruction execution.

Access 16-bit data with the MOVSX and MOVZX instructions. These instructions sign-extend and zero-extend word operands to doubleword length. This eliminates the need for an extra instruction to initialize the high word.

4. 8/16-Bit Operands

With 8-bit operands, try to use the byte opcodes, rather than using 32-bit operations on sign and zero extended bytes. Prefixes for operand size override apply to 16-bit operands, not to 8-bit operands.

Sign Extension is usually quite expensive. Often, the semantics can be maintained by zero extending 16-bit operands. Specifically, the C code in the following example does not need sign extension nor does it need prefixes for operand size overrides.

```
static short int a,b;
if (a==b) {
}
```

5. Compares

Use TEST when comparing a value in a register with 0. Test essentially AND's the operands together without writing to a destination register. If you AND a value with itself and the result sets the zero condition flag, the value was zero.

Use TEST when comparing the result of a boolean AND with an immediate constant for equality or inequality if the register is EAX. (IF (AVAR & 8) { }).

6. Address Calculations

Pull address calculations into load and store instructions. Internally, memory reference instructions can have 4 operands: a relocatable load time segment base, a base register, a displacement, and a scaled index register. In many cases, several integer instructions can be eliminated by fully using the operands of memory references.

When there is a choice to use either a base or index register, always choose the base because there is a one clock penalty on a Intel486 CPU for using an index.

7. Clearing a Register

The preferred sequence to move zero to a register is XOR REG, REG. This saves code space but sets the condition codes. In contexts where the condition codes must be preserved, use: MOV REG, 0.

8. Integer Divide

Typically, an integer divide is preceded by a CDQ instruction. (Divide instructions use EDX:EAX as the dividend and CDQ sets up EDX.) It is better to copy EAX into EDX, then right shift EDX 31 places to sign extend. The copy/shift takes the same number of clocks as CDQ on both the Pentium and Intel486 CPUs, but the copy/shift scheme allows two other instructions to execute at the same time on the Pentium CPU. If you know the value is positive, use XOR EDX, EDX.

9. Avoid Compares with Immediate Zero

Often when a value is compared with zero, the operation producing the value sets condition codes which can be tested directly by a JCC instruction. (The most notable exceptions are MOV and LEA. In these cases, use TEST.)

10. Integer Multiply by Constant

The integer multiply by an immediate can usually be replaced by a faster series of shift's, add's, sub's, and lea's.

In general, if there are 8 or fewer bits set in the binary representation of the constant, it is better not to do the integer multiply. On an Intel486 CPU, the break even point is lower: it is profitable if 6 bits or less are in the constant. Basically, shift and add for each bit set.

11. In place of using an ENTER instruction at lexical level 0, use a code sequence like:

```
PUSH EBP
MOV EBP, ESP
SUB ESP, BYTE_COUNT
```

12. Jump Instructions

The jump instructions come in two forms: one form has an eight-bit immediate for relative jumps in the range from 128 bytes back to 127 bytes forward, the other form has a full 32-bit displacement. Many assemblers use the long form in situations where the short form can be used. When it is clear that the short form may be used, explicitly specify the destination operand as being byte length. This tells the assembler to use the short form. Note that some assemblers perform this optimization automatically.

13. For fastest task switching, perform task switching in software. This allows a smaller processor state to be saved and restored. See Chapter 13 for a discussion of multitasking.

14. Minimize segment register loads and use of far pointers as much as possible. Increased protection between segments costs performance as a substantial number of clocks are required to load the segment registers.

Part V

Instruction Set

intel ®

25

Instruction Set

CHAPTER 25
INSTRUCTION SET

This chapter presents the instructions in alphabetical order. For each instruction, the forms are given for each operand combination, including object code produced, operands required, execution time, and a description. For each instruction, there is an operational description and a summary of exceptions generated.

25.1. OPERAND-SIZE AND ADDRESS-SIZE ATTRIBUTES

When executing an instruction, the processor can address memory using either 16 or 32-bit addresses. Consequently, each instruction that uses memory addresses has associated with it an address-size attribute of either 16 or 32 bits. The use of 16-bit addresses implies both the use of 16-bit displacements in instructions and the generation of 16-bit address offsets (segment relative addresses) as the result of the effective address calculations. 32-bit addresses imply the use of 32-bit displacements and the generation of 32-bit address offsets. Similarly, an instruction that accesses words (16 bits) or doublewords (32 bits) has an operand-size attribute of either 16 or 32 bits.

The attributes are determined by a combination of defaults, instruction prefixes, and (for programs executing in protected mode) size-specification bits in segment descriptors.

25.1.1. Default Segment Attribute

For programs running in protected mode, the D bit in executable-segment descriptors specifies the default attribute for both address size and operand size. These default attributes apply to the execution of all instructions in the segment. A clear D bit sets the default address size and operand size to 16 bits; a set D bit, to 32 bits.

Programs that execute in real mode or virtual-8086 mode have 16-bit addresses and operands by default.

25.1.2. Operand-Size and Address-Size Instruction Prefixes

The internal encoding of an instruction can include two byte-long prefixes: the address-size prefix, 67H, and the operand-size prefix, 66H. (A later section, "Instruction Format," shows the position of the prefixes in an instruction's encoding.) These prefixes *override* the default segment attributes for the instruction that follows. Table 25-1 shows the effect of each possible combination of defaults and overrides.

Table 25-1. Effective Size Attributes

Segment Default D = ...	0	0	0	0	1	1	1	1
Operand-Size Prefix 66H	N	N	Y	Y	N	N	Y	Y
Address-Size Prefix 67H	N	Y	N	Y	N	Y	N	Y
Effective Operand Size	16	16	32	32	32	32	16	16
Effective Address Size	16	32	16	32	32	16	32	16

Y = Yes, this instruction prefix is present
N = No, this instruction prefix is not present

25.1.3. Address-Size Attribute for Stack

Instructions that use the stack implicitly (for example: POP EAX) also have a stack address-size attribute of either 16 or 32 bits. Instructions with a stack address-size attribute of 16 use the 16-bit SP stack pointer register; instructions with a stack address-size attribute of 32 bits use the 32-bit ESP register to form the address of the top of the stack.

The stack address-size attribute is controlled by the B bit of the data-segment descriptor in the SS register. A value of zero in the B bit selects a stack address-size attribute of 16; a value of one selects a stack address-size attribute of 32.

25.2. INSTRUCTION FORMAT

All instruction encodings are subsets of the general instruction format shown in Figure 25-1. Instructions consist of optional instruction prefixes (in any order), one or two primary opcode bytes, possibly an address specifier consisting of the ModR/M byte and the SIB (Scale Index Base) byte, a displacement, if required, and an immediate data field, if required.

INSTRUCTION PREFIX	ADDRESS-SIZE PREFIX	OPERAND-SIZE PREFIX	SEGMENT OVERIDE
0 OR 1	0 OR 1	0 OR 1	0 OR 1

NUMBER OF BYTES

OPCODE	MODR/M	SIB	DISPLACEMENT	IMMEDIATE
1 OR 2	0 OR 1	0 OR 1	0,1,2 OR 4	0,1,2 OR 4

NUMBER OF BYTES

APM117

Figure 25-1. Instruction Format

Smaller encoding fields can be defined within the primary opcode or opcodes. These fields define the direction of the operation, the size of the displacements, the register encoding, or sign extension; encoding fields vary depending on the class of operation.

Most instructions that can refer to an operand in memory have an addressing form byte following the primary opcode byte(s). This byte, called the ModR/M byte, specifies the address form to be used. Certain encodings of the ModR/M byte indicate a second addressing byte, the SIB (Scale Index Base) byte, which follows the ModR/M byte and is required to fully specify the addressing form.

Addressing forms can include a displacement immediately following either the ModR/M or SIB byte. If a displacement is present, it can be 8-, 16- or 32-bits.

If the instruction specifies an immediate operand, the immediate operand always follows any displacement bytes. The immediate operand, if specified, is always the last field of the instruction.

Zero or one bytes are reserved for each group of prefixes. The prefixes are grouped as follows:

1. Instruction Prefixes: REP, REPE/REPZ, REPNE/REPNZ, LOCK
2. Segment Override Prefixes: CS, SS, DS, ES, FS, GS
3. Operand Size Override
4. Address Size Override

For each instruction, one prefix may be used from each group. The effect of redundant prefixes (more than one prefix from a group) is undefined and may vary from processor to processor. The prefixes may come in any order.

The following are the allowable instruction prefix codes:

F3H   REP prefix (used only with string instructions)

F3H   REPE/REPZ prefix (used only with string instructions)

F2H   REPNE/REPNZ prefix (used only with string instructions)

F0H   LOCK prefix

The following are the segment override prefixes:

2EH   CS segment override prefix

36H   SS segment override prefix

3EH   DS segment override prefix

26H   ES segment override prefix

64H   FS segment override prefix

65H   GS segment override prefix

66H   Operand-size override

67H   Address-size override

25.2.1. ModR/M and SIB Bytes

The ModR/M and SIB bytes follow the opcode byte(s) in many of the processor instructions. They contain the following information:

- The indexing type or register number to be used in the instruction

- The register to be used, or more information to select the instruction

- The base, index, and scale information

The ModR/M byte contains three fields of information:

- The **mod** field, which occupies the two most significant bits of the byte, combines with the r/m field to form 32 possible values: eight registers and 24 indexing modes.

- The **reg** field, which occupies the next three bits following the mod field, specifies either a register number or three more bits of opcode information. The meaning of the reg field is determined by the first (opcode) byte of the instruction.

- The **r/m** field, which occupies the three least significant bits of the byte, can specify a register as the location of an operand, or can form part of the addressing-mode encoding in combination with the **mod** field as described above.

The based indexed and scaled indexed forms of 32-bit addressing require the SIB byte. The presence of the SIB byte is indicated by certain encodings of the ModR/M byte. The SIB byte then includes the following fields:

- The **ss** field, which occupies the two most significant bits of the byte, specifies the scale factor.

- The **index** field, which occupies the next three bits following the **ss** field and specifies the register number of the index register.

- The **base** field, which occupies the three least significant bits of the byte, specifies the register number of the base register.

Figure 25-2 shows the formats of the ModR/M and SIB bytes.

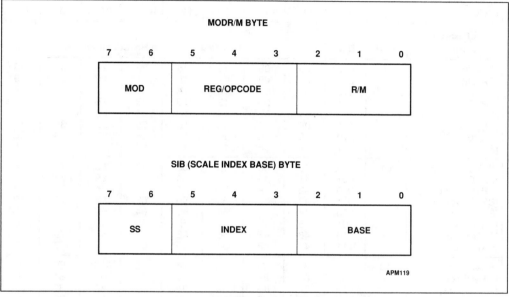

Figure 25-2. ModR/M and SIB Byte Formats

The values and the corresponding addressing forms of the ModR/M and SIB bytes are shown in Table 25-2 through Table 25-4. The 16-bit addressing forms specified by the ModR/M byte are in Table 25-2. The 32-bit addressing forms specified by the ModR/M byte are in Table 25-3. Table 25-4 shows the 32-bit addressing forms specified by the SIB byte.

Table 25-2. 16-Bit Addressing Forms with the ModR/M Byte

r8(/r) r16(/r) r32(/r) /digit (Opcode) REG =			AL AX EAX 0 000	CL CX ECX 1 001	DL DX EDX 2 010	BL BX EBX 3 011	AH SP ESP 4 100	CH BP EBP 5 101	DH SI ESI 6 110	BH DI EDI 7 111
Effective Address	**Mod**	**R/M**				**ModR/M Values in Hexadecimal**				
[BX+SI]	00	000	00	08	10	18	20	28	30	38
[BX+DI]		001	01	09	11	19	21	29	31	39
[BP+SI]		010	02	0A	12	1A	22	2A	32	3A
[BP+DI]		011	03	0B	13	1B	23	2B	33	3B
[SI]		100	04	0C	14	1C	24	2C	34	3C
[DI]		101	05	0D	15	1D	25	2D	35	3D
disp16		110	06	0E	16	1E	26	2E	36	3E
[BX]		111	07	0F	17	1F	27	2F	37	3F
[BX+SI]+disp8	01	000	40	48	50	58	60	68	70	78
[BX+DI]+disp8		001	41	49	51	59	61	69	71	79
[BP+SI]+disp8		010	42	4A	52	5A	62	6A	72	7A
[BP+DI]+disp8		011	43	4B	53	5B	63	6B	73	7B
[SI]+disp8		100	44	4C	54	5C	64	6C	74	7C
[DI]+disp8		101	45	4D	55	5D	65	6D	75	7D
[BP]+disp8		110	46	4E	56	5E	66	6E	76	7E
[BX]+disp8		111	47	4F	57	5F	67	6F	77	7F
[BX+SI]+disp16	10	000	80	88	90	98	A0	A8	B0	B8
[BX+DI]+disp16		001	81	89	91	99	A1	A9	B1	B9
[BP+SI]+disp16		010	82	8A	92	9A	A2	AA	B2	BA
[BP+DI]+disp16		011	83	8B	93	9B	A3	AB	B3	BB
[SI]+disp16		100	84	8C	94	9C	A4	AC	B4	BC
[DI]+disp16		101	85	8D	95	9D	A5	AD	B5	BD
[BP]+disp16		110	86	8E	96	9E	A6	AE	B6	BE
[BX]+disp16		111	87	8F	97	9F	A7	AF	B7	BF
EAX/AX/AL	11	000	C0	C8	D0	D8	E0	E8	F0	F8
ECX/CX/CL		001	C1	C9	D1	D9	EQ	E9	F1	F9
EDX/DX/DL		010	C2	CA	D2	DA	E2	EA	F2	FA
EBX/BX/BL		011	C3	CB	D3	DB	E3	EB	F3	FB
ESP/SP/AH		100	C4	CC	D4	DC	E4	EC	F4	FC
EBP/BP/CH		101	C5	CD	D5	DD	E5	ED	F5	FD
ESI/SI/DH		110	C6	CE	D6	DE	E6	EE	F6	FE
EDI/DI/BH		111	C7	CF	D7	DF	E7	EF	F7	FF

NOTES:

[1] **disp8** denotes an 8-bit displacement following the ModR/M byte, to be sign-extended and added to the index.

[2] **disp16** denotes a 16-bit displacement following the ModR/M byte, to be added to the index.
Default segment register is SS for the effective addresses containing a BP index, DS for other effective addresses.

Table 25-3. 32-Bit Addressing Forms with the ModR/M Byte

r8(/r) r16(/r) r32(/r) /digit (Opcode) REG =			AL AX EAX 0 000	CL CX ECX 1 001	DL DX EDX 2 010	BL BX EBX 3 011	AH SP ESP 4 100	CH BP EBP 5 101	DH SI ESI 6 110	BH DI EDI 7 111
Effective Address	**Mod**	**R/M**				**ModR/M Values in Hexadecimal**				
[EAX]	00	000	00	08	10	18	20	28	30	38
[ECX]		001	01	09	11	19	21	29	31	39
[EDX]		010	02	0A	12	1A	22	2A	32	3A
[EBX]		011	03	0B	13	1B	23	2B	33	3B
[--][--]¹		100	04	0C	14	1C	24	2C	34	3C
disp32		101	05	0D	15	1D	25	2D	35	3D
[ESI]		110	06	0E	16	1E	26	2E	36	3E
[EDI]		111	07	0F	17	1F	27	2F	37	3F
disp8[EAX]	01	000	40	48	50	58	60	68	70	78
disp8[ECX]		001	41	49	51	59	61	69	71	79
disp8[EDX]		010	42	4A	52	5A	62	6A	72	7A
disp8[EBX];		011	43	4B	53	5B	63	6B	73	7B
disp8[--][--]		100	44	4C	54	5C	64	6C	74	7C
disp8[EBP]		101	45	4D	55	5D	65	6D	75	7D
disp8[ESI]		110	46	4E	56	5E	66	6E	76	7E
disp8[EDI]		111	47	4F	57	5F	67	6F	77	7F
disp32[EAX]	10	000	80	88	90	98	A0	A8	B0	B8
disp32[ECX]		001	81	89	91	99	A1	A9	B1	B9
disp32[EDX]		010	82	8A	92	9A	A2	AA	B2	BA
disp32[EBX]		011	83	8B	93	9B	A3	AB	B3	BB
disp32[--][--]		100	84	8C	94	9C	A4	AC	B4	BC
disp32[EBP]		101	85	8D	95	9D	A5	AD	B5	BD
disp32[ESI]		110	86	8E	96	9E	A6	AE	B6	BE
disp32[EDI]		111	87	8F	97	9F	A7	AF	B7	BF
EAX/AX/AL	11	000	C0	C8	D0	D8	E0	E8	F0	F8
ECX/CX/CL		001	C1	C9	D1	D9	E1	E9	F1	F9
EDX/DX/DL		010	C2	CA	D2	DA	E2	EA	F2	FA
EBX/BX/BL		011	C3	CB	D3	DB	E3	EB	F3	FB
ESP/SP/AH		100	C4	CC	D4	DC	E4	EC	F4	FC
EBP/BP/CH		101	C5	CD	D5	DD	E5	ED	F5	FD
ESI/SI/DH		110	C6	CE	D6	DE	E6	EE	F6	FE
EDI/DI/BH		111	C7	CF	D7	DF	E7	EF	F7	FF

NOTES:

1. [--][--] means a SIB follows the ModR/M byte.

2. **disp8** denotes an 8-bit displacement following the SIB byte, to be sign-extended and added to the index.

   disp32 denotes a 32-bit displacement following the SIB byte, to be added to the index.

Table 25-4. 32-Bit Addressing Forms with the SIB Byte

r32 Base = Base =			EAX 0 000	ECX 1 001	EDX 2 010	EBX 3 011	ESP 4 100	[*] 5 101	ESI 6 110	EDI 7 111
Scaled Index	**SS**	**Index**	\multicolumn{8}{c}{**SIB Values in Hexadecimal**}
[EAX]	00	000	00	01	02	03	04	05	06	07
[ECX]		001	08	09	0A	0B	0C	0D	0E	0F
[EDX]		010	10	11	12	13	14	15	16	17
[EBX]		011	18	19	1A	1B	1C	1D	1E	1F
none		100	20	21	22	23	24	25	26	27
[EBP]		101	28	29	2A	2B	2C	2D	2E	2F
[ESI]		110	30	31	32	33	34	35	36	37
[EDI]		111	38	39	3A	3B	3C	3D	3E	3F
[EAX*2]	01	000	40	41	42	43	44	45	46	47
[ECX*2]		001	48	49	4A	4B	4C	4D	4E	4F
[ECX*2]		010	50	51	52	53	54	55	56	57
[EBX*2]		011	58	59	5A	5B	5C	5D	5E	5F
none		100	60	61	62	63	64	65	66	67
[EBP*2]		101	68	69	6A	6B	6C	6D	6E	6F
[ESI*2]		110	70	71	72	73	74	75	76	77
[EDI*2]		111	78	79	7A	7B	7C	7D	7E	7F
[EAX*4]	10	000	80	81	82	83	84	85	86	87
[ECX*4]		001	88	89	8A	8B	8C	8D	8E	8F
[EDX*4]		010	90	91	92	93	94	95	96	97
[EBX*4]		011	98	89	9A	9B	9C	9D	9E	9F
none		100	A0	A1	A2	A3	A4	A5	A6	A7
[EBP*4]		101	A8	A9	AA	AB	AC	AD	AE	AF
[ESI*4]		110	B0	B1	B2	B3	B4	B5	B6	B7
[EDI*4]		111	B8	B9	BA	BB	BC	BD	BE	BF
[EAX*8]	11	000	C0	C1	C2	C3	C4	C5	C6	C7
[ECX*8]		001	C8	C9	CA	CB	CC	CD	CE	CF
[EDX*8]		010	D0	D1	D2	D3	D4	D5	D6	D7
[EBX*8]		011	D8	D9	DA	DB	DC	DD	DE	DF
none		100	E0	E1	E2	E3	E4	E5	E6	E7
[EBP*8]		101	E8	E9	EA	EB	EC	ED	EE	EF
[ESI*8]		110	F0	F1	F2	F3	F4	F5	F6	F7
[EDI*8]		111	F8	F9	FA	FB	FC	FD	FE	FF

NOTES:

[*] means a disp32 with no base if MOD is 00, [EBP] otherwise. This provides the following addressing modes:

disp32[index]   (MOD=00)
disp8[EBP][index] (MOD=01)
disp32[EBP][index] (MOD=10)

25.2.2. How to Read the Instruction Set Pages

The following is an example of the format used for each processor instruction description in this chapter:

CMC—Complement Carry Flag

Opcode	Instruction	Clocks	Description
F5	CMC	2	Complement carry flag

The above table is followed by paragraphs labelled "Operation," "Description," "Flags Affected," "Protected Mode Exceptions," "Real Address Mode Exceptions," and, optionally, "Notes." The following sections explain the notational conventions and abbreviations used in these paragraphs of the instruction descriptions.

25.2.2.1. OPCODE COLUMN

The "Opcode" column gives the complete object code produced for each form of the instruction. When possible, the codes are given as hexadecimal bytes, in the same order in which they appear in memory. Definitions of entries other than hexadecimal bytes are as follows:

- **/digit:** (digit is between 0 and 7) indicates that the ModR/M byte of the instruction uses only the r/m (register or memory) operand. The **reg** field contains the digit that provides an extension to the instruction's opcode.

- **/r:** indicates that the ModR/M byte of the instruction contains both a register operand and an r/m operand.

- **cb, cw, cd, cp:** a 1-byte (cb), 2-byte (cw), 4-byte (cd) or 6-byte (cp) value following the opcode that is used to specify a code offset and possibly a new value for the code segment register.

- **ib, iw, id:** a 1-byte (ib), 2-byte (iw), or 4-byte (id) immediate operand to the instruction that follows the opcode, ModR/M bytes or scale-indexing bytes. The opcode determines if the operand is a signed value. All words and doublewords are given with the low-order byte first.

- **+rb, +rw, +rd:** a register code, from 0 through 7, added to the hexadecimal byte given at the left of the plus sign to form a single opcode byte. The codes are—

rb			rw			rd		
AL	=	0	AX	=	0	EAX	=	0
CL	=	1	CX	=	1	ECX	=	1
DL	=	2	DX	=	2	EDX	=	2
BL	=	3	BX	=	3	EBX	=	3

rb			rw			rd		
AH	=	4	SP	=	4	ESP	=	4
CH	=	5	BP	=	5	EBP	=	5
DH	=	6	SI	=	6	ESI	=	6
BH	=	7	DI	=	7	EDI	=	7

- **+i:** used in floating-point instructions when one of the operands is ST(i) from the FPU register stack. The number i (which can range from 0 to 7) is added to the hexadecimal byte given at the left of the plus sign to form a single opcode byte.

25.2.2.2. INSTRUCTION COLUMN

The "Instruction" column gives the syntax of the instruction statement as it would appear in an ASM386 program. The following is a list of the symbols used to represent operands in the instruction statements:

- **rel8:** a relative address in the range from 128 bytes before the end of the instruction to 127 bytes after the end of the instruction.

- **rel16, rel32:** a relative address within the same code segment as the instruction assembled. **rel16** applies to instructions with an operand-size attribute of 16 bits; **rel32** applies to instructions with an operand-size attribute of 32 bits.

- **ptr16:16, ptr16:32:** a far pointer, typically in a code segment different from that of the instruction. The notation **16:16** indicates that the value of the pointer has two parts. The value to the left of the colon is a 16-bit selector or value destined for the code segment register. The value to the right corresponds to the offset within the destination segment. **ptr16:16** is used when the instruction's operand-size attribute is 16 bits; **ptr16:32** is used with the 32-bit attribute.

- **r8:** one of the byte registers AL, CL, DL, BL, AH, CH, DH, or BH.

- **r16:** one of the word registers AX, CX, DX, BX, SP, BP, SI, or DI.

- **r32:** one of the doubleword registers EAX, ECX, EDX, EBX, ESP, EBP, ESI, or EDI.

- **imm8:** an immediate byte value. **imm8** is a signed number between −128 and +127 inclusive. For instructions in which **imm8** is combined with a word or doubleword operand, the immediate value is sign-extended to form a word or doubleword. The upper byte of the word is filled with the topmost bit of the immediate value.

- **imm16:** an immediate word value used for instructions whose operand-size attribute is 16 bits. This is a number between −32768 and +32767 inclusive.

- **imm32:** an immediate doubleword value used for instructions whose operand-size attribute is 32-bits. It allows the use of a number between +2147483647 and −2147483648 inclusive.

- **r/m8:** a one-byte operand that is either the contents of a byte register (AL, BL, CL, DL, AH, BH, CH, DH), or a byte from memory.

- **r/m16:** a word register or memory operand used for instructions whose operand-size attribute is 16 bits. The word registers are: AX, BX, CX, DX, SP, BP, SI, DI. The contents of memory are found at the address provided by the effective address computation.

- **r/m32:** a doubleword register or memory operand used for instructions whose operand-size attribute is 32-bits. The doubleword registers are: EAX, EBX, ECX, EDX, ESP, EBP, ESI, EDI. The contents of memory are found at the address provided by the effective address computation.

- **r/m64:** a quadword register or memory operand used for instructions whose operand-size attribute is 64-bits. The reg/opcode field represents the opcode. The contents of memory are found at the address provided by the effective address computation.

- **m:** a 16 or 32-bit memory operand.

- **m8:** a memory byte addressed by DS:[E]SI or ES:[E]DI (used only by string instructions).

- **m16:** a memory word addressed by DS:[E]SI or ES:[E]DI (used only by string instructions).

- **m32:** a memory doubleword addressed by DS:[E]SI or ES:[E]DI (used only by string instructions).

- **m16:16, m16:32:** a memory operand containing a far pointer composed of two numbers. The number to the left of the colon corresponds to the pointer's segment selector. The number to the right corresponds to its offset.

- **m16&32, m16&16, m32&32:** a memory operand consisting of data item pairs whose sizes are indicated on the left and the right side of the ampersand. All memory addressing modes are allowed. **m16&16** and **m32&32** operands are used by the BOUND instruction to provide an operand containing an upper and lower bounds for array indices. **m16&32** is used by LIDT and LGDT to provide a word with which to load the limit field, and a doubleword with which to load the base field of the corresponding Global and Interrupt Descriptor Table Registers.

- **moffs8, moffs16, moffs32:** (memory offset) a simple memory variable of type BYTE, WORD, or DWORD used by some variants of the MOV instruction. The actual address is given by a simple offset relative to the segment base. No ModR/M byte is used in the instruction. The number shown with **moffs** indicates its size, which is determined by the address-size attribute of the instruction.

- **Sreg:** a segment register. The segment register bit assignments are ES=0, CS=1, SS=2, DS=3, FS=4, and GS=5.

- **m32real, m64real, m80real:** (respectively) single-, double-, and extended-real floating-point operands in memory.

- **m16int, m32int, m64int**: (respectively) word-, short-, and long-integer floating-point operands in memory.

- **m/Vbyte**: *N*-byte floating-point operand in memory.

- **ST or ST(0)**: Top element of the FPU register stack.

- **ST(i)**: i[th] element from the top of the FPU register stack. (i=0..7)

25.2.2.3. CLOCKS COLUMN

The "Clocks" column gives the approximate number of clock cycles the instruction takes to execute. The clock count calculations makes the following assumptions:

- Data and instruction accesses hit in the cache.
- The target of a jump instruction is in the cache.
- No invalidate cycles contend with the instruction for use of the cache.
- Page translation hits in the TLB.
- Memory operands are aligned.
- Effective address calculations use a base register which is not the destination register of the preceding instruction.
- No exceptions are detected during execution.
- There are no write-buffer delays.

For a discussion of the performance penalties incurred when these conditions do not hold, see Appendix F.

The following symbols are used in the clock count specifications:

- **n**, which represents a number of repetitions.
- **m**, which represents the number of components in the next instruction executed, where the entire displacement (if any) counts as one component, the entire immediate data (if any) counts as one component, and every other byte of the instruction and prefix(es) each counts as one component.
- **pm=**, a clock count that applies when the instruction executes in Protected Mode. **pm=** is not given when the clock counts are the same for Protected and Real Address Modes.

When an exception occurs during the execution of an instruction and the exception handler is in another task, the instruction execution time is increased by the number of clocks to effect a task switch. This parameter depends on several factors:

- The type of TSS used to represent the new task (32 bit TSS or 16 bit TSS).
- Whether the current task is in V86 mode.
- Whether the new task is in V86 mode.
- Whether accesses hit in the cache.
- Whether a task gate on an interrupt/trap gate is used.

Table 25-5 summarizes the task switch times for exceptions, assuming cache hits and the use of task gates. For full details, see Appendix F.

Table 25-5. Task Switch Times for Exceptions

Old Task	New Task		
	to 32 bit TSS	to 16 bit TSS	to VM TSS
VM/32 bit/16 bit TSS	85	87	71

25.2.2.4.   DESCRIPTION COLUMN

The "Description" column following the "Clocks" column briefly explains the various forms of the instruction. The "Operation" and "Description" sections contain more details of the instruction's operation.

25.2.2.5.   OPERATION

The "Operation" section contains an algorithmic description of the instruction which uses a notation similar to the Algol or Pascal language. The algorithms are composed of the following elements:

- Comments are enclosed within the symbol pairs "(*" and "*)".

- Compound statements are enclosed between the keywords of the "if" statement (IF, THEN, ELSE, FI) or of the "do" statement (DO, OD), or of the "case" statement (CASE ... OF, ESAC).

- Execution continues until the END statement is encountered.

- A register name implies the contents of the register. A register name enclosed in brackets implies the contents of the location whose address is contained in that register. For example, ES:[DI] indicates the contents of the location whose ES segment relative address is in register DI. [SI] indicates the contents of the address contained in register SI relative to SI's default segment (DS) or overridden segment.

- Brackets are also used for memory operands, where they mean that the contents of the memory location is a segment-relative offset. For example, [SRC] indicates that the contents of the source operand is a segment-relative offset.

- A ← B; indicates that the value of B is assigned to A.

- The symbols =, <>, ≥, and ≤ are relational operators used to compare two values, meaning equal, not equal, greater or equal, less or equal, respectively. A relational expression such as A = B is TRUE if the value of A is equal to B; otherwise it is FALSE.

The following identifiers are used in the algorithmic descriptions:

- **OperandSize** represents the operand-size attribute of the instruction, which is either 16 or 32 bits. **AddressSize** represents the address-size attribute, which is either 16 or 32 bits. For example,

  ```
  IF instruction = CMPSW
  THEN OperandSize ← 16;
  ELSE
     IF instruction = CMPSD
     THEN OperandSize ← 32;
     FI;
  FI;
  ```

  indicates that the operand-size attribute depends on the form of the CMPS instruction used. Refer to the explanation of address-size and operand-size attributes at the beginning of this chapter for general guidelines on how these attributes are determined.

- **StackAddrSize** represents the stack address-size attribute associated with the instruction, which has a value of 16 or 32 bits, as explained earlier in the chapter.

- **SRC** represents the source operand. When there are two operands, SRC is the one on the right.

- **DEST** represents the destination operand. When there are two operands, DEST is the one on the left.

- **LeftSRC, RightSRC** distinguishes between two operands when both are source operands.

- **eSP** represents either the SP register or the ESP register depending on the setting of the B-bit for the current stack segment.

The following functions are used in the algorithmic descriptions:

- **Truncate to 16 bits(value)** reduces the size of the value to fit in 16 bits by discarding the uppermost bits as needed.

- **Addr(operand)** returns the effective address of the operand (the result of the effective address calculation prior to adding the segment base).

- **ZeroExtend(value)** returns a value zero-extended to the operand-size attribute of the instruction. For example, if OperandSize = 32, ZeroExtend of a byte value of −10 converts the byte from F6H to doubleword with hexadecimal value 000000F6H. If the value passed to ZeroExtend and the operand-size attribute are the same size, ZeroExtend returns the value unaltered.

- **SignExtend(value)** returns a value sign-extended to the operand-size attribute of the instruction. For example, if OperandSize = 32, SignExtend of a byte containing the value −10 converts the byte from F6H to a doubleword with hexadecimal value FFFFFFF6H. If the value passed to SignExtend and the operand-size attribute are the same size, SignExtend returns the value unaltered.

- **Push(value)** pushes a value onto the stack. The number of bytes pushed is determined by the operand-size attribute of the instruction. The action of Push is as follows:

  ```
  IF StackAddrSize = 16
  ```

```
THEN
      IF OperandSize = 16
      THEN
            SP ← SP – 2;
            SS:[SP] ← value; (* 2 bytes assigned starting at byte address in SP *)
      ELSE (* OperandSize = 32 *)
            SP ← SP – 4;
            SS:[SP] ← value; (* 4 bytes assigned starting at byte address in SP *)
      FI;
ELSE (* StackAddrSize = 32 *)
      IF OperandSize = 16
      THEN
            ESP ← ESP – 2;
            SS:[ESP] ← value; (* 2 bytes assigned starting at byte address in ESP*)
      ELSE (* OperandSize = 32 *)
            ESP ← ESP – 4;
            SS:[ESP] ← value; (* 4 bytes assigned starting at byte address in ESP*)
      FI;
FI;
```

- **Pop(value)** removes the value from the top of the stack and returns it. The statement EAX ← Pop( ); assigns to EAX the 32-bit value that Pop took from the top of the stack. Pop will return either a word or a doubleword depending on the operand-size attribute. The action of Pop is as follows:

```
IF StackAddrSize = 16
THEN
      IF OperandSize = 16
      THEN
            ret val ← SS:[SP]; (* 2-byte value *)
            SP ← SP + 2;
      ELSE (* OperandSize = 32 *)
            ret val ← SS:[SP]; (* 4-byte value *)
            SP ← SP + 4;
      FI;
ELSE (* StackAddrSize = 32 *)
      IF OperandSize = 16
      THEN
            ret val ← SS:[ESP]; (* 2 byte value *)
            ESP ← ESP + 2;
      ELSE (* OperandSize = 32 *)
            ret val ← SS:[ESP]; (* 4 byte value *)
            ESP ← ESP + 4;
      FI;
FI;
RETURN(ret val); (*returns a word or doubleword*)
```

Pop ST is used on floating-point instruction pages to mean *pop the FPU register stack.*

- **Bit[BitBase, BitOffset]** returns the value of a bit within a bit string, which is a sequence of bits in memory or a register. Bits are numbered from low-order to high-order within registers and within memory bytes. In memory, the two bytes of a word are stored with the low-order byte at the lower address.

  If the base operand is a register, the offset can be in the range 0..31. This offset addresses a bit within the indicated register. An example, 'BIT[EAX, 21]' is illustrated in Figure 25-3.

  If BitBase is a memory address, BitOffset can range from –2 gigabits to 2 gigabits. The addressed bit is numbered (Offset MOD 8) within the byte at address (BitBase + (BitOffset DIV 8)), where DIV is signed division with rounding towards negative infinity, and MOD returns a positive number. This is illustrated in Figure 25-4.

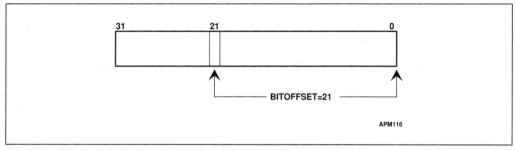

Figure 25-3. Bit Offset for BIT[EAX,21]

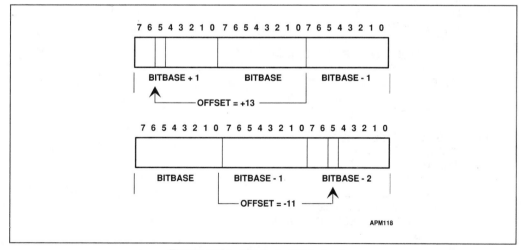

Figure 25-4. Memory Bit Indexing

- **I-O-Permission(I-O-Address, width)** returns TRUE or FALSE depending on the I/O permission bitmap and other factors. This function is defined as follows:

```
IF TSS type is 16 bit THEN RETURN FALSE; FI;
Ptr ← [TSS + 66]; (* fetch bitmap pointer *)
BitStringAddr ← SHR (I-O-Address, 3) + Ptr;
```

```
MaskShift ← I-O-Address AND 7;
CASE width OF:
    BYTE: nBitMask ← 1;
    WORD: nBitMask ← 3;
    DWORD: nBitMask ← 15;
ESAC;
mask ← SHL (nBitMask, MaskShift);
CheckString ← [BitStringAddr] AND mask;
IF CheckString = 0
THEN RETURN (TRUE);
ELSE RETURN (FALSE);
FI;
```

- **Switch-Tasks** is the task switching function described in Chapter 13.

25.2.2.6.   DESCRIPTION

The "Description" section contains further explanation of the instruction's operation.

25.2.2.7.   FLAGS AFFECTED

The "Flags Affected" section lists the flags that are affected by the instruction, as follows:

- If a flag is always cleared or always set by the instruction, the value is given (0 or 1) after the flag name. Arithmetic and logical instructions usually assign values to the status flags in the uniform manner described in Appendix C. Nonconventional assignments are described in the "Operation" section.

- The values of flags listed as "undefined" may be changed by the instruction in an indeterminate manner.

All flags not listed are unchanged by the instruction.

The floating-point instruction pages have a section called "FPU Flags Affected," which tells how each instruction can affect the four condition code bits of the FPU status word. These pages also have a section called "Numeric Exceptions," which lists the exception flags of the FPU status word that each instruction can set.

25.2.2.8.   PROTECTED MODE EXCEPTIONS

This section lists the exceptions that can occur when the instruction is executed in protected mode. The exception names are a pound sign (#) followed by two letters and an optional error code in parentheses. For example, #GP(0) denotes a general protection exception with an error code of 0. Table 25-6 associates each two-letter name with the corresponding interrupt number.

Table 25-6. Exceptions

Mnemonic	Interrupt	Description
#UD	6	Invalid opcode
#NM	7	Device not available
#DF	8	Double fault
#TS	10	Invalid TSS
#NP	11	Segment or gate not present
#SS	12	Stack fault
#GP	13	General protection fault
#PF	14	Page fault
#MF	16	Floating-point error
#AC	17	Alignment check

Chapter 14 describes the exceptions and the processor state upon entry to the exception.

Application programmers should consult the documentation provided with their operating systems to determine the actions taken when exceptions occur.

25.2.2.9. REAL ADDRESS MODE EXCEPTIONS

Because less error checking is performed by the Pentium processor in Real Address Mode, this mode has fewer exception conditions. Refer to Chapter 9 for further information on these exceptions.

25.2.2.10. VIRTUAL-8086 MODE EXCEPTIONS

Virtual 8086 tasks provide the ability to simulate Virtual 8086 machines. Virtual 8086 Mode exceptions are similar to those for the 8086 processor, but there are some differences. Refer to Chapter 22 for complete information on Virtual Mode exceptions.

AAA—ASCII Adjust after Addition

Opcode	Instruction	Clocks	Description
37	AAA	3	ASCII adjust AL after addition

Operation

```
ALcarry ← AL > 0F9H;  (* 1 if true *)
IF ((AL AND 0FH) > 9) OR (AF = 1)
THEN
    AL ← (AL + 6) AND 0FH;
    AH ← AH + 1 + ALcarry;
    AF ← 1;
    CF ← 1;
ELSE
    AF ← 0;
    CF ← 0;
    AL ← AL AND 0FH;
FI;
```

Description

Execute the AAA instruction only following an ADD instruction that leaves a byte result in the AL register. The lower nibbles of the operands of the ADD instruction should be in the range 0 through 9 (BCD digits). In this case, the AAA instruction adjusts the AL register to contain the correct decimal digit result. If the addition produced a decimal carry, the AH register is incremented, and the CF and AF flags are set. If this same addition also produced FH in the upper nibble of AL then AH is incremented again. If there was no decimal carry, the CF and AF flags are cleared and the AH register is unchanged. In either case, the AL register is left with its top nibble set to 0. To convert the AL register to an ASCII result, follow the AAA instruction with OR AL, 30H.

Flags Affected

The AF and CF flags are set if there is a decimal carry, cleared if there is no decimal carry; the OF, SF, ZF, and PF flags are undefined.

Protected Mode Exceptions

None.

Real Address Mode Exceptions

None.

Virtual 8086 Mode Exceptions

None.

AAD—ASCII Adjust AX before Division

Opcode	Instruction	Clocks	Description
D5 0A	AAD	10	ASCII adjust AX before division

Operation

regAL = AL;
regAH = AH;
AL ← (regAH * imm8 + regAL) AND 0FFH;
AH ← 0;

NOTE:

imm8 has the value of the instruction's second byte. The second byte under normally assembly of this instruction will be 0A, however, explicit modification of this byte will result in the operation described above and may alter results.

Description

The AAD instruction is used to prepare two unpacked BCD digits (the least-significant digit in the AL register, the most-significant digit in the AH register) for a division operation that will yield an unpacked result. This is accomplished by setting the AL register to AL + (second byte of opcode * AH), and then clearing the AH register. The AX register is then equal to the binary equivalent of the original unpacked two-digit number.

Flags Affected

The SF, ZF, and PF flags are set according to the result; the OF, AF, and CF flags are undefined.

Protected Mode Exceptions

None.

Real Address Mode Exceptions

None.

Virtual 8086 Mode Exceptions

None.

AAM—ASCII Adjust AX after Multiply

Opcode	Instruction	Clocks	Description
D4 0A	AAM	18	ASCII adjust AX after multiply

Operation

regAL ← AL;
AH ← regAL / imm8;
AL ← regAL MOD imm8;

NOTE:

imm8 has the value of the instruction's second byte. The second byte under normally assembly of this instruction will be 0A, however, explicit modification of this byte will result in the operation described above and may alter results.

Description

Execute the AAM instruction only after executing a MUL instruction between two unpacked BCD digits that leaves the result in the AX register. Because the result is less than 100, it is contained entirely in the AL register. The AAM instruction unpacks the AL result by dividing AL by the second byte of the opcode, leaving the quotient (most-significant digit) in the AH register and the remainder (least-significant digit) in the AL register.

Flags Affected

The SF, ZF, and PF flags are set according to the result; the OF, AF, and CF flags are undefined.

Protected Mode Exceptions

None.

Real Address Mode Exceptions

None.

Virtual 8086 Mode Exceptions

None.

AAS—ASCII Adjust AL after Subtraction

Opcode	Instruction	Clocks	Description
3F	AAS	3	ASCII adjust AL after subtraction

Operation

```
ALborrow ← AL < 6;     (* 1 if true *)
IF (AL AND 0FH) > 9 OR AF = 1
THEN
    AL ← (AL − 6) AND 0FH;
    AH ← AH − 1 − ALborrow;
    AF ← 1;
    CF ← 1;
ELSE
    CF ← 0;
    AF ← 0;
    AL ← AL AND 0FH;
FI;
```

Description

Execute the AAS instruction only after a SUB instruction that leaves the byte result in the AL register. The lower nibbles of the operands of the SUB instruction must have been in the range 0 through 9 (BCD digits). In this case, the AAS instruction adjusts the AL register so it contains the correct decimal digit result. If the subtraction produced a decimal carry, the AH register is decremented, and the CF and AF flags are set. If no decimal carry occurred, the CF and AF flags are cleared, and the AH register is unchanged. In either case, the AL register is left with its top nibble set to 0. To convert the AL result to an ASCII result, follow the AAS instruction with OR AL, 30H.

Flags Affected

The AF and CF flags are set if there is a decimal carry, cleared if there is no decimal carry; the OF, SF, ZF, and PF flags are undefined.

Protected Mode Exceptions

None.

Real Address Mode Exceptions

None.

Virtual 8086 Mode Exceptions

None.

ADC—Add with Carry

Opcode	Instruction	Clocks	Description
14 *ib*	ADC AL,*imm8*	1	Add with carry immediate byte to AL
15 *iw*	ADC AX,*imm16*	1	Add with carry immediate word to AX
15 *id*	ADC EAX,*imm32*	1	Add with carry immediate dword to EAX
80 /2 *ib*	ADC *r/m8,imm8*	1/3	Add with carry immediate byte to *r/m* byte
81 /2 *iw*	ADC *r/m16,imm16*	1/3	Add with carry immediate word to *r/m* word
81 /2 *id*	ADC *r/m32,imm32*	1/3	Add with CF immediate dword to *r/m* dword
83 /2 *ib*	ADC *r/m16,imm8*	1/3	Add with CF sign-extended immediate byte to *r/m* word
83 /2 *ib*	ADC *r/m32,imm8*	1/3	Add with CF sign-extended immediate byte into *r/m* dword
10 /*r*	ADC *r/m8,r8*	1/3	Add with carry byte register to *r/m* byte
11 /*r*	ADC *r/m16,r16*	1/3	Add with carry word register to *r/m* word
11 /*r*	ADC *r/m32,r32*	1/3	Add with CF dword register to *r/m* dword
12 /*r*	ADC *r8,r/m8*	1/2	Add with carry *r/m* byte to byte register
13 /*r*	ADC *r16,r/m16*	1/2	Add with carry *r/m* word to word register
13 /*r*	ADC *r32,r/m32*	1/2	Add with CF *r/m* dword to dword register

Operation

DEST ← DEST + SRC + CF;

Description

The ADC instruction performs an integer addition of the two operands DEST and SRC and the carry flag, CF. The result of the addition is assigned to the first operand (DEST), and the flags are set accordingly. The ADC instruction is usually executed as part of a multi-byte or multi-word addition operation. When an immediate byte value is added to a word or doubleword operand, the immediate value is first sign-extended to the size of the word or doubleword operand.

Flags Affected

The OF, SF, ZF, AF, CF, and PF flags are set according to the result.

Protected Mode Exceptions

#GP(0) if the result is in a nonwritable segment; #GP(0) for an illegal memory operand effective address in the CS, DS, ES, FS, or GS segments; #SS(0) for an illegal address in the SS segment; #PF(fault-code) for a page fault; #AC for unaligned memory reference if the current privilege level is 3.

Real Address Mode Exceptions

Interrupt 13 if any part of the operand would lie outside of the effective address space from 0 to 0FFFFH.

Virtual 8086 Mode Exceptions

Same exceptions as in Real Address Mode; #PF(fault-code) for a page fault; #AC for unaligned memory reference if the current privilege level is 3.

ADD—Add

Opcode	Instruction	Clocks	Description
04 ib	ADD AL,imm8	1	Add immediate byte to AL
05 iw	ADD AX,imm16	1	Add immediate word to AX
05 id	ADD EAX,imm32	1	Add immediate dword to EAX
80 /0 ib	ADD r/m8,imm8	1/3	Add immediate byte to r/m byte
81 /0 iw	ADD r/m16,imm16	1/3	Add immediate word to r/m word
81 /0 id	ADD r/m32,imm32	1/3	Add immediate dword to r/m dword
83 /0 ib	ADD r/m16,imm8	1/3	Add sign-extended immediate byte to r/m word
83 /0 ib	ADD r/m32,imm8	1/3	Add sign-extended immediate byte to r/m dword
00 /r	ADD r/m8,r8	1/3	Add byte register to r/m byte
01 /r	ADD r/m16,r16	1/3	Add word register to r/m word
01 /r	ADD r/m32,r32	1/3	Add dword register to r/m dword
02 /r	ADD r8,r/m8	1/2	Add r/m byte to byte register
03 /r	ADD r16,r/m16	1/2	Add r/m word to word register
03 /r	ADD r32,r/m32	1/2	Add r/m dword to dword register

Operation

DEST ← DEST + SRC;

Description

The ADD instruction performs an integer addition of the two operands (DEST and SRC). The result of the addition is assigned to the first operand (DEST), and the flags are set accordingly.

When an immediate byte is added to a word or doubleword operand, the immediate value is sign-extended to the size of the word or doubleword operand.

Flags Affected

The OF, SF, ZF, AF, CF, and PF flags are set according to the result.

Protected Mode Exceptions

#GP(0) if the result is in a nonwritable segment; #GP(0) for an illegal memory operand effective address in the CS, DS, ES, FS, or GS segments; #SS(0) for an illegal address in the SS segment; #PF(fault-code) for a page fault; #AC for unaligned memory reference if the current privilege level is 3.

Real Address Mode Exceptions

Interrupt 13 if any part of the operand would lie outside of the effective address space from 0 to 0FFFFH.

Virtual 8086 Mode Exceptions

Same exceptions as in Real Address Mode; #PF(fault-code) for a page fault; #AC for unaligned memory reference if the current privilege level is 3.

AND—Logical AND

Opcode	Instruction	Clocks	Description
24 *ib*	AND AL,*imm8*	1	AND immediate byte to AL
25 *iw*	AND AX,*imm16*	1	AND immediate word to AX
25 *id*	AND EAX,*imm32*	1	AND immediate dword to EAX
80 /4 *ib*	AND *r/m8,imm8*	1/3	AND immediate byte to *r/m* byte
81 /4 *iw*	AND *r/m16,imm16*	1/3	AND immediate word to *r/m* word
81 /4 *id*	AND *r/m32,imm32*	1/3	AND immediate dword to *r/m* dword
83 /4 *ib*	AND *r/m16,imm8*	1/3	AND sign-extended immediate byte with *r/m* word
83 /4 *ib*	AND *r/m32,imm8*	1/3	AND sign-extended immediate byte with *r/m* dword
20 /*r*	AND *r/m8,r8*	1/3	AND byte register to *r/m* byte
21 /*r*	AND *r/m16,r16*	1/3	AND word register to *r/m* word
21 /*r*	AND *r/m32,r32*	1/3	AND dword register to *r/m* dword
22 /*r*	AND *r8,r/m8*	1/2	AND *r/m* byte to byte register
23 /*r*	AND *r16,r/m16*	1/2	AND *r/m* word to word register
23 /*r*	AND *r32,r/m32*	1/2	AND *r/m* dword to dword register

Operation

DEST ← DEST AND SRC;
CF ← 0;
OF ← 0;

Description

Each bit of the result of the AND instruction is a 1 if both corresponding bits of the operands are 1; otherwise, it becomes a 0.

Flags Affected

The CF and OF flags are cleared; the PF, SF, and ZF flags are set according to the result; the AF flag is undefined.

Protected Mode Exceptions

#GP(0) if the result is in a nonwritable segment; #GP(0) for an illegal memory operand effective address in the CS, DS, ES, FS, or GS segments; #SS(0) for an illegal address in the SS segment; #PF(fault-code) for a page fault; #AC for unaligned memory reference if the current privilege level is 3.

Real Address Mode Exceptions

Interrupt 13 if any part of the operand would lie outside of the effective address space from 0 to 0FFFFH.

Virtual 8086 Mode Exceptions

Same exceptions as in Real Address Mode; #PF(fault-code) for a page fault; #AC for unaligned memory reference if the current privilege level is 3.

ARPL—Adjust RPL Field of Selector

Opcode	Instruction	Clocks	Description
63 /r	ARPL r/m16,r16	pm=7	Adjust RPL of r/m16 to not less than RPL of r16

Operation

```
IF RPL bits(0,1) of DEST < RPL bits(0,1) of SRC
THEN
    ZF ← 1;
    RPL bits(0,1) of DEST ← RPL bits(0,1) of SRC;
ELSE
    ZF ← 0;
FI;
```

Description

The ARPL instruction has two operands. The first operand is a 16-bit memory variable or word register that contains the value of a selector. The second operand is a word register. If the RPL field ("requested privilege level"—bottom two bits) of the first operand is less than the RPL field of the second operand, the ZF flag is set and the RPL field of the first operand is increased to match the second operand. Otherwise, the ZF flag is cleared and no change is made to the first operand.

The ARPL instruction appears in operating system software, not in application programs. It is used to guarantee that a selector parameter to a subroutine does not request more privilege than the caller is allowed. The second operand of the ARPL instruction is normally a register that contains the CS selector value of the caller.

Flags Affected

The ZF flag is set if the RPL field of the first operand is less than that of the second operand, otherwise ZF is cleared.

Protected Mode Exceptions

#GP(0) if the result is a nonwritable segment; #GP(0) for an illegal memory operand effective address in the CS, DS, ES, FS, or GS segments; #SS(0) for an illegal address in the SS segment; #PF(fault-code) for a page fault; #AC for unaligned memory reference if the current privilege level is 3.

Real Address Mode Exceptions

Interrupt 6; the ARPL instruction is not recognized in Real Address Mode.

Virtual 8086 Mode Exceptions

Interrupt 6; the ARPL instruction is not recognized in Virtual 8086 Mode.

BOUND—Check Array Index Against Bounds

Opcode	Instruction	Clocks	Description
62 /r	BOUND r16,m16&16	8 (within bounds) int+32 (out of bounds)	Check if r16 is within bounds
62 /r	BOUND r32,m32&32	8 (within bounds) int+32 (out of bounds)	Check if r32 is within bounds

Operation

IF (LeftSRC < [RightSRC] OR LeftSRC > [RightSRC + OperandSize/8])
  (* Under lower bound or over upper bound *)
THEN Interrupt 5;
FI;

Description

The BOUND instruction ensures that a signed array index is within the limits specified by a block of memory consisting of an upper and a lower bound. Each bound uses one word when the operand-size attribute is 16 bits and a doubleword when the operand-size attribute is 32 bits. The first operand (a register) must be greater than or equal to the first bound in memory (lower bound), and less than or equal to the second bound in memory (upper bound) plus the number of bytes occupied for the operand size. If the register is not within bounds, an Interrupt 5 occurs; the return EIP points to the BOUND instruction.

The bounds limit data structure is usually placed just before the array itself, making the limits addressable via a constant offset from the beginning of the array.

Flags Affected

None.

Protected Mode Exceptions

Interrupt 5 if the bounds test fails, as described above; #GP(0) for an illegal memory operand effective address in the CS, DS, ES, FS, or GS segments; #SS(0) for an illegal address in the SS segment; #PF(fault-code) for a page fault; #AC for unaligned memory reference if the current privilege level is 3.

The second operand must be a memory operand, not a register. If the BOUND instruction is executed with a ModR/M byte representing a register as the second operand, #UD occurs.

Real Address Mode Exceptions

Interrupt 5 if the bounds test fails; Interrupt 13 if any part of the operand would lie outside of the effective address space from 0 to 0FFFFH; Interrupt 6 if the second operand is a register.

Virtual 8086 Mode Exceptions

Same exceptions as in Real Address Mode; #PF(fault-code) for a page fault; #AC for unaligned memory reference if the current privilege level is 3.

®

BSF—Bit Scan Forward

Opcode	Instruction	Clocks	Description
0F BC	BSF r16,r/m16	6-34/6-35	Bit scan forward on r/m word
0F BC	BSF r32,r/m32	6-42/6-43	Bit scan forward on r/m dword

Operation

```
IF r/m = 0
THEN
   ZF ← 1;
   register ← UNDEFINED;
ELSE
   temp ← 0;
   ZF ← 0;
   WHILE BIT[r/m, temp] = 0
   DO
      temp ← temp + 1;
      register ← temp;
   OD;
FI;
```

Description

The BSF instruction scans the bits in the second word or doubleword operand starting with bit 0. The ZF flag is set if all the bits are 0; otherwise, the ZF flag is cleared and the destination register is loaded with the bit index of the first set bit.

Flags Affected

The ZF flag is set if all bits are 0; otherwise, the ZF flag is cleared. OF, SF, AF, PF, CF = undefined.

Protected Mode Exceptions

#GP(0) for an illegal memory operand effective address in the CS, DS, ES, FS, or GS segments; #SS(0) for an illegal address in the SS segment; #PF(fault-code) for a page fault; #AC for unaligned memory reference if the current privilege level is 3.

Real Address Mode Exceptions

Interrupt 13 if any part of the operand would lie outside of the effective address space from 0 to 0FFFFH.

Virtual 8086 Mode Exceptions

Same exceptions as in Real Address Mode; #PF(fault-code) for a page fault; #AC for unaligned memory reference if the current privilege level is 3.

BSR—Bit Scan Reverse

Opcode	Instruction	Clocks	Description
0F BD	BSR r16,r/m16	7-39/7-40	Bit scan reverse on r/m word
0F BD	BSR r32,r/m32	7-71/7-72	Bit scan reverse on r/m dword

Operation

```
IF r/m = 0
THEN
    ZF ← 1;
    register ← UNDEFINED;
ELSE
    temp ← OperandSize – 1;
    ZF ← 0;
    WHILE BIT[r/m, temp] = 0
    DO
        temp ← temp – 1;
        register ← temp;
    OD;
FI;
```

Description

The BSR instruction scans the bits in the second word or doubleword operand from the most significant bit to the least significant bit. The ZF flag is set if all the bits are 0; otherwise, the ZF flag is cleared and the destination register is loaded with the bit index of the first set bit found when scanning in the reverse direction.

Flags Affected

The ZF flag is set if all bits are 0; otherwise, the ZF flag is cleared. OS, SF, AF, PF, CF = undefined.

Protected Mode Exceptions

#GP(0) if the result is in a nonwritable segment; #GP(0) for an illegal memory operand effective address in the CS, DS, ES, FS, or GS segments; #SS(0) for an illegal address in the SS segment; #PF(fault-code) for a page fault; #AC for unaligned memory reference if the current privilege level is 3.

Real Address Mode Exceptions

Interrupt 13 if any part of the operand would lie outside of the effective address space from 0 to 0FFFFH.

Virtual 8086 Mode Exceptions

Same exceptions as in Real Address Mode; #PF(fault-code) for a page fault; #AC for unaligned memory reference if the current privilege level is 3.

BSWAP—Byte Swap

Opcode	Instruction	Clocks	Description
0F C8+rd	BSWAP r32	1	Swap bytes to convert little/big endian data in a 32-bit register to big/little endian form.

Operation

TEMP ← r32
r32(7..0) ← TEMP(31..24)
r32(15..8) ← TEMP(23..16)
r32(23..16) ← TEMP(15..8)
r32(31..24) ← TEMP(7..0)

Description

The BSWAP instruction reverses the byte order of a 32-bit register, converting a value in little/big endian form to big/little endian form. When BSWAP is used with 16-bit operand size, the result left in the destination register is undefined.

Flags Affected

None.

Protected Mode Exceptions

None.

Real Address Mode Exceptions

None.

Virtual 8086 Mode Exceptions

None.

Notes

BSWAP is not supported on Intel386 processors. Include functionally-equivalent code for Intel386 CPU's.

BT—Bit Test

Opcode	Instruction	Clocks	Description
0F A3	BT r/m16,r16	4/9	Save bit in carry flag
0F A3	BT r/m32,r32	4/9	Save bit in carry flag
0F BA /4 ib	BT r/m16,imm8	4	Save bit in carry flag
0F BA /4 ib	BT r/m32,imm8	4	Save bit in carry flag

Operation

CF ← BIT[LeftSRC, RightSRC];

Description

The BT instruction saves the value of the bit indicated by the base (first operand) and the bit offset (second operand) into the CF flag.

Flags Affected

The CF flag contains the value of the selected bit.

Protected Mode Exceptions

#GP(0) for an illegal memory operand effective address in the CS, DS, ES, FS, or GS segments; #SS(0) for an illegal address in the SS segment; #PF(fault-code) for a page fault; #AC for unaligned memory reference if the current privilege level is 3.

Real Address Mode Exceptions

Interrupt 13 if any part of the operand would lie outside of the effective address space from 0 to 0FFFFH.

Virtual 8086 Mode Exceptions

Same exceptions as in Real Address Mode; #PF(fault-code) for a page fault; #AC for unaligned memory reference if the current privilege level is 3.

Notes

The index of the selected bit can be given by the immediate constant in the instruction or by a value in a general register. Only an 8-bit immediate value is used in the instruction. This operand is taken modulo 32, so the range of immediate bit offsets is 0..31. This allows any bit within a register to be selected. For memory bit strings, this immediate field gives only the bit offset within a word or doubleword.

Immediate bit offsets larger than 31 are supported by some assemblers by using the immediate bit offset field in combination with the displacement field of the memory operand. In this case, the low-order 3 to 5 bits (3 for 16 bit operands, 5 for 32 bit operands) of the immediate bit offset are stored in the immediate bit offset field, and the high-order bits are shifted and combined with the byte displacement in the addressing mode by the assembler. The processor will ignore the high order bits if they are not zero.

When accessing a bit in memory, the processor may access four bytes starting from the memory address given by:

$$\text{Effective Address} + (4 * (\text{BitOffset DIV } 32))$$

for a 32-bit operand size, or two bytes starting from the memory address given by:

$$\text{Effective Address} + (2 * (\text{BitOffset DIV } 16))$$

for a 16-bit operand size. It may do so even when only a single byte needs to be accessed in order to reach the given bit. You must therefore avoid referencing areas of memory close to address space holes. In particular, avoid references to memory-mapped I/O registers. Instead, use the MOV instructions to load from or store to these addresses, and use the register form of these instructions to manipulate the data.

BTC—Bit Test and Complement

Opcode	Instruction	Clocks	Description
OF BB	BTC r/m16,r16	7/13	Save bit in carry flag and complement
OF BB	BTC r/m32,r32	7/13	Save bit in carry flag and complement
OF BA /7 ib	BTC r/m16,imm8	7/8	Save bit in carry flag and complement
OF BA /7 ib	BTC r/m32,imm8	7/8	Save bit in carry flag and complement

Operation

CF ← BIT[LeftSRC, RightSRC];
BIT[LeftSRC, RightSRC] ← NOT BIT[LeftSRC, RightSRC];

Description

The BTC instruction saves the value of the bit indicated by the base (first operand) and the bit offset (second operand) into the CF flag and then complements the bit.

Flags Affected

The CF flag contains the complement of the selected bit.

Protected Mode Exceptions

#GP(0) if the result is in a nonwritable segment; #GP(0) for an illegal memory operand effective address in the CS, DS, ES, FS, or GS segments; #SS(0) for an illegal address in the SS segment; #PF(fault-code) for a page fault; #AC for unaligned memory reference if the current privilege level is 3.

Real Address Mode Exceptions

Interrupt 13 if any part of the operand would lie outside of the effective address space from 0 to 0FFFFH.

Virtual 8086 Mode Exceptions

Same exceptions as in Real Address Mode; #PF(fault-code) for a page fault; #AC for unaligned memory reference if the current privilege level is 3.

Notes

The index of the selected bit can be given by the immediate constant in the instruction or by a value in a general register. Only an 8-bit immediate value may be used in the instruction. This operand is taken modulo 32, so the range of immediate bit offsets is 0..31. This allows any bit within a register to be selected. For memory bit strings, this immediate field gives only the bit offset within a word or doubleword.

Immediate bit offsets larger than 31 are supported by some assemblers by using the immediate bit offset field in combination with the displacement field of the memory operand. In this case, the low-order 3 to 5 bits (3 for 16 bit operands, 5 for 32 bit operands) of the immediate bit offset are stored in the immediate bit offset field, and the high-order bits are shifted and combined with the byte displacement in the addressing mode by the assembler. The processor will ignore the high order bits if they are not zero.

When accessing a bit in memory, the processor may access four bytes starting from the memory address given by:

$$\text{Effective Address} + (4 * (\text{BitOffset DIV } 32))$$

for a 32-bit operand size, or two bytes starting from the memory address given by:

$$\text{Effective Address} + (2 * (\text{BitOffset DIV } 16))$$

for a 16-bit operand size. It may do so even when only a single byte needs to be accessed in order to reach the given bit. Therefore, referencing areas of memory close to address space holes should be avoided. In particular, avoid references to memory-mapped I/O registers. Instead, use the MOV instructions to load from or store to these addresses, and use the register form of these instructions to manipulate the data.

BTR—Bit Test and Reset

Opcode	Instruction	Clocks	Description
0F B3	BTR r/m16,r16	7/13	Save bit in carry flag and reset
0F B3	BTR r/m32,r32	7/13	Save bit in carry flag and reset
0F BA /6 ib	BTR r/m16,imm8	7/8	Save bit in carry flag and reset
0F BA /6 ib	BTR r/m32,imm8	7/8	Save bit in carry flag and reset

Operation

CF ← BIT[LeftSRC, RightSRC];
BIT[LeftSRC, RightSRC] ← 0;

Description

The BTR instruction saves the value of the bit indicated by the base (first operand) and the bit offset (second operand) into the CF flag and then stores 0 in the bit.

Flags Affected

The CF flag contains the value of the selected bit.

Protected Mode Exceptions

#GP(0) if the result is in a nonwritable segment; #GP(0) for an illegal memory operand effective address in the CS, DS, ES, FS, or GS segments; #SS(0) for an illegal address in the SS segment; #PF(fault-code) for a page fault; #AC for unaligned memory reference if the current privilege level is 3.

Real Address Mode Exceptions

Interrupt 13 if any part of the operand would lie outside of the effective address space from 0 to 0FFFFH.

Virtual 8086 Mode Exceptions

Same exceptions as in Real Address Mode; #PF(fault-code) for a page fault; #AC for unaligned memory reference if the current privilege level is 3.

Notes

The index of the selected bit can be given by the immediate constant in the instruction or by a value in a general register. Only an 8-bit immediate value is used in the instruction. This operand is taken modulo 32, so the range of immediate bit offsets is 0..31. This allows any bit within a register to be selected. For memory bit strings, this immediate field gives only the bit offset within a word or doubleword.

Immediate bit offsets larger than 31 are supported by some assemblers by using the immediate bit offset field in combination with the displacement field of the memory operand. In thise case, the low-order 3 to 5 bits (3 for 16 bit operands, 5 for 32 bit operands) of the immediate bit offset are stored in the immediate bit offset field, and the high-order bits are shifted and combined with the byte displacement in the addressing mode by the assembler. The processor will ignore the high order bits if they are not zero.

When accessing a bit in memory, the processor may access four bytes starting from the memory address given by:

$$\text{Effective Address} + 4 * (\text{BitOffset DIV } 32)$$

for a 32-bit operand size, or two bytes starting from the memory address given by:

$$\text{Effective Address} + 2 * (\text{BitOffset DIV } 16)$$

for a 16-bit operand size. It may do so even when only a single byte needs to be accessed in order to reach the given bit. You must therefore avoid referencing areas of memory close to address space holes. In particular, avoid references to memory-mapped I/O registers. Instead, use the MOV instructions to load from or store to these addresses, and use the register form of these instructions to manipulate the data.

BTS—Bit Test and Set

Opcode	Instruction	Clocks	Description
0F AB	BTS r/m16,r16	7/13	Save bit in carry flag and set
0F AB	BTS r/m32,r32	7/13	Save bit in carry flag and set
0F BA /5 ib	BTS r/m16,imm8	7/8	Save bit in carry flag and set
0F BA /5 ib	BTS r/m32,imm8	7/8	Save bit in carry flag and set

Operation

CF ← BIT[LeftSRC, RightSRC];
BIT[LeftSRC, RightSRC] ← 1;

Description

The BTS instruction saves the value of the bit indicated by the base (first operand) and the bit offset (second operand) into the CF flag and then stores 1 in the bit.

Flags Affected

The CF flag contains the value of the selected bit.

Protected Mode Exceptions

#GP(0) if the result is in a nonwritable segment; #GP(0) for an illegal memory operand effective address in the CS, DS, ES, FS, or GS segments; #SS(0) for an illegal address in the SS segment; #PF(fault-code) for a page fault; #AC for unaligned memory reference if the current privilege level is 3.

Real Address Mode Exceptions

Interrupt 13 if any part of the operand would lie outside of the effective address space from 0 to 0FFFFH.

Virtual 8086 Mode Exceptions

Same exceptions as in Real Address Mode; #PF(fault-code) for a page fault; #AC for unaligned memory reference if the current privilege level is 3.

Notes

The index of the selected bit can be given by the immediate constant in the instruction or by a value in a general register. Only an 8-bit immediate value is used in the instruction. This operand is taken modulo 32, so the range of immediate bit offsets is 0..31. This allows any bit within a register to be selected. For memory bit strings, this immediate field gives only the bit offset within a word or doubleword.

Immediate bit offsets larger than 31 are supported by some assemblers by using the immediate bit offset field in combination with the displacement field of the memory operand. In this case, the low-order 3 to 5 bits (3 for 16 bit operands, 5 for 32 bit operands) of the immediate bit offset are stored in the immediate bit offset field, and the high-order bits are shifted and combined with the byte displacement in the addressing mode by the assembler. The processor will ignore the high order bits if they are not zero.

When accessing a bit in memory, the processor may access four bytes starting from the memory address given by:

$$\text{Effective Address} + (4 * (\text{BitOffset DIV } 32))$$

for a 32-bit operand size, or two bytes starting from the memory address given by:

$$\text{Effective Address} + (2 * (\text{BitOffset DIV } 16))$$

for a 16-bit operand size. It may do this even when only a single byte needs to be accessed in order to get at the given bit. You must therefore be careful to avoid referencing areas of memory close to address space holes. In particular, avoid references to memory-mapped I/O registers. Instead, use the MOV instructions to load from or store to these addresses, and use the register form of these instructions to manipulate the data.

CALL—Call Procedure

Opcode	Instruction	Clocks	Description
E8 cw	CALL rel16	1	Call near, displacement relative to next instruction
FF /2	CALL r/m16	2	Call near, register indirect/memory indirect
9A cd	CALL ptr16:16	4	Call intersegment, to full pointer given
9A cd	CALL ptr16:16	pm=22	Call gate, same privilege
9A cd	CALL ptr16:16	pm=44	Call gate, more privilege, no parameters
9A cd	CALL ptr16:16	pm=45+2x	Call gate, more privilege, x parameters
9A cd	CALL ptr16:16	pm=21+ts	Call to task
FF /3	CALL m16:16	5	Call intersegment, address at r/m dword
FF /3	CALL m16:16	pm=22	Call gate, same privilege
FF /3	CALL m16:16	pm=44	Call gate, more privilege, no parameters
FF /3	CALL m16:16	pm=45+2x	Call gate, more privilege, x parameters
FF /3	CALL m16:16	pm=21+ts	Call to task
E8 cd	CALL rel32	1	Call near, displacement relative to next instruction
FF /2	CALL r/m32	2	Call near, indirect
9A cp	CALL ptr16:32	4	Call intersegment, to full pointer given
9A cp	CALL ptr16:32	pm=22	Call gate, same privilege
9A cp	CALL ptr16:32	pm=44	Call gate, more privilege, no parameters
9A cp	CALL ptr16:32	pm=45+2x	Call gate, more privilege, x parameters
9A cp	CALL ptr16:32	pm=21+ts	Call to task
FF /3	CALL m16:32	5	Call intersegment, address at r/m dword
FF /3	CALL m16:32	pm=22	Call gate, same privilege
FF /3	CALL m16:32	pm=44	Call gate, more privilege, no parameters
FF /3	CALL m16:32	pm=45+2x	Call gate, more privilege, x parameters
FF /3	CALL m16:32	pm=21+ts	Call to task

NOTE: Values of ts are given by the following table:

Old Task	New Task		
	to 32 bit TSS	to 16 bit TSS	to VM TSS
VM/32 bit/16 bit TSS	85	87	71

Operation

```
IF rel16 or rel32 type of call
THEN (* near relative call *)
   IF OperandSize = 16
   THEN
      Push(IP);
      EIP ← (EIP + rel16) AND 0000FFFFH;
   ELSE (* OperandSize = 32 *)
      Push(EIP);
      EIP ← EIP + rel32;
   FI;
FI;
IF r/m16 or r/m32 type of call
THEN (* near absolute call *)
IF OperandSize = 16
   THEN
      Push(IP);
      EIP ← [r/m16] AND 0000FFFFH;
   ELSE (* OperandSize = 32 *)
      Push(EIP);
      EIP ← [r/m32];
```

```
    FI;
FI;

IF (PE = 0 OR (PE = 1 AND VM = 1))
(* real mode or virtual 8086 mode *)
    AND instruction = far CALL
    (* i.e., operand type is m16:16, m16:32, ptr16:16, ptr16:32 *)
THEN
    IF OperandSize = 16
    THEN
        Push(CS);
        Push(IP); (* address of next instruction; 16 bits *)
    ELSE
        Push(CS); (* padded with 16 high-order bits *)
        Push(EIP); (* address of next instruction; 32 bits *)
    FI;
    IF operand type is m16:16 or m16:32
    THEN (* indirect far call *)
        IF OperandSize = 16
        THEN
            CS:IP ← [m16:16];
            EIP ← EIP AND 0000FFFFH; (* clear upper 16 bits *)
        ELSE (* OperandSize = 32 *)
            CS:EIP ← [m16:32];
        FI;
    FI;
    IF operand type is ptr16:16 or ptr16:32
    THEN (* direct far call *)
        IF OperandSize = 16
        THEN
            CS:IP ← ptr16:16;
            EIP ← EIP AND 0000FFFFH; (* clear upper 16 bits *)
        ELSE (* OperandSize = 32 *)
            CS:EIP ← ptr16:32;
        FI;
    FI;
FI;

IF (PE = 1 AND VM = 0) (* Protected mode, not V86 mode *)
    AND instruction = far CALL
THEN
    If indirect, then check access of EA doubleword;
        #GP(0) if limit violation;
    New CS selector must not be null else #GP(0);
    Check that new CS selector index is within its
        descriptor table limits; else #GP(new CS selector);
    Examine AR byte of selected descriptor for various legal values;
        depending on value:
        go to CONFORMING-CODE-SEGMENT;
        go to NONCONFORMING-CODE-SEGMENT;
```

```
      go to CALL-GATE;
      go to TASK-GATE;
      go to TASK-STATE-SEGMENT;
   ELSE #GP(code segment selector);
FI;
```

CONFORMING-CODE-SEGMENT:
    DPL must be ≤ CPL ELSE #GP(code segment selector);
    Segment must be present ELSE #NP(code segment selector);
    Stack must be big enough for return address ELSE #SS(0);
    Instruction pointer must be in code segment limit ELSE #GP(0);
    Load code segment descriptor into CS register;
    Load CS with new code segment selector;
    Load EIP with zero-extend(new offset);
    IF OperandSize=16 THEN EIP ← EIP AND 0000FFFFH; FI;

NONCONFORMING-CODE-SEGMENT:
    RPL must be ≤ CPL ELSE #GP(code segment selector)
    DPL must be = CPL ELSE #GP(code segment selector)
    Segment must be present ELSE #NP(code segment selector)
    Stack must be big enough for return address ELSE #SS(0)
    Instruction pointer must be in code segment limit ELSE #GP(0)
    Load code segment descriptor into CS register
    Load CS with new code segment selector
    Set RPL of CS to CPL
    Load EIP with zero-extend(new offset);
    IF OperandSize=16 THEN EIP ← EIP AND 0000FFFFH; FI;

CALL-GATE:
    Call gate DPL must be ≥ CPL ELSE #GP(call gate selector)
    Call gate DPL must be ≥ RPL ELSE #GP(call gate selector)
    Call gate must be present ELSE #NP(call gate selector)
    Examine code segment selector in call gate descriptor:
        Selector must not be null ELSE #GP(0)
        Selector must be within its descriptor table
           limits ELSE #GP(code segment selector)
        AR byte of selected descriptor must indicate code
           segment ELSE #GP(code segment selector)
        DPL of selected descriptor must be ≤ CPL ELSE
           #GP(code segment selector)
        IF non-conforming code segment AND DPL < CPL
        THEN go to MORE-PRIVILEGE
        ELSE go to SAME-PRIVILEGE
        FI;

MORE-PRIVILEGE:
    Get new SS selector for new privilege level from TSS
        Check selector and descriptor for new SS:
           Selector must not be null ELSE #TS(0)
           Selector index must be within its descriptor

table limits ELSE #TS(SS selector)
    Selector's RPL must equal DPL of code segment
     ELSE #TS(SS selector)
    Stack segment DPL must equal DPL of code
     segment ELSE #TS(SS selector)
    Descriptor must indicate writable data segment
     ELSE #TS(SS selector)
    Segment present ELSE #SS(SS selector)
   IF OperandSize=32
   THEN
    New stack must have room for parameters plus 16 bytes
     ELSE #SS(SS selector)
    EIP must be in code segment limit ELSE #GP(0)
    Load new SS:eSP value from TSS
    Load new CS:EIP value from gate
   ELSE
    New stack must have room for parameters plus 8 bytes
     ELSE #SS(SS selector)
    IP must be in code segment limit ELSE #GP(0)
    Load new SS:eSP value from TSS
    Load new CS:IP value from gate
   FI;
   Load CS descriptor
   Load SS descriptor
   Push long pointer of old stack onto new stack
   Get word count from call gate, mask to 5 bits
   Copy parameters from old stack onto new stack
   Push return address onto new stack
   Set CPL to stack segment DPL
   Set RPL of CS to CPL

SAME-PRIVILEGE:
 IF OperandSize=32
 THEN
  Stack must have room for 6-byte return address (padded to 8 bytes)
   ELSE #SS(0)
  EIP must be within code segment limit ELSE #GP(0)
  Load CS:EIP from gate
 ELSE
  Stack must have room for 4-byte return address ELSE #SS(0)
  IP must be within code segment limit ELSE #GP(0)
  Load CS:IP from gate
 FI;
 Push return address onto stack
 Load code segment descriptor into CS register
 Set RPL of CS to CPL

TASK-GATE:
 Task gate DPL must be $\geq$ CPL ELSE #TS(gate selector)
 Task gate DPL must be $\geq$ RPL ELSE #TS(gate selector)

Task Gate must be present ELSE #NP(gate selector)
Examine selector to TSS, given in Task Gate descriptor:
    Must specify global in the local/global bit ELSE #TS(TSS selector)
    Index must be within GDT limits ELSE #TS(TSS selector)
    TSS descriptor AR byte must specify nonbusy TSS
        ELSE #TS(TSS selector)
    Task State Segment must be present ELSE #NP(TSS selector)
SWITCH-TASKS (with nesting) to TSS
IP must be in code segment limit ELSE #TS(0)

TASK-STATE-SEGMENT:
    TSS DPL must be ≥ CPL ELSE #TS(TSS selector)
    TSS DPL must be ≥ RPL ELSE #TS(TSS selector)
    TSS descriptor AR byte must specify available TSS
        ELSE #TS(TSS selector)
    Task State Segment must be present ELSE #NP(TSS selector)
SWITCH-TASKS (with nesting) to TSS
IP must be in code segment limit ELSE #TS(0)

Description

The CALL instruction causes the procedure named in the operand to be executed. When the procedure is complete (a return instruction is executed within the procedure), execution continues at the instruction that follows the CALL instruction.

The action of the different forms of the instruction are described below.

Near calls are those with destinations of type *r/m16*, *r/m32*, *rel16*, *rel32*; changing or saving the segment register value is not necessary. The CALL *rel16* and CALL *rel32* forms add a signed offset to the address of the instruction following the CALL instruction to determine the destination. The *rel16* form is used when the instruction's operand-size attribute is 16 bits; *rel32* is used when the operand-size attribute is 32 bits. The result is stored in the 32-bit EIP register. With *rel16*, the upper 16 bits of the EIP register are cleared, resulting in an offset whose value does not exceed 16 bits. CALL *r/m16* and CALL *r/m32* specify a register or memory location from which the absolute segment offset is fetched. The offset fetched from *r/m* is 32 bits for an operand-size attribute of 32 (*r/m32*), or 16 bits for an operand-size of 16 (*r/m16*). The offset of the instruction following the CALL instruction is pushed onto the stack. It will be popped by a near RET instruction within the procedure. The CS register is not changed by this form of CALL.

The far calls, CALL *ptr16:16* and CALL *ptr16:32*, use a four-byte or six-byte operand as a long pointer to the procedure called. The CALL *m16:16* and *m16:32* forms fetch the long pointer from the memory location specified (indirection). In Real Address Mode or Virtual 8086 Mode, the long pointer provides 16 bits for the CS register and 16 or 32 bits for the EIP register (depending on the operand-size attribute). These forms of the instruction push both the CS and IP or EIP registers as a return address.

In Protected Mode, both long pointer forms consult the AR byte in the descriptor indexed by the selector part of the long pointer. Depending on the value of the AR byte, the call will perform one of the following types of control transfers:

• A far call to the same protection level

- An inter-protection level far call
- A task switch

A CALL-indirect-thru-memory, which uses the stack pointer (ESP) as a base register, references memory before the CALL. The base used is the value of the ESP before the instruction executes.

For more information on Protected Mode control transfers, refer to Chapter 6 and Chapter 7.

Flags Affected

All flags are affected if a task switch occurs; no flags are affected if a task switch does not occur.

Protected Mode Exceptions

For far calls: #GP, #NP, #SS, and #TS, as indicated in the "Operation" section.

For near direct calls: #GP(0) if procedure location is beyond the code segment limits; #SS(0) if pushing the return address exceeds the bounds of the stack segment; #PF (fault-code) for a page fault; #AC for unaligned memory reference if the current privilege level is 3.

For a near indirect call: #GP(0) for an illegal memory operand effective address in the CS, DS, ES, FS, or GS segments; #SS(0) for an illegal address in the SS segment; #GP(0) if the indirect offset obtained is beyond the code segment limits; #PF(fault-code) for a page fault; #AC for unaligned memory reference if the current privilege level is 3.

Real Address Mode Exceptions

Interrupt 13 if any part of the operand would lie outside of the effective address space from 0 to 0FFFFH.

Virtual 8086 Mode Exceptions

Same exceptions as in Real Address Mode; #PF(fault-code) for a page fault; #AC for unaligned memory reference if the current privilege level is 3.

Notes

Any far call from a 32-bit code segment to a 16-bit code segment should be made from the first 64 Kbytes of the 32-bit code segment, because the operand-size attribute of the instruction is set to 16, allowing only a 16-bit return address offset to be saved.

CBW/CWDE— Convert Byte to Word/Convert Word to Doubleword

Opcode	Instruction	Clocks	Description
98	CBW	3	AX ← sign-extend of AL
98	CWDE	3	EAX ← sign-extend of AX

Operation

IF OperandSize = 16 (* instruction = CBW *)
THEN AX ← SignExtend(AL);
ELSE (* OperandSize = 32, instruction = CWDE *)
   EAX ← SignExtend(AX);
FI;

Description

The CBW instruction converts the signed byte in the AL register to a signed word in the AX register by extending the most significant bit of the AL register (the sign bit) into all of the bits of the AH register. The CWDE instruction converts the signed word in the AX register to a doubleword in the EAX register by extending the most significant bit of the AX register into the two most significant bytes of the EAX register. Note that the CWDE instruction is different from the CWD instruction. The CWD instruction uses the DX:AX register pair rather than the EAX register as a destination.

Flags Affected

None.

Protected Mode Exceptions

None.

Real Address Mode Exceptions

None.

Virtual 8086 Mode Exceptions

None.

CDQ—Convert Double to Quad

See entry for CWD/CDQ — Convert Word to Double/Convert Double to Quad.

CLC—Clear Carry Flag

Opcode	Instruction	Clocks	Description
F8	CLC	2	Clear carry flag

Operation

CF ← 0;

Description

The CLC instruction clears the CF flag. It does not affect other flags or registers.

Flags Affected

The CF flag is cleared.

Protected Mode Exceptions

None.

Real Address Mode Exceptions

None.

Virtual 8086 Mode Exceptions

None.

CLD—Clear Direction Flag

Opcode	Instruction	Clocks	Description
FC	CLD	2	Clear direction flag; SI and DI will increment during string instructions

Operation

DF ← 0;

Description

The CLD instruction clears the direction flag. No other flags or registers are affected. After a CLD instruction is executed, string operations will increment the index registers (SI and/or DI) that they use.

Flags Affected

The DF flag is cleared.

Protected Mode Exceptions

None.

Real Address Mode Exceptions

None.

Virtual 8086 Mode Exceptions

None.

CLI—Clear Interrupt Flag

Opcode	Instruction	Clocks	Description
FA	CLI	7	Clear interrupt flag; interrupts disabled when interrupt flag cleared

Operation

```
IF PE = 0
THEN
    IF ← 0;
ELSE
    IF VM = 0   (* Executing in protected Mode *)
    THEN
        IF IOPL = 3
        THEN IF ← 0;
        ELSE IF CPL ≤ IOPL
                THEN IF ← 0;
                ELSE #GP(0);
                FI;
        FI;
    ELSE  (* Executing in Virtual-8086 mode  *)
        IF IOPL = 3
        THEN IF ←
        ELSE #GP(0);
        FI;
    FI;
FI;
```

Decision Table

The following decision table indicates which action in the lower portion of the table is taken given the conditions in the upper portion of the table.

PE =	0	1	1	1	1
VM =	–	0	–	0	1
CPL	–	≤ IOPL	–	>IOPL	–
IOPL	–	–	= 3	–	< 3
IF ← 0	Y	Y	Y		
#GP(0)				Y	Y

NOTES:

–	Don't care
Blank	Action Not Taken
Y	Action in Column 1 taken

INSTRUCTION SET

Description

The CLI instruction clears the IF flag if the current privilege level is at least as privileged as IOPL. No other flags are affected. External interrupts are not recognized at the end of the CLI instruction from that point on until the IF flag is set.

Flags Affected

IF

Protected Mode Exceptions

#GP(0) if the current privilege level is greater (has less privilege) than the I/O privilege level in the flags register. The I/O privilege level specifies the least privileged level at which I/O can be performed.

Real Address Mode Exceptions

None.

Virtual 8086 Mode Exceptions

#GP(0) as for protected mode.

Notes

For information on this instruction when using virtual mode extensions, see Appendix H.

CLTS—Clear Task-Switched Flag in CR0

Opcode	Instruction	Clocks	Description
0F 06	CLTS	10	Clear task-switched flag

Operation

TS Flag in CR0 ← 0;

Description

The CLTS instruction clears the task-switched (TS) flag in the CR0 register. This flag is set by the processor every time a task switch occurs. The TS flag is used to manage processor extensions as follows:

- Every execution of an ESC instruction is trapped if the TS flag is set.
- Execution of a WAIT instruction is trapped if the MP flag and the TS flag are both set.

Thus, if a task switch was made after an ESC instruction was begun, the floating-point unit's context may need to be saved before a new ESC instruction can be issued. The fault handler saves the context and clears the TS flag.

The CLTS instruction appears in operating system software, not in application programs. It is a privileged instruction that can only be executed at privilege level 0.

Flags Affected

The TS flag is cleared (the TS flag is in the CR0 register, not the flags register).

Protected Mode Exceptions

#GP(0) if the CLTS instruction is executed with a current privilege level other than 0.

Real Address Mode Exceptions

None (valid in Real Address Mode to allow initialization for Protected Mode).

Virtual 8086 Mode Exceptions

Same exceptions as in Protected Mode.

CMC—Complement Carry Flag

Opcode	Instruction	Clocks	Description
F5	CMC	2	Complement carry flag

Operation

CF ← NOT CF;

Description

The CMC instruction reverses the setting of the CF flag. No other flags are affected.

Flags Affected

The CF flag contains the complement of its original value.

Protected Mode Exceptions

None.

Real Address Mode Exceptions

None.

Virtual 8086 Mode Exceptions

None.

CMP—Compare Two Operands

Opcode	Instruction	Clocks	Description
3C ib	CMP AL,imm8	1	Compare immediate byte to AL
3D iw	CMP AX,imm16	1	Compare immediate word to AX
3D id	CMP EAX,imm32	1	Compare immediate dword to EAX
80 /7 ib	CMP r/m8,imm8	1/2	Compare immediate byte to r/m byte
81 /7 iw	CMP r/m16,imm16	1/2	Compare immediate word to r/m word
81 /7 id	CMP r/m32,imm32	1/2	Compare immediate dword to r/m dword
83 /7 ib	CMP r/m16,imm8	1/2	Compare sign extended immediate byte to r/m word
83 /7 ib	CMP r/m32,imm8	1/2	Compare sign extended immediate byte to r/m dword
38 /r	CMP r/m8,r8	1/2	Compare byte register to r/m byte
39 /r	CMP r/m16,r16	1/2	Compare word register to r/m word
39 /r	CMP r/m32,r32	1/2	Compare dword register to r/m dword
3A /r	CMP r8,r/m8	1/2	Compare r/m byte to byte register
3B /r	CMP r16,r/m16	1/2	Compare r/m word to word register
3B /r	CMP r32,r/m32	1/2	Compare r/m dword to dword register

Operation

LeftSRC - SignExtend(RightSRC);
(* CMP does not store a result; its purpose is to set the flags *)

Description

The CMP instruction subtracts the second operand from the first but, unlike the SUB instruction, does not store the result; only the flags are changed. The CMP instruction is typically used in conjunction with conditional jumps and the SETcc instruction. (Refer to Appendix D for the list of signed and unsigned flag tests provided.) If an operand greater than one byte is compared to an immediate byte, the byte value is first sign-extended.

Flags Affected

The OF, SF, ZF, AF, PF, and CF flags are set according to the result.

Protected Mode Exceptions

#GP(0) for an illegal memory operand effective address in the CS, DS, ES, FS, or GS segments; #SS(0) for an illegal address in the SS segment; #PF(fault-code) for a page fault; #AC for unaligned memory reference if the current privilege level is 3.

Real Address Mode Exceptions

Interrupt 13 if any part of the operand would lie outside of the effective address space from 0 to 0FFFFH.

Virtual 8086 Mode Exceptions

Same exceptions as in Real Address Mode; #PF(fault-code) for a page fault; #AC for unaligned memory reference if the current privilege level is 3.

CMPS/CMPSB/CMPSW/CMPSD—Compare String Operands

Opcode	Instruction	Clocks	Description
A6	CMPS m8,m8	5	Compare bytes ES:[(E)DI] (second operand) with [(E)SI] (first operand)
A7	CMPS m16,m16	5	Compare words ES:[(E)DI] (second operand) with [(E)SI] (first operand)
A7	CMPS m32,m32	5	Compare dwords ES:[(E)DI] (second operand) with [(E)SI] (first operand)
A6	CMPSB	5	Compare bytes ES:[(E)DI] with DS:[SI]
A7	CMPSW	5	Compare words ES:[(E)DI] with DS:[SI]
A7	CMPSD	5	Compare dwords ES:[(E)DI] with DS:[SI]

Operation

```
IF (instruction = CMPSD) OR
   (instruction has operands of type DWORD)
THEN OperandSize ← 32;
ELSE OperandSize ← 16;
FI;
IF AddressSize = 16
THEN
   use SI for source-index and DI for destination-index
ELSE (* AddressSize = 32 *)
   use ESI for source-index and EDI for destination-index;
FI;
IF byte type of instruction
THEN
   set ZF based on
   [source-index] - [destination-index]; (* byte comparison *)
   IF DF = 0 THEN IncDec ← 1 ELSE IncDec ← −1; FI;
ELSE
   IF OperandSize = 16
   THEN
      set ZF based on
      [source-index] - [destination-index]; (* word comparison *)
      IF DF = 0 THEN IncDec ← 2 ELSE IncDec ← −2; FI;
   ELSE (* OperandSize = 32 *)
      set ZF based on
      [source-index] - [destination-index]; (* dword comparison *)
      IF DF = 0 THEN IncDec ← 4 ELSE IncDec ← −4; FI;
   FI;
FI;
source-index = source-index + IncDec;
destination-index = destination-index + IncDec;
```

Description

The CMPS instruction compares the byte, word, or doubleword pointed to by the source-index register with the byte, word, or doubleword pointed to by the destination-index register.

If the address-size attribute of this instruction is 16 bits, the SI and DI registers will be used for source- and destination-index registers; otherwise the ESI and EDI registers will be used. Load the correct index values into the SI and DI (or ESI and EDI) registers before executing the CMPS instruction.

The comparison is done by subtracting the operand indexed by the destination-index register from the operand indexed by the source-index register.

Note that the direction of subtraction for the CMPS instruction is [SI] – [DI] or [ESI] – [EDI]. The left operand (SI or ESI) is the source and the right operand (DI or EDI) is the destination. This is the reverse of the usual Intel convention in which the left operand is the destination and the right operand is the source.

The result of the subtraction is not stored; only the flags reflect the change. The types of the operands determine whether bytes, words, or doublewords are compared. For the first operand (SI or ESI), the DS register is used, unless a segment override byte is present. The second operand (DI or EDI) must be addressable from the ES register; no segment override is possible.

After the comparison is made, both the source-index register and destination-index register are automatically advanced. If the DF flag is 0 (a CLD instruction was executed), the registers increment; if the DF flag is 1 (an STD instruction was executed), the registers decrement. The registers increment or decrement by 1 if a byte is compared, by 2 if a word is compared, or by 4 if a doubleword is compared.

The CMPSB, CMPSW and CMPSD instructions are synonyms for the byte, word, and doubleword CMPS instructions, respectively.

The CMPS instruction can be preceded by the REPE or REPNE prefix for block comparison of CX or ECX bytes, words, or doublewords. Refer to the description of the REP instruction for more information on this operation.

Flags Affected

The OF, SF, ZF, AF, PF, and CF flags are set according to the result.

Protected Mode Exceptions

#GP(0) for an illegal memory operand effective address in the CS, DS, ES, FS, or GS segments; #SS(0) for an illegal address in the SS segment; #PF(fault-code) for a page fault; #AC for unaligned memory reference if the current privilege level is 3.

Real Address Mode Exceptions

Interrupt 13 if any part of the operand would lie outside of the effective address space from 0 to 0FFFFH.

Virtual 8086 Mode Exceptions

Same exceptions as in Real Address Mode; #PF(fault-code) for a page fault; #AC for unaligned memory reference if the current privilege level is 3.

CMPXCHG—Compare and Exchange

Opcode	Instruction	Clocks	Description
0F B0/r	CMPXCHG r/m8,r8	6	Compare AL with r/m byte. If equal, set ZF and load byte reg into r/m byte. Else, clear ZF and load r/m byte into AL.
0F B1/r	CMPXCHG r/m16,r16	6	Compare AX with r/m word. If equal, set ZF and load word reg into r/m word. Else, clear ZF and load r/m word into AX.
0F B1/r	CMPXCHG r/m32,r32	6	Compare EAX with r/m dword. If equal, set ZF and load dword reg into r/m dword. Else, clear ZF and load r/m dword into EAX.

Operation

```
IF accumulator=DEST
        ZF ← 1
        DEST ← SRC
ELSE
        ZF ← 0
        accumulator ← DEST
```

Description

The CMPXCHG instruction compares the accumulator (AL, AX, or EAX register) with DEST. If they are equal, SRC is loaded into DEST. Otherwise, DEST is loaded into the accumulator.

Flags Affected

The CF, PF, AF, SF, and OF flags are affected as if a CMP instruction had been executed with DEST and the accumulator as operands. The ZF flag is set if the destination operand and the accumulator are equal; otherwise it is cleared.

Protected Mode Exceptions

#GP(0) if the result is in a nonwritable segment; #GP(0) for an illegal memory operand effective address in the CS, DS, ES, FS, or GS segments; #SS(0) for an illegal address in the SS segment; #PF (fault code) for a page fault; #AC for unaligned memory reference if the current privilege level is 3.

Real Address Mode Exceptions

Interrupt 13 if any part of the operand would lie outside the effective address space from 0 to 0FFFFH.

Virtual 8086 Mode Exceptions

Same exceptions as in real-address mode; #PF (fault code) for a page fault; #AC for unaligned memory reference if the current privilege level is 3.

Notes

This instruction can be used with a LOCK prefix. In order to simplify interface to the processor's bus, the destination operand receives a write cycle without regard to the result of the comparison. DEST is written back if the comparison fails, and SRC is written into the destination otherwise. (The processor never produces a locked read without also producing a locked write.) This instruction is not supported on Intel386 processors. See Chapter 23 to use CMPXCHG compatible with Intel386 processors.

CMPXCHG8B—Compare and Exchange 8 Bytes

Opcode	Instruction	Clocks	Description
0F C7 m64	CMPXCHG8B r/m64	10	Compare EDX:EAX with r/m qword. If equal, set ZF and load ECX:EBX into r/m qword. Else, clear ZF and load r/m qword into EDX:EAX.

Operation

```
IF EDX:EAX=DEST
        ZF ← 1
        DEST ← ECX:EBX
ELSE
        ZF ← 0
        EDX:EAX ← DEST
```

Description

The CMPXCHG8B instruction compares the 64-bit value in EDX:EAX with DEST. EDX contains the high-order 32 bits, and EAX contains the low-order 32 bits of the 64-bit value. If they are equal, the 64-bit value in ECX:EBX is stored into DEST. ECX contains the high-order 32 bits and EBX contains the low order 32 bits. Otherwise, DEST is loaded into EDX:EAX.

Flags Affected

The ZF flag is set if the destination operand and EDX:EAX are equal; otherwise it is cleared. The CF, PF, AF, SF, and OF flags are unaffected.

Protected Mode Exceptions

#GP(0) if the result is in a nonwritable segment; #GP(0) for an illegal memory operand effective address in the CS, DS, ES, FS, or GS segments; #SS(0) for an illegal address in the SS segment; #PF (fault code) for a page fault; #AC for unaligned memory reference if the current privilege level is 3.

The destination operand must be a memory operand, not a register. If the CMPXCHG8B instruction is executed with a modr/m byte representing a register as the destination operand, #UD occurs.

Real Address Mode Exceptions

Interrupt 13 if any part of the operand would lie outside the effective address space from 0 to 0FFFFH.

Virtual 8086 Mode Exceptions

Same exceptions as in real-address mode; #PF (fault code) for a page fault; #AC for unaligned memory reference if the current privilege level is 3. #UD if modr/m byte represents a register as the destination.

Notes

This instruction can be used with a LOCK prefix. In order to simplify interface to the processor's bus, the destination operand receives a write cycle without regard to the result of the comparison. DEST is written back if the comparison fails, and SRC is written into the destination otherwise. (The processor never produces a locked read without also producing a locked write.)

The "r/m64" syntax had previously been used only in the context of floating point operations. It indicates a 64-bit value, in memory at an address determined by the modr/m byte. This instruction is not supported on Intel486 processors.

CPUID—CPU Identification

Opcode	Instruction	Clocks	Description
0F A2	CPUID	14	EAX ← CPU identification information

Operation

```
switch (EAX)
    case 0:
        EAX ← hv;(* hv=1 for the Pentium processor *)
                    (* hv is  the highest input value that is understood by CPUID.*)

        EBX ← Vendor identification string;
        EDX ← Vendor identification string;
        ECX ← Vendor identification string;
        break;

    case 1:
        EAX[3:0] ← Stepping ID;
        EAX[7:4] ← Model;
        EAX[11:8] ← Family;
        EAX[31:12] ← Reserved;

        EBX ← reserved;      (* 0 *)
        ECX ← reserved;      (* 0 *)
        EDX ← feature flags;
        break;

    default:   (* EAX > hv *)
        EAX ← reserved, undefined;
        EBX ← reserved, undefined;
        ECX ← reserved, undefined;
        EDX ← reserved, undefined;
        break;
    end-of-switch
```

Description

The CPUID instruction provides information to software about the vendor, family, model, and stepping of microprocessor on which it is executing. An input value loaded into the EAX register for this instruction indicates what information should be returned by the CPUID instruction.

Following execution of the CPUID instruction with a zero in EAX, the EAX register contains the highest input value understood by the CPUID instruction. For the Pentium processor, the value in EAX will be a one. Also included in the output of this instruction with an input value of zero in EAX is a vendor identification string contained in the EBX, EDX, and ECX registers. EBX contains the first four characters, EDX contains the next four characters and ECX contains the last four characters. For Intel processors, the vendor identification string is "GenuineIntel" as follows::

EBX ← 756e6547h (* "Genu", with G in the low nibble of BL *)
EDX ← 49656e69h (* "inel", with i in the low nibble of DL *)
ECX ← 6c65746eh (* "ntel", with n in the low nibble of CL *)

Following execution of the CPUID instruction with an input value of one loaded into the EAX register, EAX[3:0] contains the stepping id of the microprocessor, EAX[7:4] contains the model (the first model will be indicated by 0001B in these bits) and EAX[11:8] contains the family (5 for the Pentium processor family). EAX[31:12] are reserved, as well as EBX, and ECX. The Pentium processor sets the feature register, EDX, to 1BFH indicating which features the Pentium processor supports. A feature flag set to one indicates that the corresponding feature is supported. The feature set register is defined as follows:

EDX[0:0]   FPU on chip
EDX[6:1]   For more information on these bits, see Appendix H
EDX[7:7]   Machine Check Exception
EDX[8:8]   CMPXCHG8B Instruction
EDX[31:9] Reserved

Software should determine the vendor identification in order to properly interpret the feature register flag bits. For more information on the feature set register, see Appendix H.

Flags Affected

None.

Protected Mode Exceptions

None.

Real Address Mode Exceptions

None.

Virtual 8086 Mode Exceptions

None.

Notes

Refer to the guidelines in Chapter 2 "Reserved Bits".

CWD/CDQ—Convert Word to Double/Convert Double to Quad

Opcode	Instruction	Clocks	Description
99	CWD	2	DX ← sign-extend of AX
99	CDQ	2	EDX ← sign-extend of EAX

Operation

IF OperandSize = 16 (* instruction = CWD *)
THEN DX ← SignExtend(AX);
ELSE (* OperandSize = 32, instruction = CDQ *)
    EDX ← SignExtend(EAX);
FI;

Description

CWD and CDQ double the size of the source operand. The CWD instruction copies the sign (bit 15) of the word in the AX register into every bit position in the DX register. The CDQ instruction copies the sign (bit 31) of the doubleword in the EAX register into every bit position in the EDX register. The CWD instruction can be used to produce a doubleword dividend from a word before a word division, and the CDQ instruction can be used to produce a quadword dividend from a doubleword before doubleword division. The CWD and CDQ instructions are different mnemonics for the same opcode. Which one gets executed is determined by whether it is in a 16- or 32-bit segment and the presence of any operand-size override prefixes.

Flags Affected

None.

Protected Mode Exceptions

None.

Real Address Mode Exceptions

None.

Virtual 8086 Mode Exceptions

None.

CWDE—Convert Word to Doubleword

See entry for CBW/CWDE—Convert Byte to Word/Convert Word to Doubleword.

DAA—Decimal Adjust AL after Addition

Opcode	Instruction	Clocks	Description
27	DAA	3	Decimal adjust AL after addition

Operation

```
IF (((AL AND 0FH) > 09H) or EFLAGS.AF = 1)
THEN
    AL← AL + 06H;
FI;
IF ((AL AND 0F0H) > 90H) or EFLAGS.CF = 1)
THEN
    AL ← AL + 60H;
    CF ← 1;
FI;
```

Description

Execute the DAA instruction only after executing an ADD instruction that leaves a two-BCD-digit byte result in the AL register. The ADD operands should consist of two packed BCD digits. The DAA instruction adjusts the AL register to contain the correct two-digit packed decimal result.

Flags Affected

The AF and CF flags are set if there is a decimal carry, cleared if there is no decimal carry; the SF, ZF and PF flags are set according to the result. The OF flag is undefined.

Protected Mode Exceptions

None.

Real Address Mode Exceptions

None.

Virtual 8086 Mode Exceptions

None.

DAS—Decimal Adjust AL after Subtraction

Opcode	Instruction	Clocks	Description
2F	DAS	3	Decimal adjust AL after subtraction

Operation

```
tmpCF ← 0;
tmpAL ← AL;
IF (((tmpAL AND 0FH) > 9H) or AF = 1)
THEN
    AF ← 1;
    AL ← AL – 6H;
    tmpCF ← (AL < 0) OR CF;
FI;
IF ((tmpAL > 99H) or CF = 1)
THEN
    AL ← AL – 60H;
    tmpCF ← 1;
FI;
CF ← tmpCF;
```

Description

Execute the DAS instruction only after a subtraction instruction that leaves a two-BCD-digit byte result in the AL register. The operands should consist of two packed BCD digits. The DAS instruction adjusts the AL register to contain the correct packed two-digit decimal result.

Flags Affected

The AF and CF flags are set if there is a decimal borrow, cleared if there is no decimal borrow; the SF, ZF and PF flags are set according to the result. The OF flag is undefined.

Protected Mode Exceptions

None.

Real Address Mode Exceptions

None.

Virtual 8086 Mode Exceptions

None.

DEC—Decrement by 1

Opcode	Instruction	Clocks	Description
FE /1	DEC r/m8	1/3	Decrement r/m byte by 1
FF /1	DEC r/m16	1/3	Decrement r/m word by 1
FF /1	DEC r/m32	1/3	Decrement r/m dword by 1
48+rw	DEC r16	1	Decrement word register by 1
48+rd	DEC r32	1	Decrement dword register by 1

Operation

DEST ← DEST – 1;

Description

The DEC instruction subtracts 1 from the operand. The DEC instruction does not change the CF flag. To affect the CF flag, use the SUB instruction with an immediate operand of 1.

Flags Affected

The OF, SF, ZF, AF, and PF flags are set according to the result.

Protected Mode Exceptions

#GP(0) if the result is a nonwritable segment; #GP(0) for an illegal memory operand effective address in the CS, DS, ES, FS, or GS segments; #SS(0) for an illegal address in the SS segment; #PF(fault-code) for a page fault; #AC for unaligned memory reference if the current privilege level is 3.

Real Address Mode Exceptions

Interrupt 13 if any part of the operand would lie outside of the effective address space from 0 to 0FFFFH.

Virtual 8086 Mode Exceptions

Same exceptions as in Real Address Mode; #PF(fault-code) for a page fault; #AC for unaligned memory reference if the current privilege level is 3.

DIV—Unsigned Divide

Opcode	Instruction	Clocks	Description
F6 /6	DIV AL,*r/m8*	17	Unsigned divide AX by *r/m* byte (AL=Quo, AH=Rem)
F7 /6	DIV AX,*r/m16*	25	Unsigned divide DX:AX by *r/m* word (AX=Quo, DX=Rem)
F7 /6	DIV EAX,*r/m32*	41	Unsigned divide EDX:EAX by *r/m* dword (EAX=Quo, EDX=Rem)

Operation

temp ← dividend / divisor;
IF temp does not fit in quotient
THEN Interrupt 0;
ELSE
    quotient ← temp;
    remainder ← dividend MOD (*r/m*);
FI;

Note: Divisions are unsigned. The divisor is given by the **r/m** operand. The dividend, quotient, and remainder use implicit registers. Refer to the table under "Description."

Description

The DIV instruction performs an unsigned division. The dividend is implicit; only the divisor is given as an operand. The remainder is always less than the divisor. The type of the divisor determines which registers to use as follows:

Size	Dividend	Divisor	Quotient	Remainder
byte	AX	*r/m8*	AL	AH
word	DX:AX	*r/m16*	AX	DX
dword	EDX:EAX	*r/m32*	EAX	EDX

Flags Affected

The OF, SF, ZF, AF, PF, CF flags are undefined.

Protected Mode Exceptions

Interrupt 0 if the quotient is too large to fit in the designated register (AL, AX, or EAX), or if the divisor is 0; #GP(0) for an illegal memory operand effective address in the CS, DS, ES, FS, or GS segments; #SS(0) for an illegal address in the SS segment; #PF(fault-code) for a page fault; #AC for unaligned memory reference if the current privilege level is 3.

Real Address Mode Exceptions

Interrupt 0 if the quotient is too big to fit in the designated register (AL, AX, or EAX), or if the divisor is 0; Interrupt 13 if any part of the operand would lie outside of the effective address space from 0 to 0FFFFH.

Virtual 8086 Mode Exceptions

Same exceptions as in Real Address Mode; #PF(fault-code) for a page fault; #AC for unaligned memory reference if the current privilege level is 3.

ENTER—Make Stack Frame for Procedure Parameters

Opcode	Instruction	Clocks	Description
C8 *iw* 00	ENTER *imm16*,0	11	Make procedure stack frame
C8 *iw* 01	ENTER *imm16*,1	15	Make stack frame for procedure parameters
C8 *iw* ib	ENTER *imm16*,*imm8*	15+2*imm8*	Make stack frame for procedure parameters

Operation

```
level ← level MOD 32
2ndOperand <- 2ndOperand MOD 32
IF operand_size = 16 THEN Push(bp) ELSE Push(ebp) FI;
IF stkSize = 16 THEN framePtr = sp ELSE framePtr = esp FI;
FOR i ← 1 TO (2ndOperand - 1)
DO
    IF operand_size = 16
    THEN
        IF stkSize = 16
        THEN
            bp = bp - 2
            Push( [bp] )   (* word push *)
        ELSE (* stkSize = 32 *)
            ebp = ebp - 2
            Push( [ebp] )  (* word push *)
        FI;
    ELSE (* operand_size = 32 *)
        IF stkSize = 16
            bp = bp - 4
            Push( [bp] )   (* doubleword push *)
        ELSE (* stkSize = 32 *)
            ebp = ebp - 4
            Push( [ebp] )  (* doubleword push *)
        FI;
    FI;
OD;
IF stkSize = 16
THEN Push(framePtr);   (* word push *)
ELSE Pushd(framePtr); (* doubleword push *)
FI;
IF stkSize =16
THEN
    bp = framePtr
    sp = sp - 1stOperand
ELSE
    ebp = framePtr
    esp = esp - 1stOperand
FI;
```

Description

The ENTER instruction creates the stack frame required by most block-structured high-level languages. The first operand specifies the number of bytes of dynamic storage allocated on the stack for the routine being entered. The second operand gives the lexical nesting level (0 to 31) of the routine within the high-level language source code. It determines the number of stack frame pointers copied into the new stack frame from the preceding frame.

Both the operand-size attribute and the stack-size attribute are used to determine whether BP or EBP is used for the current frame pointer and SP or ESP is used for the stack pointer.

If the operand-size attribute is 16 bits, the processor uses the BP register as the frame pointer and the SP register as the stack pointer, unless the stack-size attribute is 32 bits in which case it uses EBP for the frame pointer and ESP for the stack pointer. If the operand-size attribute is 32 bits, the processor uses the EBP register for the frame pointer and the ESP register for the stack pointer, unless the stack-size attribute is 16 bits in which case it uses BP for the frame pointer and SP for the stack pointer.

If the second operand is 0, the ENTER instruction pushes the frame pointer (BP or EBP register) onto the stack; the ENTER instruction then subtracts the first operand from the stack pointer and sets the frame pointer to the current stack-pointer value.

For example, a procedure with 12 bytes of local variables would have an ENTER 12,0 instruction at its entry point and a LEAVE instruction before every RET instruction. The 12 local bytes would be addressed as negative offsets from the frame pointer.

Flags Affected

None.

Protected Mode Exceptions

#SS(0) if the SP or ESP value would exceed the stack limit at any point during instruction execution; #PF(fault-code) for a page fault.

Real Address Mode Exceptions

None.

Virtual 8086 Mode Exceptions

None.

F2XM1—Compute 2^X–1

Opcode	Instruction	Clocks	Description
D9 F0	F2XM1	13-57	Replace ST with (2ST–1)

Operation

ST ← (2ST–1);

Description

F2XM1 replaces the contents of ST with (2ST–1). ST must lie in the range –1 < ST < 1.

FPU Flags Affected

C1 as described in   Chapter 6; C0, C2, C3 undefined.

Numeric Exceptions

P, U, D, I, IS.

Protected Mode Exceptions

#NM if either EM or TS in CR0 is set.

Real Address Mode Exceptions

Interrupt 7 if either EM or TS in CR0 is set.

Virtual 8086 Mode Exceptions

#NM if either EM or TS in CR0 is set.

Notes

If the operand is outside the acceptable range, the result of F2XM1 is undefined.

Values other than 2 can be exponentiated using the formula

$x^y = 2^{(y \times \log_2 x)}$

The instructions FLDL2T and FLDL2E load the constants $\log_2 10$ and $\log_2 e$, respectively. FYL2X can be used to calculate $y \times \log_2 x$ for arbitrary positive x.

FABS—Absolute Value

Opcode	Instruction	Clocks	Description
D9 E1	FABS	1	Replace ST with its absolute value.

Operation

sign bit of ST ← 0

Description

The absolute value instruction clears the sign bit of ST. This operation leaves a positive value unchanged, or replaces a negative value with a positive value of equal magnitude.

FPU Flags Affected

C1 as described in   Chapter 6; C0, C2, C3 undefined.

Numeric Exceptions

IS

Protected Mode Exceptions

#NM if either EM or TS in CR0 is set.

Real Address Mode Exceptions

Interrupt 7 if either EM or TS in CR0 is set.

Virtual 8086 Mode Exceptions

#NM if either EM or TS in CR0 is set.

Notes

The invalid-operation exception is raised only on stack underflow. No exception is raised if the operand is a signalling NaN or is in an unsupported format.

FADD/FADDP/FIADD—Add

Opcode	Instruction	Clocks	Description
D8 /0	FADD m32 real	3/1	Add m32real to ST.
DC /0	FADD m64real	3/1	Add m64real to ST.
D8 C0+i	FADD ST, ST(i)	3/1	Add ST(i) to ST.
DC C0+i	FADD ST(i), ST	3/1	Add ST to ST(i).
DE C0+i	FADDP ST(i), ST	3/1	Add ST to ST(i) and pop ST.
DE C1	FADD	3/1	Add ST to ST(1) and pop ST.
DA /0	FIADD m32int	7/4	Add m32int to ST.
DE /0	FIADD m16int	7/4	Add m16int to ST]

Operation

DEST ← DEST +SRC;
If instruction = FADDP THEN pop ST FI;

Description

The addition instructions add the source and destination operands and return the sum to the destination. The operand at the stack top can be doubled by coding:

FADD ST, ST(0)

FPU Flags Affected

C1 as described in   ; C0, C2, C3 undefined.

Numeric Exceptions

P, U, O, D, I, IS.

Protected Mode Exceptions

#GP(0) for an illegal memory operand effective address in the CS, DS, ES, FS, or GS segments; #SS(0) for an illegal address in the SS segment; #PF (fault-code) for a page fault; #NM if either EM or TS in CR0 is set; #AC for unaligned memory reference if the current privilege level is 3.

Real Address Mode Exceptions

Interrupt 13 if any part of the operand would lie outside the effective address space from 0 to 0FFFFH; Interrupt 7 if either EM or TS in CR0 is set.

Virtual 8086 Mode Exceptions

Same exceptions as in Real Address Mode; #PF (fault code) for a page fault; #AC for unaligned memory reference if the current privilege level is 3.

Notes

If the source operand is in memory, it is automatically converted to the extended-real format.

FBLD—Load Binary Coded Decimal

Opcode	Instruction	Clocks	Description
DF /4	FBLD m80 dec	48-58	Push m80dec onto the FPU stack.

Operation

Decrement FPU stack-top pointer;
ST(0) ← SRC;

Description

FBLD converts the BCD source operand into extended-real format, and pushes it onto the FPU stack. See Figure 6-10 for BCD data layout.

FPU Flags Affected

C1 as described in   Chapter 6; C0, C2, C3 undefined.

Numeric Exceptions

IS.

Protected Mode Exceptions

#GP(0) for an illegal memory operand effective address in the CS, DS, ES, FS, or GS segments; #SS(0) for an illegal address in the SS segment; #PF (fault-code) for a page fault; #NM if either EM or TS in CR0 is set; #AC for unaligned memory reference if the current privilege level is 3.

Real Address Mode Exceptions

Interrupt 13 if any part of the operand would lie outside the effective address space from 0 to 0FFFFH; Interrupt 7 if either EM or TS in CR0 is set.

Virtual 8086 Mode Exceptions

Same exceptions as in Real Address Mode; #PF (fault code) for a page fault; #AC for unaligned memory reference if the current privilege level is 3.

Notes

The source is loaded without rounding error. The sign of the source is preserved, including the case where the value is negative zero.

The packed decimal digits are assumed to be in the range 0-9. The instruction does not check for invalid digits (A-FH), and the result of attempting to load an invalid encoding is undefined.

ST(7) must be empty to avoid causing an invalid-operation exception.

FBSTP—Store Binary Coded Decimal and Pop

Opcode	Instruction	Clocks	Description
DF /6	FBSTP m80dec	148-154	Store ST in m80dec and pop ST.

Operation

DEST ← ST(0);
 pop ST;

Description

FBSTP converts the value in ST into a packed decimal integer, stores the result at the destination in memory, and pops ST. Non-integral values are first rounded according to the RC field of the control word. See Figure 6-10 for BCD data layout.

FPU Flags Affected

C1 as described in Chapter 6; C0, C2, C3 undefined.

Numeric Exceptions

P, I, IS.

Protected Mode Exceptions

#GP(0) if the destination is in a nonwritable segment; #GP(0) for an illegal memory operand effective address in the CS, DS, ES, FS, or GS segments; #SS(0) for an illegal address in the SS segment; #PF (fault-code) for a page fault; #NM if either EM or TS in CR0 is set; #AC for unaligned memory reference if the current privilege level is 3.

Real Address Mode Exceptions

Interrupt 13 if any part of the operand would lie outside the effective address space from 0 to 0FFFFH; Interrupt 7 if either EM or TS in CR0 is set.

Virtual 8086 Mode Exceptions

Same exceptions as in Real Address Mode; #PF (fault code) for a page fault; #AC for unaligned memory reference if the current privilege level is 3.

FCHS—Change Sign

Opcode	Instruction	Clocks	Description
D9 E0	FCHS	1	Replace ST with a value of opposite sign.

Operation

sign bit of ST ← NOT (sign bit of ST)

Description

The change sign instruction inverts the sign bit of ST. This operation replaces a positive value with a negative value of equal magnitude, or vice-versa.

FPU Flags Affected

C1 as described in   Chapter 6; C0, C2, C3 undefined.

Numeric Exceptions

IS.

Protected Mode Exceptions

#NM if either EM or TS in CR0 is set.

Real Address Mode Exceptions

Interrupt 7 if either EM or TS in CR0 is set.

Virtual 8086 Mode Exceptions

#NM if either EM or TS in CR0 is set.

Notes

The invalid-operation exception is raised only on stack underflow, even if the operand is a signalling NaN or is in an unsupported format.

FCLEX/FNCLEX—Clear Exceptions

Opcode	Instruction	Clocks	Description
9B DB E2	FCLEX	9 + at least 1for FWAIT	Clear floating-point exception flags after checking for floating-point error conditions.
DB E2	FNCLEX	9	Clear floating-point exception flags without checking for floating-point error conditions.

Operation

SW[0..7] ← 0;
SW[15] ← 0;

Description

FCLEX clears the exception flags, the exception status flag, and the busy flag of the FPU status word.

FPU Flags Affected

C0, C1, C2, C3 undefined.

Numeric Exceptions

None.

Protected Mode Exceptions

#NM if either EM or TS in CR0 is set.

Real Address Mode Exceptions

Interrupt 7 if either EM or TS in CR0 is set.

Virtual 8086 Mode Exceptions

#NM if either EM or TS in CR0 is set.

Notes

FCLEX checks for unmasked floating-point error conditions before clearing the exception flags; FNCLEX does not.

FCOM/FCOMP/FCOMPP—Compare Real

Opcode	Instruction	Clocks	Description
D8 /2	FCOM m32real	4/1	Compare ST with m32real.
DC /2	FCOM m64real	4/1	Compare ST with m64real.
D8 D0+i	FCOM ST(i)	4/1	Compare ST with ST(i).
D8 D1	FCOM	4/1	Compare ST with ST(1).
D8 /3	FCOMP m32real	4/1	Compare ST with m32real and pop ST.
DC /3	FCOMP m64real	4/1	Compare ST with m64real and pop ST.
D8 D8+i	FCOMP ST(i)	4/1	Compare ST with ST(i) and pop ST.
D8 D9	FCOMP	4/1	Compare ST with ST(1) and pop ST.
DE D9	FCOMPP	4/1	Compare ST with ST(1) and pop ST twice.

Operation

```
CASE (relation of operands) OF
    Not comparable:   C3, C2, C0 ← 111;
    ST > SRC:  C3, C2, C0 ← 000;
    ST < SRC:  C3, C2, C0 ← 001;
    ST = SRC:  C3, C2, C0 ← 100;
IF instruction = FCOMP THEN pop ST; FI;
IF instruction = FCOMPP THEN pop ST; pop ST; FI;
```

FPU Flags	EFlags
C0	CF
C1	None
C2	PF
C3	ZF

Description

The compare real instructions compare the stack top to the source, which can be a register or a single- or double-real memory operand. If no operand is encoded, ST is compared to ST(1). Following the instruction, the condition codes reflect the relation between ST and the source operand.

FPU Flags Affected

C1 as described in   Chapter 6; C0, C2, C3 as specified above.

Numeric Exceptions

D, I, IS.

Protected Mode Exceptions

#GP(0) for an illegal memory operand effective address in the CS, DS, ES, FS, or GS segments; #SS(0) for an illegal address in the SS segment; #PF (fault-code) for a page fault; #NM if either EM or TS in CR0 is set; #AC for unaligned memory reference if the current privilege level is 3.

Real Address Mode Exceptions

Interrupt 13 if any part of the operand would lie outside the effective address space from 0 to 0FFFFH; Interrupt 7 if either EM or TS in CR0 is set.

Virtual 8086 Mode Exceptions

Same exceptions as in Real Address Mode; #PF (fault code) for a page fault; #AC for unaligned memory reference if the current privilege level is 3.

Notes

If either operand is a NaN or is in an undefined format, or if a stack fault occurs, the invalid-operation exception is raised, and the condition bits are set to "unordered."

The sign of zero is ignored, so that −0.0 =− +0.0.

FCOS—Cosine

Opcode	Instruction	Clocks	Description
D9 FF	FCOS	18-124	Replace ST with its cosine

Operation

IF operand is in range
THEN
    C2 ← 0;
    ST ← cos(ST);
ELSE
    C2 ← 1;
FI;

Description

The cosine instruction replaces the contents of ST with cos(ST). ST, expressed in radians, must lie in the range $| \theta | < 2^{63}$.

FPU Flags Affected

C1, C2 as described in   Chapter 6; C0, C3 undefined.

Numeric Exceptions

P, D, I, IS.

Protected Mode Exceptions

#NM if either EM or TS in CR0 is set.

Real Address Mode Exceptions

Interrupt 7 if either EM or TS in CR0 is set.

Virtual 8086 Mode Exceptions

#NM if either EM or TS in CR0 is set.

Notes

If the operand is outside the acceptable range, the C2 flag is set, and ST remains unchanged. It is the programmer's responsibility to reduce the operand to an absolute value smaller than 2^{63} by subtracting an appropriate integer multiple of 2π. See Chapter 6 for a discussion of the proper value to use for π in performing such reductions.

FDECSTP—Decrement Stack-Top Pointer

Opcode	Instruction	Clocks	Description
D9 F6	FDECSTP	1	Decrement top-of-stack pointer for FPU register stack.

Operation

IF TOP=0
THEN TOP ← 7;
ELSE TOP ← TOP−1;
FI;

Description

FDECSTP subtracts one (without carry) from the three-bit TOP field of the FPU status word.

FPU Flags Affected

C1 as described in   Chapter 6; C0, C2, C3 undefined.

Numeric Exceptions

None.

Protected Mode Exceptions

#NM if either EM or TS in CR0 is set.

Real Address Mode Exceptions

Interrupt 7 if either EM or TS in CR0 is set.

Virtual 8086 Mode Exceptions

#NM if either EM or TS in CR0 is set.

Notes

The effect of FDECSTP is to rotate the stack. If does not alter register tags or contents, nor does it transfer data.

FDIV/FDIVP/FIDIV—Divide

Opcode	Instruction	Clocks	Description
D8 /6	FDIV m32real	39	Divide ST by m32real.
DC /6	FDIV m64real	39	Divide ST by m64real.
D8 F0+i	FDIV ST, ST(i)	39	Divide ST by ST(i)
DC F8+i	FDIV ST(i), ST	39	Replace ST(i) with ST(i) ÷ ST
DE F8+i	FDIVP ST(i), ST	39	Replace ST(i) with ST(i) ÷ ST; pop ST.
DE F9	FDIVP	39	Replace ST(1) with ST(1) ÷ ST; pop ST.
DA /6	FIDIV m32int	42	Divide ST by m32int.
DE /6	FIDIV m16int	42	Divide ST by m16int.

Operation

FDIV   DEST, SCR
DEST ← DEST ÷ SCR
IF instruction = FDIVP THEN pop ST FI;

Description

The division instructions divide the stack top by the other operand and return the quotient to the destination.

FPU Flags Affected

C1 as described in   Chapter 6; C0, C2, C3 undefined.

Numeric Exceptions

P, U, O, Z, D, I, IS.

Protected Mode Exceptions

#GP(0) for an illegal memory operand effective address in the CS, DS, ES, FS, or GS segments; #SS(0) for an illegal address in the SS segment; #PF(fault-code) for a page fault; #NM if either EM or TS in CR0 is set; #AC for unaligned memory reference if the current privilege level is 3.

Real Address Mode Exceptions

Interrupt 13 if any part of the operand would lie outside the effective address space from 0 to 0FFFFH; Interrupt 7 if either EM or TS in CR0 is set.

Virtual 8086 Mode Exceptions

Same exceptions as in Real Address Mode; #PF(fault code) for a page fault; #AC for unaligned memory reference if the current privilege level is 3.

Notes

If the source operand is in memory, it is automatically converted to the extended-real format.

The performance of the division instructions depends on the PC (Precision Control) field of the FPU control word. If PC specifies a precision of 53 bits, the division instructions will execute in 33 clocks. If the specified precision is 24 bits, the division instructions will take only 19 clocks.

FDIVR/FDIVRP/FIDIVR—Reverse Divide

Opcode	Instruction	Clocks	Description
D8 /7	FDIVR m32real	39	Replaces ST with m32real ÷ ST.
DC /7	FDIVR m64real	39	Replace ST with m64real ÷ ST.
D8 F8+i	FDIVR ST, ST(i)	39	Replace ST by ST(i) ÷ ST.
DC F0+i	FDIVR ST(i), ST	39	Divide ST(i) = ST ÷ ST(i).
DE F0+i	FDIVRP ST(i), ST	39	Divide ST(i) = ST ÷ ST(i) and pop ST.
DE F1	FDIVRP	39	Divide ST(1) = ST ÷ ST(1) and pop ST.
DA /7	FIDIVR m32int	42	Replace ST with m32int ÷ ST.
DE /7	FIDIVR m16int	42	Replace ST with m16int ÷ ST.

Operation

FDIVR   DEST, SRC
DEST ← SRC ÷ DEST
IF instruction = FDIVRP THEN pop ST FI;

Description

The division instructions divide the other operand by the stack top and return the quotient to the destination.

FPU Flags Affected

C1 as described in   Chapter 6; C0, C2, C3 undefined.

Numeric Exceptions

P, U, O, Z, D, I, IS.

Protected Mode Exceptions

#GP(0) for an illegal memory operand effective address in the CS, DS, ES, FS, or GS segments; #SS(0) for an illegal address in the SS segment; #PF(fault-code) for a page fault; #NM if either EM or TS in CR0 is set; #AC for unaligned memory reference if the current privilege level is 3.

Real Address Mode Exceptions

Interrupt 13 if any part of the operand would lie outside the effective address space from 0 to 0FFFFH; Interrupt 7 if either EM or TS in CR0 is set.

Virtual 8086 Mode Exceptions

Same exceptions as in Real Address Mode; #PF(fault code) for a page fault; #AC for unaligned memory reference if the current privilege level is 3.

Notes

If the source operand is in memory, it is automatically converted to the extended-real format.

The performance of the reverse division instructions depends on the PC (Precision Control) field of the FPU control word. If PC specifies a precision of 53 bits, the reverse division instructions will execute in 33 clocks. If the specified precision is 24 bits, the reverse division instructions will take only 19 clocks.

FFREE—Free Floating-Point Register

Opcode	Instruction	Clocks	Description
DD C0+i	FFREE ST(i)	1	Tag ST(i) as *empty*.

Operation

TAG(i) ← 11B;

Description

FFREE tags the destination register as *empty*.

FPU Flags Affected

C0, C1, C2, C3 undefined.

Numeric Exceptions

None.

Protected Mode Exceptions

#NM if either EM or TS in CR0 is set.

Real Address Mode Exceptions

Interrupt 7 if either EM or TS in CR0 is set.

Virtual 8086 Mode Exceptions

#NM if either EM or TS in CR0 is set.

Notes

FFREE does not affect the contents of the destination register. The floating-point stack-top pointer (TOP) is also unaffected.

FICOM/FICOMP—Compare Integer

Opcode	Instruction	Clocks	Description
DE /2	FICOM *m16real*	8/4	Compare ST with *m16int*.
DA /2	FICOM *m32real*	8/4	Compare ST with *m32int*.
DE /3	FICOMP *m16int*	8/4	Compare ST with *m16int* and pop ST.
DA /3	FICOMP *m32int*	8/4	Compare ST with *m32int* and pop ST.

Operation

CASE (relation of operands) OF
    Not comparable: C3, C2, C0 ← 111;
   ST > SRC: C3, C2, C0 ← 000;
   ST < SRC: C3, C2, C0 ← 001;
   ST = SRC: C3, C2, C0 ← 100;
IF instruction = FICOMP THEN pop ST; FI;

FPU Flags	EFlags
C0	CF
C1	(none)
C2	PF
C3	ZF

Description

The compare integer instructions compare the stack top to the source. Following the instruction, the condition codes reflect the relation between ST and the source operand.

FPU Flags Affected

C1 as described in Chapter 6; C0, C2, C3 as specified above.

Numeric Exceptions

D, I, IS.

Protected Mode Exceptions

#GP(0) for an illegal memory operand effective address in the CS, DS, ES, FS, or GS segments; #SS(0) for an illegal address in the SS segment; #PF(fault-code) for a page fault; #NM if either EM or TS in CR0 is set; #AC for unaligned memory reference if the current privilege level is 3.

Real Address Mode Exceptions

Interupt 13 if any part of the operand would lie outside the effective address space from 0 to 0FFFFH; Interrupt 7 if either EM or TS in CR0 is set.

Virtual 8086 Mode Exceptions

Same exceptions as in Real Address Mode; #PF(fault code) for a page fault; #AC for unaligned memory reference if the current privilege level is 3.

Notes

The memory operand is converted to extended-real format before the comparison is performed.

If either operand is a NaN or is in an undefined format, or if a stack fault occurs, the invalid-operation exception is raised, and the condition bits are set to "unordered."

FILD—Load Integer

Opcode	Instruction	Clocks	Description
DF /0	FILD *m16int*	3/1	Push *m16int* onto the FPU stack.
DB /0	FILD *m32int*	3/1	Push *m32int* onto the FPU stack.
DF /5	FILD *m64int*	3/1	Push *m64int* onto the FPU stack.

Operation

Decrement FPU stack-top pointer;
ST(0) ← SRC;

Description

FILD converts the source signed integer operand into extended-real format, and pushes it onto the FPU stack.

FPU Flags Affected

C1 as described in Chapter 6; C0, C2, C3 undefined.

Numeric Exceptions

IS.

Protected Mode Exceptions

#GP(0) for an illegal memory operand effective address in the CS, DS, ES, FS, or GS segments; #SS(0) for an illegal address in the SS segment; #PF(fault-code) for page fault; #NM if either EM or TS in CR0 is set; #AC for unaligned memory reference if the current privilege level is 3.

Real Address Mode Exceptions

Interrupt 13 if any part of the operand would lie outside the effective address space from 0 to 0FFFFH; Interrupt 7 if either EM or TS in CR0 is set.

Virtual 8086 Mode Exceptions

Same exceptions as in Real Address Mode; #PF(fault code) for a page fault; #AC for unaligned memory reference if the current privilege level is 3.

Notes

The source is loaded without rounding error.

ST(7) must be empty to avoid causing an invalid-operation exception.

FINCSTP—Increment Stack-Top Pointer

Opcode	Instruction	Clocks	Description
D9 F7	FINCSTP	1	Increment top-of-stack pointer for FPU register stack.

Operation

IF TOP =7
THEN TOP ← 0;
ELSE TOP ← TOP + 1;
FI;

Description

FINCSTP adds one (without carry) to the three-bit TOP field of the FPU status word.

FPU Flags Affected

C1 as described in Chapter 6; C0, C2, C3 undefined.

Numeric Exceptions

None.

Protected Mode Exceptions

#NM if either EM or TS in CR0 is set.

Real Address Mode Exceptions

Interrupt 7 if either EM or TS in CR0 is set.

Virtual 8086 Mode Exceptions

#NM is either EM or TS in CR0 is set.

Notes

The effect of FINCSTP is to rotate the stack. It does not alter register tags or contents, nor does it transfer data. It is not equivalent to popping the stack, because it does not set the tag of the old stack-top to *empty*.

FINIT/FNINIT—Initialize Floating-Point Unit

Opcode	Instruction	Clocks	Description
DB E3	FINIT	16	Initialize FPU after checking for unmasked floating-point error condition.
DB E3	FNINIT	12	Initialize FPU without checking for unmasked floating-point error condition.

Operation

CW ← 037FH;   (* Control word *)
SW ← 0; (* Status word *)
TW ← FFFFH;   (* Tag word *)
FEA ← 0; FDS ← 0; (* Data pointer *)
FIP ← 0; FOP ← 0; FCS ← 0;   (* Instruction pointer *)

Description

The initialization instructions set the FPU into a known state, unaffected by any previous activity.

The FPU control word is set to 037FH (round to nearest, all exceptions masked, 64-bit precision). The status word is cleared (no exception flags set, stack register R0=stack-top). The stack registers are all tagged as *empty*. The error pointers (both instruction and data) are cleared.

FPU Flags Affected

C0, C1, C2, C3 cleared.

Numeric Exceptions

None.

Protected Mode Exceptions

#NM if either EM or TS in CR0 is set.

Real Address Mode Exceptions

Interrupt 7 if either EM or TS in CR0 is set.

Virtual 8086 Mode Exceptions

#NM if either EM or TS in CR0 is set.

Notes

FINIT checks for unmasked floating-point error conditions before performing the initialization; FNINIT does not.

On the Pentium processor, unlike the Intel387 math coprocessor, FINIT and FNINIT clear the error pointers.

FIST/FISTP—Store Integer

Opcode	Instruction	Clocks	Description
DF /2	FIST *m16int*	6	Store ST in *m16int*.
DB /2	FIST *m32int*	6	Store ST in *m32int*.
DF /3	FISTP *m16int*	6	Store ST in *m16int* and pop ST.
DB /3	FISTP *m32int*	6	Store ST in *m32int* and pop ST.
DF /7	FISTP *m64int*	6	Store ST in *m64int* and pop ST.

Operation

DEST ← ST(0);
IF instruction = FISTP THEN pop ST FI;

Description

FIST converts the value in ST into a signed integer according to the RC field of the control word and transfers the result to the destination. ST remains unchanged. FIST accepts word and short integer destinations; FISTP accepts these and long integers as well.

FPU Flags Affected

C1 as described in Chapter 6; C0, C2, C3 undefined.

Numeric Exceptions

P, I, IS.

Protected Mode Exceptions

#GP(0) if the destination is in a nonwritable segment; #GP(0) for an illegal memory operand effective address in the CS, DS, ES, FS, or GS segments; #SS(0) for an illegal address in the SS segment; #PF(fault-code) for a page fault; #NM if either EM or TS in CR0 is set; #AC for unaligned memory reference if the current privilege level is 3.

Real Address Mode Exceptions

Interupt 13 if any part of the operand would lie outside the effective address space from 0 to 0FFFFH; Interrupt 7 if either EM or TS in CR0 is set.

Virtual 8086 Mode Exceptions

Same exceptions as in Real Address Mode; #PF(fault code) for a page fault; #AC for unaligned memory reference if the current privilege level is 3.

Notes

Negative zero is stored with the same encoding (00..00) as positive zero. If the value is too large to represent as an integer, an I exception is raised. The masked response is to write the most negative integer to memory.

intel®

FLD—Load Real

Opcode	Instruction	Clocks	Description
D9 /0	FLD m32real	1	Push m32real onto the FPU stack.
DD /0	FLD m64real	1	Push m64real onto the FPU stack.
DB /5	FLD m80real	3	Push m80real onto the FPU stack.
D9 C0+i	FLD ST(i)	1	Push ST(i) onto the FPU stack.

Operation

Decrement FPU stack-top pointer;
ST(0) ← SRC;

Description

FLD pushes the source operand onto the FPU stack. If the source is a register, the register number used is that before the stack-top pointer is decremented. In particular, coding

FLD ST(0)

duplicates the stack top.

FPU Flags Affected

C1 as described in Chapter 6; C0, C2, C3 undefined.

Numeric Exceptions

D, I, IS.

Protected Mode Exceptions

#GP(0) for an illegal memory operand effective address in the CS, DS, ES, FS, or GS segments; #SS(0) for an illegal address in the SS segment; #PF(fault-code) for a page fault; #NM if either EM or TS in CR0 is set; #AC for unaligned memory reference if the current privilege level is 3.

Real Address Mode Exceptions

Interrupt 13 if any part of the operand would lie outside the effective address space from 0 to 0FFFFH; Interrupt 7 if either EM or TS in CR0 is set.

Virtual 8086 Mode Exceptions

Same exceptions as in Real Address Mode; #PF(fault code) for a page fault; #AC for unaligned memory reference if the current privilege level is 3.

Notes

If the source operand is in single- or double-real format, it is automatically converted to the extended-real format. Loading an extended-real operand does not require conversion, so the I and D exceptions will not occur in this case.

ST(7) must be empty to avoid causing an invalid-operation exception.

FLD1/FLDL2T/FLDL2E/ FLDPI/FLDLG2/FLDLN2/FLDZ—Load Constant

Opcode	Instruction	Clocks	Description
D9 E8	FLD1	2/2	Push +1.0 onto the FPU Stack.
D9 E9	FLDL2T	5/3	Push $\log_2 10$ onto the FPU Stack.
D9 EA	FLDL2E	5/3	Push $\log_2 e$ onto the FPU Stack.
D9 EB	FLDPI	5/3	Push π onto the FPU Stack.
D9 EC	FLDLG2	5/3	Push $\log_{10} 2$ onto the FPU Stack.
D9 ED	FLDLN2	5/3	Push $\log_e 2$ onto the FPU Stack.
D9 EE	FLDZ	2/2	Push +0.0 onto the FPU Stack.

Operation

Decrement FPU stack-top pointer;
$ST(0) \leftarrow CONSTANT$;

Description

Each of the constant instructions pushes a commonly-used constant (in extended-real format) onto the FPU stack.

FPU Flags Affected

C1 as described in Chapter 6; C0, C2, C3 undefined.

Numeric Exceptions

IS.

Protected Mode Exceptions

#NM if either EM or TS in CR0 is set.

Real Address Mode Exceptions

Interrupt 7 if either EM or TS in CR0 is set.

Virtual 8086 Mode Exceptions

#NM if either EM or TS in CR0 is set.

Notes

ST(7) must be empty to avoid an invalid exception.

An internal 66-bit constant is used and rounded to external-real format (as specified by the RC bit of the control words). The precision exception is not raised.

FLDCW—Load Control Word

Opcode	Instruction	Clocks	Description
D9 /5	FNLDCW m2byte	7	Load FPU control word from *m2byte*.

Operation

CW ← SRC;

Description

FLDCW replaces the current value of the FPU control word with the value contained in the specified memory word.

FPU Flags Affected

C0, C1, C2, C3 undefined.

Numeric Exceptions

None, except for unmasking an existing exception.

Protected Mode Exceptions

#GP(0) for an illegal memory operand effective address in the CS, DS, ES, FS, or GS segments; #SS(0) for an illegal address in the SS segment; #PF(fault-code) for a page fault; #NM if either EM or TS in CR0 is set; #AC for unaligned memory reference if the current privilege level is 3.

Real Address Mode Exceptions

Interrupt 13 if any part of the operand would lie outside the effective address space from 0 to 0FFFFH; Interrupt 7 if either EM or TS in CR0 is set.

Virtual 8086 Mode Exceptions

Same exceptions as in Real Address Mode; #PF(fault code) for a page fault; #AC for unaligned memory reference if the current privilege level is 3.

Notes

FLDCW is typically used to establish or change the FPU's mode of operation.

If an exception bit in the status word is set, loading a new control word that unmasks that exception will result in a floating-point error condition. When changing modes, the recommended procedure is to clear any pending exceptions before loading the new control word.

FLDENV—Load FPU Environment

Opcode	Instruction	Clocks	Description
D9 /4	FLDENV m14/ 28byte	rm or vm=37 16 bit pm=32 32 bit pm=33	Load FPU environment from m14byte or m28byte.

Operation

FPU environment ← SRC;

Description

FLDENV reloads the FPU environment from the memory area defined by the source operand. This data should have been written by previous FSTENV or FNSTENV instruction.

The FPU environment consists of the FPU control word, status word, tag word, and error pointers (both data and instruction). The environment layout in memory depends on both the operand size and the current operating mode of the processor. The USE attribute of the current code segment determines the operand size: the 14-byte operand applies to a USE16 segment, and the 28-byte operand applies to a USE32 segment. See Chapter 6 for figures of the environment layouts for both operand sizes in both real mode and protected mode. (In virtual-8086 mode, the real mode layout is used.) FLDENV should be executed in the same operating mode as the corresponding FSTENV or FNSTENV.

FPU Flags Affected

C0, C1, C2, C3 as loaded.

Numeric Exceptions

None, except for loading an unmasked exception.

Protected Mode Exceptions

#GP(0) for an illegal memory operand effective address in the CS, DS, ES, FS, or GS segments; #SS(0) for an illegal address in the SS segment; #PF(fault-code) for a page fault; #NM if either EM or TS in CR0 is set; #AC for unaligned memory reference if the current privilege level is 3.

Real Address Mode Exceptions

Interrupt 13 if any part of the operand would lie outside the effective address space from 0 to 0FFFFH; Interrupt 7 if either EM or TS in CR0 is set.

Virtual 8086 Mode Exceptions

Same exceptions as in Real Address Mode; #PF(fault code) for a page fault; #AC for unaligned memory reference if the current privilege level is 3.

Notes

If the environment image contains an unmasked exception, loading it will result in a floating-point error condition.

FMUL/FMULP/FIMUL—Multiply

Opcode	Instruction	Clocks	Description
D8 /1	FMUL m32real	3/1	Multiply ST by m32real.
DC /1	FMUL m64real	3/1	Multiply ST by m64real.
D8 C8+i	FMUL ST, ST(i)	3/1	Multiply ST by ST(i)
DC C8+i	FMUL ST(i), ST	3/1	Multiply ST(i) by ST.
DE C8+i	FMULP ST(i), ST	3/1	Multiply ST(i) by ST and pop ST.
DE C9	FMUL	3/1	Multiply ST(1) by ST and pop ST.
DA /1	FIMUL m32int	7/4	Multiply ST by m32int.
DE /1	FIMUL m16int	7/4	Multiply ST by m16int.

Operation

DEST ← DEST x SRC;
IF instruction = FMULP THEN pop ST FI;

Description

The multiplication instructions multiply the destination operand by the source operand and
return the product to the destination.

FPU Flags Affected

C1 as described in Chapter 6; C0, C2, C3 undefined.

Numeric Exceptions

P, U, O, D, I.

Protected Mode Exceptions

#GP(0) for an illegal memory operand effective address in the CS, DS, ES, FS, or GS
segments; #SS(0) for an illegal address in the SS segment; #PF(fault-code) for a page fault;
#NM if either EM or TS in CR0 is set; #AC for unaligned memory reference if the current
privilege level is 3.

Real Address Mode Exceptions

Interrupt 13 if any part of the operand would lie outside the effective address space from 0 to
0FFFFH; Interrupt 7 if either EM or TS in CR0 is set.

Virtual 8086 Mode Exceptions

Same exceptions as in Real Address Mode; #PF(fault code) for a page fault; #AC for unaligned
memory reference if the current privilege level is 3.

Notes

If the source operand is in memory, it is automatically converted to the extended-real format.

FNOP—No Operation

Opcode	Instruction	Clocks	Description
D9 D0	FNOP	1	No operation is performed.

Description

FNOP performs no operation. It affects nothing except instruction pointers.

FPU Flags Affected

C0, C1, C2, C3 undefined.

Numeric Exceptions

None.

Protected Mode Exceptions

#NM if either EM or TS in CR0 is set.

Real Address Mode Exceptions

Interrupt 7 if either EM or TS in CR0 is set.

Virtual 8086 Mode Exceptions

#NM if either EM or TS in CR0 is set.

intel®

FPATAN—Partial Arctangent

Opcode	Instruction	Clocks	Description
D9 F3	FPATAN	17-173	Replace ST(1) with arctan(ST(1) ÷ ST) and pop ST.

Operation

ST(1) ← arctan(ST(1) ÷ ST);
pop ST;

Description

The partial arctangent instruction computes the arctangent of ST(1) ÷ ST, and returns the computed value, expressed in radians, to ST(1). It then pops ST. The result has the same sign as the operand from ST(1), and a magnitude less than π.

FPU Flags Affected

C1 as described in Chapter 6; C0, C2, C3 undefined.

Numeric Exceptions

P, U, D, I, IS.

Protected Mode Exceptions

#NM if either EM or TS in CR0 is set.

Real Address Mode Exceptions

Interrupt 7 if either EM or TS in CR0 is set.

Virtual 8086 Mode Exceptions

#NM if either EM or TS in CR0 is set.

Notes

There is no restriction on the range of arguments that FPATAN can accept.

The fact that FPATAN takes two arguments and computes the arctangent of their ratio simplifies the calculation of other trigonometric functions. For instance, arcsin(x) (which is the arctangent of $x \div \sqrt{(1-x^2)}$) can be computed using the following sequence of operations: Push x onto the FPU stack; compute $\sqrt{(1-x^2)}$ and push the resulting value onto the stack; execute FPATAN.

FPREM—Partial Remainder

Opcode	Instruction	Clocks	Description
D9 F8	FPREM	16-64	Replace ST with the remainder obtained on dividing ST by ST(1).

Operation

EXPDIF ← exponent(ST) − exponent(ST(1));
IF EXPDIF < 64
THEN
    Q ← integer obtained by chopping ST ÷ ST(1) toward zero;
    ST ← ST − (ST(1) x Q);
    C2 ← 0;
    C0, C1, C3 ← three least-significant bits of Q; (* Q2, Q1, Q0 *)
ELSE
    C2 ← 1;
    N ← a number between 32 and 63;
    QQ ← integer obtained by chopping $(ST ÷ ST(1)) ÷ 2^{EXPDIF-N}$
        toward zero;
    $ST ← ST − (ST(1) \times QQ \times 2^{EXPDIF-N})$;
FI;

Description

The partial remainder instruction computes the remainder obtained on dividing ST by ST(1), and leaves the result in ST. The sign of the remainder is the same as the sign of the original dividend in ST. The magnitude of the remainder is less than that of the modulus.

FPU Flags Affected

C0, C1, C2, C3 as described in Chapter 6.

Numeric Exceptions

U, D, I, IS.

Protected Mode Exceptions

#NM if either EM or TS in CR0 is set.

Real Address Mode Exceptions

Interrupt 7 if either EM or TS in CR0 is set.

Virtual 8086 Mode Exceptions

#NM if either EM or TS in CR0 is set.

Notes

FPREM produces an exact result; the precision (inexact) exception does not occur and the rounding control has no effect.

The FPREM instruction is not the remainder operation specified in IEEE Std 754. To get that remainder, the FPREM1 instruction should be used. FPREM is supported for compatibility with the 8087 and Intel287 math coprocessors.

FPREM works by iterative subtraction, and can reduce the exponent of ST by no more than 63 in one execution. If FPREM succeeds in producing a remainder that is less than the modulus, the function is complete and the C2 flag is cleared. Otherwise, C2 is set, and the result in ST is called the *partial* remainder. The exponent of the partial remainder is less than the exponent of the original dividend by at least 32. Software can re-execute the instruction (using the partial remainder in ST as the dividend) until C2 is cleared. A higher-priority interrupting routine that needs the FPU can force a context switch between the instructions in the remainder loop.

An important use of FPREM is to reduce the arguments of periodic functions. When reduction is complete, FPREM provides the three least-significant bits of the quotient in flags C3, C1, and C0. This is important in argument reduction for the tangent function (using a modulus of π /4), because it locates the original angle in the correct one of eight sectors of the unit circle.

FPREM1—Partial Remainder

Opcode	Instruction	Clocks	Description
D9 F5	FPREM1	20-70	Replace ST with the remainder obtained on dividing ST by ST(1).

Operation

EXPDIF ← exponent(ST) − exponent(ST(1));
IF EXPDIF < 64
THEN
    Q ← integer obtained by rounding ST ÷ ST(1) to to the nearest integer;
        (*or the nearest even integer if the result is exactly halfway between 2 integers *)
    ST ← ST − (ST(1) x Q);
    C2 ← 0;
    C0, C1, C3 ← three least-significant bits of Q; (* Q2, Q1, Q0 *)
ELSE
    C2 ← 1;
    N ← a number between 32 and 63;
    QQ ← integer obtained by chopping (ST ÷ ST(1)) ÷ $2^{EXPDIF-N}$ toward zero;
    ST ← ST − (ST(1) x QQ x $2^{EXPDIF-N}$;
FI;

Description

The partial remainder instruction computes the remainder obtained on dividing ST by ST(1), and leaves the result in ST. The magnitude of the remainder is less than half the magnitude of the modulus.

FPU Flags Affected

C0, C1, C2, C3 as described in Chapter 6.

Numeric Exceptions

U, D, I, IS.

Protected Mode Exceptions

#NM if either EM or TS in CR0 is set.

Real Address Mode Exceptions

Interrupt 7 if either EM or TS in CR0 is set.

Virtual 8086 Mode Exceptions

#NM if either EM or TS in CR0 is set.

Notes

FPREM1 produces an exact result; the precision (inexact) exception does not occur and the rounding control has no effect.

The FPREM1 instruction is the remainder operation specified in IEEE Std 754. It differs from FPREM in the way it rounds the quotient of ST and ST(1), when the exponent difference of $^{exp}(ST) - {^{exp}}ST(1)$ is less than 64.

FPREM1 works by iterative subtraction, and can reduce the exponent of ST by no more than 63 in one execution. If FPREM1 succeeds in producing a remainder that is less than one half the modulus, the function is complete and the C2 flag is cleared. Otherwise, C2 is set, and the result in ST is called the *partial* remainder. The exponent of the partial remainder is less than the exponent of the original dividend by at least 32. Software can re-execute the instruction (using the partial remainder in ST as the dividend) until C2 is cleared. A higher-priority interrupting routine that needs the FPU can force a context switch between the instructions in the remainder loop.

An important use of FPREM1 is to reduce the arguments of periodic functions. When reduction is complete, FPREM1 provides the three least-significant bits of the quotient in flags C3, C1, and C0. This is important in argument reduction for the tangent function (using a modulus of $\pi/4$), because it locates the original angle in the correct one of eight sectors of the unit circle.

FPTAN—Partial Tangent

Opcode	Instruction	Clocks	Description
D9 F2	FPTAN	17-173	Replace ST with its tangent and push 1 onto the FPU stack.

Operation

```
IF operand is in range
THEN
    C2 ← 0;
    ST ← tan(ST);
    Decrement stack-top pointer;
    ST ← 1.0;
ELSE
    C2 ← 1;
FI;
```

Description

The partial tangent instruction replaces the contents of ST with tan(ST), and then pushes 1.0 onto the FPU stack. ST, expressed in radians, must lie in the range $| \theta | < 2^{63}$.

FPU Flags Affected

C1, C2 as described in Chapter 6; C0, C3 undefined.

Numeric Exceptions

P, U, D, I, IS.

Protected Mode Exceptions

#NM if either EM or TS in CR0 is set.

Real Address Mode Exceptions

Interrupt 7 if either EM or TS in CR0 is set.

Virtual 8086 Mode Exceptions

#NM if either EM or TS in CR0 is set.

Notes

If the operand is outside the acceptable range, the C2 flag is set, and ST remains unchanged. It is the programmer's responsibility to reduce the operand to an absolute value smaller than 2^{63} by subtracting an appropriate integer multiple of 2π. See Chapter 6 for a discussion of the proper value to use for π in performing such reductions.

The fact that FPTAN pushes 1.0 onto the FPU stack after computing tan(ST) maintains compatibility with the 8087 and Intel287 math coprocessors, and simplifies the calculation of other trigonometric functions. For instance, the cotangent (which is the reciprocal of the tangent) can be computed by executing FDIVR after FPTAN.

ST(7) must be empty to avoid an invalid-operation exception.

FRNDINT—Round to Integer

Opcode	Instruction	Clocks	Description
D9 FC	FRNDINT	9-20	Round ST to an integer.

Operation

ST ← rounded ST;

Description

The round to integer instruction rounds the value in ST to an integer according to the RC field of the FPU control word.

FPU Flags Affected

C1 as described in Chapter 6; C0, C2, C3 undefined.

Numeric Exceptions

P, D, I, IS.

Protected Mode Exceptions

#NM if either EM or TS in CR0 is set.

Real Address Mode Exceptions

Interrupt 7 if either EM or TS in CR0 is set.

Virtual 8086 Mode Exceptions

#NM if either EM or TS in CR0 is set.

FRSTOR—Restore FPU State

Opcode	Instruction	Clocks	Description
DD /4	FRSTOR m94/ 108byte	16 bit rm or vm= 75 32 bit rm or vm= 95 pm = 70	Load FPU state from m94byte or m108byte.

Operation

FPU state ← SRC;

Description

FRSTOR reloads the FPU state (environment and register stack) from the memory area defined by the source operand. This data should have been written by a previous FSAVE or FNSAVE instruction.

The FPU environment consists of the FPU control word, status word, tag word, and error pointers (both data and instruction). The environment layout in memory depends on both the operand size and the current operating mode of the processor. The USE attribute of the current code segment determines the operand size: the 14-byte operand applies to a USE16 segment, and the 28-byte operand applies to a USE32 segment. See Chapter 6 for the environment layouts for both operand sizes in both real mode and protected mode. (In virtual-8086 mode, the real mode layout is used.) The stack registers, beginning with ST and ending with ST(7), are in the 80 bytes that immediately follow the environment image. FRSTOR should be executed in the same operating mode as the corresponding FSAVE or FNSAVE.

FPU Flags Affected

C0, C1, C2, C3 as loaded.

Numeric Exceptions

None, except for loading an unmasked exception.

Protected Mode Exceptions

#GP(0) for an illegal memory operand effective address in the CS, DS, ES, FS, or GS segments; #SS(0) for an illegal address in the SS segment; #PF(fault-code) for a page fault; #NM if either EM or TS in CR0 is set; #AC for unaligned memory reference if the current privilege level is 3.

Real Address Mode Exceptions

Interrupt 13 if any part of the operand would lie outside the effective address space from 0 to 0FFFFH; Interrupt 7 if either EM or TS in CR0 is set.

Virtual 8086 Mode Exceptions

Same exceptions as in Real Address Mode; #PF(fault code) for a page fault; #AC for unaligned memory reference if the current privilege level is 3.

Notes

If the state image contains an unmasked exception, loading it will result in a floating-point error condition.

FSAVE/FNSAVE—Store FPU State

Opcode	Instruction	Clocks	Description
9B DD /6	FSAVE m94/108byte	6 bit rm or vm=127 32 bit rm or vm=151 pm=124; + at least 3 for FWAIT	Store FPU state to m94byte or m108byte after checking for unmasked floating-point error condition. Then re-initialize the FPU.
DD /6	FNSAVE m94/108byte	16 bit rm or vm=127 32 bit rm or vm=151 pm=124	Store FPU environment to m94byte or m108byte without checking for unmasked floating-point error condition. Then re-initialize the FPU.

Operation

DEST ← FPU state;
initialize FPU; (* Equivalent to FNINIT *)

Description

The save instructions write the current FPU state (environment and register stack) to the specified destination, and then re-initialize the FPU. The environment consists of the FPU control word, status word, tag word, and error pointers (both data and instruction).

The state layout in memory depends on both the operand size and the current operating mode of the processor. The USE attribute of the current code segment determines the operand size: the 94-byte operand applies to USE16 segment, and the 108-byte operand applies to a USE32 segment. Chapter 6 for the environment layouts for both operand sizes in both real mode and protected mode. (In virtual-8086 mode, the real mode layout is used.) The stack registers, beginning with ST and ending with ST(7), are stored in the 80 bytes that immediately follow the environment image.

FPU Flags Affected

C0, C1, C2, C3 cleared.

Numeric Exceptions

None.

Protected Mode Exceptions

#GP(0) if the destination is in a nonwritable segment; #GP(0) for an illegal memory operand effective address in the CS, DS, ES, FS, or GS segments; #SS(0) for an illegal address in the SS segment; #PF(fault-code) for a page fault; #NM if either EM or TS in CR0 is set; #AC for unaligned memory reference if the current privilege level is 3.

Real Address Mode Exceptions

Interrupt 13 if any part of the operand would lie outside the effective address space from 0 to 0FFFFH; Interrupt 7 if either EM or TS in CR0 is set.

Virtual 8086 Mode Exceptions

Same exceptions as in Real Address Mode; #PF(fault code) for a page fault; #AC for unaligned memory reference if the current privilege level is 3.

Notes

FSAVE and FNSAVE do not store the FPU state until all FPU activity is complete. Thus, the saved image reflects the state of the FPU after any previously decoded instruction has been executed.

If a program is to read from the memory image of the state following a save instruction, it must issue an FWAIT instruction to ensure that the storage is complete.

The save instructions are typically used when an operating system needs to perform a context switch, or an exception handler needs to use the FPU, or an application program wants to pass a "clean" FPU to a subroutine.

FSCALE—Scale

Opcode	Instruction	Clocks	Description
D9 FD	FSCALE	20-31	Scale ST by ST(1).

Operation

$$ST \leftarrow ST \times 2^{ST(1)};$$

Description

The scale instruction interprets the value in ST(1) as an integer, and adds this integer to the exponent of ST. Thus, FSCALE provides rapid multiplication or division by integral powers of 2.

FPU Flags Affected

C1 as described in Chapter 6; C0, C2, C3 undefined.

Numeric Exceptions

P, U, O, D, I, IS.

Protected Mode Exceptions

#NM if either EM or TS in CR0 is set.

Real Address Mode Exceptions

Interrupt 7 if either EM or TS in CR0 is set.

Virtual 8086 Mode Exceptions

#NM if either EM or TS in CR0 is set.

Notes

FSCALE can be used as an inverse to FXTRACT. Since FSCALE does not pop the exponent part, however, FSCALE must be followed by FSTP ST(1) in order to completely undo the effect of a preceding FXTRACT.

There is no limit on the range of the scale factor in ST(1). If the value is not integral, FSCALE uses the nearest integer smaller in magnitude; i.e., it chops the value toward 0. If the resulting integer is zero, the value in ST is not changed.

FSIN—Sine

Opcode	Instruction	Clocks	Description
D9 FE	FSIN	16-126	Replace ST with its sine.

Operation

IF operand is in range
THEN
    C2 ← 0;
    ST ← sin(ST);
ELSE
    C2 ← 1;
FI:

Description

The sine instruction replaces the contents of ST with sin(ST). ST, expressed in radians, must lie in the range $| \theta | < 2^{63}$.

FPU Flags Affected

C1, C2 as described in Chapter 6; C0, C3 undefined.

Numeric Exceptions

P, U, D, I, IS.

Protected Mode Exceptions

#NM if either EM or TS in CR0 is set.

Real Address Mode Exceptions

Interrupt 7 if either EM or TS in CR0 is set.

Virtual 8086 Mode Exceptions

#NM if either EM or TS in CR0 is set.

Notes

If the operand is outside the acceptable range, the C2 flag is set, and ST remains unchanged. It is the programmer's responsibility to reduce the operand to an absolute value smaller than 2^{63} by subtracting an appropriate integer multiple of 2π. See Chapter 6 for a discussion of the proper value to use for π in performing such reductions.

FSINCOS—Sine and Cosine

Opcode	Instruction	Clocks	Description
D9 FB	FSINCOS	17-137	Compute the sine and cosine of ST; replace ST with the sine, and then push the cosine onto the FPU stack.

Operation

```
IF operand is in range
THEN
      C2 ← 0;
      TEMP ← cos(ST);
      ST ← sin(ST);
      Decrement FPU stack-top pointer;
      ST ← TEMP;
ELSE
      C2 ← 1;
FI:
```

Description

FSINCOS computes both sin(ST) and cos(ST), replaces ST with the sine and then pushes the cosine onto the FPU stack. ST, expressed in radians, must lie in the range $| \theta | < 2^{63}$.

FPU Flags Affected

C1, C2 as described in Chapter 6; C0, C3 undefined.

Numeric Exceptions

P, U, D, I, IS.

Protected Mode Exceptions

#NM if either EM or TS in CR0 is set.

Real Address Mode Exceptions

Interrupt 7 if either EM or TS in CR0 is set.

Virtual 8086 Mode Exceptions

#NM if either EM or TS in CR0 is set.

Notes

If the operand is outside the acceptable range, the C2 flag is set, and ST remains unchanged. It is the programmer's responsibility to reduce the operand to an absolute value smaller than 2^{63}

by subtracting an appropriate integer multiple of 2π. See Chapter 6 for a discussion of the proper value to use for π in performing such reductions.

It is faster to execute FSINCOS than to execute both FSIN and FCOS.

FSQRT—Square Root

Opcode	Instruction	Clocks	Description
D9 FA	FSQRT	70	Replace ST with its square root.

Operation

ST ← square root of ST;

Description

The square root instruction replaces the value in ST with its square root.

FPU Flags Affected

C1 as described in Chapter 6; C0, C2, C3 undefined.

Numeric Exceptions

P, D, I, IS.

Protected Mode Exceptions

#NM if either EM or TS in CR0 is set.

Real Address Mode Exceptions

Interrupt 7 if either EM or TS in CR0 is set.

Virtual 8086 Mode Exceptions

#NM if either EM or TS in CR0 is set.

Notes

The square root of –0 is –0.

FST/FSTP—Store Real

Opcode	Instruction	Clocks	Description
D9 /2	FST m32real	2	Copy ST to m32real.
DD /2	FST m64real	2	Copy ST to m64real.
DD D0+i	FST ST(i)	1	Copy ST to ST(i).
D9 /3	FSTP m32real	2	Copy ST to m32real and pop ST.
DD /3	FSTP m64real	2	Copy ST to m64real and pop ST.
DB /7	FSTP m80real	3	Copy ST to m80real and pop ST.
DD D8+i	FSTP ST(i)	1	Copy ST to ST(i) and pop ST.

Operation

DEST ← ST(0);
IF instruction = FSTP THEN pop ST FI;

Description

FST copies the current value in the ST register to the destination, which can be another register or a single- or double-real memory operand. FSTP copies and then pops ST; it accepts extended-real memory operands as well as the types accepted by FST.

If the source is a register, the register number used is that before the stack is popped.

FPU Flags Affected

C1 as described in Chapter 6; C0, C2, C3 undefined.

Numeric Exceptions

Register or extended-real destinations: IS
Single- or double-real destinations: P, U, O, I, IS

Protected Mode Exceptions

#GP(0) if the destination is in a nonwritable segment; #GP(0) for an illegal memory operand effective address in the CS, DS, ES, FS, or GS segments; #SS(0) for an illegal address in the SS segment; #PF(fault-code) for a page fault; #NM if either EM or TS in CR0 is set; #AC for unaligned memory reference if the current privilege level is 3.

Real Address Mode Exceptions

Interrupt 13 if any part of the operand would lie outside the effective address space from 0 to 0FFFFH; Interrupt 7 if either EM or TS in CR0 is set.

Virtual 8086 Mode Exceptions

Same exceptions as in Real Address Mode; #PF(fault code) for a page fault; #AC for unaligned memory reference if the current privilege level is 3.

Notes

If the destination is single- or double-real, the significand is rounded to the width of the destination according to the RC field of the control word, and the exponent is converted to the width and bias of the destination format. The over/underflow condition is checked for as well.

If ST contains zero, $\pm\infty$, or a NaN, then the significand is not rounded, but chopped (on the right) to fit the destination. Nor is the exponent converted; it too is chopped on the right. These operations preserve the value's identity as ∞ or NaN (exponent all ones).

The invalid-operation exception is not raised when the destination is a nonempty stack element.

A denormal operand in ST(0) causes an underflow. No denormal operand exception is raised.

FSTCW/FNSTCW—Store Control Word

Opcode	Instruction	Clocks	Description
9B D9 /7	FSTCW m2byte	2 + at least 1 for FWAIT	Store FPU control word to m2byte after checking for unmasked floating-point error condition.
D9 /7	FNSTCW m2byte	2	Store FPU control word to m2byte without checking for unmasked floating-point error condition.

Operation

DEST ← CW;

Description

FSTCW and FNSTCW write the current value of the FPU control word to the specified destination.

FPU Flags Affected

C0, C1, C2, C3 undefined.

Numeric Exceptions

None.

Protected Mode Exceptions

#GP(0) if the destination is in a nonwritable segment; #GP(0) for an illegal memory operand effective address in the CS, DS, ES, FS, or GS segments; #SS(0) for an illegal address in the SS segment; #PF(fault-code) for a page fault; #NM if either EM or TS in CR0 is set; #AC for unaligned memory reference if the current privilege level is 3.

Real Address Mode Exceptions

Interrupt 13 if any part of the operand would lie outside the effective address space from 0 to 0FFFFH; Interrupt 7 if either EM or TS in CR0 is set.

Virtual 8086 Mode Exceptions

Same exceptions as in Real Address Mode; #PF(fault code) for a page fault; #AC for unaligned memory reference if the current privilege level is 3.

Notes

FSTCW checks for unmasked floating-point error conditions before storing the control word; FNSTCW does not.

FSTENV/FNSTENV—Store FPU Environment

Opcode	Instruction	Clocks	Description
9B D9 /6	FSTENV m14/28byte	16 bit rm or vm=50 32 bit rm or vm=48 16 bit pm=49 32 bit pm =50; + at least 3 for FWAIT	Store FPU environment to m14byte or m28byte after checking for unmasked floating-point error condition. Then mask all floating-point exceptions.
D9 /6	FNSTENV m14/28byte	16 bit rm or vm=50 32 bit rm or vm=48 16 bit pm=49 32 bit pm=50	Store FPU environment to m14byte or m28byte without checking for unmasked floating-point error condition. Then mask all floating-point exceptions.

Operation

DEST ← FPU environment;
CW[0..5] ← 111111B;

Description

The store environment instructions write the current FPU environment to the specified destination, and then mask all floating-point exceptions. The FPU environment consists of the FPU control word, status word, tag word, and error pointer (both data and instruction).

The environment layout in memory depends on both the operand size and the current operating mode of the processor. The USE attribute of the current code segment determines the operand size: the 14-byte operand applies to a USE16 segment, and the 28-byte operand applies to a USE32 segment. Figures 6-6 through 6-8 show the environment layouts for both operand sizes in both real mode and protected mode. (In virtual-8086 mode, the real mode layout is used.)

FPU Flags Affected

C0, C1, C2, C3 undefined.

Numeric Exceptions

None.

Protected Mode Exceptions

#GP(0) if the destination is in a nonwritable segment; #GP(0) for an illegal memory operand effective address in the CS, DS, ES, FS, or GS segments; #SS(0) for an illegal address in the SS segment; #PF(fault-code) for a page fault; #NM if either EM or TS in CR0 is set; #AC for unaligned memory reference if the current privilege level is 3.

Real Address Mode Exceptions

Interrupt 13 if any part of the operand would lie outside the effective address space from 0 to 0FFFFH; Interrupt 7 if either EM or TS in CR0 is set.

Virtual 8086 Mode Exceptions

Same exceptions as in Real Address Mode; #PF(fault code) for a page fault; #AC for unaligned memory reference if the current privilege level is 3.

Notes

FSTENV and FNSTENV do not store the environment until all FPU activity is complete. Thus, the saved environment reflects the state of the FPU after any previously decoded instruction has been executed.

The store environment instructions are often used by exception handlers because they provide access to the FPU error pointers. The environment is typically saved onto the memory stack. After saving the environment, FSTENV and FNSTENV sets all the exception masks in the FPU control word. This prevents floating-point errors from interrupting the exception handler.

FSTENV checks for unmasked floating-point error conditions before storing the FPU environment; FNSTENV does not.

FSTSW/FNSTSW—Store Status Word

Opcode	Instruction	Clocks	Description
9B DD /7	FSTSW m2byte	2 + at least 3 for FWAIT	Store FPU status word to *mbyte* after checking for unmasked floating-point error condition.
9B DF E0	FSTSW AX	2 + at least 3 for FWAIT	Store FPU status word to AX register after checking for unmasked floating-point error condition.
DD /7	FNSTSW m2byte	2	Store FPU status word to *m2byte* without checking for unmasked floating-point error condition.
DF E0	FNSTSW AX	2	Store FPU status word to AX register without checking for unmasked floating-point error condition.

Operation

DEST ← SW;

Description

FSTSW and FNSTSW write the current value of the FPU status word to the specified destination, which can be either a two-byte location in memory or the AX register.

FPU Flags Affected

C0, C1, C2, C3 undefined.

Numeric Exceptions

None.

Protected Mode Exceptions

#GP(0) if the destination is in a nonwritable segment; #GP(0) for an illegal memory operand effective address in the CS, DS, ES, FS, or GS segments; #SS(0) for an illegal address in the SS segment; #PF(fault-code) for a page fault; #NM if either EM or TS in CR0 is set; #AC for unaligned memory reference if the current privilege level is 3.

Real Address Mode Exceptions

Interrupt 13 if any part of the operand would lie outside the effective address space from 0 to 0FFFFH; Interrupt 7 if either EM or TS in CR0 is set.

Virtual 8086 Mode Exceptions

Same exceptions as in Real Address Mode; #PF(fault code) for a page fault; #AC for unaligned memory reference if the current privilege level is 3.

Notes

FSTSW checks for unmasked floating-point error conditions before storing the status word; FNSTSW does not.

FSTSW and FNSTSW are used primarily in conditional branching (after a comparison, FPREM, FPREM1, or FXAM instruction). They can also be used to invoke exception handlers (by polling the exception bits) in environments that do not use interrupts.

When FNSTSW AX is executed, the AX register is updated before the Pentium processor executes any further instructions. The status stored is that from the completion of the prior ESC instruction.

FSUB/FSUBP/FISUB—Subtract

Opcode	Instruction	Clocks	Description
D8 /4	FSUB m32real	3/1	Subtract m32real from ST.
DC /4	FSUB m64real	3/1	Subtract m64real from ST.
D8 E0+i	FSUB ST, ST(i)	3/1	Subtract ST(i) from ST→ST0.
DC E8+i	FSUB ST(i), ST	3/1	Replace ST(i) with ST –ST(i).
DE E8+i	FSUBP ST(i), ST	3/1	Replace ST(i) with ST –ST(i); pop ST.
DE E9	FSUBP	3/1	Replace ST(1) with ST –ST(1); pop ST.
DA /4	FISUB m32int	7/4	Subtract m32int from ST.
DE /4	FISUB m16int	7/4	Subtract m16int from ST.

Operation

DEST ← ST – Other Operand;
IF instruction = FSUBP THEN pop ST FI;

Description

The subtraction instructions subtract the other operand from the stack top and return the difference to the destination.

FPU Flags Affected

C1 as described in Chapter 6; C0, C2, C3 undefined.

Numeric Exceptions

P, U, O, D, I, IS.

Protected Mode Exceptions

#GP(0) for an illegal memory operand effective address in the CS, DS, ES, FS, or GS segments; #SS(0) for an illegal address in the SS segment; #PF(fault-code) for a page fault; #NM if either EM or TS in CR0 is set; #AC for unaligned memory reference if the current privilege level is 3.

Real Address Mode Exceptions

Interrupt 13 if any part of the operand would lie outside the effective address space from 0 to 0FFFFH; Interrupt 7 if either EM or TS in CR0 is set.

Virtual 8086 Mode Exceptions

Same exceptions as in Real Address Mode; #PF(fault code) for a page fault; #AC for unaligned memory reference if the current privilege level is 3.

Notes

If the source operand is in memory, it is automatically converted to the extended-real format.

FSUBR/FSUBRP/FISUBR—Reverse Subtract

Opcode	Instruction	Clocks	Description
D8 /5	FSUBR m32real	3/1	Replace ST with m32real – ST.
DC /5	FSUBR m64real	3/1	Replace ST with m64real – ST.
D8 E8+i	FSUBR ST, ST(i)	3/1	Replace ST with ST(i) – ST.
DC E0+i	FSUBR ST(i), ST	3/1	Subtract ST from ST(i)→ST(i).
DE E0+i	FSUBRP ST(i), ST	3/1	Subtract ST from ST(i) and pop ST.
DE E1	FSUBR	3/1	Subtract ST from ST(1) and pop ST.
DA /5	FISUBR m32int	7/4	Replace ST with m32int – ST.
DE /5	FISUBR m16int	7/4	Replace ST with m16int – ST.

Operation

DEST ← Other Operand – ST;
IF instruction = FSUBRP THEN pop ST FI;

Description

The reverse subtraction instructions subtract the stack top from the other operand and return the difference to the destination.

FPU Flags Affected

C1 as described in Chapter 6; C0, C2, C3 undefined.

Numeric Exceptions

P, U, O, D, I, IS.

Protected Mode Exceptions

#GP(0) for an illegal memory operand effective address in the CS, DS, ES, FS, or GS segments; #SS(0) for an illegal address in the SS segment; #PF(fault-code) for a page fault; #NM if either EM or TS in CR0 is set; #AC for unaligned memory reference if the current privilege level is 3.

Real Address Mode Exceptions

Interrupt 13 if any part of the operand would lie outside the effective address space from 0 to 0FFFFH; Interrupt 7 if either EM or TS in CR0 is set.

Virtual 8086 Mode Exceptions

Same exceptions as in Real Address Mode; #PF(fault code) for a page fault; #AC for unaligned memory reference if the current privilege level is 3.

Notes

If the source operand is in memory, it is automatically converted to the extended-real format.

FTST—TEST

Opcode	Instruction	Clocks	Description
D9 E4	FTST	4/1	Compare ST with 0.0.

Operation

CASE (relation of operands) OF
  Not comparable: C3, C2, C0 ← 111;
  ST > SRC: C3, C2, C0 ← 000;
  ST < SRC: C3, C2, C0 ← 001;
  ST = SRC: C3, C2, C0 ← 100;

FPU Flags	EFlags
C0	CF
C1	(none)
C2	PF
C3	ZF

Description

The test instruction compares the stack top to 0.0. Following the instruction, the condition codes reflect the result of the comparison.

FPU Flags Affected

C1 as described in Chapter 6; C0, C2, C3 as specified above.

Numeric Exceptions

D, I, IS.

Protected Mode Exceptions

#NM if either EM or TS in CR0 is set.

Real Address Mode Exceptions

Interrupt 7 if either EM or TS in CR0 is set.

Virtual 8086 Mode Exceptions

#NM if either EM or TS in CR0 is set.

Notes

If ST contains a NaN or an object of undefined format, or if a stack fault occurs, the invalid-operation exception is raised, and the condition bits are set to "unordered."

The sign of zero is ignored, so that –0.0=–+0.0.

FUCOM/FUCOMP/FUCOMPP—Unordered Compare Real

Opcode	Instruction	Clocks	Description
DD E0+i	FUCOM ST(i)	4/1	Compare ST with ST(i).
DD E1	FUCOM	4/1	Compare ST with ST(1).
DD E8+i	FUCOMP ST(i)	4/1	Compare ST with ST(i) and pop ST.
DD E9	FUCOMP	4/1	Compare ST with ST(1) and pop ST.
DA E9	FUCOMPP	4/1	Compare ST with ST(1) and pop ST twice.

Operation

CASE (relation of operands) OF
    Not comparable: C3, C2, C0 ← 111;
    ST > SRC: C3, C2, C0 ← 000;
    ST < SRC: C3, C2, C0 ← 001;
    ST = SRC: C3, C2, C0 ← 100;
IF instruction = FUCOMP THEN pop ST; FI;
IF instruction = FUCOMPP THEN pop ST; pop ST; FI;

FPU Flags	EFlags
C0	CF
C1	(none)
C2	PF
C3	ZF

Description

The unordered compare real instructions compare the stack top to the source, which must be a register. If no operand is encoded, ST is compared to ST(1). Following the instruction, the condition codes reflect the relation between ST and the source operand.

FPU Flags Affected

C1 as described in Chapter 6; C0, C2, C3 as specified above.

Numeric Exceptions

D, I, IS.

Protected Mode Exceptions

#NM if either EM or TS in CR0 is set.

Real Address Mode Exceptions

Interrupt 7 if either EM or TS in CR0 is set.

Virtual 8086 Mode Exceptions

#NM if either EM or TS in CR0 is set.

Notes

If either operand is an SNaN or is in an undefined format, or if a stack fault occurs, the invalid-operation exception is raised, and the condition bits are set to "unordered."

If either operand is a QNaN, the condition bits are set to "unordered." Unlike the ordinary compare instructions (FCOM, etc.), the unordered compare instructions do not raise the invalid-operation exception on account of a QNaN operand.

The sign of zero is ignored, so that −0.0=−+0.0.

FWAIT—Wait

Opcode	Instruction	Clocks	Description
9B	FWAIT	(1-3)	Alias for WAIT.

Description

FWAIT causes the processor to check for pending unmasked numeric exceptions before proceding.

FPU Flags Affected

C0, C1, C2, C3 undefined.

Numeric Exceptions

None.

Protected Mode Exceptions

#NM if both MP and TS in CR0 are set.

Real Address Mode Exceptions

Interrupt 7 if both MP and TS in CR0 are set.

Virtual 8086 Mode Exceptions

#NM if both MP and TS in CR0 are set.

Notes

As its opcode shows, FWAIT is not actually an ESC instruction, but an alternate mnemonic for WAIT.

Coding FWAIT after an ESC instruction ensures that any unmasked floating-point exceptions the instruction may cause are handled before the processor has a chance to modify the instruction's results.

Information about when to use FWAIT is given in Chapter 6, in the section on "Concurrent Processing."

FXAM—Examine

Opcode	Instruction	Clocks	Description
D9 E5	FXAM	21	Report the type of object in the ST register.

Operation

C1 ← sign bit of ST; (* 0 for positive, 1 for negative *)

CASE (type of object in ST) OF
    Unsupported: C3, C2, C0 ← 000;
    NaN: C3, C2, C0 ← 001;
    Normal: C3, C2, C0 ← 010;
    Infinity: C3, C2, C0 ← 011;
    Zero: C3, C2, C0 ← 100;
    Empty: C3, C2, C0 ← 101;
    Denormal: C3, C2, C0 ← 110;

FPU Flags	EFlags
C0	CF
C1	(none)
C2	PF
C3	ZF

Description

The examine instruction reports the type of object contained in the ST register by setting the FPU Flags.

FPU Flags Affected

C0, C1, C2, C3 as shown above.

Numeric Exceptions

None.

Protected Mode Exceptions

#NM if either EM or TS in CR0 is set.

Real Address Mode Exceptions

Interrupt 7 if either EM or TS in CR0 is set.

Virtual 8086 Mode Exceptions

#NM if either EM or TS in CR0 is set.

Notes

C1 bit represents the sign of ST(0) regardless of whether ST(0) is empty or full.

FXCH—Exchange Register Contents

Opcode	Instruction	Clocks	Description
D9 C8+i	FXCH ST(i)	1	Exchange the contents of ST and ST(i).
D9 C9	FXCH	1	Exchange the contents of ST and ST(1).

Operation

TEMP ← ST;
ST ← DEST;
DEST ← TEMP;

Description

FXCH swaps the contents of the destination and stack-top registers. If the destination is not coded explicitly, ST(1) is used.

FPU Flags Affected

C1 as described in Chapter 6; C0, C2, C3 undefined.

Numeric Exceptions

IS.

Protected Mode Exceptions

#NM if either EM or TS in CR0 is set.

Real Address Mode Exceptions

Interrupt 7 if either EM or TS in CR0 is set.

Virtual 8086 Mode Exceptions

#NM if either EM or TS in CR0 is set.

Notes

Many numeric instructions operate only on the stack top; FXCH provides a simple means for using these instructions on lower stack elements. For example, the following sequence takes the square root of the third register form the top (assuming that ST is nonempty):

```
FXCH ST(3)
FSQRT
FXCH ST(3)
```

FXCH can be paired with some floating point instructions (i.e., FADD, FSUB, FMUL, FLD, FCOM, FUCOM, FCHS, FTST, FABS, FDIV. This set also includes the FADDP, FSUBRP, etc. instructions). When paired, the FXCH gets executed in parallel, and does not take any additional clocks.

FXTRACT—Extract Exponent and Significand

Opcode	Instruction	Clocks	Description
D9 F4	FXTRACT	13	Separate ST into its exponent and significand; replace ST with the exponent and then push the significand onto the FPU stack.

Operation

TEMP ← significand of ST;
ST ← exponent of ST;
Decrement FPU stack-top pointer;
ST ← TEMP;

Description

FXTRACT splits the value in ST into its exponent and significand. The exponent replaces the original operand on the stack and the significand is pushed onto the stack. Following execution of FXTRACT, ST (the new stack top) contains the value of the original significand expressed as a real number: its sign is the same as the operand's, its exponent is 0 true (16,383 or 3FFFH biased), and its significand is identical to the original operand's. ST(1) contains the value of the original operand's true (unbiased) exponent expressed as a real number.

To illustrate the operation of FXTRACT, assume that ST contains a number whose true exponent is +4 (i.e., its exponent field contains 4003H). After executing FXTRACT, ST(1) will contain the real number +4.0; its sign will be positive, its exponent field will contain 4001H (+2 true) and its significand field will contain $1_\Delta 00...00B$. In other words, the value in ST(1) will be $1.0 \times 2^2 = 4$. If ST contains an operand whose true exponent is −7 (i.e., its exponent field contains 3FF8H), then FXTRACT will return an "exponent" of −7.0; after the instruction executes, ST(1)'s sign and exponent fields will contain C001H (negative sign, true exponent of 2), and its significand will be $1_\Delta 1100...00B$. In other words, the value in ST(1) will be $-1.75 \times 2^2 = -7.0$. In both cases, following FXTRACT, ST's sign and significand fields will be the same as the original operand's, and its exponent field will contain 3FFFH (0 true).

FPU Flags Affected

C1 as described in Chapter 6; C0, C2, C3 undefined.

Numeric Exceptions

Z, D, I, IS.

Protected Mode Exceptions

#NM if either EM or TS in CR0 is set.

Real Address Mode Exceptions

Interrupt 7 if either EM or TS in CR0 is set.

Virtual 8086 Mode Exceptions

#NM if either EM or TS in CR0 is set.

Notes

FXTRACT (extract exponent and significand) performs a superset of the IEEE-recommended **logb**(x) function.

If the original operand is zero, FXTRACT leaves $-\infty$ in ST(1) (the exponent) while ST is assigned the value zero with a sign equal to that of the original operand. The zero-divide exception is raised in this case, as well.

ST(7) must be empty to avoid the invalid-operation exception.

FXTRACT is useful for power and range scaling operations. Both FXTRACT and the base 2 exponential instruction F2XM1 are needed to perform a general power operation. Converting numbers in extended-real format to decimal representations (e.g., for printing or displaying) requires not only FBSTP but also FXTRACT to allow scaling that does not overflow the range of the extended format. FXTRACT can also be useful for debugging, because it allows the exponent and significand parts of a real number to be examined separately.

FYL2X—Compute y × log2x

Opcode	Instruction	Clocks	Description
D9 F1	FYL2X	22-111	Replace ST(1) with ST(1) × log$_2$ST and pop ST.

Operation

ST(1) ← ST(1) × log$_2$ST;
pop ST;

Description

FYL2X computes the base-2 logarithm of ST, multiplies the logarithm by ST(1), and returns the resulting value to ST(1). It then pops ST. The operand in ST must not be negative or zero.

FPU Flags Affected

C1 as described in Chapter 6; C0, C2, C3 undefined.

Numeric Exceptions

P, U, O, Z, D, I, IS.

Protected Mode Exceptions

#NM if either EM or TS in CR0 is set.

Real Address Mode Exceptions

Interrupt 7 if either EM or TS in CR0 is set.

Virtual 8086 Mode Exceptions

#NM if either EM or TS in CR0 is set.

Notes

If the operand in ST is negative, the invalid-operation exception is raised.

The FYL2X instruction is designed with a built-in multiplication to optimize the calculation of logarithms with arbitrary positive base:

log$_b$x = (log$_2$b)$^{-1}$ × log$_2$x

The instructions FLDL2T and FLDL2E load the constants log$_2$10 and log$_2$e, respectively.

FYL2XP1—Compute y × log₂(x +1)

Opcode	Instruction	Clocks	Description
D9 F9	FYL2XP1	22-103	Replace ST(1) with ST(1) × log₂(ST+1.0) and pop ST.

Operation

$ST(1) \leftarrow ST(1) \times \log_2(ST+1.0)$;
pop ST;

Description

FYL2XP1 computes the base-2 logarithm of (ST+1.0), multiplies the logarithm by ST(1), and returns the resulting value to ST(1). It then pops ST. The operand in ST must be in the range

$-(1-(\sqrt{2} / 2)) \leq ST \leq \sqrt{2} -1$

FPU Flags Affected

C1 as described in Chapter 6; C0, C2, C3 undefined.

Numeric Exceptions

P, U, D, I, IS.

Protected Mode Exceptions

#NM if either EM or TS in CR0 is set.

Real Address Mode Exceptions

Interrupt 7 if either EM or TS in CR0 is set.

Virtual 8086 Mode Exceptions

#NM if either EM or TS in CR0 is set.

Notes

If the operand in ST is outside the acceptable range, the result of FYL2XP1 is undefined.

The FYL2XP1 instruction provides improved accuracy over FYL2X when computing the logarithms of numbers very close to 1. When ε is small, more significant digits can be retained by providing ε as an argument to FYL2XP1 than by providing 1+ε as an argument to FYL2X.

HLT—Halt

Opcode	Instruction	Clocks	Description
F4	HLT	∞	Halt

Operation

Enter Halt state;

Description

The HLT instruction stops instruction execution and places the processor in a HALT state. An enabled interrupt, NMI, or a reset will resume execution. If an interrupt (including NMI) is used to resume execution after a HLT instruction, the saved CS:IP (or CS:EIP) value points to the instruction following the HLT instruction.

Flags Affected

None.

Protected Mode Exceptions

The HLT instruction is a privileged instruction; #GP(0) if the current privilege level is not 0.

Real Address Mode Exceptions

None.

Virtual 8086 Mode Exceptions

#GP(0); the HLT instruction is a privileged instruction.

IDIV—Signed Divide

Opcode	Instruction	Clocks	Description
F6 /7	IDIV r/m8	22	Signed divide AX (where AH must contain sign-extension of AL) by r/m byte. (Results: AL=Quo, AH=Rem)
F7 /7	IDIV AX,r/m16	30	Signed divide DX:AX (where DX must contain sign-extension of AX) by r/m word. (Results: AX=Quo, DX=Rem)
F7 /7	IDIV EAX,r/m32	46	Signed divide EDX:EAX (where EDX must contain sign-extension of EAX) by r/m dword. (Results: EAX=Quo, EDX=Rem)

Operation

```
temp ← dividend / divisor;
IF temp does not fit in quotient
THEN Interrupt 0;
ELSE
    quotient ← temp;
    remainder ← dividend MOD (r/m);
FI;
```

Notes: Divisions are signed. The dividend must be sign-extended. The divisor is given by the **r/m** operand. The dividend, quotient, and remainder use implicit registers. Refer to the table under "Description."

Description

The IDIV instruction performs a signed division. The dividend, quotient, and remainder are implicitly allocated to fixed registers. Only the divisor is given as an explicit **r/m** operand. The type of the divisor determines which registers to use as follows:

Size	Divisor	Quotient	Remainder	Dividend
byte	r/m8	AL	AH	AX
word	r/m16	AX	DX	DX:AX
dword	r/m32	EAX	EDX	EDX:EAX

If the resulting quotient is too large to fit in the destination, or if the divisor is 0, an Interrupt 0 is generated. Nonintegral quotients are truncated toward 0. The remainder has the same sign as the dividend and the absolute value of the remainder is always less than the absolute value of the divisor.

Flags Affected

The OF, SF, ZF, AF, PF, CF flags are undefined.

Protected Mode Exceptions

Interrupt 0 if the quotient is too large to fit in the designated register (AL or AX), or if the divisor is 0; #GP (0) for an illegal memory operand effective address in the CS, DS, ES, FS, or GS segments; #SS(0) for an illegal address in the SS segment; #PF(fault-code) for a page fault; #AC for unaligned memory reference if the current privilege level is 3.

Real Address Mode Exceptions

Interrupt 0 if the quotient is too large to fit in the designated register (AL or AX), or if the divisor is 0; Interrupt 13 if any part of the operand would lie outside of the effective address space from 0 to 0FFFFH.

Virtual 8086 Mode Exceptions

Same exceptions as in Real Address Mode; #PF(fault-code) for a page fault; #AC for unaligned memory reference if the current privilege level is 3.

IMUL—Signed Multiply

Opcode	Instruction	Clocks	Description
F6 /5	IMUL r/m8	11	AX← AL * r/m byte
F7 /5	IMUL r/m16	11	DX:AX ← AX * r/m word
F7 /5	IMUL r/m32	10	EDX:EAX ← EAX * r/m dword
0F AF /r	IMUL r8,r8	10	byte register ← byte register * r/m byte
0F AF /r	IMUL r16,r/m16	10	word register ← word register * r/m word
0F AF /r	IMUL r32,r/m32	10	dword register ← dword register * r/m dword
6B /r ib	IMUL r16,r/m16,imm8	10	word register ← r/m16 * sign-extended immediate byte
6B /r ib	IMUL r32,r/m32,imm8	10	dword register ← r/m32 * sign-extended immediate byte
6B /r ib	IMUL r16,imm8	10	word register ← word register * sign-extended immediate byte
6B /r ib	IMUL r32,imm8	10	dword register ← dword register * sign-extended immediate byte
69 /r iw	IMUL r16,r/m16,imm16	10	word register ← r/m16 * immediate word
69 /r id	IMUL r32,r/m32,imm32	10	dword register ← r/m32 * immediate dword
69 /r iw	IMUL r16,imm16	10	word register ← r/m16 * immediate word
69 /r id	IMUL r32,imm32	10	dword register ← r/m32 * immediate dword

Operation

result ← multiplicand * multiplier;

Description

The IMUL instruction performs signed multiplication. Some forms of the instruction use implicit register operands. The operand combinations for all forms of the instruction are shown in the "Description" column above.

The IMUL instruction clears the OF and CF flags under the following conditions (otherwise the CF and OF flags are set):

Instruction Form	Condition for Clearing CF and OF
r/m8	AL = sign-extend of AL to 16 bits
r/m16	AX = sign-extend of AX to 32 bits
r/m32	EDX:EAX = sign-extend of EAX to 32 bits
r16,r/m16	Result exactly fits within r16
r/32,r/m32	Result exactly fits within r32
r16,r/m16,imm16	Result exactly fits within r16
r32,r/m32,imm32	Result exactly fits within r32

Flags Affected

The OF and CF flags as described in the table in the "Description" section above; the SF, ZF, AF, and PF flags are undefined.

Protected Mode Exceptions

#GP(0) for an illegal memory operand effective address in the CS, DS, ES, FS, or GS segments; #SS(0) for an illegal address in the SS segment; #PF(fault-code) for a page fault; #AC for unaligned memory reference if the current privilege level is 3.

Real Address Mode Exceptions

Interrupt 13 if any part of the operand would lie outside of the effective address space from 0 to 0FFFFH.

Virtual 8086 Mode Exceptions

Same exeptions as in Real Address Mode; #PF(fault-code) for a page fault; #AC for unaligned memory reference if the current privilege level is 3.

Notes

When using the accumulator forms (IMUL **r/m8**, IMUL **r/m16**, or IMUL **r/m32**), the result of the multiplication is available even if the overflow flag is set because the result is twice the size of the multiplicand and multiplier. This is large enough to handle any possible result.

IN—Input from Port

Opcode	Instruction	Clocks	Description
E4 ib	IN AL,imm8	7,pm=4*/ 21**,vm=19	Input byte from immediate port into AL
E5 ib	IN AX,imm16	7,pm=4*/ 21**,vm=19	Input word from immediate port into AX
E5 ib	IN EAX,imm32	7,pm=4*/ 21**,vm=19	Input dword from immediate port into EAX
EC	IN AL,DX	7,pm=4*/ 21**,vm=19	Input byte from port DX into AL
ED	IN AX,DX	7,pm=4*/ 21**,vm=19	Input word from port DX into AX
ED	IN EAX,DX	7,pm=4*/ 21**,vm=19	Input dword from port DX into EAX

NOTES:
*If CPL ≤ IOPL
**If CPL ≥ IOPL

Operation

```
IF (PE = 1) AND ((VM = 1) OR (CPL > IOPL))
THEN (* Virtual 8086 mode, or protected mode with CPL > IOPL *)
   IF NOT I-O-Permission (SRC, width(SRC))
   THEN #GP(0);
   FI;
FI;
DEST ← [SRC]; (* Reads from I/O address space *)
```

Description

The IN instruction transfers a data byte or data word from the port numbered by the second operand into the register (AL, AX, or EAX) specified by the first operand. Access any port from 0 to 65535 by placing the port number in the DX register and using an IN instruction with the DX register as the second parameter. These I/O instructions can be shortened by using an 8-bit port I/O in the instruction. The upper eight bits of the port address will be 0 when 8-bit port I/O is used.

Flags Affected

None.

Protected Mode Exceptions

#GP(0) if the current privilege level is larger (has less privilege) than the I/O privilege level and any of the corresponding I/O permission bits in TSS equals 1.

Real Address Mode Exceptions

None.

Virtual 8086 Mode Exceptions

#GP(0) fault if any of the corresponding I/O permission bits in TSS equals 1.

INC—Increment by 1

Opcode	Instruction	Clocks	Description
FE /0	INC r/m8	1/3	Increment r/m byte by 1
FF /0	INC r/m16	1/3	Increment r/m word by 1
FF /0	INC r/m32	1/3	Increment r/m dword by 1
40+ rw	INC r16	1	Increment word register by 1
40+ rd	INC r32	1	Increment dword register by 1

Operation

DEST ← DEST + 1;

Description

The INC instruction adds 1 to the operand. It does not change the CF flag. To affect the CF flag, use the ADD instruction with a second operand of 1.

Flags Affected

The OF, SF, ZF, AF, and PF flags are set according to the result.

Protected Mode Exceptions

#GP(0) if the operand is in a nonwritable segment; #GP(0) for an illegal memory operand effective address in the CS, DS, ES, FS, or GS segments; #SS(0) for an illegal address in the SS segment; #PF(fault-code) for a page fault; #AC for unaligned memory reference if the current privilege level is 3.

Real Address Mode Exceptions

Interrupt 13 if any part of the operand would lie outside of the effective address space from 0 to 0FFFFH.

Virtual 8086 Mode Exceptions

Same exceptions as in Real Address Mode; #PF(fault-code) for a page fault; #AC for unaligned memory reference if the current privilege level is 3.

INS/INSB/INSW/INSD—Input from Port to String

Opcode	Instruction	Clocks	Description
6C	INS m8,DX	9,pm=6*/ 24**,VM=22	Input byte from port DX into ES:(E)DI
6D	INS m16,DX	9,pm=6*/ 24**,VM=22	Input word from port DX into ES:(E)DI
6D	INS m32,DX	9,pm=6*/ 24**,VM=22	Input dword from port DX into ES:(E)DI
6C	INSB	9,pm=6*/ 24**,VM=22	Input byte from port DX into ES:(E)DI
6D	INSW	9,pm=6*/ 24**,VM=22	Input word from port DX into ES:(E)DI
6D	INSD	9,pm=6*/ 24**,VM=22	Input dword from port DX into ES:(E)DI

NOTES:
*If CPL ≤ IOPL
**If CPL > IOPL

Operation

IF AddressSize = 16
THEN use DI for dest-index;
ELSE (* AddressSize = 32 *)
    use EDI for dest-index;
FI;
IF (PE = 1) AND ((VM = 1) OR (CPL > IOPL))
THEN (* Virtual 8086 mode, or protected mode with CPL > IOPL *)
    IF NOT I-O-Permission (SRC, width(SRC))
    THEN #GP(0);
    FI;
FI;
IF byte type of instruction
THEN
    ES:[dest-index] ← [DX]; (* Reads byte at DX from I/O address space *)
    IF DF = 0 THEN IncDec ← 1 ELSE IncDec ← −1; FI;
FI;
IF OperandSize = 16
THEN
    ES:[dest-index] ← [DX]; (* Reads word at DX from I/O address space *)
    IF DF = 0 THEN IncDec ← 2 ELSE IncDec ← −2; FI;
FI;
IF OperandSize = 32
THEN
    ES:[dest-index] ← [DX]; (* Reads dword at DX from I/O address space *)
    IF DF = 0 THEN IncDec ← 4 ELSE IncDec ← −4; FI; FI;
dest-index ← dest-index + IncDec;

Description

The INS instruction transfers data from the input port numbered by the DX register to the memory byte or word at ES:dest-index. The memory operand must be addressable from the ES register; no segment override is possible. The destination register is the DI register if the address-size attribute of the instruction is 16 bits, or the EDI register if the address-size attribute is 32 bits.

The INS instruction does not allow the specification of the port number as an immediate value. The port must be addressed through the DX register value. Load the correct value into the DX register before executing the INS instruction.

The destination address is determined by the contents of the destination index register. Load the correct index into the destination index register before executing the INS instruction.

After the transfer is made, the DI or EDI register advances automatically. If the DF flag is 0 (a CLD instruction was executed), the DI or EDI register increments; if the DF flag is 1 (an STD instruction was executed), the DI or EDI register decrements. The DI register increments or decrements by 1 if a byte is input, by 2 if a word is input, or by 4 if a doubleword is input.

The INSB, INSW and INSD instructions are synonyms of the byte, word, and doubleword INS instructions. The INS instruction can be preceded by the REP prefix for block input of CX bytes or words. Refer to the REP instruction for details of this operation.

Flags Affected

None.

Protected Mode Exceptions

#GP(0) if the current privilege level is numerically greater than the I/O privilege level and any of the corresponding I/O permission bits in TSS equals 1; #GP(0) if the destination is in a nonwritable segment; #GP(0) for an illegal memory operand effective address in the ES, segment; #PF(fault-code) for a page fault; #AC for unaligned memory reference if the current privilege level is 3.

Real Address Mode Exceptions

Interrupt 13 if any part of the operand would lie outside of the effective address space from 0 to 0FFFFH.

Virtual 8086 Mode Exceptions

#GP(0) fault if any of the corresponding I/O permission bits in TSS equals 1; #PF(fault-code) for a page fault; #AC for unaligned memory reference if the current privilege level is 3.

INT/INTO—Call to Interrupt Procedure

Opcode		Instruction	Clocks	Description
CC		INT 3	13	Interrupt 3—trap to debugger
CC		INT 3	27	Interrupt 3—Protected Mode, same privilege
CC		INT 3	44	Interrupt 3—Protected Mode, more privilege
CC		INT 3	56	Interrupt 3—from V86 mode to PL 0
CC		INT 3	19+TS	Interrupt 3—Protected Mode, via task gate
CD	*ib*	INT *imm8*	16	Interrupt numbered by immediate byte
CD	*ib*	INT *imm8*	31	Interrupt—Protected Mode, same privilege
CD	*ib*	INT *imm8*	48	Interrupt—Protected Mode, more privilege
CD	*ib*	INT *imm8*	82	Interrupt—from V86 mode to PL 0
CD	*ib*	INT *imm8*	23+TS	Interrupt—Protected Mode, via task gate
CE		INTO	Pass: 13, Fail: 4	Interrupt 4—if overflow flag is 1
CE		INTO	Pass: 27, Fail: 4	Interrupt 4—Protected Mode, same privilege
CE		INTO	Pass: 44, Fail: 4	Interrupt 4—Protected Mode, more privilege
CE		INTO	Pass: 56, Fail: 4	Interrupt 4—from V86 mode to PL 0
CE		INTO	Pass: 19+TS, Fail: 4	Interrupt 4—Protected Mode, via task gate

NOTE: Approximate values of **TS** are given by the following table:

Old Task	New Task		
	to 32-bit TSS	to 16 bit TSS	to VM TSS
V86/32 bit/16 bit TSS	85	87	71

Operation

NOTE: The following operational description applies not only to the above instructions but also to external interrupts and exceptions.

```
IF PE = 0
THEN CALL REAL-ADDRESS-MODE;
ELSE
    CALL PROTECTED-MODE;
    IF task gate
    THEN CALL TASK-GATE;
    ELSE
     CALL TRAP-OR-INT-GATE; (* PE=1, int/trap gate *)
     IF code segment is non-conforming AND DPL < CPL
     THEN
       IF VM=0
       THEN CALL INT-TO-INNER-PRIV; (*PE=1,int/trap gate,DPL<CPL, VM=0*)
       ELSE CALL INT-FROM-V86-MODE; (* PE=1, int/trap gate, DPL<CPL,
                  VM=1 *)
     FI;
     ELSE (* PE=1, int/trap gate, DPL ≥ CPL *)
        IF code segment is conforming OR code segment DPL = CPL
     THEN CALL INT-TO-SAME-PRIV;
     ELSE #GP(CS selector + EXT);  (* PE=1, int/trap gate, DPL>CPL *)
       FI;
```

```
        FI;
    FI;
FI;
END;
```

REAL-ADDRESS-MODE PROC
   Push (FLAGS);
   IF ← 0; (* Clear interrupt flag *)
   TF ← 0; (* Clear trap flag *)
   Push(CS);
   Push(IP);
   (* No error codes are pushed *)
   CS ← IDT[Interrupt number * 4].selector;
   IP ← IDT[Interrupt number * 4].offset;
(* Start execution in real address mode *)
REAL-ADDRESS-MODE ENDPROC

PROTECTED-MODE PROC
   Interrupt vector must be within IDT table limits,
      else #GP(vector number * 8+2+EXT);
   Descriptor AR byte must indicate interrupt gate, trap gate, or task gate,
      else #GP(vector number * 8+2+EXT);
   IF software interrupt (* i.e. caused by INT n, INT 3, or INTO *)
   THEN
      IF gate descriptor DPL < CPL
      THEN #GP(vector number * 8+2+EXT); (* PE=1, DPL<CPL, software interrupt *)
      FI;
   FI;
   Gate must be present, else #NP(vector number * 8+2+EXT);
PROTECTED-MODE ENDPROC

TRAP-OR-INT-GATE PROC
   Examine CS selector and descriptor given in the gate descriptor;
   Selector must be non-null, else #GP (EXT);
   Selector must be within its descriptor table limits
      ELSE #GP(selector+EXT);
   Descriptor AR byte must indicate code segment
      ELSE #GP(selector + EXT);
   Segment must be present, else #NP(selector+EXT);
TRAP-OR-INT-GATE ENDPROC

INT-TO-INNER-PRIV PROC
   (* PE=1, DPL<CPL and non-conforming, (* PE=1, int/trap gate, DPL<CPL, VM=0 *)
   Check selector and descriptor for new stack in current TSS;
      Selector must be non-null, else #TS(EXT);
      Selector index must be within its descriptor table limits
         ELSE #TS(SS selector+EXT);
      Selector's RPL must equal DPL of code segment, else #TS(SS

selector+EXT);
Stack segment DPL must equal DPL of code segment, else #TS(SS
selector+EXT);
Descriptor must indicate writable data segment, else #TS(SS
selector+EXT);
Segment must be present, else #SS(SS selector+EXT);
IF 32-bit gate
THEN New stack must have room for 20 bytes else #SS(0)
ELSE New stack must have room for 10 bytes else #SS(0)
FI;
Instruction pointer must be within CS segment boundaries else #GP(0);
Load new SS and eSP value from TSS;
IF 32-bit gate
    THEN CS:EIP ← selector:offset from gate;
 ELSE CS:IP ← selector:offset from gate;
FI;
Load CS descriptor into invisible portion of CS register;
Load SS descriptor into invisible portion of SS register;
IF 32-bit gate
THEN
    Push (long pointer to old stack) (* 3 words padded to 4 *);
    Push (EFLAGS);
    Push (long pointer to return location) (* 3 words padded to 4*);
ELSE
    Push (long pointer to old stack) (* 2 words *);
    Push (FLAGS);
    Push (long pointer to return location) (* 2 words *);
FI;
Set CPL to new code segment DPL;
Set RPL of CS to CPL;
IF interrupt gate THEN IF ← 0 (* interrupt flag to 0 (disabled) *); FI;
TF ← 0;
NT ← 0;
INT-FROM-INNER-PRIV ENDPROC

INT-FROM-V86-MODE PROC
    Check selector and descriptor for new stack in current TSS;
    Selector must be non-null, else #TS(EXT);
    Selector index must be within its descriptor table limits
        ELSE #TS(SS selector+EXT);
    Selector's RPL must equal DPL of code segment, else #TS(SS
        selector+EXT);
    Stack segment DPL must equal DPL of code segment, else #TS(SS
        selector+EXT);
    Descriptor must indicate writable data segment, else #TS(SS
        selector+EXT);
    Segment must be present, else #SS(SS selector+EXT);
    IF 32-bit gate
        THEN New stack must have room for 20 bytes else #SS(0)

```
    ELSE New stack must have room for 10 bytes else #SS(0)
    FI;
    Instruction pointer must be within CS segment boundaries else #GP(0);
    IF IOPL < 3
    THEN
        #GP(0); (*V86 monitor trap: PE=1,int/trap gate, DPL<CPL, VM=1, IOPL<3*)
    ELSE (* IOPL=3 *)
        IF GATE'S_DPL = 3
        THEN
            IF TARGET'S_CPL ≠ 0
            THEN #GP(0);
            ELSE
                TempEFlags ← EFLAGS;
                VM ← 0;
                TF ← 0;
                IF service through Interrupt Gate
                    THEN IF ← 0;
                FI;
                TempSS ← SS;
                TempESP ← ESP;
                SS ← TSS.SS0; (* Change to level 0 stack segment *)
            ESP ← TSS.ESP0; (* Change to level 0 stack pointer *)
            Push(GS); (* padded to two words *)
                Push(FS); (* padded to two words *)
            Push(DS); (* padded to two words *)
            Push(ES); (* padded to two words *)
            GS ← 0;   (* segment registers nullified - invalid in protected mode *)
                FS ← 0;
            DS ← 0;
            ES ← 0;
            Push(TempSS); (* Padded to two words *)
            Push(TempESP);
            Push(TempEFlags);
            Push(CS); (* Padded to two words *)
            Push(EIP);
                CS:EIP ← selector:offset from interrupt gate;
                (* Starts execution of new routine in Protected Mode *)
            FI;
        ELSE (* GATE'S_DPL ≠ 3 *)
            #GP(0);
        FI;
    FI;
INT-FROM-V86-MODE ENDPROC


INT-TO-SAME-PRIV PROC
    (* PE=1, DPL=CPL or conforming segment *)
    IF 32-bit gate
    THEN Current stack limits must allow pushing 10 bytes, else #SS(0);
    ELSE Current stack limits must allow pushing 6 bytes, else #SS(0);
    FI;
```

```
        IF interrupt was caused by exception with error code
        THEN Stack limits must allow push of two more bytes;
        ELSE #SS(0);
        FI;
        Instruction pointer must be in CS limit, else #GP(0);
        IF 32-bit gate
        THEN
           Push (EFLAGS);
           Push (long pointer to return location); (* 3 words padded to 4 *)
           CS:EIP ← selector:offset from gate;
        ELSE (* 16-bit gate *)
           Push (FLAGS);
           Push (long pointer to return location); (* 2 words *)
           CS:IP ← selector:offset from gate;
        FI;
        Load CS descriptor into invisible portion of CS register;
        Set the RPL field of CS to CPL;
        Push (error code); (* if any *)
        IF interrupt gate THEN IF ← 0; FI;
        TF ← 0;
        NT ← 0;
    INT-TO-SAME-PRIV ENDPROC

    TASK-GATE PROC  (* PE=1, task gate *)
        Examine selector to TSS, given in task gate descriptor;
           Must specify global in the local/global bit, else #TS(TSS selector);
           Index must be within GDT limits, else #TS(TSS selector);
           AR byte must specify available TSS (bottom bits 00001),
              else #TS(TSS selector);
           TSS must be present, else #NP(TSS selector);
        SWITCH-TASKS with nesting to TSS;
        IF interrupt was caused by fault with error code
        THEN
           Stack limits must allow push of two more bytes, else #SS(0);
           Push error code onto stack;
        FI;
        Instruction pointer must be in CS limit, else #GP(0);
    TASK-GATE ENDPROC
```

Decision Table

The following decision table indicates which action in the lower portion of the table is taken given the conditions in the upper portion of the table. Each Y in the lower section of the decision table represents a procedure defined above in the Operation section for this instruction (except #GP(0)) and the number following the Y indicates the order in which the procedure is executed.

PE	0	1	1	1	1	1	1	1
VM	-	-	-	-	-	0	1	1
IOPL	-	-	-	-	-	-	<3	=3
DPL/CPL RELATIONSHIP	-	DPL< CPL	-	DPL> CPL	DPL= CPL or C	DPL< CPL & NC	-	-
INTERRUPT TYPE	-	S/W	-	-	-	-	-	-
GATE TYPE	-	-	Task	Trap or Int	Trap or Int	Trap or Int	Trap or Int	Trap or Int
REAL-ADDRESS-MODE	Y							
PROTECTED-MODE		Y1	Y1	Y1	Y1	Y1	Y1	Y1
TRAP-OR-INT-GATE				Y2	Y2	Y2	Y2	Y2
INT-TO-INNER-PRIV						Y3		
INT-TO-SAME-PRIV					Y3			
INT-FROM-V86-MODE								Y3
TASK-GATE			Y2					
#GP		Y2		Y3			Y3	

NOTES:
-     Don't Care
Yx   Yes, Action Taken, x = the order of execution
Blank   Action Not Taken

Description

The INT n instruction generates a call to an interrupt handler. The immediate operand, from 0 to 255, gives the index number into the Interrupt Descriptor Table (IDT) of the interrupt routine to be called. In protected mode, the IDT consists of an array of eight-byte descriptors; the descriptor for the interrupt invoked must indicate an interrupt, trap, or task gate. In real-address mode, the IDT is an array of four byte-long pointers. In protected and real-address modes, the base linear address of the IDT is defined by the contents of the IDTR. The initial value of IDTR is zero upon reset into real-address mode.

When the processor is executing in virtual-8086 mode (VM=1), the IOPL determines whether the INT n causes a general protection exception (IOPL<3) or executes a protected mode interrupt to privilege level 0. The interrupt gate's DPL must be set to three and the target CPL of the interrupt service routine must be zero to execute the protected mode interrupt to privilege level 0.

The INTO conditional software instruction is identical to the INT n interrupt instruction except that the interrupt number is implicitly 4, and the interrupt is made only if the overflow flag is set.

The first 32 interrupts are reserved by Intel for system use. Some of these interrupts are used for internally generated exceptions.

The INT n instruction generally behaves like a far call except that the flags register is pushed onto the stack before the return address. Interrupt procedures return via the IRET instruction, which pops the flags and return address from the stack.

In Real Address Mode, the INT n instruction pushes the flags, the CS register, and the return IP onto the stack, in that order, then jumps to the long pointer indexed by the interrupt number.

Flags Affected

None.

Protected Mode Exceptions

#GP, #NP, #SS, and #TS as indicated under "Operation" above.

Real Address Mode Exceptions

None; if the SP or ESP register is 1, 3, or 5 before executing the INT or INTO instruction, the processor will shut down due to insufficient stack space.

Virtual 8086 Mode Exceptions

#GP(0) fault if IOPL is less than 3, for the INT n instruction only, to permit emulation; Interrupt 3 (0CCH) generates a breakpoint exception; the INTO instruction generates an overflow exception if the OF flag is set.

Notes

For obtaining information on this instruction using virtual mode extensions, see Appendix H.

INVD—Invalidate Cache

Opcode	Instruction	Clocks	Description
0F 08	INVD	15	Invalidate Entire Cache

Operation

INVALIDATE INTERNAL CACHE
SIGNAL EXTERNAL CACHE TO INVALIDATE

Description

The internal cache is invalidated, and a special-function bus cycle is issued which indicates that external caches should also be invalidated. Data held in write-back external caches is not instructed to be written back.

Flags Affected

None.

Protected Mode Exceptions

The INVD instruction is a privileged instruction; #GP(0) if the current privilege level is not 0.

Real Address Mode Exceptions

None.

Virtual 8086 Mode Exceptions

#GP(0); the INVD instruction is a privileged instruction.

Notes

INVD should be used with care. It does not write back modified cache lines; therefore, it can cause the data cache to become inconsistent with other memories in the system. Unless there is a specific requirement or benefit to invalidate a cache without writing back the modified lines (i.e., testing or fault recovery where cache coherency with main memory is not a concern), software should use the WBINVD instruction.

This instruction is implementation-dependent; its function may be implemented differently on future Intel processors.

This instruction does not wait for the external cache to complete its invalidation before the processor proceeds. It is the responsibility of hardware to respond to the external cache invalidation indication.

This instruction is not supported on Intel386 processors. See Section Chapter 9 for CPUID detection at runtime. See the WBINVD description to write back dirty data to memory.

See Chapter 18 on disabling the cache.

INVLPG—Invalidate TLB Entry

Opcode	Instruction	Clocks	Description
0F 01/7	INVLPG m	25	Invalidate TLB Entry

Operation

INVALIDATE RELEVANT TLB ENTRY(S)

Description

The INVLPG instruction is used to ensure there are no invalid entries in the TLB, the cache used for page table entries. If the TLB contains a valid entry which maps the address of the memory operand, all of the relevant TLB entries are marked invalid.

Flags Affected

None

Protected Mode Exceptions

The INVLPG instruction is a privileged instruction; #GP(0) if the current privilege level is not 0. An invalid-opcode exception is generated when used with a register operand.

Real Address Mode Exceptions

None

Virtual 8086 Mode Exceptions

An invalid-opcode exception is generated when used with a register operand. #GP(0); the INVLPG instruction is a privileged instruction.

Notes

This instruction is not supported on Intel386 processors. See Section Chapter 16 for detecting processor type at runtime.

See Chapter 18 for information on disabling the cache.

IRET/IRETD—Interrupt Return

Opcode	Instruction	Clocks	Description
CF	IRET	8	Interrupt return (from real or V86 mode)
CF	IRET	10	Interrupt return (far return and pop flags)
CF	IRET	27	Interrupt return to lesser privilege
CF	IRET	TS+10	Interrupt return, different task (NT = 1)
CF	IRETD	10	Interrupt return (far return and pop flags)
CF	IRETD	27	Interrupt return to lesser privilege
CF	IRETD	TS+10	Interrupt return, different task (NT = 1)

NOTE: Values of **TS** are given by the following table:

Old Task	New Task		
	to 32 bit TSS	to 16 bit TSS	to VM TSS
VM/32 bit/16 bit	85	87	71

Operation

```
IF PE = 0
THEN GOTO REAL_ADDRESS_MODE:;
ELSE GOTO PROTECTED_MODE;
FI;


REAL_ADDRESS_MODE;
    IF OperandSize = 32 (* Instruction = IRETD *)
    THEN EIP ← Pop( );
    ELSE (* Instruction = IRET *)
     IP ← Pop( );
    FI;
    CS ← Pop( );
    IF OperandSize = 32 (* Instruction = IRETD *)
    THEN Pop( ); EFLAGS ← Pop( );
    ELSE (* Instruction = IRET *)
     FLAGS ← Pop( );
    FI;
    END;

PROTECTED_MODE:
    IF VM = 1 (* Virtual mode: PE=1, VM=1*)
    THEN GOTO STACK_RETURN_FROM_V86; (* PE=1, VM=1 *)
    ELSE
     IF NT=1
     THEN GOTO TASK_RETURN; (* PE=1, VM=1, NT=1 *)
     ELSE
        IF VM=1 in flags image on stack
          THEN GOTO STACK_RETURN_TO_V86; (* PE=1, VM=1 in flags
                      image *)
          ELSE GOTO STACK_RETURN; (* PE=1, VM=0 in flags image *)
        FI;
     FI;
```

FI;

STACK_RETURN_FROM_V86:
    IF IOPL=3 (* Virtual mode: PE=1, VM=1, IOPL=3 *)
    THEN
        IF OperandSize = 16
            IP ← Pop();(* 16 bit pops *)
            CS ← Pop();
            FLAGS ←Pop();
        ELSE (* OperandSize = 32 *)
            EIP ← Pop(); (* 32-bit pops *)
            CS ← Pop();
            EFLAGS ←Pop(); (*VM,IOPL,VIP,and VIF EFLAG bits are not modified by IRETD*)
        FI;
    ELSE #GP(0); (* trap to virtual-8086 monitor: PE=1, VM=1, IOPL<3 *)
    FI;
END;

STACK_RETURN_TO_V86: (* Interrupted procedure was in V86 mode: PE=1, VM=1 in flags
image *)
    IF top 36 bytes of stack not within limits
    THEN #SS(0);
    FI;
    IF instruction pointer not within code segment limit   THEN #GP(0);
    FI;
    EFLAGS ← SS:[ESP + 8]; (* Sets VM in interrupted routine *)
    EIP ← Pop( );
    CS ← Pop( ); (* CS behaves as in 8086, due to VM = 1 *)
    throwaway ← Pop( ); (* pop away EFLAGS already read *)
    TempESP ← Pop( );
    TempSS ← Pop( );
    ES ← Pop( ); (* pop 2 words; throw away high-order word *)
    DS ← Pop( ); (* pop 2 words; throw away high-order word *)
    FS ← Pop( ); (* pop 2 words; throw away high-order word *)
    GS ← Pop( ); (* pop 2 words; throw away high-order word *)
     SS:ESP ← TempSS:TempESP;
    (* Resume execution in Virtual 8086 mode *)
    END;

TASK-RETURN: (* PE=1, VM=1, NT=1 *)
    Examine Back Link Selector in TSS addressed by the current task
        register:
        Must specify global in the local/global bit, else #TS(new TSS selector);
        Index must be within GDT limits, else #TS(new TSS selector);
        AR byte must specify TSS, else #TS(new TSS selector);
        New TSS must be busy, else #TS(new TSS selector);
        TSS must be present, else #NP(new TSS selector);
    SWITCH-TASKS without nesting to TSS specified by back link selector;
    Mark the task just abandoned as NOT BUSY;
    Instruction pointer must be within code segment limit ELSE #GP(0);

END;

STACK-RETURN: (* PE=1, VM=0 in flags image *)
    IF OperandSize=32
    THEN Third word on stack must be within stack limits, else #SS(0);
    ELSE Second word on stack must be within stack limits, else #SS(0);
    FI;
    Return CS selector RPL must be ≥ CPL, else #GP(Return selector);
    IF return selector RPL = CPL
    THEN GOTO RETURN-SAME-LEVEL;
    ELSE GOTO RETURN-OUTER-LEVEL;
    FI;

RETURN-SAME-LEVEL: (* PE=1, VM=0 in flags image, RPL=CPL *)
    IF OperandSize=32
    THEN
        Top 12 bytes on stack must be within limits, else #SS(0);
        Return CS selector (at eSP+4) must be non-null, else #GP(0);
    ELSE
        Top 6 bytes on stack must be within limits, else #SS(0);
        Return CS selector (at eSP+2) must be non-null, else #GP(0);
    FI;
    Selector index must be within its descriptor table limits, else #GP
        (Return selector);
    AR byte must indicate code segment, else #GP(Return selector);
    IF non-conforming
    THEN code segment DPL must = CPL;
    ELSE #GP(Return selector); (* PE=1,VM=0 in flags image,RPL=CPL,non-conforming,DPL≠
CPL *)
    FI;
    IF conforming
     THEN IF DPL>CPL
        #GP(Return selector); (* PE=1,VM=0 in flags image,RPL=CPL,conforming,DPL>CPL *)
    Segment must be present, else #NP(Return selector);
    Instruction pointer must be within code segment boundaries, else #GP(0);
    FI;
    IF OperandSize=32 put comments here
    THEN
        Load CS:EIP from stack;
        Load CS-register with new code segment descriptor;
        Load EFLAGS with third doubleword from stack;
        Increment eSP by 12;
    ELSE
        Load CS-register with new code segment descriptor;
        Load FLAGS with third word on stack;
        Increment eSP by 6;
    FI;
    END;

RETURN-OUTER-LEVEL:

IF OperandSize=32
THEN Top 20 bytes on stack must be within limits, else #SS(0);
ELSE Top 10 bytes on stack must be within limits, else #SS(0);
FI;
Examine return CS selector and associated descriptor:
    Selector must be non-null, ELSE #GP(0);
    Selector index must be within its descriptor table limits;
        ELSE #GP(Return selector);
    AR byte must indicate code segment, else #GP(Return selector);
 IF non-conforming
    THEN code segment DPL must = CS selector RPL;
    ELSE #GP(Return selector);
    FI;
    IF conforming
    THEN code segment DPL must be > CPL;
    ELSE #GP(Return selector);
    FI;
    Segment must be present, else #NP(Return selector);
Examine return SS selector and associated descriptor:
    Selector must be non-null, else #GP(0);
    Selector index must be within its descriptor table limits
        ELSE #GP(SS selector);
    Selector RPL must equal the RPL of the return CS selector
        ELSE #GP(SS selector);
    AR byte must indicate a writable data segment, else #GP(SS selector);
    Stack segment DPL must equal the RPL of the return CS selector
        ELSE #GP(SS selector);
    SS must be present, else #NP(SS selector);
Instruction pointer must be within code segment limit ELSE #GP(0);
IF OperandSize=32
THEN
    Load CS:EIP from stack;
    Load EFLAGS with values at (eSP+8);
ELSE
    Load CS:IP from stack;
    Load FLAGS with values at (eSP+4);
FI;
Load SS:eSP from stack;
Set CPL to the RPL of the return CS selector;
Load the CS register with the CS descriptor;
Load the SS register with the SS descriptor;
FOR each of ES, FS, GS, and DS
DO;
    IF the current value of the register is not valid for the outer level;
    THEN zero the register and clear the valid flag;
    FI;
    To be valid, the register setting must satisfy the following properties:
        Selector index must be within descriptor table limits;
        AR byte must indicate data or readable code segment;
        IF segment is data or non-conforming code,

THEN DPL must be > CPL, or DPL must be < RPL;
OD;
END:

Description

In Real Address Mode, the IRET instruction pops the instruction pointer, the CS register, and the flags register from the stack and resumes the interrupted routine.

In Protected Mode, the action of the IRET instruction depends on the setting of the nested task flag (NT) bit in the flag register. When the new flag image is popped from the stack, the IOPL bits in the flag register are changed only when CPL equals 0.

If the NT flag is cleared, the IRET instruction returns from an interrupt procedure without a task switch. The code returned to must be equally or less privileged than the interrupt routine (as indicated by the RPL bits of the CS selector popped from the stack). If the destination code is less privileged, the IRET instruction also pops the stack pointer and SS from the stack.

If the NT flag is set, the IRET instruction reverses the operation of a CALL or INT that caused a task switch. The updated state of the task executing the IRET instruction is saved in its task state segment. If the task is reentered later, the code that follows the IRET instruction is executed.

Flags Affected

All flags are affected; the flags register is popped from stack.

Protected Mode Exceptions

#GP, #NP, or #SS, as indicated under "Operation" above; #PF(fault-code) for a page fault; #AC for unaligned memory reference if the current privilege level is 3.

Real Address Mode Exceptions

Interrupt 13 if any part of the operand being popped lies beyond address 0FFFFH.

Virtual 8086 Mode Exceptions

#GP(0) fault occurs if the I/O privilege level is less than 3, to permit emulation; #PF(fault-code) for a page fault; #AC for unaligned memory reference if the current privilege level is 3.

Notes

For obtaining information on this instruction using virtual mode extensions, see Appendix H.

Jcc—Jump if Condition is Met

Opcode	Instruction	Clocks	Description
77 cb	JA rel8	1	Jump short if above (CF=0 and ZF=0)
73 cb	JAE rel8	1	Jump short if above or equal (CF=0)
72 cb	JB rel8	1	Jump short if below (CF=1)
76 cb	JBE rel8	1	Jump short if below or equal (CF=1 or ZF=1)
72 cb	JC rel8	1	Jump short if carry (CF=1)
E3 cb	JCXZ rel8	6,5	Jump short if CX register is 0
E3 cb	JECXZ rel8	6,5	Jump short if ECX register is 0
74 cb	JE rel8	1	Jump short if equal (ZF=1)
74 cb	JZ rel8	1	Jump short if 0 (ZF=1)
7F cb	JG rel8	1	Jump short if greater (ZF=0 and SF=OF)
7D cb	JGE rel8	1	Jump short if greater or equal (SF=OF)
7C cb	JL rel8	1	Jump short if less (SF<>OF)
7E cb	JLE rel8	1	Jump short if less or equal (ZF=1 or SF<>OF)
76 cb	JNA rel8	1	Jump short if not above (CF=1 or ZF=1)
72 cb	JNAE rel8	1	Jump short if not above or equal (CF=1)
73 cb	JNB rel8	1	Jump short if not below (CF=0)
77 cb	JNBE rel8	1	Jump short if not below or equal (CF=0 and ZF=0)
73 cb	JNC rel8	1	Jump short if not carry (CF=0)
75 cb	JNE rel8	1	Jump short if not equal (ZF=0)
7E cb	JNG rel8	1	Jump short if not greater (ZF=1 or SF<>OF)
7C cb	JNGE rel8	1	Jump short if not greater or equal (SF<>OF)
7D cb	JNL rel8	1	Jump short if not less (SF=OF)
7F cb	JNLE rel8	1	Jump short if not less or equal (ZF=0 and SF=OF)
71 cb	JNO rel8	1	Jump short if not overflow (OF=0)
7B cb	JNP rel8	1	Jump short if not parity (PF=0)
79 cb	JNS rel8	1	Jump short if not sign (SF=0)
75 cb	JNZ rel8	1	Jump short if not zero (ZF=0)
70 cb	JO rel8	1	Jump short if overflow (OF=1)
7A cb	JP rel8	1	Jump short if parity (PF=1)
7A cb	JPE rel8	1	Jump short if parity even (PF=1)
7B cb	JPO rel8	1	Jump short if parity odd (PF=0)
78 cb	JS rel8	1	Jump short if sign (SF=1)
74 cb	JZ rel8	1	Jump short if zero (ZF = 1)
0F 87 cw/cd	JA rel16/32	1	Jump near if above (CF=0 and ZF=0)
0F 83 cw/cd	JAE rel16/32	1	Jump near if above or equal (CF=0)
0F 82 cw/cd	JB rel16/32	1	Jump near if below (CF=1)
0F 86 cw/cd	JBE rel16/32	1	Jump near if below or equal (CF=1 or ZF=1)
0F 82 cw/cd	JC rel16/32	1	Jump near if carry (CF=1)
0F 84 cw/cd	JE rel16/32	1	Jump near if equal (ZF=1)
0F 84 cw/cd	JZ rel16/32	1	Jump near if 0 (ZF=1)
0F 8F cw/cd	JG rel16/32	1	Jump near if greater (ZF=0 and SF=OF)
0F 8D cw/cd	JGE rel16/32	1	Jump near if greater or equal (SF=OF)
0F 8C cw/cd	JL rel16/32	1	Jump near if less (SF<>OF)
0F 8E cw/cd	JLE rel16/32	1	Jump near if less or equal (ZF=1 or SF<>OF)
0F 86 cw/cd	JNA rel16/32	1	Jump near if not above (CF=1 or ZF=1)
0F 82 cw/cd	JNAE rel16/32	1	Jump near if not above or equal (CF=1)
0F 83 cw/cd	JNB rel16/32	1	Jump near if not below (CF=0)
0F 87 cw/cd	JNBE rel16/32	1	Jump near if not below or equal (CF=0 and ZF=0)
0F 83 cw/cd	JNC rel16/32	1	Jump near if not carry (CF=0)
0F 85 cw/cd	JNE rel16/32	1	Jump near if not equal (ZF=0)
0F 8E cw/cd	JNG rel16/32	1	Jump near if not greater (ZF=1 or SF<>OF)
0F 8C cw/cd	JNGE rel16/32	1	Jump near if not greater or equal (SF<>OF)
0F 8D cw/cd	JNL rel16/32	1	Jump near if not less (SF=OF)
0F 8F cw/cd	JNLE rel16/32	1	Jump near if not less or equal (ZF=0 and SF=OF)
0F 81 cw/cd	JNO rel16/32	1	Jump near if not overflow (OF=0)
0F 8B cw/cd	JNP rel16/32	1	Jump near if not parity (PF=0)
0F 89 cw/cd	JNS rel16/32	1	Jump near if not sign (SF=0)
0F 85 cw/cd	JNZ rel16/32	1	Jump near if not zero (ZF=0)
0F 80 cw/cd	JO rel16/32	1	Jump near if overflow (OF=1)
0F 8A cw/cd	JP rel16/32	1	Jump near if parity (PF=1)
0F 8A cw/cd	JPE rel16/32	1	Jump near if parity even (PF=1)
0F 8B cw/cd	JPO rel16/32	1	Jump near if parity odd (PF=0)
0F 88 cw/cd	JS rel16/32	1	Jump near if sign (SF=1)
0F 84 cw/cd	JZ rel16/32	1	Jump near if 0 (ZF=1)

NOTES:

Where two clocks counts appear, the first clock count is for the true condition (branch taken); the second clock count is for the false condition (branch not taken). *rel16/32* indicates that these instructions map to two; one with a 16-bit relative displacement, the other with a 32-bit relative displacement, depending on the operand-size attribute of the instruction.

Operation

```
IF condition
THEN
    EIP ← EIP + SignExtend(rel8/16/32);
    IF OperandSize = 16
    THEN EIP ← EIP AND 0000FFFFH;
    FI;
FI;
```

Description

Conditional jumps (except the JCXZ instruction) test the flags which have been set by a previous instruction. The conditions for each mnemonic are given in parentheses after each description above. The terms "less" and "greater" are used for comparisons of signed integers; "above" and "below" are used for unsigned integers.

If the given condition is true, a jump is made to the location provided as the operand. Instruction coding is most efficient when the target for the conditional jump is in the current code segment and within −128 to +127 bytes of the next instruction's first byte. The jump can also target −32768 thru +32767 (segment size attribute 16) or -2^{31} thru $+2^{31}-1$ (segment size attribute 32) relative to the next instruction's first byte. When the target for the conditional jump is in a different segment, use the opposite case of the jump instruction (i.e., the JE and JNE instructions), and then access the target with an unconditional far jump to the other segment. For example, you cannot code—

JZ FARLABEL;

You must instead code—

```
    JNZ BEYOND;
    JMP FARLABEL;
BEYOND:
```

Because there can be several ways to interpret a particular state of the flags, ASM386 provides more than one mnemonic for most of the conditional jump opcodes. For example, if you compared two characters in AX and want to jump if they are equal, use the JE instruction; or, if you ANDed the AX register with a bit field mask and only want to jump if the result is 0, use the JZ instruction, a synonym for the JE instruction.

The JCXZ instruction differs from other conditional jumps because it tests the contents of the CX or ECX register for 0, not the flags. The JCXZ instruction is useful at the beginning of a conditional loop that terminates with a conditional loop instruction (such as LOOPNE TARGET LABEL. The JCXZ instruction prevents entering the loop with the CX or ECX register equal to zero, which would cause the loop to execute 64K or 2^{32} times instead of zero times.

Flags Affected

None.

Protected Mode Exceptions

#GP(0) if the offset jumped to is beyond the limits of the code segment.

Real Address Mode Exceptions

None.

Virtual 8086 Mode Exceptions

None

Notes

The JCXZ instruction takes longer to execute than a two-instruction sequence which compares the count register to zero and jumps if the count is zero.

All branches are converted into 16-byte code fetches regardless of jump address or cacheability.

JMP—Jump

Opcode	Instruction	Clocks	Description
EB cb	JMP rel8	1	Jump short
E9 cw	JMP rel16	1	Jump near, displacement relative to next instruction
FF /4	JMP r/m16	2	Jump near indirect
EA cd	JMP ptr16:16	3	Jump intersegment, 4-byte immediate address
EA cd	JMP ptr16:16	18	Jump to call gate, same privilege
EA cd	JMP ptr16:16	19+TS	Jump via task state segment
EA cd	JMP ptr16:16	20+TS	Jump via task gate
FF /5	JMP m16:16	4	Jump r/m16:16 indirect and intersegment
FF /5	JMP m16:16	18	Jump to call gate, same privilege
FF /5	JMP m16:16	19+TS	Jump via task state segment
FF /5	JMP m16:16	20+TS	Jump via task gate
E9 cd	JMP rel32	1	Jump near, displacement relative to next instruction
FF /4	JMP r/m32	2	Jump near, indirect
EA cp	JMP ptr16:32	3	Jump intersegment, 6-byte immediate address
EA cp	JMP ptr16:32	18	Jump to call gate, same privilege
EA cp	JMP ptr16:32	19+TS	Jump via task state segment
EA cp	JMP ptr16:32	20+TS	Jump via task gate
FF /5	JMP m16:32	4	Jump intersegment, address at r/m dword
FF /5	JMP m16:32	18	Jump to call gate, same privilege
FF /5	JMP m16:32	19+TS	Jump via task state segment
FF /5	JMP m16:32	20+TS	Jump via task gate

NOTE: Values of **ts** are given by the following table:

Old Task	New Task		
	to 32 bit TSS	to 16 bit TSS	to VM TSS
VM/32 bit/16 bit TSS	85	87	71

Operation

IF instruction = relative JMP   (* i.e. operand is rel8, rel16, or rel32 *)
THEN
    EIP ← EIP + rel8/16/32;
    IF OperandSize = 16
    THEN EIP ← EIP AND 0000FFFFH;
    FI;
FI;

IF instruction = near indirect JMP
    (* i.e. operand is r/m16 or r/m32 *)
THEN
    IF OperandSize = 16
    THEN
        EIP ← [r/m16] AND 0000FFFFH;
    ELSE (* OperandSize = 32 *)
        EIP ← [r/m32;
    FI;
FI;

IF (PE = 0 OR (PE = 1 AND VM = 1)) (* real mode or V86 mode *)
    AND instruction = far JMP

```
    (* i.e., operand type is m16:16, m16:32, ptr16:16, ptr16:32 *)
THEN GOTO REAL-OR-V86-MODE;
    IF operand type = m16:16 or m16:32
    THEN (* indirect *)
        IF OperandSize = 16
        THEN
            CS:IP ← [m16:16];
            EIP ← EIP AND 0000FFFFH; (* clear upper 16 bits *)
        ELSE (* OperandSize = 32 *)
            CS:EIP ← [m16:32];
        FI;
    FI;
    IF operand type = ptr16:16 or ptr16:32
    THEN
        IF OperandSize = 16
        THEN
            CS:IP ← ptr16:16;
            EIP ← EIP AND 0000FFFFH; (* clear upper 16 bits *)
        ELSE (* OperandSize = 32 *)
            CS:EIP ← ptr16:32;
        FI;
    FI;
FI;


IF (PE = 1 AND VM = 0) (* Protected mode, not V86 mode *)
    AND instruction = far JMP
THEN
    IF operand type = m16:16 or m16:32
    THEN (* indirect *)
        check access of EA dword;
        #GP(0) or #SS(0) IF limit violation;
    FI;
    Destination selector is not null ELSE #GP(0)
    Destination selector index is within its descriptor table limits ELSE #GP(selector)
    Depending on AR byte of destination descriptor:
        GOTO CONFORMING-CODE-SEGMENT;
        GOTO NONCONFORMING-CODE-SEGMENT;
        GOTO CALL-GATE;
        GOTO TASK-GATE;
        GOTO TASK-STATE-SEGMENT;
    ELSE #GP(selector); (* illegal AR byte in descriptor *)
FI;


CONFORMING-CODE-SEGMENT:
    Descriptor DPL must be ≤ CPL ELSE #GP(selector);
    Segment must be present ELSE #NP(selector);
    Instruction pointer must be within code-segment limit ELSE #GP(0);
    IF OperandSize = 32
    THEN Load CS:EIP from destination pointer;
    ELSE Load CS:IP from destination pointer;
```

FI;
Load CS register with new segment descriptor;

NONCONFORMING-CODE-SEGMENT:
    RPL of destination selector must be ≤ CPL ELSE #GP(selector);
    Descriptor DPL must be = CPL ELSE #GP(selector);
    Segment must be present ELSE # NP(selector);
    Instruction pointer must be within code-segment limit ELSE #GP(0);
    IF OperandSize = 32
    THEN Load CS:EIP from destination pointer;
    ELSE Load CS:IP from destination pointer;
    FI;
    Load CS register with new segment descriptor;
    Set RPL field of CS register to CPL;

CALL-GATE:
    Descriptor DPL must be ≥ CPL ELSE #GP(gate selector);
    Descriptor DPL must be ≥ gate selector RPL ELSE #GP(gate selector);
    Gate must be present ELSE #NP(gate selector);
    Examine selector to code segment given in call gate descriptor:
        Selector must not be null ELSE #GP(0);
        Selector must be within its descriptor table limits ELSE
          #GP(CS selector);
        Descriptor AR byte must indicate code segment
          ELSE #GP(CS selector);
        IF non-conforming
        THEN code-segment descriptor DPL must = CPL
        ELSE #GP(CS selector);
        FI;
        IF conforming
        THEN code-segment descriptor DPL must be ≤ CPL;
        ELSE #GP(CS selector);
        Code segment must be present ELSE #NP(CS selector);
        Instruction pointer must be within code-segment limit ELSE #GP(0);
        IF OperandSize = 32
        THEN Load CS:EIP from call gate;
        ELSE Load CS:IP from call gate;
        FI;
    Load CS register with new code-segment descriptor;
    Set RPL of CS to CPL

TASK-GATE:
    Gate descriptor DPL must be ≥ CPL ELSE #GP(gate selector);
    Gate descriptor DPL must be ≥ gate selector RPL ELSE #GP(gate selector);
    Task Gate must be present ELSE #NP(gate selector);
    Examine selector to TSS, given in Task Gate descriptor:
        Must specify global in the local/global bit ELSE #GP(TSS selector);
        Index must be within GDT limits ELSE #GP(TSS selector);
        Descriptor AR byte must specify available TSS (bottom bits 00001);
          ELSE #GP(TSS selector);

Task State Segment must be present ELSE #NP(TSS selector);
SWITCH-TASKS (without nesting) to TSS;
Instruction pointer must be within code-segment limit ELSE #GP(0);

TASK-STATE-SEGMENT:
TSS DPL must be ≥ CPL ELSE #GP(TSS selector);
TSS DPL must be ≥ TSS selector RPL ELSE #GP(TSS selector);
Descriptor AR byte must specify available TSS (bottom bits 00001)
ELSE #GP(TSS selector);
Task State Segment must be present ELSE #NP(TSS selector);
SWITCH-TASKS (without nesting) to TSS;
Instruction pointer must be within code-segment limit ELSE #GP(0);

Description

The JMP instruction transfers control to a different point in the instruction stream without recording return information.

The action of the various forms of the instruction are shown below.

Jumps with destinations of type *r/m16*, *r/m32*, *rel16*, and *rel32* are near jumps and do not involve changing the segment register value.

The JMP *rel16* and JMP *rel32* forms of the instruction add an offset to the address of the instruction following the JMP to determine the destination. The *rel16* form is used when the instruction's operand-size attribute is 16 bits (segment size attribute 16 only); *rel32* is used when the operand-size attribute is 32 bits (segment size attribute 32 only). The result is stored in the 32-bit EIP register. With *rel16*, the upper 16 bits of the EIP register are cleared, which results in an offset whose value does not exceed 16 bits.

The JMP *r/m16* and JMP *r/m32* forms specify a register or memory location from which the absolute offset from the procedure is fetched. The offset fetched from **r/m** is 32 bits for an operand-size attribute of 32 bits (*r/m32*), or 16 bits for an operand-size attribute of 16 bits (*r/m16*).

The JMP *ptr16:16* and *ptr16:32* forms of the instruction use a four-byte or six-byte operand as a long pointer to the destination. The JMP *m16:16* and *m16:32* forms fetch the long pointer from the memory location specified (indirection). In Real Address Mode or Virtual 8086 Mode, the long pointer provides 16 bits for the CS register and 16 or 32 bits for the EIP register (depending on the operand-size attribute). In Protected Mode, both long pointer forms consult the Access Rights (AR) byte in the descriptor indexed by the selector part of the long pointer. Depending on the value of the AR byte, the jump will perform one of the following types of control transfers:

- A jump to a code segment at the same privilege level
- A task switch

For more information on protected mode control transfers, refer to Chapter 12 and Chapter 13.

Flags Affected

All if a task switch takes place; none if no task switch occurs.

Protected Mode Exceptions

Far jumps: #GP, #NP, #SS, and #TS, as indicated in the list above.

Near direct jumps: #GP(0) if procedure location is beyond the code segment limits; #AC for unaligned memory reference if the current privilege level is 3.

Near indirect jumps: #GP(0) for an illegal memory operand effective address in the CS, DS, ES, FS, or GS segments: #SS(0) for an illegal address in the SS segment; #GP if the indirect offset obtained is beyond the code segment limits; #PF(fault-code) for a page fault; #AC for unaligned memory reference if the current privilege level is 3.

Real Address Mode Exceptions

Interrupt 13 if any part of the operand would be outside of the effective address space from 0 to 0FFFFH.

Virtual 8086 Mode Exceptions

Same exceptions as under Real Address Mode; #PF(fault-code) for a page fault; #AC for unaligned memory reference if the current privilege level is 3.

Notes

All branches are converted into 16-byte code fetches regardless of jump address or cacheability.

LAHF—Load Flags into AH Register

Opcode	Instruction	Clocks	Description
9F	LAHF	2	Load: AH = flags SF ZF xx AF xx PF xx CF

Operation

AH ← SF:ZF:xx:AF:xx:PF:xx:CF;

Description

The LAHF instruction transfers the low byte of the flags word to the AH register. The bits, from MSB to LSB, are sign, zero, indeterminate, auxiliary, carry, indeterminate, parity, indeterminate, and carry.

Flags Affected

None.

Protected Mode Exceptions

None.

Real Address Mode Exceptions

None.

Virtual 8086 Mode Exceptions

None.

LAR—Load Access Rights Byte

Opcode	Instruction	Clocks	Description
0F 02 /r	LAR r16,r/m16	8	r16 ← r/m16 masked by FF00
0F 02 /r	LAR r32,r/m32	8	r32 ← /m32 masked by 00FxFF00

Description

The LAR instruction stores a marked form of the second doubleword of the descriptor for the source selector if the selector is visible at the current privilege level (modified by the selector's RPL) and is a valid descriptor type within the descriptor limits. The destination register is loaded with the high-order doubleword of the descriptor masked by 00FxFF00, and the ZF flag is set. The x indicates that the four bits corresponding to the upper four bits of the limit are undefined in the value loaded by the LAR instruction. If the selector is invisible or of the wrong type, the ZF flag is cleared.

If the 32-bit operand size is specified, the entire 32-bit value is loaded into the 32-bit destination register. If the 16-bit operand size is specified, the lower 16-bits of this value are stored in the 16-bit destination register.

All code and data segment descriptors are valid for the LAR instruction.

The valid special segment and gate descriptor types for the LAR instruction are given in the following table:

Type	Name	Valid/Invalid
0	Invalid	Invalid
1	Available 16-bit TSS	Valid
2	LDT	Valid
3	Busy 16-bit TSS	Valid
4	16-bit call gate	Valid
5	16-bit /32 bit task gate	Valid
6	16-bit trap gate	Invalid
7	16-bit interrupt gate	Invalid
8	Invalid	Invalid
9	Available 32-bit TSS	Valid
A	Invalid	Invalid
B	Busy 32-bit TSS	Valid
C	32-bit call gate	Valid
D	Invalid	Invalid
E	32-bit trap gate	Invalid
F	32-bit interrupt gate	Invalid

Flags Affected

The ZF flag is set unless the selector is invisible or of the wrong type, in which case the ZF flag is cleared.

Protected Mode Exceptions

#GP(0) for an illegal memory operand effective address in the CS, DS, ES, FS, or GS segments; #SS(0) for an illegal address in the SS segment; #PF(fault-code) for a page fault; #AC for unaligned memory reference if the current privilege level is 3.

Real Address Mode Exceptions

Interrupt 6; the LAR instruction is unrecognized in Real Address Mode.

Virtual 8086 Mode Exceptions

Same exceptions as in Real Address Mode.

LDS/LES/LFS/LGS/LSS—Load Full Pointer

Opcode	Instruction	Clocks	Description
C5 /r	LDS r16,m16:16	4	Load DS:r16 with pointer from memory
C5 /r	LDS r32,m16:32	4	Load DS:r32 with pointer from memory
0F B2 /r	LSS r16,m16:16	4/pm=8	Load SS:r16 with pointer from memory
0F B2 /r	LSS r32,m16:32	4/pm=8	Load SS:r32 with pointer from memory
C4 /r	LES r16,m16:16	4	Load ES:r16 with pointer from memory
C4 /r	LES r32,m16:32	4	Load ES:r32 with pointer from memory
0F B4 /r	LFS r16,m16:16	4	Load FS:r16 with pointer from memory
0F B4 /r	LFS r32,m16:32	4	Load FS:r32 with pointer from memory
0F B5 /r	LGS r16,m16:16	4	Load GS:r16 with pointer from memory
0F B5 /r	LGS r32,m16:32	4	Load GS:r32 with pointer from memory

Operation

```
CASE instruction OF
    LSS: Sreg is SS; (* Load SS register *)
    LDS: Sreg is DS; (* Load DS register *)
    LES: Sreg is ES; (* Load ES register *)
    LFS: Sreg is FS; (* Load FS register *)
    LGS: Sreg is DS; (* Load GS register *)
ESAC;
IF (OperandSize = 16)
THEN
    r16 ← [Effective Address]; (* 16-bit transfer *)
    Sreg ← [Effective Address + 2]; (* 16-bit transfer *)
    (* In Protected Mode, load the descriptor into the segment register *)
ELSE (* OperandSize = 32 *)
    r32 ← [Effective Address]; (* 32-bit transfer *)
    Sreg ← [Effective Address + 4]; (* 16-bit transfer *)
    (* In Protected Mode, load the descriptor into the segment register *)
FI;
```

Description

The LGS, LSS, LDS, LES, and LFS instructions read a full pointer from memory and store it in the selected segment register:register pair. The full pointer loads 16 bits into the segment register SS, DS, ES, FS, or GS. The other register loads 32 bits if the operand-size attribute is 32 bits, or loads 16 bits if the operand-size attribute is 16 bits. The other 16- or 32-bit register to be loaded is determined by the **r16** or **r32** register operand specified.

When an assignment is made to one of the segment registers, the descriptor is also loaded into the segment register. The data for the register is obtained from the descriptor table entry for the selector given.

A null selector (values 0000-0003) can be loaded into DS, ES, FS, or GS registers without causing a protection exception. (Any subsequent reference to a segment whose corresponding segment register is loaded with a null selector to address memory causes a #GP(0) exception. No memory reference to the segment occurs.)

The following is a listing of the Protected Mode checks and actions taken in the loading of a segment register:

IF SS is loaded:
  IF selector is null THEN #GP(0); FI;
  Selector index must be within its descriptor table limits ELSE
    #GP(selector);
  Selector's RPL must equal CPL ELSE #GP(selector);
  AR byte must indicate a writable data segment ELSE #GP(selector);
  DPL in the AR byte must equal CPL ELSE #GP(selector);
  Segment must be marked present ELSE #SS(selector);
  Load SS with selector;
  Load SS with descriptor;

IF DS, ES, FS, or GS is loaded with non-null selector:
  Selector index must be within its descriptor table limits ELSE
    #GP(selector);
  AR byte must indicate data or readable code segment ELSE
    #GP(selector);
  IF data or nonconforming code
  THEN both the RPL and the CPL must be less than or equal to DPL in
    AR byte;
  ELSE #GP(selector);
  Segment must be marked present ELSE #NP(selector);
Load segment register with selector and RPL bits;
Load segment register with descriptor;

IF DS, ES, FS or GS is loaded with a null selector:
  Load segment register with selector;
  Clear descriptor valid bit;

Flags Affected

None.

Protected Mode Exceptions

#GP(0) for an illegal memory operand effective address in the CS, DS, ES, FS, or GS segments; #SS(0) for an illegal address in the SS segment; the second operand must be a memory operand, not a register—if a register then #UD Fault; #GP(0) if a null selector is loaded into SS; #PF(fault-code) for a page fault; #AC for unaligned memory reference if the current privilege level is 3.

Real Address Mode Exceptions

The second operand must be a memory operand, not a register; Interrupt 13 if any part of the operand would lie outside of the effective address space from 0 to 0FFFFH.

Virtual 8086 Mode Exceptions

Same exceptions as in Real Address Mode; #PF(fault-code) for a page fault; #AC for unaligned memory reference if the current privilege level is 3.

LEA—Load Effective Address

Opcode	Instruction	Clocks	Description
8D /r	LEA r16,m	1	Store effective address for m in register r16
8D /r	LEA r32,m	1	Store effective address for m in register r32
8D /r	LEA r16,m	1	Store effective address for m in register r16
8D /r	LEA r32,m	1	Store effective address for m in register r32

Operation

```
IF OperandSize = 16 AND AddressSize = 16
THEN r16 ← Addr(m);
ELSE
    IF OperandSize = 16 AND AddressSize = 32
    THEN
        r16 ← Truncate_to_16bits(Addr(m));        (* 32-bit address *)
    ELSE
        IF OperandSize = 32 AND AddressSize = 16
        THEN
            r32 ← Truncate_to_16bits(Addr(m)) and zero extend;
        ELSE
            IF OperandSize = 32 AND AddressSize = 32
            THEN    r32 ← Addr(m);
            FI;
        FI;
    FI;
FI;
```

Description

The LEA instruction calculates the effective address (offset part) and stores it in the specified register. The operand-size attribute of the instruction (represented by OperandSize in the algorithm under "Operation" above) is determined by the chosen register. The address-size attribute (represented by AddressSize) is determined by the attribute of the code segment. (See the "Operand-Size and Address-Size Attributes" section at the beginning of this chapter.) The address-size and operand-size attributes affect the action performed by the LEA instruction, as follows:

Operand Size	Address Size	Action Performed
16	16	16-bit effective address is calculated and stored in requested 16-bit register destination.
16	32	32-bit effective address is calculated. The lower 16 bits of the address are stored in the requested 16-bit register destination.
32	16	16-bit effective address is calculated. The 16-bit address is zero-extended and stored in the requested 32-bit register destination.
32	32	32-bit effective address is calculated and stored in the requested 32-bit register destination.

Flags Affected

None.

Protected Mode Exceptions

#UD if the second operand is a register.

Real Address Mode Exceptions

Interrupt 6 if the second operand is a register.

Virtual 8086 Mode Exceptions

Same exceptions as in Real Address Mode.

Notes

Different assemblers may use different algorithms based on the size attribute and symbolic reference of the second operand.

LEAVE—High Level Procedure Exit

Opcode	Instruction	Clocks	Description
C9	LEAVE	3	Set SP to BP, then pop BP
C9	LEAVE	3	Set ESP to EBP, then pop EBP

Operation

```
IF StackAddrSize = 16
THEN
    SP ← BP;
ELSE (* StackAddrSize = 32 *)
    ESP ← EBP;
FI;
IF OperandSize = 16
THEN
    BP ← Pop();
ELSE (* OperandSize = 32 *)
    EBP ← Pop();
FI;
```

Description

The LEAVE instruction reverses the actions of the ENTER instruction. By copying the frame pointer to the stack pointer, the LEAVE instruction releases the stack space used by a procedure for its local variables. The old frame pointer is popped into the BP or EBP register, restoring the caller's frame. A subsequent RET **nn** instruction removes any arguments pushed onto the stack of the exiting procedure.

Flags Affected

None.

Protected Mode Exceptions

#SS(0) if the BP register does not point to a location within the limits of the current stack segment.

Real Address Mode Exceptions

Interrupt 13 if any part of the operand would lie outside of the effective address space from 0 to 0FFFFH.

Virtual 8086 Mode Exceptions

Same exceptions as in Real Address Mode.

LES—Load Full Pointer

See entry for LDS/LES/LFS/LGS/LSS.

LFS—Load Full Pointer

See entry for LDS/LES/LFS/LGS/LSS.

LGDT/LIDT—Load Global/Interrupt Descriptor Table Register

Opcode	Instruction	Clocks	Description
0F 01 /2	LGDT *m16&32*	6	Load *m* into GDTR
0F 01 /3	LIDT *m16&32*	6	Load *m* into IDTR

Operation

```
IF instruction = LIDT
THEN
    IF OperandSize = 16
    THEN IDTR.Limit:Base ← m16:24 (* 24 bits of base loaded *)
    ELSE IDTR.Limit:Base ← m16:32
    FI;
ELSE (* instruction = LGDT *)
    IF OperandSize = 16
    THEN GDTR.Limit:Base ← m16:24 (* 24 bits of base loaded *)
    ELSE GDTR.Limit:Base ← m16:32;
    FI;
FI;
```

Description

The LGDT and LIDT instructions load a linear base address and limit value from a six-byte data operand in memory into the GDTR or IDTR, respectively. If a 16-bit operand is used with the LGDT or LIDT instruction, the register is loaded with a 16-bit limit and a 24-bit base, and the high-order eight bits of the six-byte data operand are not used. If a 32-bit operand is used, a 16-bit limit and a 32-bit base is loaded; the high-order eight bits of the six-byte operand are used as high-order base address bits.

The SGDT and SIDT instructions always store into all 48 bits of the six-byte data operand. With the 16-bit processors, the upper eight bits are undefined after the SGDT or SIDT instruction is executed. With the 32-bit processors, the upper eight bits are written with the high-order eight address bits, for both a 16-bit operand and a 32-bit operand. If the LGDT or LIDT instruction is used with a 16-bit operand to load the register stored by the SGDT or SIDT instruction, the upper eight bits are stored as zeros.

The LGDT and LIDT instructions appear in operating system software; they are not used in application programs. They are the only instructions that directly load a linear address (i.e., not a segment relative address) in Protected Mode.

Flags Affected

None.

Protected Mode Exceptions

#GP(0) if the current privilege level is not 0; #UD if the source operand is a register; #GP(0) for an illegal memory operand effective address in the CS, DS, ES, FS, or GS segments; #SS(0) for an illegal address in the SS segment; #PF(fault-code) for a page fault.

Real Address Mode Exceptions

Interrupt 13 if any part of the operand would lie outside of the effective address space from 0 to 0FFFFH; Interrupt 6 if the source operand is a register.

Note: These instructions are valid in Real Address Mode to allow power-up initialization for Protected Mode.

Virtual 8086 Mode Exceptions

Same exceptions as in Real Address Mode; #PF(fault-code) for a page fault.

LGS—Load Full Pointer

See entry for LDS/LES/LFS/LGS/LSS.

LLDT—Load Local Descriptor Table Register

Opcode	Instruction	Clocks	Description
0F 00 /2	LLDT r/m16	9	Load selector r/m16 into LDTR

Operation

LDTR ← SRC;

Description

The LLDT instruction loads the Local Descriptor Table register (LDTR). The word operand (memory or register) to the LLDT instruction should contain a selector to the Global Descriptor Table (GDT). The GDT entry should be a Local Descriptor Table. If so, then the LDTR is loaded from the entry. The descriptor registers DS, ES, SS, FS, GS, and CS are not affected. The LDT field in the task state segment does not change.

The selector operand can be 0; if so, the LDTR is marked invalid. All descriptor references (except by the LAR, VERR, VERW or LSL instructions) cause a #GP fault.

The LLDT instruction is used in operating system software; it is not used in application programs.

Flags Affected

None.

Protected Mode Exceptions

#GP(0) if the current privilege level is not 0; #GP(selector) if the selector operand does not point into the Global Descriptor Table, or if the entry in the GDT is not a Local Descriptor Table; #NP(selector) if the LDT descriptor is not present; #GP(0) for an illegal memory operand effective address in the CS, DS, ES, FS, or GS segments; #SS(0) for an illegal address in the SS segment; #PF(fault-code) for a page fault.

Real Address Mode Exceptions

Interrupt 6; the LLDT instruction is not recognized in Real Address Mode.

Virtual 8086 Mode Exceptions

Same exceptions as in Real Address Mode (because the instruction is not recognized, it will not execute or perform a memory reference).

Note

The operand-size attribute has no effect on this instruction.

LIDT—Load Interrupt Descriptor Table Register

See entry for LGDT/LIDT—Load Global Descriptor Table Register/Load Interrupt Descriptor Table Register.

LMSW—Load Machine Status Word

Opcode	Instruction	Clocks	Description
0F 01 /6	LMSW r/m16	8	Load r/m16 in machine status word

Operation

MSW ← r/m16; (* 16 bits is stored in the machine status word *)

Description

The LMSW instruction loads the machine status word (part of the CR0 register) from the source operand. This instruction can be used to switch to Protected Mode; if so, it must be followed by an intrasegment jump to flush the instruction queue. The LMSW instruction will not switch back to Real Address Mode.

The LMSW instruction is used only in operating system software. It is not used in application programs.

Flags Affected

None.

Protected Mode Exceptions

#GP(0) if the current privilege level is not 0; #GP(0) for an illegal memory operand effective address in the CS, DS, ES, FS, or GS segments; #SS(0) for an illegal address in the SS segment; #PF(fault-code) for a page fault.

Real Address Mode Exceptions

Interrupt 13 if any part of the operand would lie outside of the effective address space from 0 to 0FFFFH.

Virtual 8086 Mode Exceptions

Same exceptions as in Protected Mode.

Notes

The operand-size attribute has no effect on this instruction. This instruction is provided for compatibility with the Intel286 processor; programs for the Intel386, Intel486, and Pentium processors should use the MOV CR0, ... instruction instead. The LMSW instruction does not affect the PG, ET, or NE bits, and it cannot be used to clear the PE bit.

LOCK—Assert LOCK# Signal Prefix

Opcode	Instruction	Clocks	Description
F0	LOCK	1	Assert LOCK# signal for the next instruction

Description

The LOCK prefix causes the LOCK# signal of the Pentium processor to be asserted during execution of the instruction that follows it. In a multiprocessor environment, this signal can be used to ensure that the Pentium processor has exclusive use of any shared memory while LOCK# is asserted. The read-modify-write sequence typically used to implement test-and-set on the Pentium processor is the BTS instruction.

The LOCK prefix functions only with the following instructions:

BTS, BTR, BTC	mem, reg/imm
XCHG	reg, mem
XCHG	mem, reg
ADD, OR, ADC, SBB, AND, SUB, XOR	mem, reg/imm
NOT, NEG, INC, DEC	mem
CMPXCHG, XADD	

An undefined opcode trap will be generated if a LOCK prefix is used with any instruction not listed above.

The XCHG instruction always asserts LOCK# regardless of the presence or absence of the LOCK prefix.

The integrity of the LOCK prefix is not affected by the alignment of the memory field. Memory locking is observed for arbitrarily misaligned fields.

Flags Affected

None.

Protected Mode Exceptions

#UD if the LOCK prefix is used with an instruction not listed in the "Description" section above; other exceptions can be generated by the subsequent (locked) instruction.

Real Address Mode Exceptions

Interrupt 6 if the LOCK prefix is used with an instruction not listed in the "Description" section above; exceptions can still be generated by the subsequent (locked) instruction.

Virtual 8086 Mode Exceptions

#UD if the LOCK prefix is used with an instruction not listed in the "Description" section above; exceptions can still be generated by the subsequent (locked) instruction.

LODS/LODSB/LODSW/LODSD—Load String Operand

Opcode	Instruction	Clocks	Description
AC	LODS m8	2	Load byte [(E)SI] into AL
AD	LODS m16	2	Load word [(E)SI] into AX
AD	LODS m32	2	Load dword [(E)SI] into EAX
AC	LODSB	2	Load byte DS:[(E)SI] into AL
AD	LODSW	2	Load word DS:[(E)SI] into AX
AD	LODSD	2	Load dword DS:[(E)SI] into EAX

Operation

```
AddressSize = 16
THEN use SI for source-index
ELSE (* AddressSize = 32 *)
   use ESI for source-index;
FI;
IF byte type of instruction
THEN
   AL ← [source-index]; (* byte load *)
   IF DF = 0 THEN IncDec ← 1 ELSE IncDec ← –1; FI;
ELSE
   IF OperandSize = 16
   THEN
      AX ← [source-index]; (* word load *)
      IF DF = 0 THEN IncDec ← 2 ELSE IncDec ← –2; FI;
   ELSE (* OperandSize = 32 *)
      EAX ← [source-index]; (* dword load *)
      IF DF = 0 THEN IncDec ← 4 ELSE IncDec ← –4; FI;
   FI;
FI;
source-index ← source-index + IncDec
```

Description

The LODS instruction loads the AL, AX, or EAX register with the memory byte, word, or doubleword at the location pointed to by the source-index register. After the transfer is made, the source-index register is automatically advanced. If the DF flag is 0 (the CLD instruction was executed), the source index increments; if the DF flag is 1 (the STD instruction was executed), it decrements. The increment or decrement is 1 if a byte is loaded, 2 if a word is loaded, or 4 if a doubleword is loaded.

If the address-size attribute for this instruction is 16 bits, the SI register is used for the source-index register; otherwise the address-size attribute is 32 bits, and the ESI register is used. The address of the source data is determined solely by the contents of the ESI or SI register. Load the correct index value into the SI register before executing the LODS instruction. The LODSB, LODSW, and LODSD instructions are synonyms for the byte, word, and doubleword LODS instructions.

The LODS instruction can be preceded by the REP prefix; however, the LODS instruction is used more typically within a LOOP construct, because further processing of the data moved into the EAX, AX, or AL register is usually necessary.

Flags Affected

None.

Protected Mode Exceptions

#GP(0) for an illegal memory operand effective address in the CS, DS, ES, FS, or GS segments; #SS(0) for an illegal address in the SS segment; #PF(fault-code) for a page fault; #AC for unaligned memory reference if the current privilege level is 3.

Real Address Mode Exceptions

Interrupt 13 if any part of the operand would lie outside of the effective address space from 0 to 0FFFFH.

Virtual 8086 Mode Exceptions

Same exceptions as in Real Address Mode; #PF(fault-code) for a page fault; #AC for unaligned memory reference if the current privilege level is 3.

LOOP/LOOPcond—Loop Control with CX Counter

Opcode	Instruction	Clocks	Description
E2 cb	LOOP rel8	5/6	DEC count; jump short if count <> 0
E1 cb	LOOPE rel8	7/8	DEC count; jump short if count <> 0 and ZF=1
E1 cb	LOOPZ rel8	7/8	DEC count; jump short if count <> 0 and ZF=1
E0 cb	LOOPNE rel8	7/8	DEC count; jump short if count <> 0 and ZF=0
E0 cb	LOOPNZ rel8	7/8	DEC count; jump short if count <> 0 and ZF=0

Operation

```
IF AddressSize = 16 THEN CountReg is CX ELSE CountReg is ECX; FI;
CountReg ← CountReg – 1;

IF instruction <> LOOP
THEN
   IF (instruction = LOOPE) OR (instruction = LOOPZ)
   THEN BranchCond ← (ZF = 1) AND (CountReg <> 0);
   FI;
   IF (instruction = LOOPNE) OR (instruction = LOOPNZ)
   THEN BranchCond ← (ZF = 0) AND (CountReg <> 0);
   FI;
FI;

IF BranchCond
THEN
   IF OperandSize = 16
   THEN
      IP ← IP + SignExtend(rel8);
   ELSE (* OperandSize = 32 *)
      EIP ← EIP + SignExtend(rel8);
   FI;
FI;
```

Description

The LOOP instruction decrements the count register without changing any of the flags. Conditions are then checked for the form of the LOOP instruction being used. If the conditions are met, a short jump is made to the label given by the operand to the LOOP instruction. If the address-size attribute is 16 bits, the CX register is used as the count register; otherwise the ECX register is used. The operand of the LOOP instruction must be in the range from 128 (decimal) bytes before the instruction to 127 bytes ahead of the instruction.

The LOOP instructions provide iteration control and combine loop index management with conditional branching. Use the LOOP instruction by loading an unsigned iteration count into the count register, then code the LOOP instruction at the end of a series of instructions to be iterated. The destination of the LOOP instruction is a label that points to the beginning of the iteration.

Flags Affected

None.

Protected Mode Exceptions

#GP(0) if the offset jumped to is beyond the limits of the current code segment.

Real Address Mode Exceptions

None.

Virtual 8086 Mode Exceptions

None.

Notes

The unconditional LOOP instruction takes longer to execute than a two-instruction sequence which decrements the count register and jumps if the count does not equal zero.

All branches are converted into 16-byte code fetches regardless of jump address or cacheability.

LSL—Load Segment Limit

Opcode	Instruction	Clocks	Description
0F 03 /r	LSL r16,r/m16	8	Load: r16 ← segment limit, selector r/m16 (byte granular)
0F 03 /r	LSL r32,r/m32	8	Load: r32 ← segment limit, selector r/m32 (byte granular)
0F 03 /r	LSL r16,r/m16	8	Load: r16 ← segment limit, selector r/m16 (page granular)
0F 03 /r	LSL r32,r/m32	8	Load: r32 ← segment limit, selector r/m32 (page granular)

Description

The LSL instruction loads a register with an unscrambled segment limit, and sets the ZF flag, provided that the source selector is visible at the current privilege level and RPL, within the descriptor table, and that the descriptor is a type accepted by the LSL instruction. Otherwise, the ZF flag is cleared, and the destination register is unchanged. The segment limit is loaded as a byte granular value. If the descriptor has a page granular segment limit, the LSL instruction will translate it to a byte limit before loading it in the destination register (shift left 12 the 20-bit "raw" limit from descriptor, then OR with 00000FFFH).

The 32-bit forms of the LSL instruction store the 32-bit byte granular limit in the 32-bit destination register. For 16-bit operand sizes, the limit is computed to form a valid 32-bit limit. However, the upper 16 bits are chopped and only the low-order 16 bits are loaded into the destination operand.

Code and data segment descriptors are valid for the LSL instruction.

The valid special segment and gate descriptor types for the LSL instruction are given in the following table:

Type	Name	Valid/Invalid
0	Invalid	Invalid
1	Available 16-bit TSS	Valid
2	LDT	Valid
3	Busy 16-bit TSS	Valid
4	16-bit call gate	Invalid
5	16-bit/32-bit task gate	Invalid
6	16-bit trap gate	Invalid
7	16-bit interrupt gate	Invalid
8	Invalid	Invalid
9	Available 32-bit TSS	Valid
A	Invalid	Invalid
B	Busy 32-bit TSS	Valid
C	32-bit call gate	Invalid
D	Invalid	Invalid
E	32-bit trap gate	Invalid
F	32-bit interrupt gate	Invalid

Flags Affected

The ZF flag is set unless the selector is invisible or of the wrong type, in which case the ZF flag is cleared.

Protected Mode Exceptions

#GP(0) for an illegal memory operand effective address in the CS, DS, ES, FS, or GS segments; #SS(0) for an illegal address in the SS segment; #PF(fault-code) for a page fault; #AC for unaligned memory reference if the current privilege level is 3.

Real Address Mode Exceptions

Interrupt 6; the LSL instruction is not recognized in Real Address Mode.

Virtual 8086 Mode Exceptions

Same exceptions as in Real Address Mode (because the instruction is not recognized, it will not execute or perform a memory reference).

LSS—Load Full Pointer

See entry for LDS/LES/LFS/LGS/LSS.

LTR—Load Task Register

Opcode	Instruction	Clocks	Description
0F 00 /3	LTR r/m16	10	Load EA word into task register

Description

The LTR instruction loads the task register with a selector from the source register or memory location specified by the operand. The loaded TSS is marked busy. A task switch does not occur.

The LTR instruction is used only in operating system software; it is not used in application programs.

Flags Affected

None.

Protected Mode Exceptions

#GP(0) for an illegal memory operand effective address in the CS, DS, ES, FS, or GS segments; #SS(0) for an illegal address in the SS segment; #GP(0) if the current privilege level is not 0; #GP(selector) if the object named by the source selector is not a TSS or is already busy; #NP(selector) if the TSS is marked "not present"; #PF(fault-code) for a page fault.

Real Address Mode Exceptions

Interrupt 6; the LTR instruction is not recognized in Real Address Mode.

Virtual 8086 Mode Exceptions

Same exceptions as in Real Address Mode.

Notes

The operand-size attribute has no effect on this instruction.

MOV—Move Data

Opcode	Instruction	Clocks	Description
88 /r	MOV r/m8,r8	1	Move byte register to r/m byte
89 /r	MOV r/m16,r16	1	Move word register to r/m word
89 /r	MOV r/m32,r32	1	Move dword register to r/m dword
8A /r	MOV r8,r/m8	1	Move r/m byte to byte register
8B /r	MOV r16,r/m16	1	Move r/m word to word register
8B /r	MOV r32,r/m32	1	Move r/m dword to dword register
8C /r	MOV r/m16,Sreg*	1	Move segment register to r/m word
8E /r	MOV Sreg,r/m16	2/3**	Move r/m word to segment register
A0	MOV AL,moffs8	1	Move byte at (seg:offset) to AL
A1	MOV AX,moffs16	1	Move word at (seg:offset) to AX
A1	MOV EAX,moffs32	1	Move dword at (seg:offset) to EAX
A2	MOV moffs8,AL	1	Move AL to (seg:offset)
A3	MOV moffs16,AX	1	Move AX to (seg:offset)
A3	MOV moffs32,EAX	1	Move EAX to (seg:offset)
B0+ rb	MOV reg8,imm8	1	Move immediate byte to register
B8+ rw	MOV reg16,imm16	1	Move immediate word to register
B8+ rd	MOV reg32,imm32	1	Move immediate dword to register
C6 /0	MOV r/m8,imm8	1	Move immediate byte to r/m byte
C7 /0	MOV r/m16,imm16	1	Move immediate word to r/m word
C7 /0	MOV r/m32,imm32	1	Move immediate dword to r/m dword

NOTES:

moffs8, moffs16, and **moffs32** all consist of a simple offset relative to the segment base. The 8, 16, and 32 refer to the size of the data. The address-size attribute of the instruction determines the size of the offset, either 16 or 32 bits.

*In 32-bit mode, use 16-bit operand size prefix (a byte with the value 67H preceding the instruction).
**In protected mode, MOV SS, rm16/32 takes 7 clocks.

Operation

DEST ← SRC;

Description

The MOV instruction copies the second operand to the first operand.

If the destination operand is a segment register (DS, ES, SS, etc.), then data from a descriptor is also loaded into the shadow portion of the register. The data for the register is obtained from the descriptor table entry for the selector given. A null selector (values 0000-0003) can be loaded into the DS, ES, FS, and GS registers without causing an exception; however, use of these registers causes a #GP(0) exception, and no memory reference occurs.

A MOV into SS instruction inhibits all interrupts until after the execution of the next instruction (which should be a MOV into ESP instruction).

Loading a segment register under Protected Mode results in special checks and actions, as described in the following listing:

IF SS is loaded;
THEN
    IF selector is null THEN #GP(0);
    Selector index must be within its descriptor table limits else #GP(selector);
    Selector's RPL must equal CPL else #GP(selector);
    AR byte must indicate a writable data segment else #GP(selector);
    DPL in the AR byte must equal CPL else #GP(selector);

Segment must be marked present else #SS(selector);
    Load SS with selector;
    Load SS with descriptor.
FI;
IF DS, ES, FS or GS is loaded with non-null selector;
THEN
    Selector index must be within its descriptor table limits
        else #GP(selector);
    AR byte must indicate data or readable code segment else #GP(selector);
    IF data or nonconforming code segment
    THEN both the RPL and the CPL must be less than or equal to DPL in AR byte;
    ELSE #GP(selector);
    FI;
    Segment must be marked present else #NP(selector);
    Load segment register with selector;
    Load segment register with descriptor;
FI;
IF DS, ES, FS or GS is loaded with a null selector;
THEN
    Load segment register with selector;
    Clear descriptor valid bit;
FI;

Flags Affected

None.

Protected Mode Exceptions

#GP, #SS, and #NP if a segment register is being loaded; otherwise, #GP(0) if the destination is in a nonwritable segment; #GP(0) for an illegal memory operand effective address in the CS, DS, ES, FS, or GS segments; #SS(0) for an illegal address in the SS segment; #PF(fault-code) for a page fault; #AC for unaligned memory reference if the current privilege level is 3.

Real Address Mode Exceptions

Interrupt 13 if any part of the operand would lie outside of the effective address space from 0 to 0FFFFH.

Virtual 8086 Mode Exceptions

Same exceptions as in Real Address Mode; #PF(fault-code) for a page fault; #AC for unaligned memory reference if the current privilege level is 3.

MOV—Move to/from Control Registers

Opcode	Instruction	Clocks	Description
0F 22 /r	MOV CR0,r32	22	Move (register) to (control register 0)
0F 22 /r	MOV CR2,r32	12	Move (register) to (control register 2)
0F 22 /r	MOV CR4,r32	21/46	Move (register) to (control register 3)
0F 22 /r	MOV CR4,r32	14	Move (register) to (control register 4)
0F 20 /r	MOV r32,CR0-4	4	Move (control register) to (register)

Operation

DEST ← SRC;

Description

The above forms of the MOV instruction store or load CR0, CR2, CR3, and CR4 to or from a general purpose register.

Thirty-two bit operands are always used with these instructions, regardless of the operand-size attribute.

Flags Affected

The OF, SF, ZF, AF, PF, and CF flags are undefined.

Protected Mode Exceptions

#GP(0) if the current privilege level is not 0. #GP(0) if an attempt is made to write a 1 to any reserved bits of CR4.

Real Address Mode Exceptions

Interrupt 13 if an attempt is made to write a 1 to any reserved bits of CR4.

Virtual 8086 Mode Exceptions

#GP(0) if instruction execution is attempted.

Notes

The *reg* field within the ModR/M byte specifies which of the special registers in each category is involved. The two bits in the *mod* field are always 11. The *r/m* field specifies the general register involved.

Always set undefined or reserved bits to the value previously read.

MOV—Move to/from Debug Registers

Opcode	Instruction	Clocks	Description
0F 21/r	MOV r32, DR0-DR3	11	Move (debug register) to (register)
0F 21/r	MOV r32, DR4-DR5	12	Move (debug register) to (register)
0F 21/r	MOV r32, DR6-DR7	11	Move (debug register) to (register)
0F 23 /r	MOV DR0-DR3, r32	11	Move (register) to (debug register)
0F 23 /r	MOV DR4-DR5, r32	12	Move (register) to (debug register)
0F 23 /r	MOV DR6-DR7,r32	11	Move (register) to (debug register)

Operation

```
IF ((DE = 1)  and (SRC or DEST = DR4 or DR5))
THEN
    #UD;
ELSE
    DEST ← SRC;
```

Description

The above forms of the MOV instruction store or load the DR0, DR1, DR2, DR3, DR6 and DR7 debug registers to or from a general purpose register.

Thirty-two bit operands are always used with these instructions, regardless of the operand-size attribute.

When the DE (Debug Extension) bit in CR4 is clear, MOV instructions using debug registers operate in a manner that is compatible with Intel386 and Intel486 CPU's. References to DR4 and DR5 refer to DR6 and DR7, respectively. When the DE bit in CR4 is set, attempts to execute MOV instructions using DR4 and DR5 result in an Undefined Opcode (#UD) exception.

Flags Affected

The OF, SF, ZF, AF, PF, and CF flags are undefined.

Protected Mode Exceptions

#GP(0) if the current privilege level is not 0. #UD if the DE (Debug Extensions) bit of CR4 is set and a MOV instruction is executed using DR4 or DR5.

Real Address Mode Exceptions

#GP(0) if an attempt is made to write a 1 to any reserved bits of CR4. #UD if the DE (Debug Extensions) bit of CR4 is set and a MOV instruction is executed using DR4 or DR5.

Virtual 8086 Mode Exceptions

#GP(0) if instruction execution is attempted.

Notes

The instructions must be executed at privilege level 0 or in real-address mode; otherwise, a protection exception will be raised.

The *reg* field within the ModR/M byte specifies which of the special registers in each category is involved. The two bits in the *mod* field are always 11. The *r/m* field specifies the general register involved.

Always set undefined or reserved bits to the value previously read.

MOVS/MOVSB/MOVSW/MOVSD—Move Data from String to String

Opcode	Instruction	Clocks	Description
A4	MOVS m8,m8	4	Move byte [(E)SI] to ES:[(E)DI]
A5	MOVS m16,m16	4	Move word [(E)SI] to ES:[(E)DI]
A5	MOVS m32,m32	4	Move dword [(E)SI] to ES:[(E)DI]
A4	MOVSB	4	Move byte DS:[(E)SI] to ES:[(E)DI]
A5	MOVSW	4	Move word DS:[(E)SI] to ES:[(E)DI]
A5	MOVSD	4	Move dword DS:[(E)SI] to ES:[(E)DI]

Operation

```
IF (instruction = MOVSD) OR (instruction has doubleword operands)
THEN OperandSize ← 32;
ELSE OperandSize ← 16;
IF AddressSize = 16
THEN use SI for source-index and DI for destination-index;
ELSE (* AddressSize = 32 *)
   use ESI for source-index and EDI for destination-index;
FI;
IF byte type of instruction
THEN
   [destination-index] ← [source-index]; (* byte assignment *)
   IF DF = 0 THEN IncDec ← 1 ELSE IncDec ← −1; FI;
ELSE
   IF OperandSize = 16
   THEN
      [destination-index] ← [source-index]; (* word assignment *)
      IF DF = 0 THEN IncDec ← 2 ELSE IncDec ← −2; FI;
   ELSE (* OperandSize = 32 *)
      [destination-index] ← [source-index]; (* doubleword assignment *)
      IF DF = 0 THEN IncDec ← 4 ELSE IncDec ← −4; FI;
   FI;
FI;
source-index ← source-index + IncDec;
destination-index ← destination-index + IncDec;
```

Description

The MOVS instruction copies the byte or word at [(E)SI] to the byte or word at ES:[(E)DI]. The destination operand must be addressable from the ES register; no segment override is possible for the destination. A segment override can be used for the source operand; the default is the DS register.

The addresses of the source and destination are determined solely by the contents of the (E)SI and (E)DI registers. Load the correct index values into the (E)SI and (E)DI registers before executing the MOVS instruction. The MOVSB, MOVSW, and MOVSD instructions are synonyms for the byte, word, and doubleword MOVS instructions.

After the data is moved, both the (E)SI and (E)DI registers are advanced automatically. If the DF flag is 0 (the CLD instruction was executed), the registers are incremented; if the DF flag is

1 (the STD instruction was executed), the registers are decremented. The registers are incremented or decremented by 1 if a byte was moved, 2 if a word was moved, or 4 if a doubleword was moved.

The MOVS instruction can be preceded by the REP prefix for block movement of ECX bytes or words. Refer to the REP instruction for details of this operation.

Flags Affected

None.

Protected Mode Exceptions

#GP(0) if the result is in a nonwritable segment; #GP(0) for an illegal memory operand effective address in the CS, DS, ES, FS, or GS segments; #SS(0) for an illegal address in the SS segment; #PF(fault-code) for a page fault; #AC for unaligned memory reference if the current privilege level is 3.

Real Address Mode Exceptions

Interrupt 13 if any part of the operand would lie outside of the effective address space from 0 to 0FFFFH.

Virtual 8086 Mode Exceptions

Same exceptions as in Real Address Mode; #PF(fault-code) for a page fault; #AC for unaligned memory reference if the current privilege level is 3.

MOVSX—Move with Sign-Extend

Opcode	Instruction	Clocks	Description
0F BE /r	MOVSX r16,r/m8	3	Move byte to word with sign-extend
0F BE /r	MOVSX r32,r/m8	3	Move byte to dword, sign-extend
0F BF /r	MOVSX r32,r/m16	3	Move word to dword, sign-extend

Operation

DEST ← SignExtend(SRC);

Description

The MOVSX instruction reads the contents of the effective address or register as a byte or a word, sign-extends the value to the operand-size attribute of the instruction (16 or 32 bits), and stores the result in the destination register.

Flags Affected

None.

Protected Mode Exceptions

#GP(0) for an illegal memory operand effective address in the CS, DS, ES, FS or GS segments; #SS(0) for an illegal address in the SS segment; #PF(fault-code) for a page fault; #AC for unaligned memory reference if the current privilege level is 3.

Real Address Mode Exceptions

Interrupt 13 if any part of the operand would lie outside of the effective address space from 0 to 0FFFFH.

Virtual 8086 Mode Exceptions

Same exceptions as in Real Address Mode; #PF(fault-code) for a page fault; #AC for unaligned memory reference if the current privilege level is 3.

MOVZX—Move with Zero-Extend

Opcode	Instruction	Clocks	Description
0F B6 /r	MOVZX r16,r/m8	3	Move byte to word with zero-extend
0F B6 /r	MOVZX r32,r/m8	3	Move byte to dword, zero-extend
0F B7 /r	MOVZX r32,r/m16	3	Move word to dword, zero-extend

Operation

DEST ← ZeroExtend(SRC);

Description

The MOVZX instruction reads the contents of the effective address or register as a byte or a word, zero extends the value to the operand-size attribute of the instruction (16 or 32 bits), and stores the result in the destination register.

Flags Affected

None.

Protected Mode Exceptions

#GP(0) for an illegal memory operand effective address in the CS, DS, ES, FS, or GS segments; #SS(0) for an illegal address in the SS segment; #PF(fault-code) for a page fault; #AC for unaligned memory reference if the current privilege level is 3.

Real Address Mode Exceptions

Interrupt 13 if any part of the operand would lie outside of the effective address space from 0 to 0FFFFH.

Virtual 8086 Mode Exceptions

Same exceptions as in Real Address Mode; #PF(fault-code) for a page fault; #AC for unaligned memory reference if the current privilege level is 3.

MUL—Unsigned Multiplication of AL, AX, or EAX

Opcode	Instruction	Clocks	Description
F6 /4	MUL AL,r/m8	11	Unsigned multiply (AX ← AL * r/m byte)
F7 /4	MUL AX,r/m16	11	Unsigned multiply (DX:AX ← AX * r/m word)
F7 /4	MUL EAX,r/m32	10	Unsigned multiply (EDX:EAX ← EAX * r/m dword)

Operation

```
IF byte-size operation
THEN AX ← AL * r/m8
ELSE (* word or doubleword operation *)
   IF OperandSize = 16
   THEN DX:AX ← AX * r/m16
   ELSE (* OperandSize = 32 *)
      EDX:EAX ← EAX * r/m32
   FI;
FI;
```

Description

The MUL instruction performs unsigned multiplication. Its actions depend on the size of its operand, as follows:

- A byte operand is multiplied by the AL value; the result is left in the AX register. The CF and OF flags are cleared if the AH value is 0; otherwise, they are set.

- A word operand is multiplied by the AX value; the result is left in the DX:AX register pair. The DX register contains the high-order 16 bits of the product. The CF and OF flags are cleared if the DX value is 0; otherwise, they are set.

- A doubleword operand is multiplied by the EAX value and the result is left in the EDX:EAX register. The EDX register contains the high-order 32 bits of the product. The CF and OF flags are cleared if the EDX value is 0; otherwise, they are set.

Flags Affected

The OF and CF flags are cleared if the upper half of the result is 0; otherwise they are set; the SF, ZF, AF, and PF flags are undefined.

Protected Mode Exceptions

#GP(0) for an illegal memory operand effective address in the CS, DS, ES, FS, or GS segments; #SS(0) for an illegal address in the SS segment; #PF(fault-code) for a page fault; #AC for unaligned memory reference if the current privilege level is 3.

Real Address Mode Exceptions

Interrupt 13 if any part of the operand would lie outside of the effective address space from 0 to 0FFFFH.

Virtual 8086 Mode Exceptions

Same exceptions as in Real Address Mode; #PF(fault-code) for a page fault; #AC for unaligned memory reference if the current privilege level is 3.

NEG—Two's Complement Negation

Opcode	Instruction	Clocks	Description
F6 /3	NEG r/m8	1/3	Two's complement negate r/m byte
F7 /3	NEG r/m16	1/3	Two's complement negate r/m word
F7 /3	NEG r/m32	1/3	Two's complement negate r/m dword

Operation

IF $r/m = 0$ THEN CF ← 0 ELSE CF ← 1; FI;
r/m ← − r/m

Description

The NEG instruction replaces the value of a register or memory operand with its two's complement. The operand is subtracted from zero, and the result is placed in the operand.

The CF flag is set, unless the operand is zero, in which case the CF flag is cleared.

Flags Affected

The CF flag is set unless the operand is zero, in which case the CF flag is cleared; the OF, SF, ZF, and PF flags are set according to the result.

Protected Mode Exceptions

#GP(0) if the result is in a nonwritable segment; #GP(0) for an illegal memory operand effective address in the CS, DS, ES, FS, or GS segments; #SS(0) for an illegal address in the SS segment; #PF(fault-code) for a page fault; #AC for unaligned memory reference if the current privilege level is 3.

Real Address Mode Exceptions

Interrupt 13 if any part of the operand would lie outside of the effective address space from 0 to 0FFFFH.

Virtual 8086 Mode Exceptions

Same exceptions as in real-address mode; #PF(fault-code) for a page fault; #AC for unaligned memory reference if the current privilege level is 3.

NOP—No Operation

Opcode	Instruction	Clocks	Description
90	NOP	1	No operation

Description

The NOP instruction performs no operation. The NOP instruction is a one-byte instruction that takes up space but affects none of the machine context except the (E)IP register.

The NOP instruction is an alias mnemonic for the XCHG (E)AX, (E)AX instruction.

Flags Affected

None.

Protected Mode Exceptions

None.

Real Address Mode Exceptions

None.

Virtual 8086 Mode Exceptions

None.

®

NOT—One's Complement Negation

Opcode	Instruction	Clocks	Description
F6 /2	NOT r/m8	1/3	Reverse each bit of r/m byte
F7 /2	NOT r/m16	1/3	Reverse each bit of r/m word
F7 /2	NOT r/m32	1/3	Reverse each bit of r/m dword

Operation

r/m ← NOT r/m;

Description

The NOT instruction inverts the operand; every 1 becomes a 0, and vice versa.

Flags Affected

None.

Protected Mode Exceptions

#GP(0) if the result is in a nonwritable segment; #GP(0) for an illegal memory operand effective address in the CS, DS, ES, FS, or GS segments; #SS(0) for an illegal address in the SS segment; #PF(fault-code) for a page fault; #AC for unaligned memory reference if the current privilege level is 3.

Real Address Mode Exceptions

Interrupt 13 if any part of the operand would lie outside of the effective address space from 0 to 0FFFFH.

Virtual 8086 Mode Exceptions

Same exceptions as in real-address mode; #PF(fault-code) for a page fault; #AC for unaligned memory reference if the current privilege level is 3.

OR—Logical Inclusive OR

Opcode	Instruction	Clocks	Description
0C ib	OR AL,imm8	1	OR immediate byte to AL
0D iw	OR AX,imm16	1	OR immediate word to AX
0D id	OR EAX,imm32	1	OR immediate dword to EAX
80 /1 ib	OR r/m8,imm8	1/3	OR immediate byte to r/m byte
81 /1 iw	OR r/m16,imm16	1/3	OR immediate word to r/m word
81 /1 id	OR r/m32,imm32	1/3	OR immediate dword to r/m dword
83 /1 ib	OR r/m16,imm8	1/3	OR sign-extended immediate byte with r/m word
83 /1 ib	OR r/m32,imm8	1/3	OR sign-extended immediate byte with r/m dword
08 /r	OR r/m8,r8	1/3	OR byte register to r/m byte
09 /r	OR r/m16,r16	1/3	OR word register to r/m word
09 /r	OR r/m32,r32	1/3	OR dword register to r/m dword
0A /r	OR r8,r/m8	1/2	OR byte register to r/m byte
0B /r	OR r16,r/m16	1/2	OR word register to r/m word
0B /r	OR r32,r/m32	1/2	OR dword register to r/m dword

Operation

DEST ← DEST OR SRC;
CF ← 0;
OF ← 0

Description

The OR instruction computes the inclusive OR of its two operands and places the result in the first operand. Each bit of the result is 0 if both corresponding bits of the operands are 0; otherwise, each bit is 1.

Flags Affected

The OF and CF flags are cleared; the SF, ZF, and PF flags are set according to the result; the AF flag is undefined.

Protected Mode Exceptions

#GP(0) if the result is in a nonwritable segment; #GP(0) for an illegal memory operand effective address in the CS, DS, ES, FS, or GS segments; #SS(0) for an illegal address in the SS segment; #PF(fault-code) for a page fault; #AC for unaligned memory reference if the current privilege level is 3.

Real Address Mode Exceptions

Interrupt 13 if any part of the operand would lie outside of the effective address space from 0 to 0FFFFH.

Virtual 8086 Mode Exceptions

Same exceptions as in real-address mode; #PF(fault-code) for a page fault; #AC for unaligned memory reference if the current privilege level is 3.

OUT—Output to Port

Opcode	Instruction	Clocks	Description
E6 ib	OUT imm8,AL	12,pm=9*/ 26**,vm=24	Output byte AL to immediate port number
E7 ib	OUT imm8,AX	12,pm=9*/ 26**,vm=24	Output word AX to immediate port number
E7 ib	OUT imm8,EAX	12,pm=9*/ 26**,vm=24	Output dword EAX to immediate port number
EE	OUT DX,AL	12,pm=9*/ 25**,vm=24	Output byte AL to port number in DX
EF	OUT DX,AX	12,pm=9*/ 25**,vm=24	Output word AX to port number in DX
EF	OUT DX,EAX	12,pm=9*/ 25**,vm=24	Output dword EAX to port number in DX

NOTES:

*If CPL ≤ IOPL
**If CPL > IOPL

Operation

IF (PE = 1) AND ((VM = 1) OR (CPL > IOPL))
THEN (* Virtual 8086 mode, or protected mode with CPL > IOPL *)
   IF NOT I-O-Permission (DEST, width(DEST))
   THEN #GP(0);
   FI;
FI;
[DEST] ← SRC; (* I/O address space used *)

Description

The OUT instruction transfers a data byte or data word from the register (AL, AX, or EAX) given as the second operand to the output port numbered by the first operand. Output to any port from 0 to 65535 is performed by placing the port number in the DX register and then using an OUT instruction with the DX register as the first operand. If the instruction contains an eight-bit port ID, that value is zero-extended to 16 bits.

Flags Affected

None.

Protected Mode Exceptions

#GP(0) if the current privilege level is higher (has less privilege) than the I/O privilege level and any of the corresponding I/O permission bits in the TSS equals 1.

Real Address Mode Exceptions

None.

Virtual 8086 Mode Exceptions

#GP(0) fault if any of the corresponding I/O permission bits in the TSS equals 1.

Notes

After the OUT or OUTS instructions are executed, the Pentium processor ensures that the EWBE# has been sampled active before beginning to execute the next instruction. Note that the instruction may be prefetched if EWBE# is not active, but it willl not execute until EWBE# is sampled active.

OUTS/OUTSB/OUTSW/OUTSD—Output String to Port

Opcode	Instruction	Clocks	Description
6E	OUTS DX,*r/m8*	13,*pm*=10*/ 27**,VM=25	Output byte [(E)SI] to port in DX
6F	OUTS DX,*r/m16*	13,*pm*=10*/ 27**,VM=25	Output word [(E)SI] to port in DX
6F	OUTS DX,*r/m32*	13,*pm*=10*/ 27**,VM=25	Output dword [(E)SI] to port in DX
6E	OUTSB	13,*pm*=10*/ 27**,VM=25	Output byte DS:[(E)SI] to port in DX
6F	OUTSW	13,*pm*=10*/ 27**,VM=25	Output word DS:[(E)SI] to port in DX
6F	OUTSD	13,*pm*=10*/ 27**,VM=25	Output dword DS:[(E)SI] to port in DX

NOTES:

*If CPL ≤ IOPL
**If CPL > IOPL

Operation

IF AddressSize = 16
THEN use SI for source-index;
ELSE (* AddressSize = 32 *)
   use ESI for source-index;
FI;

IF (PE = 1) AND ((VM = 1) OR (CPL > IOPL))
THEN (* Virtual 8086 mode, or protected mode with CPL > IOPL *)
   IF NOT I-O-Permission (DEST, width(DEST))
   THEN #GP(0);
   FI;
FI;
IF byte type of instruction
THEN
   [DX] ← [source-index]; (* Write byte at DX I/O address *)
   IF DF = 0 THEN IncDec ← 1 ELSE IncDec ← –1; FI;
FI;
IF OperandSize = 16
THEN
   [DX] ← [source-index]; (* Write word at DX I/O address *)
   IF DF = 0 THEN IncDec ← 2 ELSE IncDec ← –2; FI;
FI;
IF OperandSize = 32
THEN
   [DX] ← [source-index]; (* Write dword at DX I/O address *)
   IF DF = 0 THEN IncDec ← 4 ELSE IncDec ← –4; FI;
   FI;
FI;
source-index ← source-index + IncDec;

Description

The OUTS instruction transfers data from the memory byte, word, or doubleword at the source-index register to the output port addressed by the DX register. If the address-size attribute for this instruction is 16 bits, the SI register is used for the source-index register; otherwise, the address-size attribute is 32 bits, and the ESI register is used for the source-index register.

The OUTS instruction does not allow specification of the port number as an immediate value. The port must be addressed through the DX register value. Load the correct value into the DX register before executing the OUTS instruction.

The address of the source data is determined by the contents of source-index register. Load the correct index value into the SI or ESI register before executing the OUTS instruction.

After the transfer, source-index register is advanced automatically. If the DF flag is 0 (the CLD instruction was executed), the source-index register is incremented; if the DF flag is 1 (the STD instruction was executed), it is decremented. The amount of the increment or decrement is 1 if a byte is output, 2 if a word is output, or 4 if a doubleword is output.

The OUTSB, OUTSW, and OUTSD instructions are synonyms for the byte, word, and doubleword OUTS instructions. The OUTS instruction can be preceded by the REP prefix for block output of ECX bytes or words. Refer to the REP instruction for details on this operation.

Flags Affected

None.

Protected Mode Exceptions

#GP(0) if the current privilege level is greater than the I/O privilege level and any of the corresponding I/O permission bits in TSS equals 1; #GP(0) for an illegal memory operand effective address in the CS, DS, ES, FS, or GS segments; #SS(0) for an illegal address in the SS segment; #PF(fault-code) for a page fault; #AC for unaligned memory reference if the current privilege level is 3.

Real Address Mode Exceptions

Interrupt 13 if any part of the operand would lie outside of the effective address space from 0 to 0FFFFH.

Virtual 8086 Mode Exceptions

#GP(0) fault if any of the corresponding I/O permission bits in TSS equals 1; #PF(fault-code) for a page fault; #AC for unaligned memory reference if the current privilege level is 3.

Notes

After the OUT or OUTS instructions are executed, the Pentium processor ensures that the

EWBE# has been sampled active before beginning to execute the next instruction. Note that the instruction may be prefetched if EWBE# is not active, but it will not execute until EWBE# is sampled active.

POP—Pop a Word from the Stack

Opcode	Instruction	Clocks	Description
8F /0	POP m16	3	Pop top of stack into memory word
8F /0	POP m32	3	Pop top of stack into memory dword
58+ rw	POP r16	1	Pop top of stack into word register
58+ rd	POP r32	1	Pop top of stack into dword register
1F	POP DS	3	Pop top of stack into DS
07	POP ES	3	Pop top of stack into ES
17	POP SS	3	Pop top of stack into SS
0F A1	POP FS	3	Pop top of stack into FS
0F A9	POP GS	3	Pop top of stack into GS

Operation

```
IF StackAddrSize = 16
THEN
    IF OperandSize = 16
    THEN
        DEST ← (SS:SP); (* copy a word *)
        SP ← SP + 2;
    ELSE (* OperandSize = 32 *)
        DEST ← (SS:SP); (* copy a dword *)
        SP ← SP + 4;
    FI;
ELSE (* StackAddrSize = 32 * )
    IF OperandSize = 16
    THEN
        DEST ← (SS:ESP); (* copy a word *)
        ESP ← ESP + 2;
    ELSE (* OperandSize = 32 *)
        DEST ← (SS:ESP); (* copy a dword *)
        ESP ← ESP + 4;
    FI;
FI;
```

Description

The POP instruction replaces the previous contents of the memory, the register, or the segment register operand with the word on the top of the Pentium processor stack, addressed by SS:SP (address-size attribute of 16 bits) or SS:ESP (address-size attribute of 32 bits). The stack pointer SP is incremented by 2 for an operand-size of 16 bits or by 4 for an operand-size of 32 bits. It then points to the new top of stack.

The POP CS instruction is not a Pentium processor instruction. Popping from the stack into the CS register is accomplished with a RET instruction.

If the destination operand is a segment register (DS, ES, FS, GS, or SS), the value popped must be a selector. In protected mode, loading the selector initiates automatic loading of the descriptor information associated with that selector into the hidden part of the segment register; loading also initiates validation of both the selector and the descriptor information.

A null value (0000-0003) may be popped into the DS, ES, FS, or GS register without causing a protection exception. An attempt to reference a segment whose corresponding segment register is loaded with a null value causes a #GP(0) exception. No memory reference occurs. The saved value of the segment register is null.

A POP SS instruction inhibits all interrupts, including NMI, until after execution of the next instruction. This allows sequential execution of POP SS and MOV eSP, eBP instructions without danger of having an invalid stack during an interrupt. However, use of the LSS instruction is the preferred method of loading the SS and eSP registers.

A POP-to-memory instruction, which uses the stack pointer (ESP) as a base register, references memory after the POP. The base used is the value of the ESP after the instruction executes.

Loading a segment register while in protected mode results in special checks and actions, as described in the following listing:

IF SS is loaded:
    IF selector is null THEN #GP(0);
    Selector index must be within its descriptor table limits ELSE
       #GP(selector);
    Selector's RPL must equal CPL ELSE #GP(selector);
    AR byte must indicate a writable data segment ELSE #GP(selector);
    DPL in the AR byte must equal CPL ELSE #GP(selector);
    Segment must be marked present ELSE #SS(selector);
    Load SS register with selector;
    Load SS register with descriptor;

IF DS, ES, FS or GS is loaded with non-null selector:
    AR byte must indicate data or readable code segment ELSE
       #GP(selector);
    IF data or nonconforming code
    THEN both the RPL and the CPL must be less than or equal to DPL in
       AR byte
    ELSE #GP(selector);
    FI;
    Segment must be marked present ELSE #NP(selector);
    Load segment register with selector;
    Load segment register with descriptor;

IF DS, ES, FS, or GS is loaded with a null selector:
    Load segment register with selector
    Clear valid bit in invisible portion of register

Flags Affected

None.

Protected Mode Exceptions

#GP, #SS, and #NP if a segment register is being loaded; #SS(0) if the current top of stack is not within the stack segment; #GP(0) if the result is in a nonwritable segment; #GP(0) for an illegal memory operand effective address in the CS, DS, ES, FS, or GS segments; #SS(0) for an illegal address in the SS segment; #PF(fault-code) for a page fault; #AC for unaligned memory reference if the current privilege level is 3.

Real Address Mode Exceptions

Interrupt 13 if any part of the operand would lie outside of the effective address space from 0 to 0FFFFH.

Virtual 8086 Mode Exceptions

Same exceptions as in real-address mode; #PF(fault-code) for a page fault; #AC for unaligned memory reference if the current privilege level is 3.

Notes

Back-to-back PUSH/POP instruction sequences are allowed without incurring an additional clock.

The stack segment descriptor's B bit will determine the size of Stack Addr Size.

Pop ESP instructions increments the stack pointer (ESP) before data at the old top of stack is written into the destination.

POPA/POPAD—Pop all General Registers

Opcode	Instruction	Clocks	Description
61	POPA	5	Pop DI, SI, BP, BX, DX, CX, and AX
61	POPAD	5	Pop EDI, ESI, EBP, EDX, ECX, and EAX

Operation

IF OperandSize = 16 (* instruction = POPA *)
THEN
   DI ←Pop();
   SI ← Pop();
   BP ← Pop();
   increment SP by 2 (* skip next 2 bytes of stack *)
   BX ← Pop();
   DX ← Pop();
   CX ← Pop();
   AX ← Pop();
ELSE (* OperandSize = 32, instruction = POPAD *)
   EDI ← Pop();
   ESI ← Pop();
   EBP ← Pop();
   increment SP by 4 (* skip next 4 bytes of stack *)
   EBX ← Pop();
   EDX ← Pop();
   ECX ← Pop();
   EAX ← Pop();
FI;

Description

The POPA instruction pops the eight 16-bit general registers. However, the SP value is discarded instead of loaded into the SP register. The POPA instruction reverses a previous PUSHA instruction, restoring the general registers to their values before the PUSHA instruction was executed. The first register popped is the DI register.

The POPAD instruction pops the eight 32-bit general registers. The ESP value is discarded instead of loaded into the ESP register. The POPAD instruction reverses the previous PUSHAD instruction, restoring the general registers to their values before the PUSHAD instruction was executed. The first register popped is the EDI register.

Flags Affected

None.

Protected Mode Exceptions

#SS(0) if the starting or ending stack address is not within the stack segment; #PF(fault-code) for a page fault.

Real Address Mode Exceptions

Interrupt 13 if any part of the operand would lie outside of the effective address space from 0 to 0FFFFH.

Virtual 8086 Mode Exceptions

Same exceptions as in real-address mode; #PF(fault-code) for a page fault.

POPF/POPFD—Pop Stack into FLAGS or EFLAGS Register

Opcode	Instruction	Clocks	Description
9D	POPF	*pm*= 4,*rm and vm*= 6	Pop top of stack FLAGS
9D	POPFD	*pm*= 4,*rm and vm*= 6	Pop top of stack into EFLAGS

Operation

```
IF VM=0 (* Not in Virtual-8086 Mode *)
THEN
    IF OperandSize=32;
    THEN EFLAGS ← Pop() AND 277FD7H;
    ELSE FLAGS ← Pop();
    FI;
ELSE  (* In Virtual-8086 Mode *)
    IF IOPL=3
    THEN
        IF OperandSize=32
        THEN
            TempEflags ← Pop();
            EFLAGS ← ((EFLAGS AND 1B3000H) OR (TempEflags AND ~1B3000H))
                    (* VM, RF, IOPL, VIP, and VIF of EFLAGS bits are not modified
                       by POPFD *)
        ELSE
            FLAGS ← Pop()
        FI;
    ELSE
        #GP(0);  (* trap to virtual-8086 monitor *)
    FI;
FI;
```

Description

The POPF and POPFD instructions pop the word or doubleword on the top of the stack and store the value in the FLAGS register. If the operand-size attribute of the instruction is 16 bits, then a word is popped and the value is stored in the FLAGS register. If the operand-size attribute is 32 bits, then a doubleword is popped and the value is stored in the EFLAGS register.

When the IOPL is less than 3 in virtual-8086 mode, the POPF instruction causes a general protection exception. When the IOPL is equal to 3 while executing in virtual-8086 mode, POPF pops a word into the FLAGS register.

Refer to Chapter 3 and Chapter 10 for information about the FLAGS and EFLAGS registers. Note that bits 16 and 17 of the EFLAGS register, called the VM and RF flags, respectively, are not affected by the POPF or POPFD instruction.

The I/O privilege level is altered only when executing at privilege level 0. The interrupt flag is altered only when executing at a level at least as privileged as the I/O privilege level. (Real-address mode is equivalent to privilege level 0.) If a POPF instruction is executed with insufficient privilege, an exception does not occur, but the privileged bits do not change.

Flags Affected

All flags except the VM, RF, IOPL, VIF and VIP flags.

Protected Mode Exceptions

#SS(0) if the top of stack is not within the stack segment.

Real Address Mode Exceptions

Interrupt 13 if any part of the operand would lie outside of the effective address space from 0 to 0FFFFH.

Virtual 8086 Mode Exceptions

#GP(0) fault if the I/O privilege level is less than 3 in order to permit emulation. #GP(0) if an attempt is made to execute POPF with an operand-size override prefix.

Notes

For information on the effect of POPF and POPFD when using virtual mode extensions, see Appendix H.

PUSH—Push Operand onto the Stack

Opcode	Instruction	Clocks	Description
FF /6	PUSH r/m16	1/2	Push memory word
FF /6	PUSH r/m32	1/2	Push memory dword
50+rw	PUSH r16	1	Push register word
50+rd	PUSH r32	1	Push register dword
6A	PUSH imm8	1	Push immediate byte
68	PUSH imm16	1	Push immediate word
68	PUSH imm32	1	Push immediate dword
0E	PUSH CS	1	Push CS
16	PUSH SS	1	Push SS
1E	PUSH DS	1	Push DS
06	PUSH ES	1	Push ES
0F A0	PUSH FS	1	Push FS
0F A8	PUSH GS	1	Push GS

Operation

```
IF StackAddrSize = 16
THEN
   IF OperandSize = 16 THEN
      SP ← SP – 2;
      (SS:SP) ← (SOURCE); (* word assignment *)
   ELSE
      SP ← SP – 4;
      (SS:SP) ← (SOURCE); (* dword assignment *)
   FI;
ELSE (* StackAddrSize = 32 *)
   IF OperandSize = 16
   THEN
      ESP ← ESP – 2;
      (SS:ESP) ← (SOURCE); (* word assignment *)
   ELSE
      ESP ← ESP – 4;
      (SS:ESP) ← (SOURCE); (* dword assignment *)
   FI;
FI;
```

Description

The PUSH instruction decrements the stack pointer by 2 if the operand-size attribute of the instruction is 16 bits; otherwise, it decrements the stack pointer by 4. The PUSH instruction then places the operand on the new top of stack, which is pointed to by the stack pointer.

The PUSH ESP instruction pushes the value of the ESP register as it existed before the instruction. This differs from the 8086, where the PUSH SP instruction pushes the new value (decremented by 2).

Likewise, a PUSH-from-memory instruction, which uses the stack pointer (ESP) as a base register, references memory before the PUSH. The base used is the value of the ESP before the instruction executes.

PUSHA/PUSHAD—Push all General Registers

Opcode	Instruction	Clocks	Description
60	PUSHA	5	Push AX, CX, DX, BX, original SP, BP, SI, and DI
60	PUSHAD	5	Push EAX, ECX, EDX, EBX, original ESP, EBP, ESI, and EDI

Operation

```
IF OperandSize = 16 (* PUSHA instruction *)
THEN    Temp ← (SP);
   Push(AX);
   Push(CX);
   Push(DX);
   Push(BX);
   Push(Temp);
   Push(BP);
   Push(SI);
   Push(DI);
ELSE (* OperandSize = 32, PUSHAD instruction *)
   Temp ← (ESP);
   Push(EAX);
   Push(ECX);
   Push(EDX);
   Push(EBX);
   Push(Temp);
   Push(EBP);
   Push(ESI);
   Push(EDI);
FI;
```

Description

The PUSHA and PUSHAD instructions save the 16-bit or 32-bit general registers, respectively, on the Pentium processor stack. The PUSHA instruction decrements the stack pointer (SP) by 16 to hold the eight word values. The PUSHAD instruction decrements the stack pointer (ESP) by 32 to hold the eight doubleword values. Because the registers are pushed onto the stack in the order in which they were given, they appear in the 16 or 32 new stack bytes in reverse order. The last register pushed is the DI or EDI register.

Flags Affected

None.

Protected Mode Exceptions

#SS(0) if the starting or ending stack address is outside the stack segment limit; #PF(fault-code) for a page fault.

Real Address Mode Exceptions

Before executing the PUSHA or PUSHAD instruction, the Pentium processor shuts down if the SP or ESP register equals 1, 3, or 5; if the SP or ESP register equals 7, 9, 11, 13, or 15, exception 13 occurs.

Virtual 8086 Mode Exceptions

Same exceptions as in real-address mode; #PF(fault-code) for a page fault.

®

PUSHF/PUSHFD—Push Flags Register onto the Stack

Opcode	Instruction	Clocks	Description
9C	PUSHF	pm=3, rm and vm=4	Push FLAGS
9C	PUSHFD	pm=3, rm and vm=4	Push EFLAGS

Operation

```
IF VM=0 (* Not in Virtual-8086 Mode *)
THEN
    IF OperandSize = 32
    THEN push(EFLAGS AND 0FCFFFFH);    (* VM and RF EFLAG bits are cleared *)
    ELSE push(FLAGS);
    FI;
ELSE (* In Virtual-8086 Mode *)
    IF IOPL=3
    THEN
        IF OperandSize = 32
        THEN push(EFLAGS AND 0FCFFFFH); (* VM and RF EFLAGS bits are cleared *)
        ELSE push(FLAGS);
        FI;
    ELSE
        #GP(0); (* Trap to virtual-8086 monitor *)
    FI;
FI;
```

Description

The PUSHF instruction decrements the stack pointer by 2 and copies the FLAGS register to the new top of stack; the PUSHFD instruction decrements the stack pointer by 4, and the EFLAGS register is copied to the new top of stack which is pointed to by SS:ESP. Refer to Chapter 3 and Chapter 10 for information on the EFLAGS register.

Flags Affected

None.

Protected Mode Exceptions

#SS(0) if the new value of the ESP register is outside the stack segment boundaries.

Real Address Mode Exceptions

None; the processor shuts down due to a lack of stack space.

Virtual 8086 Mode Exceptions

#GP(0) fault if the I/O privilege level is less than 3, to permit emulation.

Notes

For information on this instruction when using virtual mode extensions, see Appendix H.

RCL/RCR/ROL/ROR——Rotate

Opcode	Instruction	Clocks	Description
D0 /2	RCL r/m8,1	1/3	Rotate 9 bits (CF,r/m byte) left once
D2 /2	RCL r/m8,CL	7-24/9-26	Rotate 9 bits (CF,r/m byte) left CL times
C0 /2 ib	RCL r/m8,imm8	8-25/10-27	Rotate 9 bits (CF,r/m byte) left imm8 times
D1 /2	RCL r/m16,1	1/3	Rotate 17 bits (CF,r/m word) left once
D3 /2	RCL r/m16,CL	7-24/9-26	Rotate 17 bits (CF,r/m word) left CL times
C1 /2 ib	RCL r/m16,imm8	8-25/10-27	Rotate 17 bits (CF,r/m word) left imm8 times
D1 /2	RCL r/m32,1	1/3	Rotate 33 bits (CF,r/m dword) left once
D3 /2	RCL r/m32,CL	7-24/9-26	Rotate 33 bits (CF,r/m dword) left CL times
C1 /2 ib	RCL r/m32,imm8	8-25/10-27	Rotate 33 bits (CF,r/m dword) left imm8 times
D0 /3	RCR r/m8,1	1/3	Rotate 9 bits (CF,r/m byte) right once
D2 /3	RCR r/m8,CL	7-24/9-26	Rotate 9 bits (CF,r/m byte) right CL times
C0 /3 ib	RCR r/m8,imm8	8-25/10-27	Rotate 9 bits (CF,r/m byte) right imm8 times
D1 /3	RCR r/m16,1	1/3	Rotate 17 bits (CF,r/m word) right once
D3 /3	RCR r/m16,CL	7-24/9-26	Rotate 17 bits (CF,r/m word) right CL times
C1 /3 ib	RCR r/m16,imm8	8-25/10-27	Rotate 17 bits (CF,r/m word) right imm8 times
D1 /3	RCR r/m32,1	1/3	Rotate 33 bits (CF,r/m dword) right once
D3 /3	RCR r/m32,CL	7-24/9-26	Rotate 33 bits (CF,r/m dword) right CL times
C1 /3 ib	RCR r/m32,imm8	8-25/10-27	Rotate 33 bits (CF,r/m dword) right imm8 times
D0 /0	ROL r/m8,1	1/3	Rotate 8 bits r/m byte left once
D2 /0	ROL r/m8,CL	4	Rotate 8 bits r/m byte left CL times
C0 /0 ib	ROL r/m8,imm8	1/3	Rotate 8 bits r/m byte left imm8 times
D1 /0	ROL r/m16,1	1/3	Rotate 16 bits r/m word left once
D3 /0	ROL r/m16,CL	4	Rotate 16 bits r/m word left CL times
C1 /0 ib	ROL r/m16,imm8	1/3	Rotate 16 bits r/m word left imm8 times
D1 /0	ROL r/m32,1	1/3	Rotate 32 bits r/m dword left once
D3 /0	ROL r/m32,CL	4	Rotate 32 bits r/m dword left CL times
C1 /0 ib	ROL r/m32,imm8	1/3	Rotate 32 bits r/m dword left imm8 times
D0 /1	ROR r/m8,1	1/3	Rotate 8 bits r/m byte right once
D2 /1	ROR r/m8,CL	4	Rotate 8 bits r/m byte right CL times
C0 /1 ib	ROR r/m8,imm8	1/3	Rotate 8 bits r/m word right imm8 times
D1 /1	ROR r/m16,1	1/3	Rotate 16 bits r/m word right once
D3 /1	ROR r/m16,CL	4	Rotate 16 bits r/m word right CL times
C1 /1 ib	ROR r/m16,imm8	1/3	Rotate 16 bits r/m word right imm8 times
D1 /1	ROR r/m32,1	1/3	Rotate 32 bits r/m dword right once
D3 /1	ROR r/m32,CL	4	Rotate 32 bits r/m dword right CL times
C1 /1 ib	ROR r/m32,imm8	1/3	Rotate 32 bits r/m dword right imm8 times

Operation

```
(* ROL - Rotate Left *)
temp ← COUNT;
WHILE (temp <> 0)
DO
    tmpcf ← high-order bit of (r/m);
    r/m ← r/m * 2 + (tmpcf);
    temp ← temp – 1;
OD;
IF COUNT = 1
THEN
    IF high-order bit of r/m <> CF
    THEN OF ← 1;
    ELSE OF ← 0;
    FI;
ELSE OF ← undefined;
FI;
(* ROR - Rotate Right *)
```

```
temp ← COUNT;
WHILE (temp <> 0 )
DO
    tmpcf ← low-order bit of (r/m);
    r/m ← r/m / 2 + (tmpcf * 2^width(r/m));
    temp ← temp – 1;
DO;
IF COUNT = 1
THEN
    IF (high-order bit of r/m) <> (bit next to high-order bit of r/m)
    THEN OF ← 1;
    ELSE OF ← 0;
    FI;
ELSE OF ← undefined;
FI;
```

Description

Each rotate instruction shifts the bits of the register or memory operand given. The left rotate instructions shift all the bits upward, except for the top bit, which is returned to the bottom. The right rotate instructions do the reverse: the bits shift downward until the bottom bit arrives at the top.

For the RCL and RCR instructions, the CF flag is part of the rotated quantity. The RCL instruction shifts the CF flag into the bottom bit and shifts the top bit into the CF flag; the RCR instruction shifts the CF flag into the top bit and shifts the bottom bit into the CF flag. For the ROL and ROR instructions, the original value of the CF flag is not a part of the result, but the CF flag receives a copy of the bit that was shifted from one end to the other.

The rotate is repeated the number of times indicated by the second operand, which is either an immediate number or the contents of the CL register. To reduce the maximum instruction execution time, the Pentium processor does not allow rotation counts greater than 31. If a rotation count greater than 31 is attempted, only the bottom five bits of the rotation are used. The 8086 does not mask rotation counts. The Pentium processor in Virtual 8086 Mode does mask rotation counts.

The OF flag is defined only for the single-rotate forms of the instructions (second operand is a 1). It is undefined in all other cases. For left shifts/rotates, the CF bit after the shift is XORed with the high-order result bit. For right shifts/rotates, the high-order two bits of the result are XORed to get the OF flag.

Flags Affected

The OF flag is affected only for single-bit rotates; the OF flag is undefined for multi-bit rotates; the CF flag contains the value of the bit shifted into it; the SF, ZF, AF, and PF flags are not affected.

Protected Mode Exceptions

#GP(0) if the result is in a nonwritable segment; #GP(0) for an illegal memory operand effective address in the CS, DS, ES, FS, or GS segments; #SS(0) for an illegal address in the

SS segment; #PF(fault-code) for a page fault; #AC for unaligned memory reference if the current privilege level is 3.

Real Address Mode Exceptions

Interrupt 13 if any part of the operand would lie outside of the effective address space from 0 to 0FFFFH.

Virtual 8086 Mode Exceptions

Same exceptions as in Real Address Mode; #PF(fault-code) for a page fault; #AC for unaligned memory reference if the current privilege level is 3.

RDMSR—Read from Model Specific Register

Opcode	Instruction	Clocks	Description
0F 32	RDMSR	20-24	Read Model Specific Register indicated by ECX into EDX:EAX

Operation

EDX:EAX ← MSR[ECX];

Description

The value in ECX specifies one of the 64-bit Model Specific Registers of the Pentium processor. The content of that Model-Specific Register is copied into EDX:EAX. EDX is loaded with the high-order 32 bits, and EAX is loaded with the low-order 32 bits.

The following values are used to select model specific registers on the Pentium processor:

Value (in Hex)	Register Name	Description
00H	Machine Check Address	Stores address of cycle causing the exception
01H	Machine Check Type	Stores cycle type of cycle causing the exception

For other values used to perform cache, TLB, and BTB testing and performance monitoring, see Appendix H.

Flags Affected

None.

Protected Mode Exceptions

#GP(0) if either the current privilege level is not 0 or the value in ECX does not specify a Model-Specific Register that is implemented in the Pentium processor.

Real Address Mode Exceptions

#GP if the value in ECX does not specify a Model-Specific Register that is implemented in the Pentium processor.

Virtual 8086 Mode Exceptions

#GP(0) if instruction execution is attempted.

Notes

This instruction must be executed at privilege level 0 or in real-address mode; otherwise, a protection exception will be generated.

If less than 64 bits are implemented in a model specific register, the value returned to EDX:EAX, in the locations corresponding to the unimplemented bits, is unpredictable.

RDMSR is used to read the content of Model-Specific Registers that control functions for testability, execution tracing, performance monitoring and machine check errors. Refer to the *Pentium™ Processor Data Book* for more information.

The values 3H, 0FH, and values above 13H are reserved. Do not execute RDMSR with reserved values in ECX.

REP/REPE/REPZ/REPNE/REPNZ—Repeat Following String Operation

Opcode	Instruction	Clocks	Description
F3 6C	REP INS r/m8, DX	11+3(E)CX, pm=8+3(E)CX*'/25+ 3(E)CX*², VM=23+3(E)CX	Input (E)CX bytes from port DX into ES:[(E)DI]
F3 6D	REP INS r/m16,DX	11+3(E)CX, pm=8+3(E)CX*'/25+ 3(E)CX*², VM=23+3(E)CX	Input (E)CX words from port DX into ES:[(E)DI]
F3 6D	REP INS r/m32,DX	11+3(E)CX, pm=8+3(E)CX*'/25+ 3(E)CX*², VM=23+3(E)CX	Input (E)CX dwords from port DX into ES:[(E)DI]
F3 A4	REP MOVS m8,m8	6*⁰,13**, 13+(E)CX*⁰	Move (E)CX bytes from [(E)SI] to ES:[(E)DI]
F3 A5	REP MOVS m16,m16	6*⁰,13**, 13(E)CX*⁰	Move (E)CX words from [(E)SI] to ES:[(E)DI]
F3 A5	REP MOVS m32,m32	6*⁰,13**, 13(E)CX*⁰	Move (E)CX dwords from [(E)SI] to ES:[(E)DI]
F3 6E	REP OUTS DX,r/m8	13+4(E)CX, pm=10+4(E)CX*'27 +4(E)CX*² vm=25+4(E)CX	Output (E)CX bytes from [(E)SI] to port DX
F3 6F	REP OUTS DX,r/m16	13+4(E)CX, pm=10+4(E)CX*'27 +4(E)CX*² vm=25+4(E)CX	Output (E)CX words from [(E)SI] to port DX
F3 6F	REP OUTS DX,r/m32	13+4(E)CX, pm=10+4(E)CX*'27 +4(E)CX*² vm=25+4(E)CX	Output (E)CX dwords from [(E)SI] to port DX
F3 AC	REP LODS AL	7*⁰,7+3(E)CX*⁰	Load (E)CX bytes from [(E)SI] to AL
F3 AD	REP LODS AX	7*⁰,7+3(E)CX*⁰	Load (E)CX words from [(E)SI] to AX
F3 AD	REP LODS EAX	7*⁰,7+3(E)CX*⁰	Load (E)CX dwords from [(E)SI] to EAX
F3 AA	REP STOS m8	6*⁰,9(E)CX*⁰	Fill (E)CX bytes at ES:[(E)DI] with AL
F3 AB	REP STOS m16	6*⁰,9(E)CX*⁰	Fill (E)CX words at ES:[(E)DI] with AX
F3 AB	REP STOS m32	6*⁰,9(E)CX*⁰	Fill (E)CX dwords at ES:[(E)DI] with EAX
F3 A6	REPE CMPS m8,m8	7*⁰,9+4(E)CX*⁰	Find nonmatching bytes in ES:[(E)DI] and [(E)SI]
F3 A7	REPE CMPS m16,m16	7*⁰,9+4(E)CX*⁰	Find nonmatching words in ES:[(E)DI] and [(E)SI]
F3 A7	REPE CMPS m32,m32	7*⁰,9+4(E)CX*⁰	Find nonmatching dwords in ES:[(E)DI] and [(E)SI]
F3 AE	REPE SCAS m8	7*⁰,9+4(E)CX*⁰	Find non-AL byte starting at ES:[(E)DI]
F3 AF	REPE SCAS m16	7*⁰,9+4(E)CX*⁰	Find non-AX word starting at ES:[(E)DI]
F3 AF	REPE SCAS m32	7*⁰,9+4(E)CX*⁰	Find non-EAX dword starting at ES:[(E)DI]
F2 A6	REPNE CMPS m8,m8	7*⁰,8+4(E)CX*⁰	Find matching bytes in ES:[(E)DI] and [(E)SI]
F2 A7	REPNE CMPS m16,m16	7*⁰,8+4(E)CX*⁰	Find matching words in ES:[(E)DI] and [(E)SI]
F2 A7	REPNE CMPS m32,m32	7*⁰,8+4(E)CX*⁰	Find matching dwords in ES:[(E)DI] and [(E)SI]
F2 AE	REPNE SCAS m8	7*⁰,9+4(E)CX*⁰	Find AL, starting at ES:[(E)DI]
F2 AF	REPNE SCAS m16	7*⁰,9+4(E)CX*⁰	Find AX, starting at ES:[(E)DI]
F2 AF	REPNE SCAS m32	7*⁰,9+4(E)CX*⁰	Find EAX, starting at ES:[(E)DI]

NOTES:

*1 If CPL ≤ IOPL

*2 If CPL > IOPL

*3 (E) CX=0

*4 (E) CX =1

*5 (E) CX > 1

*6 (E) CX > 0

Operation

```
IF AddressSize = 16
THEN use CX for CountReg;
ELSE (* AddressSize = 32 *) use ECX for CountReg;
FI;
WHILE CountReg <> 0
DO
   service pending interrupts (if any);
   perform primitive string instruction;
   CountReg ← CountReg − 1;
   IF primitive operation is CMPSB, CMPSW, CMPSD, SCASB, SCASW, or SCASD
   THEN
      IF (instruction is REP/REPE/REPZ) AND (ZF=0)
      THEN exit WHILE loop
      ELSE
         IF (instruction is REPNZ or REPNE) AND (ZF=1)
         THEN exit WHILE loop;
         FI;
      FI;
   FI;
OD;
```

Description

The REP, REPE (repeat while equal), and REPNE (repeat while not equal) prefixes are applied to string operation. Each prefix causes the string instruction that follows to be repeated the number of times indicated in the count register or (for the REPE and REPNE prefixes) until the indicated condition in the ZF flag is no longer met.

Synonymous forms of the REPE and REPNE prefixes are the REPZ and REPNZ prefixes, respectively.

The REP prefixes apply only to one string instruction at a time. To repeat a block of instructions, use the LOOP instruction or another looping construct.

The precise action for each iteration is as follows:

1. If the address-size attribute is 16 bits, use the CX register for the count register; if the address-size attribute is 32 bits, use the ECX register for the count register.

2. Check the count register. If it is zero, exit the iteration, and move to the next instruction.

3. Acknowledge any pending interrupts.

4. Perform the string operation once.

5. Decrement the CX or count register by one; no flags are modified.

6. Check the ZF flag if the string operation is a SCAS or CMPS instruction. If the repeat condition does not hold, exit the iteration and move to the next instruction. Exit the iteration if the prefix is REPE and the ZF flag is 0 (the last comparison was not equal), or if the prefix is REPNE and the ZF flag is one (the last comparison was equal).

7. Return to step 2 for the next iteration.

Repeated CMPS and SCAS instructions can be exited if the count is exhausted or if the ZF flag fails the repeat condition. These two cases can be distinguished by using either the JCXZ instruction, or by using the conditional jumps that test the ZF flag (the JZ, JNZ, and JNE instructions).

Flags Affected

The ZF flag is affected by the REP CMPS and REP SCAS as described above.

Protected Mode Exceptions

None.

Real Address Mode Exceptions

None.

Virtual 8086 Mode Exceptions

None.

Notes

Not all I/O ports can handle the rate at which the REP INS and REP OUTS instructions execute.

Do not use the REP prefix with the LOOP instruction. Proper LOOP operation is not guaranteed when used with the REP prefix and the effect of this combination is unpredictable.

The behavior of the REP prefix is undefined when used with non-string instructions.

When a page fault occurs during CMPS or SCAS instructions that are prefixed with REPNE, the EFLAGS value is restored to the state prior to the execution of the instruction. Since SCAS and CMPS do not use EFLAGS as an input, the processor can resume the instruction after the page fault handler.

RET—Return from Procedure

Opcode	Instruction	Clocks	Description
C3	RET	2	Return (near) to caller
CB	RET	4	Return (far) to caller, same privilege
CB	RET	23	Return (far), lesser privilege, switch stacks
C2 iw	RET imm16	3	Return (near), pop imm16 bytes of parameters
CA iw	RET imm16	4	Return (far), same privilege, pop imm16 bytes
CA iw	RET imm16	23	Return (far), lesser privilege, pop imm16 bytes

Operation

```
IF instruction = near RET
THEN;
   IF OperandSize = 16
   THEN
      IP ← Pop();
      EIP ← EIP AND 0000FFFFH;
   ELSE (* OperandSize = 32 *)
      EIP ← Pop();
   FI;
   IF instruction has immediate operand THEN eSP ← eSP + imm16; FI;
FI;


IF (PE = 0 OR (PE = 1 AND VM = 1))
   (* real mode or virtual 8086 mode *)
   AND instruction = far RET
THEN;
   IF OperandSize = 16
   THEN
      IP ← Pop();
      EIP ← EIP AND 0000FFFFH;
      CS ← Pop(); (* 16-bit pop *)
   ELSE (* OperandSize = 32 *)
      EIP ← Pop();
      CS ← Pop(); (* 32-bit pop, high-order 16-bits discarded *)
   FI;
   IF instruction has immediate operand THEN eSP ← eSP + imm16; FI;
FI;


IF (PE = 1 AND VM = 0) (* Protected mode, not V86 mode *)
   AND instruction = far RET
THEN
   IF OperandSize=32
   THEN Third word on stack must be within stack limits else #SS(0);
   ELSE Second word on stack must be within stack limits else #SS(0);
   FI;
   Return selector RPL must be ≥ CPL ELSE #GP(return selector)
   IF return selector RPL = CPL
   THEN GOTO SAME-LEVEL;
   ELSE GOTO OUTER-PRIVILEGE-LEVEL;
```

```
    FI;
FI;
SAME-LEVEL:
    Return selector must be non-null ELSE #GP(0)
    Selector index must be within its descriptor table limits ELSE
        #GP(selector)
    Descriptor AR byte must indicate code segment ELSE #GP(selector)
    IF non-conforming
    THEN code segment DPL must equal CPL;
    ELSE #GP(selector);
    FI;
    IF conforming
    THEN code segment DPL must be ≤ CPL;
    ELSE #GP(selector);
    FI;
    Code segment must be present ELSE #NP(selector);
    Top word on stack must be within stack limits ELSE #SS(0);
    IP must be in code segment limit ELSE #GP(0);
    IF OperandSize=32
    THEN
        Load CS:EIP from stack
        Load CS register with descriptor
        Increment eSP by 8 plus the immediate offset if it exists
    ELSE (* OperandSize=16 *)
        Load CS:IP from stack
        Load CS register with descriptor
        Increment eSP by 4 plus the immediate offset if it exists
    FI;
OUTER-PRIVILEGE-LEVEL:
    IF OperandSize=32
    THEN Top (16+immediate) bytes on stack must be within stack limits
        ELSE #SS(0);
    ELSE Top (8+immediate) bytes on stack must be within stack limits ELSE
        #SS(0);
    FI;
    Examine return CS selector and associated descriptor:
        Selector must be non-null ELSE #GP(0);
        Selector index must be within its descriptor table limits ELSE
            #GP(selector)
        Descriptor AR byte must indicate code segment ELSE #GP(selector);
        IF non-conforming
        THEN code segment DPL must equal return selector RPL
        ELSE #GP(selector);
        FI;
        IF conforming
        THEN code segment DPL must be ≤ return selector RPL;
        ELSE #GP(selector);
        FI;
        Segment must be present ELSE #NP(selector)
```

Examine return SS selector and associated descriptor:
　Selector must be non-null ELSE #GP(0);
　Selector index must be within its descriptor table limits
　　ELSE #GP(selector);
　Selector RPL must equal the RPL of the return CS selector ELSE
　　#GP(selector);
　Descriptor AR byte must indicate a writable data segment ELSE
　　#GP(selector);
　Descriptor DPL must equal the RPL of the return CS selector ELSE
　　#GP(selector);
　Segment must be present ELSE #NP(selector);
IP must be in code segment limit ELSE #GP(0);
Set CPL to the RPL of the return CS selector;
IF OperandSize=32
THEN
　Load CS:EIP from stack;
　Set CS RPL to CPL;
　Increment eSP by 8 plus the immediate offset if it exists;
　Load SS:eSP from stack;
ELSE (* OperandSize=16 *)
　Load CS:IP from stack;
　Set CS RPL to CPL;
　Increment eSP by 4 plus the immediate offset if it exists;
　Load SS:eSP from stack;
FI;
Load the CS register with the return CS descriptor;
Load the SS register with the return SS descriptor;
For each of ES, FS, GS, and DS
DO
　IF the current register setting is not valid for the outer level,
　　set the register to null (selector ← AR ← 0);
　To be valid, the register setting must satisfy the following properties:
　　Selector index must be within descriptor table limits;
　　Descriptor AR byte must indicate data or readable code segment;
　　IF segment is data or non-conforming code, THEN
　　　DPL must be ≥ CPL, or DPL must be ≥ RPL;
　　FI;
OD;

Description

The RET instruction transfers control to a return address located on the stack. The address is usually placed on the stack by a CALL instruction, and the return is made to the instruction that follows the CALL instruction.

The optional numeric parameter to the RET instruction gives the number of stack bytes (OperandMode=16) or words (OperandMode=32) to be released after the return address is popped. These items are typically used as input parameters to the procedure called.

For the intrasegment (near) return, the address on the stack is a segment offset, which is popped into the instruction pointer. The CS register is unchanged. For the intersegment (far) return, the address on the stack is a long pointer. The offset is popped first, followed by the selector.

In real mode, the CS and IP registers are loaded directly. In Protected Mode, an intersegment return causes the processor to check the descriptor addressed by the return selector. The AR byte of the descriptor must indicate a code segment of equal or lesser privilege (or greater or equal numeric value) than the current privilege level. Returns to a lesser privilege level cause the stack to be reloaded from the value saved beyond the parameter block.

The DS, ES, FS, and GS segment registers can be cleared by the RET instruction during an interlevel transfer. If these registers refer to segments that cannot be used by the new privilege level, they are cleared to prevent unauthorized access from the new privilege level.

Flags Affected

None.

Protected Mode Exceptions

#GP, #NP, or #SS, as described under "Operation" above; #PF(fault-code) for a page fault.

Real Address Mode Exceptions

Interrupt 13 if any part of the operand would be outside the effective address space from 0 to 0FFFFH.

Virtual 8086 Mode Exceptions

Same exceptions as in Real Address Mode; #PF(fault-code) for a page fault.

ROL/ROR—Rotate

See entry for RCL/RCR/ROL/ROR.

RSM—Resume from System Management Mode

Opcode	Instruction	Clocks	Description
0F AA	RSM	83	Resume operation of interrupted program

Operation

Resume operation of a program interrupted by a System Management Mode interrupt

Description

The processor state is restored from the dump created upon entrance to SMM. Note, however, that the contents of the model-specific registers are not affected. The processor leaves SMM and returns control to the interrupted application or operating system. If the processor detects any invalid state information, it enters the shutdown state. This happens in any of the following situations:

● The value stored in the State Dump Base field is not a 32 Kbyte aligned address.

● Any reserved bit of CR4 is set to 1.

● Any combination of bits in CR0 is illegal; namely, (PG=1 and PE=0) or (NW=1 and CD=0).

Flags Affected

All.

Protected Mode Exceptions

#UD if an attempt is made to execute this instruction when the processor is not in System Management Mode.

Real Address Mode Exceptions

#UD if an attempt is made to execute this instruction when the processor is not in System Management Mode.

Virtual 8086 Mode Exceptions

#UD if an attempt is made to execute this instruction when the processor is not in System Management Mode.

Notes

Please refer to Chapter 20 for more information about System Management Mode and the behavior of the RSM instruction.

SAHF—Store AH into Flags

Opcode	Instruction	Clocks	Description
9E	SAHF	2	Store AH into flags SF ZF xx AF xx PF xx CF

Operation

SF:ZF:xx:AF:xx:PF:xx:CF ← AH;

Description

The SAHF instruction loads the SF, ZF, AF, PF, and CF flags with values from the AH register, from bits 7, 6, 4, 2, and 0, respectively.

Flags Affected

The SF, ZF, AF, PF, and CF flags are loaded with values from the AH register.

Protected Mode Exceptions

None.

Real Address Mode Exceptions

None.

Virtual 8086 Mode Exceptions

None.

SAL/SAR/SHL/SHR—Shift Instructions

Opcode	Instruction	Clocks	Description
D0 /4	SAL r/m8,1	1/3	Multiply r/m byte by 2, once
D2 /4	SAL r/m8,CL	4	Multiply r/m byte by 2, CL times
C0 /4 ib	SAL r/m8,imm8	1/3	Multiply r/m byte by 2, imm8 times
D1 /4	SAL r/m16,1	1/3	Multiply r/m word by 2, once
D3 /4	SAL r/m16,CL	4	Multiply r/m word by 2, CL times
C1 /4 ib	SAL r/m16,imm8	1/3	Multiply r/m word by 2, imm8 times
D1 /4	SAL r/m32,1	1/3	Multiply r/m dword by 2, once
D3 /4	SAL r/m32,CL	4	Multiply r/m dword by 2, CL times
C1 /4 ib	SAL r/m32,imm8	1/3	Multiply r/m dword by 2, imm8 times
D0 /7	SAR r/m8,1	1/3	Signed divide[1] r/m byte by 2, once
D2 /7	SAR r/m8,CL	4	Signed divide[1] r/m byte by 2, CL times
C0 /7 ib	SAR r/m8,imm8	1/3	Signed divide[1] r/m byte by 2, imm8 times
D1 /7	SAR r/m16,1	1/3	Signed divide[1] r/m word by 2, once
D3 /7	SAR r/m16,CL	4	Signed divide[1] r/m word by 2, CL times
C1 /7 ib	SAR r/m16,imm8	1/3	Signed divide[1] r/m word by 2, imm8 times
D1 /7	SAR r/m32,1	1/3	Signed divide[1] r/m dword by 2, once
D3 /7	SAR r/m32,CL	4	Signed divide[1] r/m dword by 2, CL times
C1 /7 ib	SAR r/m32,imm8	1/3	Signed divide[1] r/m dword by 2, imm8 times
D0 /4	SHL r/m8,1	1/3	Multiply r/m byte by 2, once
D2 /4	SHL r/m8,CL	4	Multiply r/m byte by 2, CL times
C0 /4 ib	SHL r/m8,imm8	1/3	Multiply r/m byte by 2, imm8 times
D1 /4	SHL r/m16,1	1/3	Multiply r/m word by 2, once
D3 /4	SHL r/m16,CL	4	Multiply r/m word by 2, CL times
C1 /4 ib	SHL r/m16,imm8	1/3	Multiply r/m word by 2, imm8 times
D1 /4	SHL r/m32,1	1/3	Multiply r/m dword by 2, once
D3 /4	SHL r/m32,CL	4	Multiply r/m dword by 2, CL times
C1 /4 ib	SHL r/m32,imm8	1/3	Multiply r/m dword by 2, imm8 times
D0 /5	SHR r/m8,1	1/3	Unsigned divide r/m byte by 2, once
D2 /5	SHR r/m8,CL	4	Unsigned divide r/m byte by 2, CL times
C0 /5 ib	SHR r/m8,imm8	1/3	Unsigned divide r/m byte by 2, imm8 times
D1 /5	SHR r/m16,1	1/3	Unsigned divide r/m word by 2, once
D3 /5	SHR r/m16,CL	4	Unsigned divide r/m word by 2, CL times
C1 /5 ib	SHR r/m16,imm8	1/3	Unsigned divide r/m word by 2, imm8 times
D1 /5	SHR r/m32,1	1/3	Unsigned divide r/m dword by 2, once
D3 /5	SHR r/m32,CL	4	Unsigned divide r/m dword by 2, CL times
C1 /5 ib	SHR r/m32,imm8	1/3	Unsigned divide r/m dword by 2, imm8 times

NOTES:

[1]Not the same division as IDIV; rounding is toward negative infinity.

Operation

```
(* COUNT is the second parameter *)
(temp) ← COUNT;
WHILE (temp <> 0)
DO
   IF instruction is SAL or SHL
   THEN CF ← high-order bit of r/m;
   FI;
   IF instruction is SAR or SHR
   THEN CF ← low-order bit of r/m;
   FI;
   IF instruction = SAL or SHL
   THEN r/m ← r/m * 2;
   FI;
   IF instruction = SAR
   THEN r/m ← r/m /2 (*Signed divide, rounding toward negative infinity*);
```

```
    FI;
    IF instruction = SHR
    THEN r/m ← r/m / 2; (* Unsigned divide *);
    FI;
    temp ← temp − 1;
OD;
* Determine overflow for the various instructions *)
IF COUNT = 1
THEN
    IF instruction is SAL or SHL
    THEN OF ← high-order bit of r/m <> (CF);
    FI;
    IF instruction is SAR
    THEN OF ← 0;
    FI;
    IF instruction is SHR
    THEN OF ← high-order bit of operand;
    FI;
ELSE OF ← undefined;
FI;
```

Description

The SAL instruction (or its synonym, SHL) shifts the bits of the operand upward. The high-order bit is shifted into the CF flag, and the low-order bit is cleared.

The SAR and SHR instructions shift the bits of the operand downward. The low-order bit is shifted into the CF flag. The effect is to divide the operand by two. The SAR instruction performs a signed divide with rounding toward negative infinity (not the same as the IDIV instruction); the high-order bit remains the same. The SHR instruction performs an unsigned divide; the high-order bit is cleared.

The shift is repeated the number of times indicated by the second operand, which is either an immediate number or the contents of the CL register. To reduce the maximum execution time, the Pentium processor does not allow shift counts greater than 31. If a shift count greater than 31 is attempted, only the bottom five bits of the shift count are used. (The 8086 uses all eight bits of the shift count.)

The OF flag is affected only if the single-shift forms of the instructions are used. For left shifts, the OF flag is cleared if the high bit of the answer is the same as the result of the CF flag (i.e., the top two bits of the original operand were the same); the OF flag is set if they are different. For the SAR instruction, the OF flag is cleared for all single shifts. For the SHR instruction, the OF flag is set to the high-order bit of the original operand.

Flags Affected

If count = 0, the flags are not affected.

The CF flag contains the value of the last bit shifted out. The CF flag is undefined for SHL and SHR instructions in which the shift lengths are greater than or equal to the size of the operand to be shifted.

The OF flag is affected for single shifts; the OF flag is undefined for multiple shifts; the CF, ZF, PF, and SF flags are set according to the result.

Protected Mode Exceptions

#GP(0) if the result is in a nonwritable segment; #GP(0) for an illegal memory operand effective address in the CS, DS, ES, FS, or GS segments; #SS(0) for an illegal address in the SS segment; #PF(fault-code) for a page fault; #AC for unaligned memory reference if the current privilege level is 3.

Real Address Mode Exceptions

Interrupt 13 if any part of the operand would lie outside of the effective address space from 0 to 0FFFFH.

Virtual 8086 Mode Exceptions

Same exceptions as in Real Address Mode; #PF(fault-code) for a page fault; #AC for unaligned memory reference if the current privilege level is 3.

SBB—Integer Subtraction with Borrow

Opcode	Instruction	Clocks	Description
1C *ib*	SBB AL,*imm8*	1	Subtract with borrow immediate byte from AL
1D *iw*	SBB AX,*imm16*	1	Subtract with borrow immediate word from AX
1D *id*	SBB EAX,*imm32*	1	Subtract with borrow immediate dword from EAX
80 /3 *ib*	SBB *r/m8,imm8*	1/3	Subtract with borrow immediate byte from *r/m* byte
81 /3 *iw*	SBB *r/m16,imm16*	1/3	Subtract with borrow immediate word from *r/m* word
81 /3 *id*	SBB *r/m32,imm32*	1/3	Subtract with borrow immediate dword from *r/m* dword
83 /3 *ib*	SBB *r/m16,imm8*	1/3	Subtract with borrow sign-extended immediate byte from *r/m* word
83 /3 *ib*	SBB *r/m32,imm8*	1/3	Subtract with borrow sign-extended immediate byte from *r/m* dword
18 /*r*	SBB *r/m8,r8*	1/3	Subtract with borrow byte register from *r/m* byte
19 /*r*	SBB *r/m16,r16*	1/3	Subtract with borrow word register from *r/m* word
19 /*r*	SBB *r/m32,r32*	1/3	Subtract with borrow dword register from *r/m* dword
1A /*r*	SBB *r8,r/m8*	1/2	Subtract with borrow *r/m* byte from byte register
1B /*r*	SBB *r16,r/m16*	1/2	Subtract with borrow *r/m* word from word register
1B /*r*	SBB *r32,r/m32*	1/2	Subtract with borrow *r/m* dword from dword register

Operation

F SRC is a byte and DEST is a word or dword
THEN DEST = DEST − (SignExtend(SRC) + CF)
ELSE DEST ← DEST − (SRC + CF);

Description

The SBB instruction adds the second operand (SRC) to the CF flag and subtracts the result from the first operand (DEST). The result of the subtraction is assigned to the first operand (DEST), and the flags are set accordingly.

When an immediate byte value is subtracted from a word operand, the immediate value is first sign-extended.

Flags Affected

The OF, SF, ZF, AF, PF, and CF flags are set according to the result.

Protected Mode Exceptions

#GP(0) if the result is in a nonwritable segment; #GP(0) for an illegal memory operand effective address in the CS, DS, ES, FS, or GS segments; #SS(0) for an illegal address in the SS segment; #PF(fault-code) for a page fault; #AC for unaligned memory reference if the current privilege level is 3.

Real Address Mode Exceptions

Interrupt 13 if any part of the operand would lie outside of the effective address space from 0 to 0FFFFH.

Virtual 8086 Mode Exceptions

Same exceptions as in Real Address Mode; #PF(fault-code) for a page fault; #AC for unaligned memory reference if the current privilege level is 3.

SCAS/SCASB/SCASW/SCASD—Compare String Data

Opcode	Instruction	Clocks	Description
AE	SCAS m8	4	Compare bytes AL-ES:[(E)DI], update (E)DI
AF	SCAS m16	4	Compare words AX-ES:[(E)DI], update (E)DI
AF	SCAS m32	4	Compare dwords EAX-ES:[(E)DI], update (E)DI
AE	SCASB	4	Compare bytes AL-ES:[(E)DI], update (E)DI
AF	SCASW	4	Compare words AX-ES:[(E)DI], update (E)DI
AF	SCASD	4	Compare dwords EAX-ES:[(E)DI], update (E)DI

Operation

```
IF AddressSize = 16
THEN use DI for dest-index;
ELSE (* AddressSize = 32 *) use EDI for dest-index;
FI;
IF byte type of instruction
THEN
   AL – [dest-index]; (* Compare byte in AL and dest *)
   IF DF = 0 THEN IncDec ← 1 ELSE IncDec ← –1; FI;
ELSE
   IF OperandSize = 16
   THEN
      AX – [dest-index]; (* compare word in AL and dest *)
      IF DF = 0 THEN IncDec ← 2 ELSE IncDec ← –2; FI;
   ELSE (* OperandSize = 32 *)
      EAX – [dest-index];(* compare dword in EAX and dest *)
      IF DF = 0 THEN IncDec ← 4 ELSE IncDec ← –4; FI;
   FI;
FI;
dest-index = dest-index + IncDec
```

Description

The SCAS instruction subtracts the memory byte or word at the destination register from the AL, AX or EAX register. The result is discarded; only the flags are set. The operand must be addressable from the ES segment; no segment override is possible.

If the address-size attribute for this instruction is 16 bits, the DI register is used as the destination register; otherwise, the address-size attribute is 32 bits and the EDI register is used.

The address of the memory data being compared is determined solely by the contents of the destination register, not by the operand to the SCAS instruction. The operand validates ES segment addressability and determines the data type. Load the correct index value into the DI or EDI register before executing the SCAS instruction.

After the comparison is made, the destination register is automatically updated. If the direction flag is 0 (the CLD instruction was executed), the destination register is incremented; if the direction flag is 1 (the STD instruction was executed), it is decremented. The increments or decrements are by 1 if bytes are compared, by 2 if words are compared, or by 4 if doublewords are compared.

The SCASB, SCASW, and SCASD instructions are synonyms for the byte, word and doubleword SCAS instructions that don't require operands. They are simpler to code, but provide no type or segment checking.

The SCAS instruction can be preceded by the REPE or REPNE prefix for a block search of CX or ECX bytes or words. Refer to the REP instruction for further details.

Flags Affected

The OF, SF, ZF, AF, PF, and CF flags are set according to the result.

Protected Mode Exceptions

#GP(0) for an illegal memory operand effective address in the ES segment; #PF(fault-code) for a page fault; #AC for unaligned memory reference if the current privilege level is 3.

Real Address Mode Exceptions

Interrupt 13 if any part of the operand would lie outside of the effective address space from 0 to 0FFFFH.

Virtual 8086 Mode Exceptions

Same exceptions as in Real Address Mode; #PF(fault-code) for a page fault; #AC for unaligned memory reference if the current privilege level is 3.

SETcc—Byte Set on Condition

Opcode	Instruction	Clocks	Description
0F 97	SETA r/m8	1/2	Set byte if above (CF=0 and ZF=0)
0F 93	SETAE r/m8	1/2	Set byte if above or equal (CF=0)
0F 92	SETB r/m8	1/2	Set byte if below (CF=1)
0F 96	SETBE r/m8	1/2	Set byte if below or equal (CF=1 or (ZF=1)
0F 92	SETC r/m8	1/2	Set if carry (CF=1)
0F 94	SETE r/m8	1/2	Set byte if equal (ZF=1)
0F 9F	SETG r/m8	1/2	Set byte if greater (ZF=0 and SF=OF)
0F 9D	SETGE r/m8	1/2	Set byte if greater or equal (SF=OF)
0F 9C	SETL r/m8	1/2	Set byte if less (SF<>OF)
0F 9E	SETLE r/m8	1/2	Set byte if less or equal (ZF=1 or SF<>OF)
0F 96	SETNA r/m8	1/2	Set byte if not above (CF=1 or ZF=1)
0F 92	SETNAE r/m8	1/2	Set byte if not above or equal (CF=1)
0F 93	SETNB r/m8	1/2	Set byte if not below (CF=0)
0F 97	SETNBE r/m8	1/2	Set byte if not below or equal (CF=0 and ZF=0)
0F 93	SETNC r/m8	1/2	Set byte if not carry (CF=0)
0F 95	SETNE r/m8	1/2	Set byte if not equal (ZF=0)
0F 9E	SETNG r/m8	1/2	Set byte if not greater (ZF=1 or SF<>OF)
0F 9C	SETNGE r/m8	1/2	Set if not greater or equal (SF<>OF)
0F 9D	SETNL r/m8	1/2	Set byte if not less (SF=OF)
0F 9F	SETNLE r/m8	1/2	Set byte if not less or equal (ZF=0 and SF=OF)
0F 91	SETNO r/m8	1/2	Set byte if not overflow (OF=0)
0F 9B	SETNP r/m8	1/2	Set byte if not parity (PF=0)
0F 99	SETNS r/m8	1/2	Set byte if not sign (SF=0)
0F 95	SETNZ r/m8	1/2	Set byte if not zero (ZF=0)
0F 90	SETO r/m8	1/2	Set byte if overflow (OF=1)
0F 9A	SETP r/m8	1/2	Set byte if parity (PF=1)
0F 9A	SETPE r/m8	1/2	Set byte if parity even (PF=1)
0F 9B	SETPO r/m8	1/2	Set byte if parity odd (PF=0)
0F 98	SETS r/m8	1/2	Set byte if sign (SF=1)
0F 94	SETZ r/m8	1/2	Set byte if zero (ZF=1)

Operation

IF condition THEN r/m8 ← 1 ELSE r/m8 ← 0; FI;

Description

The SETcc instruction stores a 1 byte at the destination specified by the effective address or register if the condition is met, or a 0 byte if the condition is not met.

Flags Affected

None.

Protected Mode Exceptions

#GP(0) if the result is in a non-writable segment; #GP(0) for an illegal memory operand effective address in the CS, DS, ES, FS, or GS segments; #SS(0) for an illegal address in the SS segment; #PF(fault-code) for a page fault; #AC for unaligned memory reference if the current privilege level is 3.

Real Address Mode Exceptions

Interrupt 13 if any part of the operand would lie outside of the effective address space from 0 to 0FFFFH.

Virtual 8086 Mode Exceptions

Same exceptions as in Real Address Mode; #PF(fault-code) for a page fault.

SGDT/SIDT—Store Global/Interrupt Descriptor Table Register

Opcode	Instruction	Clocks	Description
0F 01 /0	SGDT m	4	Store GDTR to m
0F 01 /1	SIDT m	4	Store IDTR to m

Operation

DEST ← 48-bit BASE/LIMIT register contents;

Description

The SGDT and SIDT instructions copy the contents of the descriptor table register to the six bytes of memory indicated by the operand. The LIMIT field of the register is assigned to the first word at the effective address. If the operand-size attribute is 16 bits, the next three bytes are assigned the BASE field of the register, and the fourth byte is undefined. Otherwise, if the operand-size attribute is 32 bits, the next four bytes are assigned the 32-bit BASE field of the register.

The SGDT and SIDT instructions are used only in operating system software; they are not used in application programs.

Flags Affected

None.

Protected Mode Exceptions

Interrupt 6 if the destination operand is a register; #GP(0) if the destination is in a nonwritable segment; #GP(0) for an illegal memory operand effective address in the CS, DS, ES, FS, or GS segments; #SS(0) for an illegal address in the SS segment; #PF(fault-code) for a page fault; #AC for unaligned memory reference if the current privilege level is 3.

Real Address Mode Exceptions

Interrupt 6 if the destination operand is a register; Interrupt 13 if any part of the operand would lie outside of the effective address space from 0 to 0FFFFH.

Virtual 8086 Mode Exceptions

Same exceptions as in Real Address Mode; #PF(fault-code) for a page fault; #AC for unaligned memory reference if the current privilege level is 3.

Compatibility Note

The 16-bit forms of the SGDT and SIDT instructions are compatible with the Intel 286 processor, if the value in the upper eight bits is not referenced. The Intel 286 processor stores 1's in these upper bits, whereas the 32-bit processors store 0's if the operand-size attribute is 16 bits. These bits were specified as undefined by the SGDT and SIDT instructions in the *80286 Programming Reference Manual* (Order No. 210498).

SHL/SHR—Shift Instructions

See entry for SAL/SAR/SHL/SHR.

SHLD—Double Precision Shift Left

Opcode	Instruction	Clocks	Description
0F A4	SHLD *r/m16,r16,imm8*	4	*r/m16* gets SHL of *r/m16* concatenated with *r16*
0F A4	SHLD *r/m32,r32,imm8*	4	*r/m32* gets SHL of *r/m32* concatenated with *r32*
0F A5	SHLD *r/m16,r16*,CL	4/5	*r/m16* gets SHL of *r/m16* concatenated with *r16*
0F A5	SHLD *r/m32,r32*,CL	4/5	*r/m32* gets SHL of *r/m32* concatenated with *r32*

Operation

(* count is an unsigned integer corresponding to the last operand of the instruction, either an immediate byte or the byte in register CL *)
ShiftAmt ← count MOD 32;
inBits ← register; (* Allow overlapped operands *)
IF ShiftAmt = 0
THEN no operation
ELSE
   IF ShiftAmt ≥ OperandSize
   THEN (* Bad parameters *)
     r/m ← UNDEFINED;
     CF, OF, SF, ZF, AF, PF ← UNDEFINED;
   ELSE (* Perform the shift *)
     CF ← BIT[Base, OperandSize − ShiftAmt];
       (* Last bit shifted out on exit *)
     FOR i ← OperandSize − 1 DOWNTO ShiftAmt
     DO
       BIT[Base, i] ← BIT[Base, i − ShiftAmt];
     OF;
     FOR i ← ShiftAmt − 1 DOWNTO 0
     DO
       BIT[Base, i] ← BIT[inBits, i − ShiftAmt + OperandSize];
     OD;
     Set SF, ZF, PF (*r/m*);
       (* SF, ZF, PF are set according to the value of the result *)
     AF ← UNDEFINED;
   FI;
FI;

Description

The SHLD instruction shifts the first operand provided by the **r/m** field to the left as many bits as specified by the count operand. The second operand (**r16** or **r32**) provides the bits to shift in from the right (starting with bit 0). The result is stored back into the **r/m** operand. The register remains unaltered.

The count operand is provided by either an immediate byte or the contents of the CL register. These operands are taken MODULO 32 to provide a number between 0 and 31 by which to shift. Because the bits to shift are provided by the specified registers, the operation is useful for multiprecision shifts (64 bits or more). The SF, ZF and PF flags are set according to the value of the result. The CF flag is set to the value of the last bit shifted out. The OF and AF flags are left undefined.

Flags Affected

If count = 0, the flags are not affected.

The SF, ZF, and PF, flags are set according to the result; the CF flag is set to the value of the last bit shifted out; after a shift of one bit position, the OF flag is set if a sign change occurred, otherwise it is cleared; after a shift of more than one bit position, the OF flag is undefined; the AF flag is undefined, except for a shift count of zero, which does not affect any flags.

Protected Mode Exceptions

#GP(0) if the result is in a nonwritable segment; #GP(0) for an illegal memory operand effective address in the CS, DS, ES, FS, or GS segments; #SS(0) for an illegal address in the SS segment; #PF(fault-code) for a page fault; #AC for unaligned memory reference if the current privilege level is 3.

Real Address Mode Exceptions

Interrupt 13 if any part of the operand would lie outside of the effective address space from 0 to 0FFFFH.

Virtual 8086 Mode Exceptions

Same exceptions as in Real Address Mode; #PF(fault-code) for a page fault; #AC for unaligned memory reference if the current privilege level is 3.

SHRD—Double Precision Shift Right

Opcode	Instruction	Clocks	Description
0F AC	SHRD r/m16,r16,imm8	4	r/m16 gets SHR of r/m16 concatenated with r16
0F AC	SHRD r/m32,r32,imm8	4	r/m32 gets SHR of r/m32 concatenated with r32
0F AD	SHRD r/m16,r16,CL	4/5	r/m16 gets SHR of r/m16 concatenated with r16
0F AD	SHRD r/m32,r32,CL	4/5	r/m32 gets SHR of r/m32 concatenated with r32

Operation

(* count is an unsigned integer corresponding to the last operand of the instruction, either an immediate byte or the byte in register CL *)
ShiftAmt ← count MOD 32;
inBits ← register; (* Allow overlapped operands *)
IF ShiftAmt = 0
THEN no operation
ELSE
   IF ShiftAmt ≥ OperandSize
   THEN (* Bad parameters *)
     r/m ← UNDEFINED;
     CF, OF, SF, ZF, AF, PF ← UNDEFINED;
   ELSE (* Perform the shift *)
     CF ← BIT[r/m, ShiftAmt − 1]; (* last bit shifted out on exit *)
     FOR i ← 0 TO OperandSize − 1 − ShiftAmt
     DO
       BIT[r/m, i] ← BIT[r/m, i − ShiftAmt];
     OD;
     FOR i ← OperandSize − ShiftAmt TO OperandSize−1
     DO
       BIT[r/m,i] ← BIT[inBits,i+ShiftAmt − OperandSize];
     OD;
       (* SF, ZF, PF are set according to the value of the result *)
     Set SF, ZF, PF (r/m);
     AF ←UNDEFINED;
   FI;
FI;

Description

The SHRD instruction shifts the first operand provided by the r/m field to the right as many bits as specified by the count operand. The second operand (r16 or r32) provides the bits to shift in from the left (starting with bit 31). The result is stored back into the r/m operand. The register remains unaltered.

The count operand is provided by either an immediate byte or the contents of the CL register. These operands are taken MODULO 32 to provide a number between 0 and 31 by which to shift. Because the bits to shift are provided by the specified register, the operation is useful for multi-precision shifts (64 bits or more). The SF, ZF and PF flags are set according to the value of the result. The CF flag is set to the value of the last bit shifted out. The OF and AF flags are left undefined.

Flags Affected

If count = 0, the flags are not affected.

The SF, ZF, and PF flags are set according to the result; the CF flag is set to the value of the last bit shifted out; after a shift of one bit position, the OF flag is set if a sign change occurred, otherwise it is cleared; after a shift of more than one bit position, the OF flag is undefined; the AF flag is undefined, except for a shift count of zero, which does not affect any flags.

Protected Mode Exceptions

#GP(0) if the result is in a nonwritable segment; #GP(0) for an illegal memory operand effective address in the CS, DS, ES, FS, or GS segments; #SS(0) for an illegal address in the SS segment; #PF(fault-code) for a page fault; #AC for unaligned memory reference if the current privilege level is 3.

Real Address Mode Exceptions

Interrupt 13 if any part of the operand would lie outside of the effective address space from 0 to 0FFFFH.

Virtual 8086 Mode Exceptions

Same exceptions as in Real Address Mode; #AC for unaligned memory reference if the current privilege level is 3.

SIDT—Store Interrupt Descriptor Table Register

See entry for SGDT/SIDT.

SLDT—Store Local Descriptor Table Register

Opcode	Instruction	Clocks	Description
0F 00 /0	SLDT r/m16	2	Store LDTR to EA word

Operation

r/m16 ← LDTR;

Description

The SLDT instruction stores the Local Descriptor Table Register (LDTR) in the two-byte register or memory location indicated by the effective address operand. This register is a selector that points into the Global Descriptor Table.

The SLDT instruction is used only in operating system software. It is not used in application programs.

Flags Affected

None.

Protected Mode Exceptions

#GP(0) if the result is in a nonwritable segment; #GP(0) for an illegal memory operand effective address in the CS, DS, ES, FS, or GS segments; #SS(0) for an illegal address in the SS segment; #PF(fault-code) for a page fault; #AC for unaligned memory reference if the current privilege level is 3.

Real Address Mode Exceptions

Interrupt 6; the SLDT instruction is not recognized in Real Address Mode.

Virtual 8086 Mode Exceptions

Same exceptions as in Real Address Mode (because the instruction is not recognized, it will not execute or perform a memory reference).

Notes

When the destination is a 32-bit register, the 16-bit source operand is copied into the lower 16 bits of the destination register, and the upper 16 bits of the register are undefined. With a 16-bit register operand, only the lower 16 bits of the destination are affected (the upper 16 bits remain unchanged). With a memory operand, the source is written to memory as a 16-bit quantity, regardless of operand size. As a result, 32-bit software should always treat the destination as 16-bits and mask bits 16-31, if necessary.

SMSW—Store Machine Status Word

Opcode	Instruction	Clocks	Description
0F 01 /4	SMSW r/m16	4	Store machine status word to EA word

Operation

r/m16 ← MSW;

Description

The SMSW instruction stores the machine status word (part of the CR0 register) in the two-byte register or memory location indicated by the effective address operand.

Flags Affected

None.

Protected Mode Exceptions

#GP(0) if the result is in a nonwritable segment; #GP(0) for an illegal memory operand effective address in the CS, DS, ES, FS, or GS segments; #SS(0) for an illegal address in the SS segment; #PF(fault-code) for a page fault; #AC for unaligned memory reference if the current privilege level is 3.

Real Address Mode Exceptions

Interrupt 13 if any part of the operand would lie outside of the effective address space from 0 to 0FFFFH.

Virtual 8086 Mode Exceptions

Same exceptions as in Real Address Mode; #PF(fault-code) for a page fault; #AC for unaligned memory reference if the current privilege level is 3.

Notes

This instruction is provided for compatibility with the Intel 286 processor; programs for the Pentium processor should use the MOV ..., CR0 instruction.

When the destination is a 32-bit register, the 16-bit source operand is copied into the lower 16 bits of the destination register, and the upper 16 bits of the register are undefined. With a 16-bit register operand, only the lower 16 bits of the destination are affected (the upper 16 bits remain unchanged). With a memory operand, the source is written to memory as a 16-bit quantity, regardless of operand size. As a result, 32-bit software should always treat the destination as 16-bits and mask bits 16-31, if necessary.

STC—Set Carry Flag

Opcode	Instruction	Clocks	Description
F9	STC	2	Set carry flag

Operation

CF ← 1;

Description

The STC instruction sets the CF flag.

Flags Affected

The CF flag is set.

Protected Mode Exceptions

None.

Real Address Mode Exceptions

None.

Virtual 8086 Mode Exceptions

None.

STD—Set Direction Flag

Opcode	Instruction	Clocks	Description
FD	STD	2	Set direction flag so (E)SI and/or (E)DI decrement

Operation

DF ← 1;

Description

The STD instruction sets the direction flag, causing all subsequent string operations to decrement the index registers, (E)SI and/or (E)DI, on which they operate.

Flags Affected

The DF flag is set.

Protected Mode Exceptions

None.

Real Address Mode Exceptions

None.

Virtual 8086 Mode Exceptions

None.

STI—Set Interrupt Flag

Opcode	Instruction	Clocks	Description
FB	STI	7	Set interrupt flag; interrupts enabled at the end of the next instruction

Operation

```
IF PE=0  (* Executing in real-address mode *)
THEN
    IF ← 1;  (* Set Interrupt Flag *)
ELSE  (* Executing in protected mode or virtual-8086 mode *)
    IF VM=0  (* Executing in protected mode*)
    THEN
        IF IOPL=3
        THEN IF ← 1;  (* Set Interrupt Flag *)
        ELSE IF  CPL ≤IOPL
           THEN IF ← 1;
           ELSE #GP(0);
           FI;
        FI;
    ELSE  (* Executing in Virtual-8086 mode *)
        #GP(0); (* Trap to virtual-8086 monitor *)
    FI;
FI;
```

Decision Table

The following decision table indicates which action in the lower portion of the table is taken given the conditions in the upper portion of the table.

PE =	0	1	1	1
VM =	–	0	0	1
CPL	–	≤ IOPL	> IOPL	=3
IOPL	–	–	–	=3
IF ← 1	Y	Y		Y
#GP(0)			Y	

NOTES:

–	Don't care
Blank	Action not taken
Y	Action in Column 1 taken

Description

The STI instruction sets the IF. The processor then responds to external interrupts after executing the next instruction if the next instruction allows the IF flag to remain enabled. If external interrupts are disabled and the STI instruction is followed by the RET instruction (such as at the end of a subroutine), the RET instruction is allowed to execute before external interrupts are recognized. Also, if external interrupts are disabled and the STI instruction is followed by a CLI instruction which clears the IF flag, then external interrupts are not recognized because the CLI instruction clears the IF flag during its execution.

Flags Affected

The IF flag is set.

Protected Mode Exceptions

#GP(0) if the current privilege level is greater (has less privilege) than the I/O privilege level.

Real Address Mode Exceptions

None.

Virtual 8086 Mode Exceptions

#GP(0) as for protected mode.

Notes

In case of an NMI, trap, or fault following STI the interrupt will be taken before executing the next sequential instruction in the code.

For information on this instruction when using virtual mode extensions, see Appendix H.

STOS/STOSB/STOSW/STOSD—Store String Data

Opcode	Instruction	Clocks	Description
AA	STOS m8	3	Store AL in byte ES:[(E)DI], update (E)DI
AB	STOS m16	3	Store AX in word ES:[(E)DI], update (E)DI
AB	STOS m32	3	Store EAX in dword ES:[(E)DI], update (E)DI
AA	STOSB	3	Store AL in byte ES:[(E)DI], update (E)DI
AB	STOSW	3	Store AX in word ES:[(E)DI], update (E)DI
AB	STOSD	3	Store EAX in dword ES:[(E)DI], update (E)DI

Operation

```
IF AddressSize = 16
THEN use ES:DI for DestReg
ELSE (* AddressSize = 32 *) use ES:EDI for DestReg;
FI;
IF byte type of instruction
THEN
    (ES:DestReg) ← AL;
    IF DF = 0
    THEN DestReg ← DestReg + 1;
    ELSE DestReg ← DestReg – 1;
    FI;
ELSE IF OperandSize = 16
    THEN
        (ES:DestReg) ← AX;
        IF DF = 0
        THEN DestReg ← DestReg + 2;
        ELSE DestReg ← DestReg – 2;
        FI;
    ELSE (* OperandSize = 32 *)
        (ES:DestReg) ← EAX;
        IF DF = 0
        THEN DestReg ← DestReg + 4;
        ELSE DestReg ← DestReg – 4;
        FI;
    FI;
FI;
```

Description

The STOS instruction transfers the contents of the AL, AX, or EAX register to the memory byte or word given by the destination register relative to the ES segment. The destination register is the DI register for an address-size attribute of 16 bits or the EDI register for an address-size attribute of 32 bits.

The destination operand must be addressable from the ES register. A segment override is not possible.

The address of the destination is determined by the contents of the destination register, not by the explicit operand of the STOS instruction. This operand is used only to validate ES segment addressability and to determine the data type. Load the correct index value into the destination register before executing the STOS instruction.

After the transfer is made, the (E)DI register is automatically updated. If the DF flag is 0 (the CLD instruction was executed), the (E)DI register is incremented; if the DF flag is 1 (the STD instruction was executed), the (E)DI register is decremented. The (E)DI register is incremented or decremented by 1 if a byte is stored, by 2 if a word is stored, or by 4 if a doubleword is stored.

The STOSB, STOSW, and STOSD instructions are synonyms for the byte, word, and doubleword STOS instructions, that do not require an operand. They are simpler to use, but provide no type or segment checking.

The STOS instruction can be preceded by the REP prefix for a block fill of CX or ECX bytes, words, or doublewords. Refer to the REP instruction for further details.

Flags Affected

None.

Protected Mode Exceptions

#GP(0) if the result is in a nonwritable segment; #GP(0) for an illegal memory operand effective address in the ES segment; #PF(fault-code) for a page fault; #AC for unaligned memory reference if the current privilege level is 3.

Real Address Mode Exceptions

Interrupt 13 if any part of the operand would lie outside of the effective address space from 0 to 0FFFFH.

Virtual 8086 Mode Exceptions

Same exceptions as in Real Address Mode; #PF(fault-code) for a page fault; #AC for unaligned memory reference if the current privilege level is 3.

STR—Store Task Register

Opcode	Instruction	Clocks	Description
0F 00 /1	STR r/m16	2	Store task register to EA word

Operation

r/m ← task register;

Description

The contents of the task register are copied to the two-byte register or memory location indicated by the effective address operand.

The STR instruction is used only in operating system software. It is not used in application programs.

Flags Affected

None.

Protected Mode Exceptions

#GP(0) if the result is in a nonwritable segment; #GP(0) for an illegal memory operand effective address in the CS, DS, ES, FS, or GS segments; #SS(0) for an illegal address in the SS segment; #PF(fault-code) for a page fault; #AC for unaligned memory reference if the current privilege level is 3.

Real Address Mode Exceptions

Interrupt 6; the STR instruction is not recognized in Real Address Mode.

Virtual 8086 Mode Exceptions

Same exceptions as in Real Address Mode.

Notes

When the destination is a 32-bit register, the 16-bit source operand is copied into the lower 16 bits of the destination register, and the upper 16 bits of the register are undefined. With a 16-bit register operand, only the lower 16 bits of the destination are affected (the upper 16 bits remain unchanged). With a memory operand, the source is written to memory as a 16-bit quantity, regardless of operand size. As a result, 32-bit software should always treat the destination as 16-bits and mask bits 16-31, if necessary.

SUB—Integer Subtraction

Opcode	Instruction	Clocks	Description
2C ib	SUB AL,imm8	1	Subtract immediate byte from AL
2D iw	SUB AX,imm16	1	Subtract immediate word from AX
2D id	SUB EAX,imm32	1	Subtract immediate dword from EAX
80 /5 ib	SUB r/m8,imm8	1/3	Subtract immediate byte from r/m byte
81 /5 iw	SUB r/m16,imm16	1/3	Subtract immediate word from r/m word
81 /5 id	SUB r/m32,imm32	1/3	Subtract immediate dword from r/m dword
83 /5 ib	SUB r/m16,imm8	1/3	Subtract sign-extended immediate byte from r/m word
83 /5 ib	SUB r/m32,imm8	1/3	Subtract sign-extended immediate byte from r/m dword
28 /r	SUB r/m8,r8	1/3	Subtract byte register from r/m byte
29 /r	SUB r/m16,r16	1/3	Subtract word register from r/m word
29 /r	SUB r/m32,r32	1/3	Subtract dword register from r/m dword
2A /r	SUB r8,r/m8	1/2	Subtract r/m byte from byte register
2B /r	SUB r16,r/m16	1/2	Subtract r/m word from word register
2B /r	SUB r32,r/m32	1/2	Subtract r/m dword from dword register

Operation

```
IF SRC is a byte and DEST is a word or dword
THEN DEST = DEST – SignExtend(SRC);
ELSE DEST ← DEST – SRC;
FI;
```

Description

The SUB instruction subtracts the second operand (SRC) from the first operand (DEST). The first operand is assigned the result of the subtraction, and the flags are set accordingly.

When an immediate byte value is subtracted from a word operand, the immediate value is first sign-extended to the size of the destination operand.

Flags Affected

The OF, SF, ZF, AF, PF, and CF flags are set according to the result.

Protected Mode Exceptions

#GP(0) if the result is in a nonwritable segment; #GP(0) for an illegal memory operand effective address in the CS, DS, ES, FS, or GS segments; #SS(0) for an illegal address in the SS segment; #PF(fault-code) for a page fault; #AC for unaligned memory reference if the current privilege level is 3.

Real Address Mode Exceptions

Interrupt 13 if any part of the operand would lie outside of the effective address space from 0 to 0FFFFH.

Virtual 8086 Mode Exceptions

Same exceptions as in Real Address Mode; #PF(fault-code) for a page fault; #AC for unaligned memory reference if the current privilege level is 3.

TEST—Logical Compare

Opcode	Instruction	Clocks	Description
A8 *ib*	TEST AL,*imm8*	1	AND immediate byte with AL
A9 *iw*	TEST AX,*imm16*	1	AND immediate word with AX
A9 *id*	TEST EAX,*imm32*	1	AND immediate dword with EAX
F6 /0 *ib*	TEST *r/m8,imm8*	1/2	AND immediate byte with *r/m* byte
F7 /0 *iw*	TEST *r/m16,imm16*	1/2	AND immediate word with *r/m* word
F7 /0 *id*	TEST *r/m32,imm32*	1/2	AND immediate dword with *r/m* dword
84 /*r*	TEST *r/m8,r8*	1/2	AND byte register with *r/m* byte
85 /*r*	TEST *r/m16,r16*	1/2	AND word register with *r/m* word
85 /*r*	TEST *r/m32,r32*	1/2	AND dword register with *r/m* dword

Operation

DEST : = LeftSRC AND RightSRC;
CF ← 0;
OF ← 0;

Description

The TEST instruction computes the bit-wise logical AND of its two operands. Each bit of the result is 1 if both of the corresponding bits of the operands are 1; otherwise, each bit is 0. The result of the operation is discarded and only the flags are modified.

Flags Affected

The OF and CF flags are cleared; the SF, ZF, and PF flags are set according to the result.

Protected Mode Exceptions

#GP(0) for an illegal memory operand effective address in the CS, DS, ES, FS, or GS segments; #SS(0) for an illegal address in the SS segment; #PF(fault-code) for a page fault; #AC for unaligned memory reference if the current privilege level is 3.

Real Address Mode Exceptions

Interrupt 13 if any part of the operand would lie outside of the effective address space from 0 to 0FFFFH.

Virtual 8086 Mode Exceptions

Same exceptions as in Real Address Mode; #PF(fault-code) for a page fault; #AC for unaligned memory reference if the current privilege level is 3.

VERR, VERW—Verify a Segment for Reading or Writing

Opcode	Instruction	Clocks	Description
0F 00 /4	VERR r/m16	7	Set ZF=1 if segment can be read, selector in r/m16
0F 00 /5	VERW r/m16	7	Set ZF=1 if segment can be written, selector in r/m16

Operation

```
IF segment with selector at (r/m) is accessible
   with current protection level
   AND ((segment is readable for VERR) OR
      (segment is writable for VERW))
THEN ZF ← 1;
ELSE ZF ← 0;
FI;
```

Description

The two-byte register or memory operand of the VERR and VERW instructions contains the value of a selector. The VERR and VERW instructions determine whether the segment denoted by the selector is reachable from the current privilege level and whether the segment is readable (VERR) or writable (VERW). If the segment is accessible, the ZF flag is set; if the segment is not accessible, the ZF flag is cleared. To set the ZF flag, the following conditions must be met:

- The selector must denote a descriptor within the bounds of the table (GDT or LDT); the selector must be "defined."

- The selector must denote the descriptor of a code or data segment (not that of a task state segment, LDT, or a gate).

- For the VERR instruction, the segment must be readable. For the VERW instruction, the segment must be a writable data segment.

- If the code segment is readable and conforming, the descriptor privilege level (DPL) can be any value for the VERR instruction. Otherwise, the DPL must be greater than or equal to (have less or the same privilege as) both the current privilege level and the selector's RPL.

The validation performed is the same as if the segment were loaded into the DS, ES, FS, or GS register, and the indicated access (read or write) were performed. The ZF flag receives the result of the validation. The selector's value cannot result in a protection exception, enabling the software to anticipate possible segment access problems.

Flags Affected

The ZF flag is set if the segment is accessible, cleared if it is not.

Protected Mode Exceptions

Faults generated by illegal addressing of the memory operand that contains the selector; the selector is not loaded into any segment register, and no faults attributable to the selector operand are generated.

#GP(0) for an illegal memory operand effective address in the CS, DS, ES, FS, or GS segments; #SS(0) for an illegal address in the SS segment; #PF(fault-code) for a page fault; #AC for unaligned memory reference if the current privilege level is 3.

Real Address Mode Exceptions

Interrupt 6; the VERR and VERW instructions are not recognized in Real Address Mode.

Virtual 8086 Mode Exceptions

Same exceptions as in Real Address Mode; #AC for unaligned memory reference if the current privilege level is 3.

WAIT—Wait

Opcode	Instruction	Clocks	Description
9B	WAIT	1	Causes processor to check for numeric exceptions.

Description

WAIT causes the processor to check for pending unmasked numeric exceptions before proceding.

Flags Affected

None.

Protected Mode Exceptions

#NM if both MP and TS in CR0 are set.

Real Address Mode Exceptions

Interrupt 7 if both MP and TS in CR0 are set.

Virtual 8086 Mode Exceptions

#NM if both MP and TS in CR0 are set.

Notes

Coding WAIT after an ESC instruction ensures that any unmasked floating-point exceptions the instruction may cause are handled before the processor has a chance to modify the instruction's results.

FWAIT is an alternate mnemonic for WAIT.

Information about when to use WAIT (FWAIT) is given in Chapter 6, in the section on "Concurrent Processing."

WBINVD—Write-Back and Invalidate Cache

Opcode	Instruction	Clocks	Description
0F 09	WBINVD	2000+	Write-Back and Invalidate Entire Cache

Operation

FLUSH INTERNAL CACHE
SIGNAL EXTERNAL CACHE TO WRITE-BACK
SIGNAL EXTERNAL CACHE TO FLUSH

Description

The internal cache is flushed, and a special-function bus cycle is issued which indicates that external cache should write-back its contents to main memory. Another special-function bus cycle follows, directing the external cache to flush itself.

Flags Affected

None.

Protected Mode Exceptions

The WBINVD instruction is a privileged instruction; #GP(0) if the current privilege level is not 0.

Real Address Mode Exceptions

None.

Virtual 8086 Mode Exceptions

#GP(0); the WBINVD instruction is a privileged instruction.

Notes

INVD should be used with care. It does not write back modified cache lines; therefore, it can cause the data cache to become inconsistent with other memories in the system. Unless there is a specific requirement or benefit to invalidate a cache without writing back the modified lines (i.e., testing or fault recovery where cache coherency with main memory is not a concern), software should use the WBINVD instruction.

This instruction is implementation-dependent; its function may be implemented differently on future Intel processors.

It is the responsibility of hardware to respond to the external cache write-back and flush indications.

This instruction is not supported on Intel386 processors. See Chapter 16 for detecting processor type at runtime. See Chapter 18 on disabling the cache.

WRMSR—Write to Model Specific Register

Opcode	Instruction	Clocks	Description
0F 30	WRMSR	30-45	Write the value in EDX:EAX to Model Specific Register indicated by ECX

Operation

MSR[ECX] ← EDX:EAX;

Description

The value in ECX specifies one of the 64-bit Model Specific Registers of the Pentium processor. The contents of EDX:EAX is copied into that Model-Specific Register. The high-order 32 bits are copied from EDX and the low-order 32 bits are copied from EAX.

The following values are used to select model specific registers on the Pentium processor:

Value (in Hex)	Register Name	Description
00H	Machine Check Address	Stores address of cycle causing the exception
01H	Machine Check Type	Stores cycle type of cycle causing the exception

For other values used to perform cache, TLB, and BTB testing and performance monitoring, see Appendix H.

Flags Affected

None.

Protected Mode Exceptions

#GP(0) if either the current privilege level is not 0 or the value in ECX does not specify a Model-Specific Register that is implemented in the Pentium processor.

Real Address Mode Exceptions

#GP(0) if the value in ECX does not specify a Model-Specific Register that is implemented in the Pentium processor. No error code is pushed.

Virtual 8086 Mode Exceptions

#GP(0) if instruction execution is attempted.

Notes

Always set undefined or reserved bits to the value previously read.

WRMSR is used to write the content of Model-Specific Registers that control functions for testability, execution tracing, performance monitoring, and machine check errors. Refer to the *Pentium™ Processor Data Book* for more information.

The values 3H, 0FH, and values above 13H are reserved. Do not execute WRMSR with reserved values in ECX.

XADD—Exchange and Add

Opcode	Instruction	Clocks	Description
0F C0/r	XADD r/m8,r8	3/4	Exchange byte register and r/m byte; load sum into r/m byte.
0F C1/r	XADD r/m16,r16	3/4	Exchange word register and r/m word; load sum into r/m word.
0F C1/r	XADD r/m32,r32	3/4	Exchange dword register and r/m dword; load sum into r/m dword.

Operation

TEMP ← SRC + DEST
SRC ← DEST
DEST ← TEMP

Description

The XADD instruction loads DEST into SRC, and then loads the sum of DEST and the original value of SRC into DEST.

Flags Affected

The CF, PF, AF, SF, ZF, and OF flags are affected as if an ADD instruction had been executed.

Protected Mode Exceptions

#GP(0) if the result is in a nonwritable segment; #GP(0) for an illegal memory operand effective address in the CS, DS, ES, FS, or GS segments; #SS(0) for an illegal address in the SS segment; #PF(fault-code) for a page fault; #NM if either EM or TS in CR0 is set; #AC for unaligned memory reference if the current privilege level is 3.

Real Address Mode Exceptions

Interrupt 13 if any part of the operand would lie outside the effective address space from 0 to 0FFFFH.

Virtual 8086 Mode Exceptions

Same exceptions as in real-address mode; #PF(fault code) for a page fault; #AC for unaligned memory reference if the current privilege level is 3.

Notes

This instruction can be used with a LOCK prefix. The Intel386 DX microprocessor does not implement this instruction. If this instruction is used, you should provide an equivalent code sequence that runs on an Intel386 DX processor as well. See Section Chapter 9 for detecting a Pentium processor at runtime.

XCHG—Exchange Register/Memory with Register

Opcode	Instruction	Clocks	Description
90+rw	XCHG AX,r16	2	Exchange word register with AX
90+rw	XCHG r16,AX	2	Exchange word register with AX
90+rd	XCHG EAX,r32	2	Exchange dword register with EAX
90+rd	XCHG r32,EAX	2	Exchange dword register with EAX
86 /r	XCHG r/m8,r8	3	Exchange byte register with EA byte
86 /r	XCHG r8,r/m8	3	Exchange byte register with EA byte
87 /r	XCHG r/m16,r16	3	Exchange word register with EA word
87 /r	XCHG r16,r/m16	3	Exchange word register with EA word
87 /r	XCHG r/m32,r32	3	Exchange dword register with EA dword
87 /r	XCHG r32,r/m32	3	Exchange dword register with EA dword

Operation

temp ← DEST
DEST ← SRC
SRC ← temp

Description

The XCHG instruction exchanges two operands. The operands can be in either order. If a memory operand is involved, the LOCK# signal is asserted for the duration of the exchange, regardless of the presence or absence of the LOCK prefix or of the value of the IOPL.

Flags Affected

None.

Protected Mode Exceptions

#GP(0) if either operand is in a nonwritable segment; #GP(0) for an illegal memory operand effective address in the CS, DS, ES, FS, or GS segments; #SS(0) for an illegal address in the SS segment; #PF(fault-code) for a page fault; #AC for unaligned memory reference if the current privilege level is 3.

Real Address Mode Exceptions

Interrupt 13 if any part of the operand would lie outside of the effective address space from 0 to 0FFFFH.

Virtual 8086 Mode Exceptions

Same exceptions as in Real Address Mode; #PF(fault-code) for a page fault; #AC for unaligned memory reference if the current privilege level is 3.

Note

XCHG can be used for BSWAP for 16-bit data.

XLAT/XLATB—Table Look-up Translation

Opcode	Instruction	Clocks	Description
D7	XLAT *m8*	4	Set AL to memory byte DS:[(E)BX + unsigned AL]
D7	XLATB	4	Set AL to memory byte DS:[(E)BX + unsigned AL]

Operation

IF AddressSize = 16
THEN
    AL ← (BX + ZeroExtend(AL))
ELSE (* AddressSize = 32 *)
    AL ← (EBX + ZeroExtend(AL));
FI;

Description

The XLAT instruction changes the AL register from the table index to the table entry. The AL register should be the unsigned index into a table addressed by the DS:BX register pair (for an address-size attribute of 16 bits) or the DS:EBX register pair (for an address-size attribute of 32 bits).

The operand to the XLAT instruction allows for the possibility of a segment override. The XLAT instruction uses the contents of the BX register even if they differ from the offset of the operand. The offset of the operand should have been moved into the BX or EBX register with a previous instruction.

The no-operand form, the XLATB instruction, can be used if the BX or EBX table will always reside in the DS segment.

Flags Affected

None.

Protected Mode Exceptions

#GP(0) for an illegal memory operand effective address in the CS, DS, ES, FS, or GS segments; #SS(0) for an illegal address in the SS segment; #PF(fault-code) for a page fault; #AC for unaligned memory reference if the current privilege level is 3.

Real Address Mode Exceptions

Interrupt 13 if any part of the operand would lie outside of the effective address space from 0 to 0FFFFH.

Virtual 8086 Mode Exceptions

Same exceptions as in Real Address Mode; #PF(fault-code) for a page fault; #AC for unaligned memory reference if the current privilege level is 3.

XOR—Logical Exclusive OR

Opcode	Instruction	Clocks	Description
34 ib	XOR AL,imm8	1	Exclusive-OR immediate byte to AL
35 iw	XOR AX,imm16	1	Exclusive-OR immediate word to AX
35 id	XOR EAX,imm32	1	Exclusive-OR immediate dword to EAX
80 /6 ib	XOR r/m8,imm8	1/3	Exclusive-OR immediate byte to r/m byte
81 /6 iw	XOR r/m16,imm16	1/3	Exclusive-OR immediate word to r/m word
81 /6 id	XOR r/m32,imm32	1/3	Exclusive-OR immediate dword to r/m dword
83 /6 ib	XOR r/m16,imm8	1/3	XOR sign-extended immediate byte with r/m word
83 /6 ib	XOR r/m32,imm8	1/3	XOR sign-extended immediate byte with r/m dword
30 /r	XOR r/m8,r8	1/3	Exclusive-OR byte register to r/m byte
31 /r	XOR r/m16,r16	1/3	Exclusive-OR word register to r/m word
31 /r	XOR r/m32,r32	1/3	Exclusive-OR dword register to r/m dword
32 /r	XOR r8,r/m8	1/2	Exclusive-OR byte register to r/m byte
33 /r	XOR r16,r/m16	1/2	Exclusive-OR word register to r/m word
33 /r	XOR r32,r/m32	1/2	Exclusive-OR dword register to r/m dword

Operation

DEST ← LeftSRC XOR RightSRC
CF ← 0
OF ← 0

Description

The XOR instruction computes the exclusive OR of the two operands. Each bit of the result is 1 if the corresponding bits of the operands are different; each bit is 0 if the corresponding bits are the same. The answer replaces the first operand.

Flags Affected

The CF and OF flags are cleared; the SF, ZF, and PF flags are set according to the result; the AF flag is undefined.

Protected Mode Exceptions

#GP(0) if the result is in a nonwritable segment; #GP(0) for an illegal memory operand effective address in the CS, DS, ES, FS, or GS segments; #SS(0) for an illegal address in the SS segment; #PF(fault-code) for a page fault; #AC for unaligned memory reference if the current privilege level is 3.

Real Address Mode Exceptions

Interrupt 13 if any part of the operand would lie outside of the effective address space from 0 to 0FFFFH.

Virtual 8086 Mode Exceptions

Same exceptions as in Real Address Mode; #PF(fault-code) for a page fault; #AC for unaligned memory reference if the current privilege level is 3.

intel®

A

Opcode Map

The opcode tables in this section aid in interpreting Pentium processor object code. Use the high-order four bits of the opcode as an index to a row of the opcode table; use the low-order four bits as an index to a column of the table. If the opcode is 0FH, refer to the two-byte opcode table and use the second byte of the opcode to index the rows and columns of that table.

The escape opcode tables for floating-point instructions identify the high-order eight bits of the opcode at the top of each page. If the accompanying modR/M byte is in the range 00h-BFh, bits 3 through 5 identified along the top row of the third table on each page, along with the REG bits of the modR/M, determine the opcode. ModR/M bytes outside the range 00h-BFh are mapped by the bottom two tables on each page.

A.1. KEY TO ABBREVIATIONS

Operands are identified by a two-character code of the form Zz. The first character, an uppercase letter, specifies the addressing method; the second character, a lowercase letter, specifies the type of operand.

A.2. CODES FOR ADDRESSING METHOD

A Direct address; the instruction has no modR/M byte; the address of the operand is encoded in the instruction; no base register, index register, or scaling factor can be applied; e.g., far JMP (EA).

C The reg field of the modR/M byte selects a control register; e.g., MOV (0F20, 0F22).

D The reg field of the modR/M byte selects a debug register; e.g., MOV (0F21,0F23).

E A modR/M byte follows the opcode and specifies the operand. The operand is either a general register or a memory address. If it is a memory address, the address is computed from a segment register and any of the following values: a base register, an index register, a scaling factor, a displacement.

F Flags Register.

G The reg field of the modR/M byte selects a general register; e.g., AX (000).

I Immediate data. The value of the operand is encoded in subsequent bytes of the instruction.

J The instruction contains a relative offset to be added to the instruction pointer register; e.g., JMP short, LOOP.

M The modR/M byte may refer only to memory; e.g., BOUND, LES, LDS, LSS, LFS, LGS, CMPXCHG8B.

O The instruction has no modR/M byte; the offset of the operand is coded as a word or double word (depending on address size attribute) in the instruction. No base register, index register, or scaling factor can be applied; e.g., MOV (A0–A3).

R The mod field of the modR/M byte may refer only to a general register; e.g., MOV (0F20–0F24, 0F26).

S The reg field of the modR/M byte selects a segment register; e.g., MOV (8C,8E).

T The reg field of the modR/M byte selects a test register; e.g., MOV (0F24,0F26).

X Memory addressed by the DS:SI register pair; e.g., MOVS, CMPS, OUTS, LODS.

Y Memory addressed by the ES:DI register pair; e.g., MOVS, CMPS, INS, STOS, SCAS.

A.3.   CODES FOR OPERAND TYPE

a Two one-word operands in memory or two double-word operands in memory, depending on operand size attribute (used only by BOUND).

b Byte (regardless of operand size attribute).

c Byte or word, depending on operand size attribute.

d Double word (regardless of operand size attribute).

p Thirty-two bit or 48-bit pointer, depending on operand size attribute.

q Quad word (regardless of operand size attribute).

s Six-byte pseudo-descriptor.

v Word or double word, depending on operand size attribute.

w Word (regardless of operand size attribute).

A.4.   REGISTER CODES

When an operand is a specific register encoded in the opcode, the register is identified by its name; e.g., AX, CL, or ESI. The name of the register indicates whether the register is 32-, 16-, or 8-bits wide. A register identifier of the form eXX is used when the width of the register depends on the operand size attribute; for example, eAX indicates that the AX register is used when the operand size attribute is 16 and the EAX register is used when the operand size attribute is 32.

A.5.   OPCODE LOOK-UP EXAMPLES

This section provides several examples to demonstrate how the following opcode maps are used. See Chapter 25 for detailed information on the modR/M byte, register values and the various addressing forms.

A.5.1.   One-Byte Opcode Integer Instructions

Given the hexadecimal opcode, the instruction and its operands can be determined:

Opcode: 030500000000H

LSB address					MSB address
03	05	00	00	00	00

Looking at the one-byte opcode map, the first digit (0) of the opcode indicates the row and the second digit (3) indicates the column. The instruction located at row 0, column 3 is an ADD instruction using the operand types Gv, Ev. The first operand of type Gv indicates a general register that is a word or doubleword depending on the operand size attribute. The second operand (Ev) indicates that a modR/M byte follows specifying whether the operand is a word or doubleword general register or a memory address. The modR/M byte for this instruction is 05H indicating (see Chapter 25) that a 32-bit displacement follows (00000000H). The reg/opcode portion of the modR/M byte (bits 3-5) is 000 indicating the EAX register. Thus, it can be determined that the instruction for this opcode is ADD EAX, mem_op and the offset of mem_op is 00000000H.

A.5.2. Two-Byte Opcode Integer Instructions

Instructions that begin with 0FH can be found in the two-byte opcode map. The second opcode byte is then used to reference a particular row and column. For example, the opcode 0FA405000000003H, is located on the first page of the two-byte opcode map in row A, column 4. This indicates a SHLD instruction with the operands EvGvIb. These operands are defined as follows:

Ev   = modR/M byte follows opcode to specify word or doubleword operand

Gv   = reg field of modR/M byte selects a general register

Ib   = immediate data encoded in subsequent byte of instruction.

The third byte is the modR/M byte (05H). The mod and opcode/reg fields indicate that a 32-bit displacement follows and the EAX register is the source (see Chapter 25 for information on the modR/M byte).

The next part of the opcode is the 32-bit displacement for the destination memory operand (00000000H) and finally the immediate byte representing the count of the shift (03H).

By this breakdown, it has been shown that this opcode represents the instruction:

SHLD DS:00000000H, EAX, 3

A.5.3. Escape Opcodes

The escape opcode maps are slightly different than the integer opcode maps. For instructions that have a modR/M byte in the range of 00H-BFH, bits 3-5 of the modR/M byte are used to determine the opcode. ModR/M bytes outside the range 00H-BFH are mapped by the tables at the bottom of each page.

A.5.3.1. OPCODES WITH MODR/M BYTES IN THE 00H-BFH RANGE

The opcode DD0504000000 can be interpreted as follows. This instruction can be located on the page indicating DD as the first byte. Since the modR/M byte is in the 00H-BFH range (05H or 00000101B), bits 3-5 (000) of this byte indicate the opcode to be an FLD double-real instruction. The double-real to be loaded is at 00000004H which is the following 32-bit displacement in this opcode.

A.5.3.2. OPCODES WITH MODR/M BYTES OUTSIDE THE 00H-BFH RANGE

Since the opcode of D8C1 has a modR/M byte outside the range 00H-BFH, the bottom two tables are used to determine this escape instruction on the page with D8 as the first byte. C1 indicates row C, column 1 which is an FADD instruction using ST, ST(1) as the operands.

One-Byte Opcode Map

	0	1	2	3	4	5	6	7
0	ADD						PUSH	POP
	Eb,Gb	Ev,Gv	Gb,Eb	Gv,Ev	AL,Ib	eAX,Iv	ES	ES
1	ADC						PUSH	POP
	Eb,Gb	Ev,Gv	Gb,Eb	Gv,Ev	AL,Ib	eAX,Iv	SS	SS
2	AND						SEG	DAA
	Eb,Gb	Ev,Gv	Gb,Eb	Gv,Ev	AL,Ib	eAX,Iv	=ES	
3	XOR						SEG	AAA
	Eb,Gb	Ev,Gv	Gb,Eb	Gb,Ev	AL,Ib	eAX,Iv	=SS	
4	INC general register							
	eAX	eCX	eDX	eBX	eSP	eBP	eSI	eDI
5	PUSH general register							
	eAX	eCX	eDX	eBX	eSP	eBP	eSI	eDI
6	PUSHA PUSHAD	POPA POPAD	BOUND Gv,Ma	ARPL Ew,Gw	SEG =FS	SEG =GS	Operand Size	Address Size
7	Short-displacement jump on condition (Jb)							
	JO	JNO	JB/JNAE/J	JNB/JAE/J	JZ	JNZ	JBE	JNBE
8	Immediata Grpl		MOVB*	Grpl	TEST		XCHG	
	Eb,Ib	Ev,Iv	AL,immed	Eb,Ib	Eb,Gb	Ev,Gv	Eb,Gb	Ev,Gv
9	NOP	XCHG word or double-word register with eAX						
		eCX	eDX	eBX	eSP	eBP	eSI	eDI
A	MOV				MOVSB	MOVSW	CMPSB	CMPSW
	AL,Ob	eAX,Ov	Ob,AL	Ov,eAX	Xb,Yb	Xv,Yv	Xb,Yb	Xv,Yv
B	MOV immediate byte into byte register							
	AL	CL	DL	BL	AH	CH	DH	BH
C	Shift Grp2a		RET near		LES	LDS	MOV	
	Eb,Ib	Ev,Ib	Iw		Gv,Mp	Gv,Mp	Eb,Ib	Ev,Iv
D	Shift Grp2				AAM	AAD	*	XLAT
	Eb,1	Ev,1	Eb,CL	Ev,CL				
E	LOOPN	LOOPE	LOOP	JCXZ/JEC	IN		OUT	
	Jb	Jb	Jb	Jb	AL,Ib	eAX,Ib	Ib,AL	Ib,eAX
F	LOCK	*	REPNE	REP	HLT	CMC	Unary Grp3	
				REPE			Eb	Ev

*Reserved

One-Byte Opcode Map

	8	9	A	B	C	D	E	F
0	OR						PUSH	2-byte
	Eb,Gb	Ev,Gv	Gb,Eb	Gv,Ev	AL,Ib	eAX,Iv	CS	escape
1	SBB						PUSH	POP
	Eb,Gb	Ev,Gv	Gb,Eb	Gv,Ev	AL,Ib	eAX,Iv	DS	DS
2	SUB						SEG	DAS
	Eb,Gb	Ev,Gv	Gb,Eb	Gv,Ev	AL,Ib	eAX,Iv	=CS	
3	CMP						SEG	AAS
	Eb,Gb	Ev,Gv	Gb,Eb	Gv,Ev	AL,Ib	eAX,Iv	=DS	
4	DEC general register							
	eAX	eCX	eDX	eBX	eSP	eBP	eSI	eDI
5	POP into general register							
	eAX	eCX	eDX	eBX	eSP	eBP	eSI	eDI
6	PUSH	IMUL	PUSH	IMUL	INSB	INSW/D	OUTSB	OUTSW/D
	Iv	Gv,Ev,Iv	Ib	Gv,Ev,Ib	Yb,DX	Yv,DX	Dx,Xb	DX,Xv
7	Short-displacement jump on condition (Jb)							
	JS	JNS	JP	JNP	JL	JNL	JLE	JNLE
8	MOV				MOV	LEA	MOV	POP
	Eb,Gb	Ev,Gv	Gb,Eb	Gv,Ev	Ew,Sw	Gv,M	Sw,Ew	Ev
9	CBW	CWD/CDQ	CALL	WAIT	PUSHF	POP	SAHF	LAHF
			aP		Fv	Fv		
A	TEST		STOSB	STOSW/D	LODSB	LODSW/D	SCASB	SCASW/D
	AL,Ib	eAX,Iv	Yb,AL	Yv,eAX	AL,Xb	eAX,Xv	AL,Yb	eAX,Yv
B	MOV immediate word or double into word or double register							
	eAX	eCX	eDX	eBX	eSP	eBP	eSI	eDI
C	ENTER	LEAVE	RET far	RET far	INT	INT	INTO	IRET
	Iw, Ib		Iw		3	Ib		
D	ESC (Escape to coprocessor instruction set)							
E	CALL	JMP			IN		OUT	
	Jv	Jv	Ap	Jb	AL,DX	eAX,DX	DX,AL	DX,eAX
F	CLC	STC	CLI	STI	CLD	STD	INC/DEC	INC/DEC
							Grp4	Grp5

Two Byte Opcode Map (First byte is 0FH)

	0	1	2	3	4	5	6	7
0	Grp6	Grp7	LAR Gv,Ew	LSL Gv,Ew			CLTS	*
1	MOV* Eb,Gb	MOV* Gv,Ev	MOV* Gb,Eb	MOV* Ev,Gv				
2	MOV Rd,Cd	MOV Rd,Dd	MOV Cd,Rd	MOV Dd,Rd	MOV* Rd,Td		MOV* Td,Rd	
3	WRMSR	RDTSC	RDMSR					
4								
5								
6								
7								
8	Long-displacement jump on condition (Jv)							
	JO	JNO	JB	JNB	JZ	JNZ	JBE	JNBE
9	Byte Set on condition (Eb)							
	SETO	SETNO	SETB	SETNB	SETZ	SETNZ	SETBE	SETNBE
A	PUSH FS	POP FS	CPUID	BT Ev,Gv	SHLD Ev,Gv,Ib	SHLD Ev,Gv,CL	A step* CMPXCHG	A step* CMPXCHG
B	CMPXCH~ Eb,Gb	CMPXCH~ Ev,Gv	LSS Mp	BTR Ev,Gv	LFS Mp	LGS Mp	MOVZX Gv,Eb	MOVZX Gv,Ew
C	XADD Eb,Gb	XADD Ev,Gv						Group 9
D								
E								
F								

*Reserved

Two-Byte Opcode Map (First byte is 0FH)

	8	9	A	B	C	D	E	F
0	INVD	WBINVD						
1								
2								
3								
4								
5								
6								
7								
8	Long-displacement jump on condition (Jv)							
	JS	JNS	JP	JNP	JL	JNL	JLE	JNLE
	Byte set on condition (Eb)							
9	SETS Eb	SETNS Eb	SETP Eb	SETNP Eb	SETL Eb	SETNL Eb	SETLE Eb	SETNLE Eb
A	PUSH GS	POP GS	RSM	BTS Ev,Gv	SHRD Ev,Gv,Ib	SHRD Ev,Gv,CL		IMUL Gv,Ev
B			Grp-8 Ev,Ib	BTC Ev,Gv	BSF Gv,Ev	BSR Gv,Ev	MOVSX Gv,Eb	Gv,Ew
C	BSWAP EAX	BSWAP ECX	BSWAP EDX	BSWAP EBX	BSWAP ESP	BSWAP EBP	BSWAP ESI	BSWAP EDI
D								
E								
F								

A.5.3.2.1. Opcodes Determined by Bits 5,4,3 of ModR/M Byte

mod			nnn			R/M	

Group	000	001	010	011	100	101	110	111
1	ADD	OR	ADC	SBB	AND	SUB	XOR	CMP
2	ROL	ROR	RCL	RCR	SHL SAL	SHR		SAR
3	TEST lb/lv		NOT	NEG	MUL AL/eAX	IMUL AL/eAX	DIV AL/eAX	IDIV AL/eAX
4	INC Eb	DEC Eb						
5	INC Ev	DEC Ev	CALL Ev	CALL Ep	JMP Ev	JMP Ep	PUSH Ev	
6	SLDT Ew	STR Ew	LLDT Ew	LTR Ew	VERR Ew	VERW Ew		
7	SGDT Ms	SIDT Ms	LGDT Ms	LIDT Ms	SMSW Ew		LMSW Ew	INVLPG
8					BT	BTS	BTR	BTC
9		CMPXCH 8BMq						

A.5.3.2.2.   Escape Opcodes with D8 as First Byte

mod	nnn	R/M

ModR/M bytes in range of 00h-BFh, nnn are mapped according to the following table (opcode is determined by bits 5,4,3 of modR/M byte).

000	001	010	011	100	101	110	111
FADD single-real	FMUL single-real	FCOM single-real	FCOMP single-real	FSUB single-real	FSUBR single-real	FDIV single-real	FDIVR single-real

ModR/M bytes outside the range 00h-BFh are mapped by the tables below:

	0	1	2	3	4	5	6	7
C	FADD							
	ST,ST(0)	ST,ST(1)	ST,ST(2)	ST,ST(3)	ST,ST(4)	ST,ST(5)	ST,ST(6)	ST,ST(7)
D	FCOM							
	ST,ST(0)	ST,ST(1)	ST,T(2)	ST,ST(3)	ST,ST(4)	ST,ST(5)	ST,ST(6)	ST,ST(7)
E	FSUB							
	ST,ST(0)	ST,ST(1)	ST,ST(2)	ST,ST(3)	ST,ST(4)	ST,ST(5)	ST,ST(6)	ST,ST(7)
F	FDIV							
	ST,ST(0)	ST,ST(1)	ST,ST(2)	ST,ST(3)	ST,ST(4)	ST,ST(5)	ST,ST(6)	ST,ST(7)

	8	9	A	B	C	D	E	F
C	FMUL							
	ST,ST(0)	ST,ST(1)	ST,ST(2)	ST,ST(3)	ST,ST(4)	ST,ST(5)	ST,ST(6)	ST,ST(7)
D	FCOMP							
	ST,ST(0)	ST,ST(1)	ST,T(2)	ST,ST(3)	ST,ST(4)	ST,ST(5)	ST,ST(6)	ST,ST(7)
E	FSUBR							
	ST,ST(0)	ST,ST(1)	ST,ST(2)	ST,ST(3)	ST,ST(4)	ST,ST(5)	ST,ST(6)	ST,ST(7)
F	FDIVR							
	ST,ST(0)	ST,ST(1)	ST,ST(2)	ST,ST(3)	ST,ST(4)	ST,ST(5)	ST,ST(6)	ST,ST(7)

A.5.3.2.3. Escape Opcodes with D9 as First Byte

mod	nnn	R/M

ModR/M bytes in range of 00h-BFh, nnn are mapped according to the following table (opcode is determined by bits 5,4,3 of modR/M byte).

000	001	010	011	100	101	110	111
FLD		FST	FSTP	FLDENV	FLDCW	FSTENV	FSTCW
single-real		single-real	single-real	14/28	2 bytes	14/28	2 bytes

ModR/M bytes outside the range 00h-BFh are mapped by the tables below:

	0	1	2	3	4	5	6	7
C				FLD				
	ST,ST(0)	ST,ST(1)	ST,ST(2)	ST,ST(3)	ST,ST(4)	ST,ST(5)	ST,ST(6)	ST,ST(7)
D	FNOP							
E	FCHS	FABS			FTST	FXAM		
F	F2XM1	FYL2X	FPTAN	FPATAN	FXTRACT	FPREM1	FDECSTP	FINCSTP

	8	9	A	B	C	D	E	F
C				FXCH				
	ST,ST(0)	ST,ST(1)	ST,ST(2)	ST,ST(3)	ST,ST(4)	ST,ST(5)	ST,ST(6)	ST,ST(7)
D								
E	FLD1	FLDL2T	FLDL2E	FLDPI	FLDLG2	FLDLN2	FLDZ	
F	FPREM	FYL2XP1	FSQRT	FSINCOS	FRNDINT	FSCALE	FSIN	FCOS

A.5.3.2.4. Escape Opcodes with DA as First Byte

mod	nnn	R/M

ModR/M bytes in range of 00h-BFh, nnn are mapped according to the following table (opcode is determined by bits 5,4,3 of modR/M byte).

000	001	010	011	100	101	110	111
FIADD short-int*	FIMUL short-int*	FICOM short-int*	FICOMP short-int*	FISUB short-int*	FISUBR short-int*	FIDIV short-int*	FIDIVR short-int*

ModR/M bytes outside the range 00h-BFh are mapped by the tables below:

	0	1	2	3	4	5	6	7
C								
D								
E								
F								

	8	9	A	B	C	D	E	F
C								
D								
E		FUCOMPP						
F								

NOTE: *Short-int = 32 bit integer.

A.5.3.2.5. Escape Opcodes with DB as First Byte

mod	nnn	R/M

ModR/M bytes in range of 00h-BFh, nnn are mapped according to the following table (opcode is determined by bits 5,4,3 of modR/M byte).

000	001	010	011	100	101	110	111
FILD		FIST	FISTP		FLD		FSTP
short-int*		short-int*	short-int*		ext-real		ext-real

ModR/M bytes outside the range 00h-BFh are mapped by the tables below:

	0	1	2	3	4	5	6	7
C								
D								
E			FCLEX	FINIT				
F								

	8	9	A	B	C	D	E	F
C								
D								
E								
F								

NOTE: *Short-int = 32 bit integer.

A.5.3.2.6.   Escape Opcodes with DC as First Byte

mod	nnn	R/M

ModR/M bytes in range of 00h-BFh, nnn are mapped according to the following table (opcode is determined by bits 5,4,3 of modR/M byte).

000	001	010	011	100	101	110	111
FADD double-real	FMUL double-real	FCOM double-real	FCOMP double-real	FSUB double-real	FSUBR double-real	FDIV double-real	FDIVR double-real

ModR/M bytes outside the range 00h-BFh are mapped by the tables below:

	0	1	2	3	4	5	6	7
C	FADD							
	ST(0),ST	ST(1),ST	ST(2),ST	ST(3),ST	ST(4),ST	ST(5),ST	ST(6),ST	ST(7),ST
D								
E	FSUBR							
	ST(0),ST	ST(1),ST	ST(2),ST	ST(3),ST	ST(4),ST	ST(5),ST	ST(6),ST	ST(7),ST
F	FDIVR							
	ST(0),ST	ST(1),ST	ST(2),ST	ST(3),ST	ST(4),ST	ST(5),ST	ST(6),ST	ST(7),ST

	8	9	A	B	C	D	E	F
C	FMUL							
	ST(0),ST	ST(1),ST	ST(2),ST	ST(3),ST	ST(4),ST	ST(5),ST	ST(6),ST	ST(7),ST
D								
E	FSUB							
	ST(0),ST	ST(1),ST	ST(2),ST	ST(3),ST	ST(4),ST	ST(5),ST	ST(6),ST	ST(7),ST
F	FDIV							
	ST(0),ST	ST(1),ST	ST(2),ST	ST(3),ST	ST(4),ST	ST(5),ST	ST(6),ST	ST(7),ST

A.5.3.2.7. Escape Opcodes with DD as First Byte

mod	nnn	R/M

ModR/M bytes in range of 00h-BFh, nnn are mapped according to the following table (opcode is determined by bits 5,4,3 of modR/M byte).

000	001	010	011	100	101	110	111
FLD double-real		FST double-real	FSTP double-real	FRSTOR 98/108bytes		FSAVE 98/108bytes	FSTSW 2 bytes

ModR/M bytes outside the range 00h-BFh are mapped by the tables below:

	0	1	2	3	4	5	6	7
C	FFREE							
	ST(0)	ST(1)	ST(2)	ST(3)	ST(4)	ST(5)	ST(6)	ST(7)
D	FST							
	ST(0)	ST(1)	ST(2)	ST(3)	ST(4)	ST(5)	ST(6)	ST(7)
E	FUCOM							
	ST(0),ST	ST(1),ST	ST(2),ST	ST(3),ST	ST(4),ST	ST(5),ST	ST(6),ST	ST(7),ST
F								

	8	9	A	B	C	D	E	F
C								
D	FSTP							
	ST(0)	ST(1)	ST(2)	ST(3)	ST(4)	ST(5)	ST(6)	ST(7)
E	FUCOMP							
	ST(0)	ST(1)	ST(2)	ST(3)	ST(4)	ST(5)	ST(6)	ST(7)
F								

A.5.3.2.8.   Escape Opcodes with DE as First Byte

mod	nnn	R/M

ModR/M bytes in range of 00h-BFh, nnn are mapped according to the following table (opcode is determined by bits 5,4,3 of modR/M byte).

000	001	010	011	100	101	110	111
FIADD word-int	FIMUL word-int	FICOM word-int	FICOMP word-int	FISUB word-int	FISUBR word-int	FIDIV word-int	FIDIVR word-int

ModR/M bytes outside the range 00h-BFh are mapped by the tables below:

	0	1	2	3	4	5	6	7
C	FADDP							
	ST(0),ST	ST(1),ST	ST(2),ST	ST(3),ST	ST(4),ST	ST(5),ST	ST(6),ST	ST(7),ST
D								
E	FSUBRP							
	ST(0),ST	ST(1),ST	ST(2),ST	ST(3),ST	ST(4),ST	ST(5),ST	ST(6),ST	ST(7),ST
F	FDIVRP							
	ST(0),ST	ST(1),ST	ST(2),ST	ST(3),ST	ST(4),ST	ST(5),ST	ST(6),ST	ST(7),ST

	8	9	A	B	C	D	E	F
C	FMULP							
	ST(0),ST	ST(1),ST	ST(2),ST	ST(3),ST	ST(4),ST	ST(5),ST	ST(6),ST	ST(7),ST
D		FCOMPP						
E	FSUBP							
	ST(0),ST	ST(1),ST	ST(2),ST	ST(3),ST	ST(4),ST	ST(5),ST	ST(6),ST	ST(7),ST
F	FDIVP							
	ST(0),ST	ST(1),ST	ST(2),ST.	ST(3),ST	ST(4),ST	ST(5),ST	ST(6),ST	ST(7),ST

A.5.3.2.9. Escape Opcodes with DF As First Byte

mod	nnn	R/M

ModR/M bytes in range of 00h-BFh, nnn are mapped according to the following table (opcode is determined by bits 5,4,3 of modR/M byte).

000	001	010	011	100	101	110	111
FILD word-int		FIST word-int	FISTP word-int	FBLD packed-BCD	FILD long-int	FBSTP packed-BCD	FISTP long-int

ModR/M bytes outside the range 00h-BFh are mapped by the tables below:

	0	1	2	3	4	5	6	7
C								
D								
E	FSTSW AX							
F								

	8	9	A	B	C	D	E	F
C								
D								
E								
F								

intel®

B

Flag Cross-Reference

This flag cross-reference is a summary of the flags affected by each instruction. For detailed information on how flags are affected for different modes of operation on the Pentium processor, see Chapter 25.

B.1. KEY TO CODES

T	= instruction tests flag
M	= instruction modifies flag (either sets or resets depending on operands)
0	= instruction resets flag
1	= instruction sets flag
—	= instruction's effect on flag is undefined
R	= instruction restores prior value of flag\<xin\>
blank	= instruction does not affect flag

Instruction	OF	SF	ZF	AF	PF	CF	TF	IF	DF	NT	RF
AAA	—	—	—	TM	—	M					
AAD	—	M	M	—	M	—					
AAM	—	M	M	—	M	—					
AAS	—	—	—	TM	—	M					
ADC	M	M	M	M	M	TM					
ADD	M	M	M	M	M	M					
AND	0	M	M	—	M	0					
ARPL			M								
BOUND											
BSF/BSR	—	—	M	—	—	—					
BSWAP											
BT/BTS/BTR/BTC	—	—	—	—	—	M					
CALL											
CBW											
CLC						0					
CLD									0		
CLI								0			
CLTS											
CMC						M					
CMP	M	M	M	M	M	M					

Instruction	OF	SF	ZF	AF	PF	CF	TF	IF	DF	NT	RF
CMPS	M	M	M	M	M	M			T		
CMPXCHG	M	M	M	M	M	M					
CMPXCHG8B			M								
CPUID											
CWD											
DAA	—	M	M	TM	M	TM					
DAS	—	M	M	TM	M	TM					
DEC	M	M	M	M	M						
DIV	—	—	—	—	—	—					
ENTER											
ESC											
HLT											
IDIV	—	—	—	—	—	—					
IMUL	M	—	—	—	—	M					
IN											
INC	M	M	M	M	M						
INS									T		
INT							0			0	
INTO	T						0			0	
INVD											
INVLPG											
IRET	R	R	R	R	R	R	R	R	R	T	
Jcond	T	T	T		T	T					
JCXZ											
JMP											
LAHF											
LAR			M								
LDS/LES/LSS/LFS/LGS											
LEA											
LEAVE											
LGDT/LIDT/LLDT/LMSW											
LOCK											
LODS									T		
LOOP											
LOOPE/LOOPNE			T								
LSL			M								
LTR											
MOV											
MOV control, debug, test	—	—	—	—	—	—					
MOVS									T		
MOVSX/MOVZX											
MUL	M	—	—	—	—	M					
NEG	M	M	M	M	M	M					
NOP											
NOT											
OR	0	M	M	—	M	0					
OUT											
OUTS									T		

Instruction	OF	SF	ZF	AF	PF	CF	TF	IF	DF	NT	RF
POP/POPA											
POPF	R	R	R	R	R	R	R	R	R	R	
PUSH/PUSHA/PUSHF											
RCL/RCR 1	M					TM					
RCL/RCR count	—					TM					
RDMSR											
RDTSC											
REP/REPE/REPNE											
RET											
ROL/ROR 1	M					M					
ROL/ROR count	—					M					
RSM	M	M	M	M	M	M	M	M	M	M	M
SAHF		R	R	R	R	R					
SAL/SAR/SHL/SHR 1	M	M	M	—	M	M					
SAL/SAR/SHL/SHR count	—	M	M	—	M	M					
SBB	M	M	M	M	M	TM					
SCAS	M	M	M	M	M	M			T		
SET cond	T	T	T		T	T					
SGDT/SIDT/SLDT/SMSW											
SHLD/SHRD	—	M	M	—	M	M					
STC						1					
STD									1		
STI								1			
STOS									T		
STR											
SUB	M	M	M	M	M	M					
TEST	0	M	M	—	M	0					
VERR/VERRW			M								
WAIT											
WBINVD											
WRMSR											
XADD	M	M	M	M	M	M					
XCHG											
XLAT											
XOR	0	M	M	—	M	0					

intel®

C

Status Flag Summary

C.1. STATUS FLAGS FUNCTIONS

Bit	Name	Function
0	CF	Carry Flag—Set on high-order bit carry or borrow; cleared otherwise.
2	PF	Parity Flag—Set if low-order eight bits of result contain an even number of 1 bits; cleared otherwise.
4	AF	Adjust Flag—Set on carry from or borrow to the low order four bits of AL; cleared otherwise. Used for decimal arithmetic.
6	ZF	Zero Flag—Set if result is zero; cleared otherwise.
7	SF	Sign Flag—Set equal to high-order bit of result (0 is positive, 1 if negative).
11	OF	Overflow Flag—Set if result is too large a positive number or too small a negative number (excluding sign-bit) to fit in destination operand; cleared otherwise.

C.2. KEY TO CODES

T	= instruction tests flag
M	= instruction modifies flag either sets or resets depending on operands)
0	= instruction resets flag
—	= instruction's effect on flag is undefined
blank	= instruction does not affect flag

Instruction	OF	SF	ZF	AF	PF	CF
AAA	—	—	—	TM	—	M
AAS	—	—	—	TM	—	M
AAD	—	M	M	—	M	—
AAM	—	M	M	—	M	—
DAA	—	M	M	TM	M	TM
DAS	—	M	M	TM	M	TM
ADC	M	M	M	M	M	TM
ADD	M	M	M	M	M	M
XADD	M	M	M	M	M	M
SBB	M	M	M	M	M	TM
SUB	M	M	M	M	M	M
CMP	M	M	M	M	M	M
CMPS	M	M	M	M	M	M
CMPXCHG	M	M	M	M	M	M
CMPXCHG8B			M			
SCAS	M	M	M	M	M	M
NEG	M	M	M	M	M	M
DEC	M	M	M	M	M	
INC	M	M	M	M	M	
IMUL	M	—	—	—	—	M
MUL	M	—	—	—	—	M
RCL/RCR 1	M					TM
RCL/RCR count	—					TM
ROL/ROR 1	M					M
ROL/ROR count	—					M
SAL/SAR/SHL/SHR 1	M	M	M	—	M	M
SAL/SAR/SHL/SHR count	—	M	M	—	M	M
SHLD/SHRD	—	M	M	—	M	M
BSF/BSR	—	—	M	—	—	—
BT/BTS/BTR/BTC	—	—	—	—	—	M
AND	0	M	M	—	M	0
OR	0	M	M	—	M	0
TEST	0	M	M	—	M	0
XOR	0	M	M	—	M	0

intel®

D

Condition Codes

Note: The terms "above" and "below" refer to the relation between two unsigned values (neither the SF flag nor the OF flag is tested). The terms "greater" and "less" refer to the relation between two signed values (the SF and OF flags are tested).

D.1.   DEFINITION OF CONDITIONS

For Conditional Instructions Jcond and SETcond

Mnemonic	Meaning	Instruction Subcode	Condition Tested
O	Overflow	0000	OF = 1
NO	No overflow	0001	OF = 0
B NAE	Below Neither above nor equal	0010	CF = 1
NB AE	Not below Above or equal	0011	CF = 0
E Z	Equal Zero	0100	ZF = 1
NE NZ	Not equal Not zero	0101	ZF = 0
BE NA	Below or equal Not above	0110	(CF or ZF) = 1
NBE A	Neither below nor equal Above	0111	(CF or ZF) = 0
S	Sign	1000	SF = 1
NS	No sign	1001	SF = 0
P PE	Parity Parity even	1010	PF = 1
NP PO	No parity Parity odd	1011	PF = 0
L NGE	Less Neither greater nor equal	1100	(SF xor OF) = 1
NL GE	Not less Greater or equal	1101	(SF xor OF) = 0
LE NG	Less or equal Not greater	1110	((SF xor OF) or ZF) = 1
NLE G	Neither less nor equal Greater	1111	((SF xor OF) or ZF) = 0

intel®

E

Numeric Exception
Summary

The following table lists the instruction mnemonics in alphabetical order. For each mnemonic, it summarizes the exceptions that the instruction may cause. When writing numeric programs that may be used in an environment that employs numerics exception handlers, assembly-language programmers should be aware of the possible exceptions for each instruction in order to determine the need for exception synchronization. Chapter 18 explains the need for exception synchronization.

Mnemonic	Instruction	IS	I	D	Z	O	U	P
F2XM1	2^X-1	Y	Y	Y			Y	Y
FABS	Absolute value	Y						
FADD(P)	Add real	Y	Y	Y		Y	Y	Y
FBLD	BCD load	Y						
FBSTP	BCD store and pop	Y	Y					Y
FCHS	Change sign	Y						
FCLEX	Clear exceptions							
FCOM(P)(P)	Compare real	Y	Y	Y				
FCOS	Cosine	Y	Y	Y			Y	Y
FDECSTP	Decrement stack pointer							
FDIV(R)(P)	Divide real	Y	Y	Y	Y	Y	Y	Y
FFREE	Free register							
FIADD	Integer add	Y	Y	Y		Y	Y	Y
FICOM(P)	Integer compare	Y	Y	Y				
FIDIV	Integer divide	Y	Y	Y	Y		Y	Y
FIDIVR	Integer divide reversed	Y	Y	Y	Y	Y	Y	Y
FILD	Integer load	Y						
FIMUL	Integer multiply	Y	Y	Y		Y	Y	Y
FINCSTP	Increment stack pointer							
FINIT	Initialize processor							
FIST(P)	Integer store	Y	Y					Y
FISUB(R)	Integer subtract	Y	Y	Y		Y	Y	Y
FLD extended or stack	Load real	Y						
FLD single or double	Load real	Y	Y	Y				
FLD1	Load + 1.0	Y						
FLDCW	Load Control word	Y	Y	Y	Y	Y	Y	Y
FLDENV	Load environment	Y	Y	Y	Y	Y	Y	Y
FLDL2E	Load $\log_2 e$	Y						
FLDL2T	Load $\log_2 10$	Y						
FLDLG2	Load $\log_{10} 2$	Y						
FLDLN2	Load $\log_e 2$	Y						

Mnemonic	Instruction	IS	I	D	Z	O	U	P
FLDPI	Load π	Y						
FLDZ	Load + 0.0	Y						
FMUL(P)	Multiply real	Y	Y	Y		Y	Y	Y
FNOP	No operation							
FPATAN	Partial arctangent	Y	Y	Y			Y	Y
FPREM	Partial remainder	Y	Y	Y			Y	
FPREM1	IEEE partial remainder	Y	Y	Y			Y	
FPTAN	Partial tangent	Y	Y	Y			Y	Y
FRNDINT	Round to integer	Y	Y	Y				Y
FRSTOR	Restore state	Y	Y	Y	Y	Y	Y	Y
FSAVE	Save state							
FSCALE	Scale	Y	Y	Y		Y	Y	Y
FSIN	Sine	Y	Y	Y			Y	Y
FSINCOS	Sine and cosine	Y	Y	Y			Y	Y
FSQRT	Square root	Y	Y	Y				Y
FST(P) stack or extended	Store real	Y						
FST(P) single or double	Store real	Y	Y	Y		Y	Y	Y
FSTCW	Store control word							
FSTENV	Store environment							
FSTSW (AX)	Store status word							
FSUB(R)(P)	Subtract real	Y	Y	Y		Y	Y	Y
FTST	Test	Y	Y	Y				
FUCOM(P)(P)	Unordered compare real	Y	Y	Y				
FWAIT	CPU Wait							
FXAM	Examine							
FXCH	Exchange registers	Y						
FXTRACT	Extract	Y	Y	Y	Y			
FYL2X	$Y \cdot \log_2 X$	Y	Y	Y	Y	Y	Y	Y
FYL2XP1	$Y \cdot \log_2(X + 1)$	Y	Y	Y			Y	Y

IS   — Invalid operand due to stack overflow/underflow
I   — Invalid operand due to other cause
D   — Denormal operand
Z   — Zero-divide
O   — Overflow
U   — Underflow
P   — Inexact result (precision)

intel®

F

Instruction Format
and Timing

Table F-2, Table F-3, and Table F-5 list all instructions along with instruction encoding diagrams and clock counts.

F.1. INTEGER INSTRUCTION FORMAT AND TIMING

The following sections explain how to use each of the columns of Table F-2.

Format

All instruction encodings are subsets of the general instruction format shown in Figure F-1. Instructions consist of one or two primary opcode bytes, possibly an address specifier consisting of the **mod r/m** byte and scale-index-base byte, a displacement if required, and an immediate data field if required.

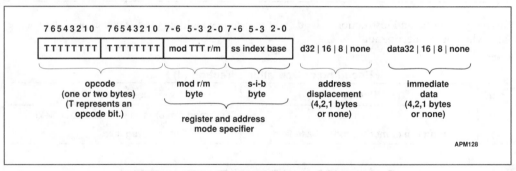

Figure F-1. General Instruction Format

Within the primary opcode or opcodes, smaller encoding fields may be defined. These fields vary according to the class of operation. The fields define such information as direction of the operation, size of displacements, register encoding, or sign extension.

Almost all instructions referring to an operand in memory have an addressing mode byte following the primary opcode byte(s). This byte, the **mod r/m** byte, specifies the address mode to be used. Certain encodings of the **mod r/m** byte indicate that a second addressing byte, the scale-index-base byte, follows the **mod r/m** byte to fully specify the addressing mode.

Addressing modes can include a displacement immediately following the **mod r/m** byte or scale-index-base byte. If a displacement is present, the possible sizes are 8, 16, or 32 bits.

If the instruction specifies an immediate operand, the immediate operand follows any displacement bytes. The immediate operand, if specified, is always the last field of the instruction.

Figure F-1 illustrates several of the fields that can appear in an instruction, such as the **mod** field and the **r/m** field, but the figure does not show all fields. Several smaller fields also appear in certain instructions, sometimes within the opcode bytes themselves. Table F-0 is a complete list of all fields appearing in the instruction set. Subsequent tables list the values for each of the fields.

Table F-1. Fields within Instructions

Field Name	Description	Number of Bits
d	Specifies direction of data operation	1
eee	Specifies a special-purpose (test, debug, or control) register	
reg	General register specifier	3
s	Specifies if an immediate data field must be sign-extended	1
sreg2	Segment register specifier for CS, SS, DS, ES	2
sreg3	Segment register specifier for CS, SS, DS, ES, FS, GS	3
tttn	For conditional instructions, specifies a condition asserted or a condition negated	4
w	Specifies if data is byte of full-sized (full-sized is either 16 or 32 bits)	1

In many two-operand instructions, the **d** field indicates which operand is considered the source and which is the destination.

Encoding of Operation Direction (d) Field

d	Source	Destination
0	**reg** field	**mod r/m** or **mod ss index base** field
1	**mod r/m** or **mod ss index base** field	**reg** field

Encoding of Special-Purpose Register (eee) Field

eee	Control Register	Debug Register
000	CR0	DR0
001	*reserved*	DR1
010	CR2	DR2
011	CR3	DR3
100	*CR4*	*reserved*
101	*reserved*	*reserved*
110	*reserved*	DR6
111	*reserved*	DR7

NOTE: Do not use reserved encodings.

Encoding of reg Field When w Field is Not Present in Instruction

reg Field	Register Selected During 16-Bit Data Operations	Register Selected During 32-Bit Data Operations
000	AX	EAX
001	CX	ECX
010	DX	EDX
011	BX	EBX
100	SP	ESP
101	BP	EBP
110	SI	ESI
111	DI	EDI

Encoding of reg Field When w Field is Present in Instruction

reg	Register Specified by reg Field During 16-Bit Data Operations		reg	Register Specified by reg Field During 32-Bit Data Operations	
	Function of w Field			Function of w Field	
	When w = 0	When w = 1		When w = 0	When w = 1
000	AL	AX	000	AL	EAX
001	CL	CX	001	CL	ECX
010	DL	DX	010	DL	EDX
011	BL	BX	011	BL	EBX
100	AH	SP	100	AH	ESP
101	CH	BP	101	CH	EBP
110	DH	SI	110	DH	ESI
111	BH	DI	111	BH	EDI

The s field occurs primarily in instructions with immediate data fields. The s field has an effect only if the size of the immediate data is 8 bits and is being placed in a 16-bit or 32-bit destination.

Encoding of Sign-Extend (s) Field

s	Effect on Immediate Data8	Effect on Immediate Data16 or Data32
0	None	None
1	Sign-extend data8 to fill 16-bit or 32-bit destination	None

Encoding of the Segment Register (sreg) Field

2-Bit sreg2 Field	Segment Register Selected
00	ES
01	CS
10	SS
11	DS

3-Bit sreg3 Field	Segment Register Selected
000	ES
001	CS
010	SS
011	DS
100	FS
101	GS
110	*do not use*
111	*do not use*

For the conditional instructions (conditional jumps and set on condition), **tttn** is encoded such that **ttt** gives the condition to test and **n** indicates whether to use the condition (**n** = 0) or its negation (**n** = 1).

Encoding of Conditional Test (tttn) Field

t t t n	Mnemonic	Condition
0000	O	Overflow
0001	NO	No overflow
0010	B, NAE	Below, Not above or equal
0011	NB, AE	Not below, Above or equal
0100	E, Z	Equal, Zero
0101	NE, NZ	Not equal, Not zero
0110	BE, NA	Below or equal, Not above
0111	NBE, A	Not below or equal, Above
1000	S	Sign
1001	NS	Not sign
1010	P, PE	Parity, Parity Even
1011	NP, PO	Not parity, Parity Odd
1100	L, NGE	Less than, Not greater than or equal to
1101	NL, GE	Not less than, Greater than or equal to
1110	LE, NG	Less than or equal to, Not greater than
1111	NLE, G	Not less than or equal to, Greater than

For any given instruction performing a data operation, the instruction is executing as a 32-bit operation or a 16-bit operation. Within the constraints of the operation size, the **w** field encodes the operand size as either one byte or the full operation size, as shown in the following table.

Encoding of Operand Length (w) Field

w Field	Operand Size During 16-Bit Data Operations	Operand Size During 32-Bit Data Operations
0	8 bits	8 bits
1	16 bits	32 bits

Clock Counts

To calculate elapsed time for an instruction, multiply the instruction clock count as listed in the tables by the processor clock period (for example, 15 ns for a 66-MHz processor).

The clock count tables assume that data and instruction access hit their respective caches. A cache miss forces the processor to run an external bus cycle. The 64-bit burst bus of the Pentium processor is defined as r-b-w, where:

$r = $ The number of clocks in the first cycle of a burst read or the number of clocks per data cycle in a nonburst read.

$b = $ The number of clocks for the second and subsequent cycles in a burst read.

$w = $ The number of clocks for a write.

The fastest bus the Pentium processor can support is 2-1-2, assuming zero wait states. The clock counts in the cache miss penalty column assume a 2-1-2 bus. For slower busses, add $r - 2$ clocks to the cache miss penalty for the first quadword accessed. Other factors also affect instruction clock counts.

To simplify the tables, the following assumptions are made:

1. The external bus is available for reads or writes at all times. Otherwise, add clocks to reads until the bus is available. The processor stalls if the write buffers become full and the external bus is busy. In that case, add clocks to writes until the bus becomes available.

2. If the write buffers become full, subsequent writes are delayed until the write buffers become empty. For the worst case, add w clocks.

3. Accesses are aligned. Add three clocks to each misaligned access.

4. Operands are in the data cache. Add 3 + (number of wait states) for each cache miss.

5. The target of a jump is in the code cache. If not, add r clocks for accessing the destination instruction of a jump. If the destination instruction is not completely contained in the first qword read, add a maximum of $3b$ clocks. If the destination instruction is not completely contained in the first 32-byte burst, add a maximum of another $r + 3b$ clocks. The penalty for branch misprediction is three clocks.

6. Cache fills complete before subsequent accesses to the same line. If a read misses the cache during a cache fill due to a previous read or prefetch, the read must wait for the cache fill to complete. If a read or write accesses a cache line still being filled, it must wait for the fill to complete.

7. Page translation hits in TLB. A TLB miss typically adds from 13 to 28 clocks to the instruction depending on whether the Accessed or Dirty bit of the page entries needs to be

set in memory. This assumes that neither page entry is in the data cache and that a page fault does not occur during address translation.

8. No exceptions are detected during instruction execution. Refer to the Interrupt Clock Counts Table for extra clocks if an interrupt is detected.

9. Instructions that read multiple consecutive data items (for example, task switch, POPA, etc.) and miss the cache are assumed to start the first access on a 32-byte boundary. If not, an extra cache line fill may be necessary, which may add up to $r + 3b$ clocks to the cache miss penalty.

10. No address generation interlocks (AGI). AGIs occur when a register being used as part of an address calculation is the destination register of a previous instruction in either the pipelines. AGIs cause a one clock delay.

The following abbreviations are used in the clock count columns:

TS   The time for a task switch, which depends on the target TSS type as shown in the Task Switch Clock Counts Table.

INT The time for an interrupt, which depends on processor mode and type of gate used, as shown in the Interrupt Clock Counts Table.

Task Switch Clock Counts Table

Method		Value of TS
From	To	
32-Bit, 16-Bit, or V86 TSS	32-Bit TSS	85
32-Bit, 16-Bit, or V86 TSS	16-Bit TSS	85
32-Bit, 16-Bit, or V86 TSS	V86 TSS	71

Interrupt Clock Counts Table

Method	Value of INT		
	Cache Hit	Miss Penalty	Notes
Real Mode	11	3	
Protected Mode			
Interrupt/Trap gate, same level	25	6	9
Interrupt/Trap gate, different level	42	12	9
Task gate	17 + TS	3	9,10
Virtual 8086 Mode			
Interrupt/Trap, same level	13	3	
Interrupt/Trap gate, different level	54	12	
Task gate	17 + TS	3	10

Notes

The following abbreviations in the Notes column help to interpret the other columns:

16/32   Clocks apply to 16- and 32-bit modes respectively

L/NL	Clocks apply to loop and no loop cases respectively
MN/MX	Clocks shown define a range from minimum to maximum
P	Clocks apply to protected mode
R	Clocks apply to real-address mode
RV/P	First clock applies to real and V86 mode; second applies to protected mode
T/NT	Clocks apply to taken and not taken cases respectively
U/L	Clocks apply to unlocked and locked cases respectively
1.	Assuming that the operand address and stack address fall in different cache interleaves.
2.	Always locked. Always forced to miss cache.
4.	Clocks = {quotient(count/operand length)}*7 + 9 = 8 if count $\leq$ operand length (8/16/32).
5.	Clocks = {quotient(count/operand length)}*7 + 9 = 9 if count $\leq$ operand length (8/16/32).
8.	Penalty for cache miss: add 2 clocks for every stack value copied to the new stack frame.
9.	Add 8 clocks for each load of an unaccessed descriptor.
10.	Refer to Task Switch Clock Counts Table for value of TS.
For notes 12 − 13:	b = 0 − 3, nonzero byte number; i = 0 − 1, nonzero nibble number; n = 0 − 3, nonzero bit number in nibble.
12.	Clocks= 8 + 4(b + 1) + 3(i + 1) + 3(n + 1) = 6 if second operand = 0.
13.	Clocks= 9 + 4(b + 1) + 3(i + 1) + 3(n + 1) = 7 if second operand = 0.
For notes 14 − 15:	n = bit position (0 − 31).
14.	Clocks= 7 + 2(32 − n) = 6 if second operand = 0.
15.	Clocks= 8 + 2(32 − n) = 7 if second operand = 0.
16.	Assuming that the two string addresses fall in different cache interleaves.
21.	Refer to the Interrupt Clock Counts Table for value of INT.
23.	Add $r + 3b$ for instruction cache miss. Add 3 for branch misprediction.
24.	Clocks shown define a range from minimum to maximum.
25.	Add $r + 3b$ for instruction cache miss.

Pairing

The following abbreviations are used in the Pairing column:

PV   Pairable if issued to V-pipe
NP   Not pairable, executes in U-pipe
UV   Pairable in either pipe
PU   Pairable if issued to U-pipe

Table F-2. Integer Clock Count Summary

Instruction	Format	Clocks	Notes
AAA – ASCII Adjust after **Addition**	0011 0111	3	
AAD – ASCII Adjust AX before **Division**	1101 0101 : 0000 1010	10	
AAM – ASCII Adjust AX after **Multiply**	1101 0100 : 0000 1010	18	
AAS – ASCII Adjust AL after **Subtraction**	0011 1111	3	
ADC – ADD with Carry			
reg1 to reg2	0001 000w : 11 reg1 reg2	1	
reg2 to reg1	0001 001w : 11 reg1 reg2	1	
memory to register	0001 001w : mod reg r/m	2	
register to memory	0001 000w : mod reg r/m	3	U/L
immediate to register	1000 00sw : 11 010 reg : immediate data	1	
immediate to accumulator	0001 010w : immediate data	1	
immediate to memory	1000 00sw : mod 010 r/m : immediate data	3	U/L
ADD – Add			
reg1 to reg2	0000 000w : 11 reg1 reg2	1	
reg2 to reg1	0000 001w : 11 reg1 reg2	1	
memory to register	0000 001w : mod reg r/m	2	
register to memory	0000 000w : mod reg r/m	3	U/L
immediate to register	1000 00sw : 11 000 reg : immediate data	1	
immediate to accumulator	0000 010w : immediate data	1	
immediate to memory	1000 00sw : mod 000 r/m : immediate data	3	U/L
AND – Logical AND			
reg1 to reg2	0010 000w : 11 reg1 reg2	1	
reg2 to reg1	0010 001w : 11 reg1 reg2	1	
memory to register	0010 001w : mod reg r/m	2	
register to memory	0010 000w : mod reg r/m	3	U/L
immediate to register	1000 00sw : 11 100 reg : immediate data	1	
immediate to accumulator	0010 010w : immediate data	1	
immediate to memory	1000 00sw : mod 100 r/m : immediate data	3	U/L
ARPL – Adjust RPL Field of Selector			
from register	0110 0011 : 11 reg1 reg2	7	
from memory	0110 0011 : mod reg r/m	7	
BOUND – Check Array Against **Bounds**	0110 0010 : mod reg r/m		
if within bounds		8	
if out of bounds		INT + 32	21

Table F-2. Integer Clock Count Summary (Contd.)

Instruction	Format	Clocks	Notes
BSF – Bit Scan Forward			
reg1, reg2	0000 1111 : 1011 1100 : 11 reg2 reg1		
word		6–34	MN/MX, 12
doubleword		6–42	MN/MX, 12
memory, reg	0000 1111 : 1011 1100 : mod reg r/m		
word		6–35	MN/MX, 13
doubleword		6–43	MN/MX, 13
BSR – Bit Scan Reverse			
reg1, reg2	0000 1111 : 1011 1101 : 11 reg2 reg1		
word		7–39	MN/MX,14
doubleword		7–71	MN/MX,14
memory, reg	0000 1111 : 1011 1101 : mod reg r/m		
word		7–40	MN/MX,15
doubleword		7–72	MN/MX,15
BSWAP – Byte Swap	0000 1111 : 1100 1 reg	1	
BT – Bit Test			
register, immediate data	0000 1111 : 1011 1010 : 11 100 reg: imm8	4	
memory, immediate imm8 data	0000 1111 : 1011 1010 : mod 100 r/m :	4	
reg1, reg2	0000 1111 : 1010 0011 : 11 reg2 reg1	4	
memory, reg	0000 1111 : 1010 0011 : mod reg r/m	9	
BTC – Bit Test and Complement			
register, immediate data	0000 1111 : 1011 1010 : 11 111 reg: imm8	7	
memory, immediate imm8 data	0000 1111 : 1011 1010 : mod 111 r/m :	8	U/L
reg1, reg2	0000 1111 : 1011 1011 : 11 reg2 reg1	7	
memory, reg	0000 1111 : 1011 1011 : mod reg r/m	13	U/L
BTR – Bit Test and Reset			
register, immediate data	0000 1111 : 1011 1010 : 11 110 reg: imm8	7	
memory, immediate imm8 data	0000 1111 : 1011 1010 : mod 110 r/m :	8	U/L
reg1, reg2	0000 1111 : 1011 0011 : 11 reg2 reg1	7	
memory, reg	0000 1111 : 1011 0011 : mod reg r/m	13	U/L
BTS – Bit Test and Set			
register, immediate data	0000 1111 : 1011 1010 : 11 101 reg: imm8	7	
memory, immediate imm8 data	0000 1111 : 1011 1010 : mod 101 r/m :	8	U/L
reg1, reg2	0000 1111 : 1010 1011 : 11 reg2 reg1	7	
memory, reg	0000 1111 : 1010 1011 : mod reg r/m	13	U/L
CALL – Call Procedure (in same segment)			
direct	1110 1000 : full displacement	1	23
register indirect	1111 1111 : 11 010 reg	2	23
memory indirect	1111 1111 : mod 010 r/m	2	23

Table F-2. Integer Clock Count Summary (Contd.)

Instruction	Format	Clocks	Notes
CALL – Call Procedure (in other segment)			
direct	1001 1010 : unsigned full offset, selector	4	R,23
to same level		4–13	P,9,23,24
thru gate to same level		22	P,9,25
to inner level, no parameters		44	P,9,25
to inner level, x parameters (d)words		45+2x	P,9,25
to TSS		21+TS	P,10,9,25
thru task gate		22+TS	P,10,9,25
indirect	1111 1111 : mod 011 r/m	5	R,23
to same level		5–14	P,9,23,24
thru gate to same level		22	P,9,25
to inner level, no parameters		44	P,9,25
to inner level, x parameters (d)words		45+2x	P,9,25
to TSS		21+TS	P,10,9,25
thru task gate		22+TS	P,10,9,25
CBW – Convert Byte to Word **CWDE – Convert Word to Doubleword**	1001 1000	3	
CLC – Clear Carry Flag	1111 1000	2	
CLD – Clear Direction Flag	1111 1100	2	
CLI – Clear Interrupt Flag	1111 1010	7	
CLTS – Clear Task-Switched **Flag in CR0**	0000 1111 : 0000 0110	10	
CMC – Complement Carry Flag	1111 0101	2	
CMP – Compare Two Operands			
reg1 with reg2	0011 100w : 11 reg1 reg2	1	
reg2 with reg1	0011 101w : 11 reg1 reg2	1	
memory with register	0011 100w : mod reg r/m	2	
register with memory	0011 101w : mod reg r/m	2	
immediate with register	1000 00sw : 11 111 reg : immediate data	1	
immediate with accumulator	0011 110w : immediate data	1	
immediate with memory	1000 00sw : mod 111 r/m	2	
CMPS/CMPSB/CMPSW/CMPSD **– Compare String Operands**	1010 011w	5	16
CMPXCHG – Compare and Exchange			
reg1, reg2	0000 1111 : 1011 000w : 11 reg2 reg1	5	
memory, reg	0000 1111 : 1011 000w : mod reg r/m	6	U/L
CMPXCHG8B – Compare and **Exchange 8 Bytes**			
memory, reg	0000 1111 : 1100 0111 : mod reg r/m	10	U/L
CWD – Convert Word to Dword **CDQ – Convert Dword to Qword**	1001 1001	2	
DAA – Decimal Adjust AL after **Addition**	0010 0111	3	

Table F-2. Integer Clock Count Summary (Contd.)

Instruction	Format	Clocks	Notes
DAS – Decimal Adjust AL after Subtraction	0010 1111	3	
DEC – Decrement by 1			
reg	1111 111w : 11 001 reg	1	
or	0100 1 reg	1	
memory	1111 111w : mod 001 r/m	3	U/L
DIV – Unsigned Divide			
accumulator by register	1111 011w : 11 110 reg		
divisor —	byte	17	
	word	25	
	doubleword	41	
accumulator by memory	1111 011w : mod 110 r/m		
divisor —	byte	17	
	word	25	
	doubleword	41	
ENTER – Make Stack Frame level (L) for Procedure Parameters	1100 1000 : 16-bit displacement : 8-bit		
L = 0		11	
L = 1		15	
L > 1		15 + 2L	8
HLT – Halt	1111 0100		
IDIV – Signed Divide			
accumulator by register	1111 011w : 11 111 reg		
divisor —	byte	22	
	word	30	
	doubleword	46	
accumulator by memory	1111 011w : mod 111 r/m		
divisor —	byte	22	
	word	30	
	doubleword	46	
IMUL – Signed Multiply			
accumulator with register	1111 011w : 11 101 reg		
multiplier —	byte	11	
	word	11	
	doubleword	10	
accumulator with memory	1111 011w : mod 101 reg		
multiplier —	byte	11	
	word	11	
	doubleword	10	

Table F-2. Integer Clock Count Summary (Contd.)

Instruction	Format	Clocks	Notes
reg1 with reg2	0000 1111 : 1010 1111 : 11 : reg1 reg2		
multiplier —	byte	10	
	word	10	
	doubleword	10	
register with memory	0000 1111 : 1010 1111 : mod reg r/m		
multiplier —	byte	10	
	word	10	
	doubleword	10	
reg1 with imm. to reg2	0110 10s1 : 11 reg1 reg2 : immediate data		
multiplier —	byte	10	
	word	10	
	doubleword	10	
mem. with imm. to reg	0110 10s1 : mod reg r/m : immediate data		
multiplier —	byte	10	
	word	10	
	doubleword	10	
INC – Increment by 1			
reg	1111 111w : 11 000 reg	1	
or	0100 0 reg	1	
memory	1111 111w : mod 000 r/m	3	U/L
INT n – Interrupt Type n	1100 1101 : type	INT + 6	21,25
INT – Single-Step Interrupt 3	1100 1100	INT + 5	21,25
INTO – Interrupt 4 on Overflow	1100 1110		
taken		INT + 5	21,25
not taken		4	21,25
INVD – Invalidate Cache	0000 1111 : 0000 1000	15	
INVLPG – Invalidate TLB Entry	0000 1111 : 0000 0001 : mod 111 r/m	29	
IRET/IRETD – Interrupt Return	1100 1111		
real mode or virtual 8086 mode		7	R,23
protected mode to same level		10–19	P,9,23,24
to outer level		27	P,9,25
to nested task		10 + TS	P,9,10,25
Jcc – Jump if Condition is Met			
8-bit displacement	0111 tttn : 8-bit displacement	1	23
full displacement	0000 1111 : 1000 tttn : full displacement	1	23
JCXZ/JECXZ – Jump on CX/ECX Zero	1110 0011 : 8-bit displacement	6/5	T/NT,23
address size prefix differentiates JCXZ from JECXZ			

Table F-2. Integer Clock Count Summary (Contd.)

Instruction	Format	Clocks	Notes
JMP – Unconditional Jump (to same segment)			
short	1110 1011 : 8-bit displacement	1	23
direct	1110 1001 : full displacement	1	23
register indirect	1111 1111 : 11 100 reg	2	23
memory indirect	1111 1111 : mod 100 r/m	2	23
JMP – Unconditional Jump (to other segment)			
direct intersegment	1110 1010 : unsigned full offset, selector	3	R,23
to same level		3–12	P,9,23,24
thru call gate ro same level		18	P,9,25
thru TSS		19 + TS	P,10,9,25
thru task gate		20 + TS	P,10,9,25
indirect intersegment	1111 1111 : mod 101 r/m	4	R,23
to same level		4–13	P,9,23,24
thru call gate ro same level		18	P,9,25
thru TSS		19 + TS	P,10,9,25
thru task gate		20 + TS	P,10,9,25
LAHF – Load Flags into AH Register	1001 1111	2	
LAR – Load Access Rights Byte			
from register	0000 1111 : 0000 0010 : 11 reg1 reg2	8	
from memory	0000 1111 : 0000 0010 : mod reg r/m	8	
LDS – Load Pointer to DS	1100 0101 : mod reg r/m	4–13	9,24
LEA – Load Effective Address	1000 1101 : mod reg r/m	1	
LEAVE – High Level Procedure Exit	1100 1001	3	
LES – Load Pointer to ES	1100 0100 : mod reg r/m	4–13	9,24
LFS – Load Pointer to FS	0000 1111 : 1011 0100 : mod reg r/m	4–13	9,24
LGDT – Load Global Descriptor Table Register	0000 1111 : 0000 0001 : mod 010 r/m	6	
LGS – Load Pointer to GS	0000 1111 : 1011 0101 : mod reg r/m	4–13	9,24
LIDT – Load Interrupt Descriptor Table Register	0000 1111 : 0000 0001 : mod 011 r/m	6	
LLDT – Load Local Descriptor Table Register			
LDTR from register	0000 1111 : 0000 0000 : 11 010 reg	9	
LDTR from memory	0000 1111 : 0000 0000 : mod 010 r/m	9	
LMSW – Load Machine Status Word			
from register	0000 1111 : 0000 0001 : 11 110 reg	8	
from memory	0000 1111 : 0000 0001 : mod 110 r/m	8	
LOCK – Assert LOCK# Signal Prefix	1111 0000	1	
LODS/LODSB/LODSW/LODSD – Load String Operand	1010 110w	2	
LOOP – Loop Count	1110 0010 : 8-bit displacement	5/6	L/NL,23

Table F-2. Integer Clock Count Summary (Contd.)

Instruction	Format	Clocks	Notes
LOOPZ/LOOPE – Loop Count while Zero/Equal	1110 0001 : 8-bit displacement	7/8	L/NL,23
LOOPNZ/LOOPNE – Loop Count while not Zero/Equal	1110 0000 : 8-bit displacement	7/8	L/NL,23
LSL – Load Segment Limit			
from register	0000 1111 : 0000 0011 : 11 reg1 reg2	8	
from memory	0000 1111 : 0000 0011 : mod reg r/m	8	
LSS – Load Pointer to SS	0000 1111 : 1011 0010 : mod reg r/m	4–13/ 8–17	RV/P,9,24
LTR – Load Task Register			
from register	0000 1111 : 0000 0000 : 11 011 reg	10	
from memory	0000 1111 : 0000 0000 : mod 011 r/m	10	
MOV – Move Data			
reg1 to reg2	1000 100w : 11 reg1 reg2	1	
reg2 to reg1	1000 101w : 11 reg1 reg2	1	
memory to reg	1000 101w : mod reg r/m	1	
reg to memory	1000 100w : mod reg r/m	1	
immediate to reg	1100 011w : 11 000 reg : immediate data	1	
or	1011 w reg : immediate data	1	
immediate to memory	1100 011w : mod 000 r/m : immediate data	1	
memory to accumulator	1010 000w : full displacement	1	
accumulator to memory	1010 001w : full displacement	1	
MOV – Move to/from Control Registers			
CR0 from register	0000 1111 : 0010 0010 : 11 000 reg	22	
CR2 from register	0000 1111 : 0010 0010 : 11 010reg	12	
CR3 from register	0000 1111 : 0010 0010 : 11 011 reg	21	
CR4 from register	0000 1111 : 0010 0010 : 11 100 reg	14	
register from CR0-4	0000 1111 : 0010 0000 : 11 eee reg	4	
MOV – Move to/from Debug Registers			
DR0-3 from register	0000 1111 : 0010 0011 : 11 eee reg	11	
DR4-5 from register	0000 1111 : 0010 0011 : 11 eee reg	12	
DR6-7 from register	0000 1111 : 0010 0011 : 11 eee reg	11	
register from DR6-7	0000 1111 : 0010 0001 : 11 eee reg	11	
register from DR4-5	0000 1111 : 0010 0001 : 11 eee reg	12	
register from DR0-3	0000 1111 : 0010 0001 : 11 eee reg	2	

Table F-2. Integer Clock Count Summary (Contd.)

Instruction	Format	Clocks	Notes
MOV – Move to/from Segment Registers			
reg to segment reg	1000 1110 : 11 sreg3 reg	2–11	9,24
reg to SS	1000 1110 : 11 sreg3 reg	2–11/ 8–17	RV/P,9,24
memory to segment reg	1000 1110 : mod sreg3 r/m	3	9,24
memory to SS	1000 1110 : mod sreg3 r/m	3–12/ 8–17	RV/P,9,24
segment reg to reg	1000 1100 : 11 sreg3 reg	1	
segment reg to memory	1000 1100 : mod sreg3 r/m	1	
MOVS/MOVSB/MOVSW/ MOVSD – Move Data from String to String	1010 010w	4	16
MOVSX – Move with Sign-Extend			
reg2 to reg1	0000 1111 : 1011 111w : 11 reg1 reg2	3	
memory to reg	0000 1111 : 1011 111w : mod reg r/m	3	
MOVZX – Move with Zero-Extend			
reg2 to reg1	0000 1111 : 1011 011w : 11 reg1 reg2	3	
memory to reg	0000 1111 : 1011 011w : mod reg r/m	3	
MUL – Unsigned Multiplication of AL or AX			
accumulator with register	1111 011w : 11 100 reg		
multiplier —	byte	11	
	word	11	
	doubleword	10	
accumulator with memory	1111 011w : mod 100 reg		
multiplier —	byte	11	
	word	11	
	doubleword	10	
NEG – Two's Complement Negation			
reg	1111 011w : 11 011 reg	1	
memory	1111 011w : mod 011 r/m	3	U/L
NOP – No Operation	1001 0000	1	
NOT – One's Complement Negation			
reg	1111 011w : 11 010 reg	1	
memory	1111 011w : mod 010 r/m	3	U/L
OR – Logical Inclusive OR			
reg1 to reg2	0000 100w : 11 reg1 reg2	1	
reg2 to reg1	0000 101w : 11 reg1 reg2	1	
memory to register	0000 101w : mod reg r/m	2	
register to memory	0000 100w : mod reg r/m	3	U/L
immediate to register	1000 00sw : 11 001 reg : immediate data	1	
immediate to accumulator	0000 110w : immediate data	1	
immediate to memory	1000 00sw : mod 001 r/m : immediate data	3	U/L

Table F-2. Integer Clock Count Summary (Contd.)

Instruction	Format	Clocks	Notes
POP – Pop a Word from the Stack			
reg	1000 1111 : 11 000 reg	1	
or	0101 1 reg	1	
memory	1000 1111 : mod 000 r/m	3	1
POP – Pop a Segment Register from the Stack			
segment reg CS, DS, ES	000 sreg2 111	3–12	9,24
segment reg SS	000 sreg2 111	3–12/ 8–17	RV/P,9,24
segment reg FS, GS	0000 1111: 10 sreg3 001	3–12	9,24
POPA/POPAD – Pop All General Registers	0110 0001	5	
POPF/POPFD – Pop Stack into FLAGS or EFLAGS Register	1001 1101	4/14	RV/P
PUSH – Push Operand onto the Stack			
reg	1111 1111 : 11 110 reg	1	
or	0101 0 reg	1	
memory	1111 1111 : mod 110 r/m	2	1
immediate	0110 10s0 : immediate data	1	
PUSH – Push Segment Register onto the Stack			
segment reg CS,DS,ES,SS	000 sreg2 110	1	
segment reg FS,GS	0000 1111: 10 sreg3 000	1	
PUSHA/PUSHAD – Push All General Registers	0110 0000	5	
PUSHF/PUSHFD – Push Flags Register onto the Stack	1001 1100	3/9	RV/P
RCL – Rotate thru Carry Left			
reg by 1	1101 000w : 11 010 reg	1	
memory by 1	1101 000w : mod 010 r/m	3	
reg by CL	1101 001w : 11 010 reg	7–24	MN/MX,4
memory by CL	1101 001w : mod 010 r/m	9–26	MN/MX,5
reg by immediate count	1100 000w : 11 010 reg : imm8 data	8–25	MN/MX,4
memory by immediate count	1100 000w : mod 010 r/m : imm8 data	10–27	MN/MX,5
RCR – Rotate thru Carry Right			
reg by 1	1101 000w : 11 011 reg	1	
memory by 1	1101 000w : mod 011 r/m	3	
reg by CL	1101 001w : 11 011 reg	7–24	MN/MX,4
memory by CL	1101 001w : mod 011 r/m	9–26	MN/MX,5
reg by immediate count	1100 000w : 11 011 reg : imm8 data	8–25	MN/MX,4
memory by immediate count	1100 000w : mod 011 r/m : imm8 data	10–27	MN/MX,5
RDMSR – Read from Model- Specific Register	0000 1111 : 0011 0010	20–24	MN/MX

Table F-2. Integer Clock Count Summary (Contd.)

Instruction	Format	Clocks	Notes
REP LODS – Load String	1111 0011 : 1010 110w		
C = 0		7	
C > 0		7 + 3c	16
REP MOVS – Move String	1111 0011 : 1010 010w		
C = 0		6	
C = 1		13	16
C > 1		13 + c	16
REP STOS – Store String	1111 0011 : 1010 101w		
C = 0		6	
C > 0		9 + c	
REPE CMPS – Compare String (Find Non-Match)	1111 0011 : 1010 011w		
C = 0		7	
C > 0		8 + 4c	16
REPE SCAS – Scan String (Find Non-AL/AX/EAX)	1111 0011 : 1010 111w		
C = 0		7	
C > 0		8 + 4c	16
REPNE CMPS – Compare String (Find Match)	1111 0010 : 1010 011w		
C = 0		7	
C > 0		9 + 4c	16
REPNE SCAS – Scan String (Find AL/AX/EAX)	1111 0010 : 1010 111w		
C = 0		7	
C > 0		8 + 4c	16
RET – Return from Procedure (to same segment)			
	1100 0011	2	
adding immediate to SP	1100 0010 : 16-bit displacement	3	
RET – Return from Procedure (to other segment)			
intersegment	1100 1011	4	R,23
to same level		4–13	P,9,23,24
to outer level		23	P,9,25
adding immediate to SP	1100 1010 : 16-bit displacement	4	R,23
to same level		4–13	P,9,23,24
to outer level		23	P,9,25
ROL – Rotate (not thru Carry) Left			
reg by 1	1101 000w : 11 000 reg	1	
memory by 1	1101 000w : mod 000 r/m	3	
reg by CL	1101 001w : 11 000 reg	4	
memory by CL	1101 001w : mod 000 r/m	4	
reg by immediate count	1100 000w : 11 000 reg : imm8 data	1	
memory by immediate count	1100 000w : mod 000 r/m : imm8 data	3	

Table F-2. Integer Clock Count Summary (Contd.)

Instruction	Format	Clocks	Notes
ROR – Rotate (not thru Carry) Right			
reg by 1	1101 000w : 11 001 reg	1	
memory by 1	1101 000w : mod 001 r/m	3	
reg by CL	1101 001w : 11 001 reg	4	
memory by CL	1101 001w : mod 001 r/m	4	
reg by immediate count	1100 000w : 11 001 reg : imm8 data	1	
memory by immediate count	1100 000w : mod 001 r/m : imm8 data	3	
RSM – Resume from System Management Mode	0000 1111 : 1010 1010		
SAHF – Store AH into Flags	1001 1110	2	
SAL – Shift Arithmetic Left	same instruction as SHL		
SAR – Shift Arithmetic Right			
reg by 1	1101 000w : 11 111 reg	1	
memory by 1	1101 000w : mod 111 r/m	3	
reg by CL	1101 001w : 11 111 reg	4	
memory by CL	1101 001w : mod 111 r/m	4	
reg by immediate count	1100 000w : 11 111 reg : imm8 data	1	
memory by immediate count	1100 000w : mod 111 r/m : imm8 data	3	
SBB – Integer Subtraction with Borrow			
reg1 to reg2	0001 100w : 11 reg1 reg2	1	
reg2 to reg1	0001 101w : 11 reg1 reg2	1	
memory to register	0001 101w : mod reg r/m	2	
register to memory	0001 100w : mod reg r/m	3	U/L
immediate to register	1000 00sw : 11 011 reg : immediate data	1	
immediate to accumulator	0001 110w : immediate data	1	
immediate to memory	1000 00sw : mod 011 r/m : immediate data	3	U/L
SCAS/SCASB/SCASW/SCASD – Scan String	1101 111w	4	
SETcc – Byte Set on Condition			
reg	0000 1111 : 1001 tttn : 11 000 reg	1	
memory	0000 1111 : 1001 tttn : mod 000 r/m	2	
SGDT – Store Global Descriptor Table Register	0000 1111 : 0000 0001 : mod 000 r/m	4	
SHL – Shift Left			
reg by 1	1101 000w : 11 100 reg	1	
memory by 1	1101 000w : mod 100 r/m	3	
reg by CL	1101 001w : 11 100 reg	4	
memory by CL	1101 001w : mod 100 r/m	4	
reg by immediate count	1100 000w : 11 100 reg : imm8 data	1	
memory by immediate count	1100 000w : mod 100 r/m : imm8 data	3	

Table F-2. Integer Clock Count Summary (Contd.)

Instruction	Format	Clocks	Notes
SHLD – Double Precision Shift Left			
register by immediate count imm8	0000 1111 : 1010 0100 : 11 reg2 reg1 :	4	
memory by immediate count imm8	0000 1111 : 1010 0100 : mod reg r/m :	4	
register by CL	0000 1111 : 1010 0101 : 11 reg2 reg1	4	
memory by CL	0000 1111 : 1010 0101 : mod reg r/m	5	
SHR – Shift Right			
reg by 1	1101 000w : 11 101 reg	1	
memory by 1	1101 000w : mod 101 r/m	3	
reg by CL	1101 001w : 11 101 reg	4	
memory by CL	1101 001w : mod 101 r/m	4	
reg by immediate count	1100 000w : 11 101 reg : imm8 data	1	
memory by immediate count	1100 000w : mod 101 r/m : imm8 data	3	
SHRD – Double Precision Shift Right			
register by immediate count imm8	0000 1111 : 1010 1100 : 11 reg2 reg1 :	4	
memory by immediate count imm8	0000 1111 : 1010 1100 : mod reg r/m :	4	
register by CL	0000 1111 : 1010 1101 : 11 reg2 reg1	4	
memory by CL	0000 1111 : 1010 1101 : mod reg r/m	5	
SIDT – Store Interrupt Descriptor Table Register	0000 1111 : 0000 0001 : mod 001 r/m	4	
SLDT – Store Local Descriptor Table Register			
to register	0000 1111 : 0000 0000 : 11 000 reg	2	
to memory	0000 1111 : 0000 0000 : mod 000 r/m	2	
SMSW – Store Machine Status Word			
to register	0000 1111 : 0000 0001 : 11 100 reg	4	
to memory	0000 1111 : 0000 0001 : mod 100 r/m	4	
STC – Set Carry Flag	1111 1001	2	
STD – Set Direction Flag	1111 1101	2	
STI – Set Interrupt Flag	1111 1011	7	
STOS/STOSB/STOSW/STOSD – Store String Data	1010 101w	3	
STR – Store Task Register			
to register	0000 1111 : 0000 0000 : 11 001 reg	2	
to memory	0000 1111 : 0000 0000 : mod 001 r/m	2	
SUB – Integer Subtraction			
reg1 to reg2	0010 100w : 11 reg1 reg2	1	
reg2 to reg1	0010 101w : 11 reg1 reg2	1	
memory to register	0010 101w : mod reg r/m	2	
register to memory	0010 100w : mod reg r/m	3	U/L
immediate to register	1000 00sw : 11 101 reg : immediate data	1	
immediate to accumulator	0010 110w : immediate data	1	
immediate to memory	1000 00sw : mod 101 r/m : immediate data	3	U/L

Table F-2. Integer Clock Count Summary (Contd.)

Instruction	Format	Clocks	Notes
TEST – Logical Compare			
reg1 and reg2	1000 010w : 11 reg1 reg2	2	
memory and register	1000 010w : mod reg r/m	1	
immediate and register	1111 011w : 11 000 reg : immediate data	1	
immediate and accumulator	1010 100w : immediate data	1	
immediate and memory	1111 011w : mod 000 r/m : immediate data	2	
VERR – Verify a Segment for Reading			
register	0000 1111 : 0000 0000 : 11 100 reg	7	
memory	0000 1111 : 0000 0000 : mod 100 r/m	7	
VERW – Verify a Segment for Writing			
register	0000 1111 : 0000 0000 : 11 101 reg	7	
memory	0000 1111 : 0000 0000 : mod 101 r/m	7	
WAIT – Wait	1001 1011	1/1	
WBINVD – Write-Back and Invalidate Data Cache	0000 1111 : 0000 1001	2000+	
WRMSR – Write to Model- **Specific Register**	0000 1111 : 0011 0000	30–45	MN/MX
XADD – Exchange and Add			
reg1, reg2	0000 1111 : 1100 000w : 11 reg2 reg1	3	
memory, reg	0000 1111 : 1100 000w : mod reg r/m	4	U/L
XCHG – Exchange Register/Memory with Register			
reg1 with reg2	1000 011w : 11 reg1 reg2	3	2
accumulator with reg	1001 0 reg	2	2
memory with reg	1000 011w : mod reg r/m	3	2
XLAT/XLATB – Table Look-up **Translation**	1101 0111	4	
XOR – Logical Exclusive OR			
reg1 to reg2	0011 000w : 11 reg1 reg2	1	
reg2 to reg1	0011 001w : 11 reg1 reg2	1	
memory to register	0011 001w : mod reg r/m	2	
register to memory	0011 000w : mod reg r/m	3	U/L
immediate to register	1000 00sw : 11 110 reg : immediate data	1	
immediate to accumulator	0011 010w : immediate data	1	
immediate to memory	1000 00sw : mod 110 r/m : immediate data	3	U/L

Table F-2. Integer Clock Count Summary (Contd.)

Instruction	Format	Clocks	Notes
Prefix Bytes			
address size	0110 0111	1	
LOCK	1111 0000	1	
operand size	0110 0110	1	
CS segment override	0010 1110	1	
DS segment override	0011 1110	1	
ES segment override	0010 0110	1	
FS segment override	0110 0100	1	
GS segment override	0110 0101	1	
SS segment override	0011 0110	1	
External Interrupt		INT + 14	21
NMI – Non-Maskable Interrupt		INT + 6	21
Page Fault		INT + 40	21
Virtual 8086 Mode Exceptions			
CLI		INT + 9	21
STI		INT + 9	21
INT n		INT + 9	
PUSHF		INT + 9	21
POPF		INT + 9	21
IRET		INT + 9	
IN			
fixed port		INT + 34	21
variable port		INT + 34	21
OUT			
fixed port		INT + 34	21
variable port		INT + 34	21
INS		INT + 34	21
OUTS		INT + 34	21
REP INS		INT + 34	21
REP OUTS		INT + 34	21

F.2. I/O INSTRUCTION FORMAT AND TIMING

Table F-3. I/O Instructions Clock Count Summary

Instruction	Format	Real Mode	Protected Mode CPL≤ IOPL	Protected Mode CPL>I OPL	Virtual 8086 Mode	Notes
IN – Input from:						
fixed port number	1110 010w : port	7	4	21	19	
variable port	1110 110w	7	4	21	19	
OUT – Output to:						
fixed port number	1110 011w : port	12	9	26	24	
variable port	1110 111w	12	9	26	24	
INS – Input from DX Port	0110 110w	9	6	24	22	
OUTS – Output to DX Port	0110 111w	13	10	27	25	1
REP INS – Input String 110w	1111 0011 : 0110	11 + 3c	8 + 3c	25 + 3c	23 + 3c	2
REP OUTS – Output String 111w	1111 0011 : 0110	13 + 4c	10 + 4c	27 + 4c	25 + 4c	3

NOTES:

1. Two clock cache miss penalty in all cases.
2. c = count in CX or ECX
3. Cache miss penalty in all modes: Add 2 clocks for every 16 bytes. Entire penalty on second operation.

F.3. FLOATING-POINT INSTRUCTION FORMAT AND TIMING

The following sections explain how to use the columns of Table F-5.

F.3.1. Format

Instructions for the FPU assume one of the five forms shown in Table F-4. In all cases, instructions are at least two bytes long and begin with the bit pattern 11011.

Table F-4. General Floating-Point Instruction Format

	Instruction								Optional Fields	
	First Byte				Second Byte					
1	11011	OPA	1	mod	1	OPB	r/m		s-i-b	disp
2	11011	MF	OPA	mod	OPB		r/m		s-i-b	disp
3	11011	d	P	OPA	1	1	OPB	R	ST(i)	
4	11011	0	0	1	1	1	1	OP		
5	11011	0	1	1	1	1	1	OP		
	15–11	10	9	8	7	6	5	4	3	2 1 0

MF = Memory Format
00 — 32-bit real
01 — 32-bit integer
10 — 64-bit real
11 — 16-bit integer

P = Pop
0 — Do not pop stack
1 — Pop stack after operation

d = Destination
0 — Destination is ST(0)
1 — Destination is ST(i)

R XOR d = 0 — Destination OP Source
R XOR d = 1 — Source OP Destination

ST(i) = Register stack element *i*
000 = Stack Top
001 = Second stack element
.
.
.
111 = Eighth stack element

The **mod** (mode field) and **r/m** (register/memory specifier) have the same interpretation as the corresponding fields of the integer instructions. The **s-i-b** (scale index base) and **disp** (displacement) are optionally present in instructions that have **mod** and **r/m** fields. Their presence depends on the values of **mod** and **r/m**, as for integer instructions.

F.3.2.   Clock Counts

Two clock counts separated by a slash (/) are the latency and throughput, respectively. Throughput may be less than latency due to pipelining.

Two clock counts separated by a dash indicate a range of possible timings.

F.3.3.   Notes

1. If CW.PC indicates 24-bit precision, subtract 20 clocks.   If CW.PC indicates 53-bit precision, subtract 6 clocks.

2. If there is a numeric error pending from a previous instruction, add 60 clocks.

3. FXCH takes 0 clocks when paired. Second FXCH will pair in V-pipe if two FXCH instructions are issued back-to-back.

4. FMUL followed by FMUL has throughput of 2.

F.3.4.   Pairing

FX — Pairs with FXCH

NP — No pairing.

Table F-5. Floating-Point Clock Count Summary

Instruction	Format	Clocks	Notes
F2XM1 – Compute $2^{ST(0)}$ – 1	11011 001 : 1111 0000	13–57	
FABS – Absolute Value	11011 001 : 1110 0001	1/1	
FADD – Add			
ST(0) ← ST(0) + 32-bit memory	11011 000 : mod 000 r/m	3/1	
ST(0) ← ST(0) + 64-bit memory	11011 100 : mod 000 r/m	3/1	
ST(d) ← ST(0) + ST(i)	11011 d00 : 11 000 ST(i)	3/1	
FADDP – Add and Pop			
ST(0) ← ST(0) + ST(i)	11011 110 : 11 000 ST(i)	3/1	
FBLD – Load Binary Coded Decimal	11011 111 : mod 100 r/m	48–58	
FBSTP – Store Binary Coded Decimal and Pop	11011 111 : mod 110 r/m	148–154	
FCHS – Change Sign	11011 001 : 1110 0000	1/1	
FCLEX – Clear Exceptions	11011 011 : 1110 0010	9/9	2
FCOM – Compare Real			
32-bit memory	11011 000 : mod 010 r/m	4/1	
64-bit memory	11011 100 : mod 010 r/m	4/1	
ST(i)	11011 000 : 11 010 ST(i)	4/1	
FCOMP – Compare Real and Pop			
32-bit memory	11011 000 : mod 011 r/m	4/1	
64-bit memory	11011 100 : mod 011 r/m	4/1	
ST(i)	11011 000 : 11 011 ST(i)	4/1	
FCOMPP – Compare Real and Pop Twice	11011 110 : 11 011 001	4/1	
FCOS – Cosine of ST(0)	11011 001 : 1111 1111	18–124	
FDECSTP – Decrement Stack-Top Pointer	11011 001 : 1111 0110	1/1	
FDIV – Divide			
ST(0) ← ST(0) ÷ 32-bit memory	11011 000 : mod 110 r/m	39	1
ST(0) ← ST(0) ÷ 64-bit memory	11011 100 : mod 110 r/m	39	1
ST(d) ← ST(0) ÷ ST(i)	11011 d00 : 1111 R ST(i)	39	1
FDIVP – Divide and Pop			
ST(0) ← ST(0) ÷ ST(i)	11011 110 : 1111 1 ST(i)	39	1
FDIVR – Reverse Divide			
ST(0) ← 32-bit memory ÷ ST(0)	11011 000 : mod 111 r/m	39	1
ST(0) ← 64-bit memory ÷ ST(0)	11011 100 : mod 111 r/m	39	1
ST(d) ← ST(i) ÷ ST(0)	11011 d00 : 1111 R ST(i)	39	1
FDIVRP – Reverse Divide and Pop			
ST(0) ← ST(i) ÷ ST(0)	11011 110 : 1111 0 ST(i)	39	1
FFREE – Free ST(i) Register	11011 101 : 1100 0 ST(i)	1/1	
FIADD – Add Integer			
ST(0) ← ST(0) + 16-bit memory	11011 110 : mod 000 r/m	7/4	
ST(0) ← ST(0) + 32-bit memory	11011 010 : mod 000 r/m	7/4	

Table F-5. Floating-Point Clock Count Summary (Contd.)

Instruction	Format	Clocks	Notes
FICOM – Compare Integer			
16-bit memory	11011 110 : mod 010 r/m	8/4	
32-bit memory	11011 010 : mod 010 r/m	8/4	
FICOMP – Compare Integer and Pop			
16-bit memory	11011 110 : mod 011 r/m	8/4	
32-bit memory	11011 010 : mod 011 r/m	8/4	
FIDIV			
ST(0) ← ST(0) + 16-bit memory	11011 110 : mod 110 r/m	42	1
ST(0) ← ST(0) + 32-bit memory	11011 010 : mod 110 r/m	42	1
FIDIVR			
ST(0) ← ST(0) + 16-bit memory	11011 110 : mod 111 r/m	42	1
ST(0) ← ST(0) + 32-bit memory	11011 010 : mod 111 r/m	42	1
FILD – Load Integer			
16-bit memory	11011 111 : mod 000 r/m	3/1	
32-bit memory	11011 011 : mod 000 r/m	3/1	
64-bit memory	11011 111 : mod 101 r/m	3/1	
FIMUL			
ST(0) ← ST(0) + 16-bit memory	11011 110 : mod 001 r/m	7/4	
ST(0) ← ST(0) + 32-bit memory	11011 010 : mod 001 r/m	7/4	
FINCSTP – Increment Stack Pointer	11011 001 : 1111 0111	1/1	
FINIT – Initialize Floating-Point Unit	11011 011 : 1110 0011	16/12	2
FIST – Store Integer			
16-bit memory	11011 111 : mod 010 r/m	6/6	
32-bit memory	11011 011 : mod 010 r/m	6/6	
FISTP – Store Integer and Pop			
16-bit memory	11011 111 : mod 011 r/m	6/6	
32-bit memory	11011 011 : mod 011 r/m	6/6	
64-bit memory	11011 111 : mod 111 r/m	6/6	
FISUB			
ST(0) ← ST(0) + 16-bit memory	11011 110 : mod 100 r/m	7/4	
ST(0) ← ST(0) + 32-bit memory	11011 010 : mod 100 r/m	7/4	
FISUBR			
ST(0) ← ST(0) + 16-bit memory	11011 110 : mod 101 r/m	7/4	
ST(0) ← ST(0) + 32-bit memory	11011 010 : mod 101 r/m	7/4	
FLD – Load Real			
32-bit memory	11011 001 : mod 000 r/m	1/1	
64-bit memory	11011 101 : mod 000 r/m	1/1	
80-bit memory	11011 011 : mod 101 r/m	3/3	
ST(i)	11011 001 : 11 000 ST(i)	1/1	
FLD1 – Load +1.0 into ST(0)	11011 001 : 1110 1000	2/2	

Table F-5. Floating-Point Clock Count Summary (Contd.)

Instruction	Format	Clocks	Notes
FLDCW – **Load Control Word**	11011 001 : mod 101 r/m	7/7	
FLDENV – **Load FPU Environment**	11011 001 : mod 100 r/m		
real and v86 modes, 16-bit address		37	
real and v86 modes, 32-bit address		37	
protected mode, 16-bit address		32	
protected mode, 32-bit address		33	
FLDL2E – **Load log$_2$(ε) into ST(0)**	11011 001 : 1110 1010	5/3	
FLDL2T – **Load log$_2$(10) into ST(0)**	11011 001 : 1110 1001	5/3	
FLDLG2 – **Load log$_{10}$(2) into ST(0)**	11011 001 : 1110 1100	5/3	
FLDLN2 – **Load log$_\varepsilon$(2) into ST(0)**	11011 001 : 1110 1101	5/3	
FLDPI – **Load π into ST(0)**	11011 001 : 1110 1011	5/3	
FLDZ – **Load +0.0 into ST(0)**	11011 001 : 1110 1110	2/2	
FMUL – **Multiply**			
ST(0) ← ST(0) × 32-bit memory	11011 000 : mod 001 r/m	3/1	4
ST(0) ← ST(0) × 64-bit memory	11011 100 : mod 001 r/m	3/1	4
ST(d) ← ST(0) × ST(i)	11011 d00 : 1100 1 ST(i)	3/1	4
FMULP – **Multiply**			
ST(0) ← ST(0) × ST(i)	11011 110 : 1100 1 ST(i)	3/1	
FNOP – **No Operation**	11011 001 : 1101 0000	1/1	
FPATAN – **Partial Arctangent**	11011 001 : 1111 0011	19–134	
FPREM – **Partial Remainder**	11011 001 : 1111 1000	16–64	
FPREM1 – **Partial Remainder (IEEE)**	11011 001 : 1111 0101	20–70	
FPTAN – **Partial Tangent**	11011 001 : 1111 0010	17–173	
FRNDINT – **Round to Integer**	11011 001 : 1111 1100	9–20	
FRSTOR – **Restore FPU State**	11011 101 : mod 100 r/m		
real and v86 modes, 16-bit address		75/75	
real and v86 modes, 32-bit address		95/95	
protected mode, 16-bit address		70/70	
protected mode, 32-bit address		70/70	
FSAVE – **Store FPU State**	1101 101 : mod 110 r/m		
real and v86 modes, 16-bit address		127/127	2
real and v86 modes, 32-bit address		151/151	2
protected mode, 16-bit address		124/124	2
protected mode, 32-bit address		124/124	2
FSCALE – **Scale**	11011 001 : 1111 1101	20–31	
FSIN – **Sine**	11011 001 : 1111 1110	16–126	
FSINCOS – **Sine and Cosine**	11011 001 : 1111 1011	17–137	
FSQRT – **Square Root**	11011 001 : 1111 1010	70/70	
FST – **Store Real**			
32-bit memory	11011 001 : mod 010 r/m	2/2	
64-bit memory	11011 101 : mod 010 r/m	2/2	
ST(i)	11011 101 : 11 010 ST(i)	1/1	

Table F-5. Floating-Point Clock Count Summary (Contd.)

Instruction	Format	Clocks	Notes
FSTCW – Store Control Word	11011 001 : mod 111 r/m	2/2	2
FSTENV – Store FPU Environment	11011 001 : mod 110 r/m		
real and v86 modes, 16-bit address		50/50	2
real and v86 modes, 32-bit address		48/50	2
protected mode, 16-bit address		49/50	2
protected mode, 32-bit address		50/50	2
FSTP – Store Real and Pop			
32-bit memory	11011 001 : mod 011 r/m	2/2	
64-bit memory	11011 101 : mod 011 r/m	2/2	
80-bit memory	11011 011 : mod 111 r/m	3/3	
ST(i)	11011 101 : 11 011 ST(i)	1/1	
FSTSW – Store Status Word into AX	11011 111 : 1110 0000	6/2	2
FSTSW – Store Status Word into Memory	11011 101 : mod 111 r/m	5/2	2
FSUB – Subtract			
ST(0) ← ST(0) – 32-bit memory	11011 000 : mod 100 r/m	3/1	
ST(0) ← ST(0) – 64-bit memory	11011 100 : mod 100 r/m	3/1	
ST(d) ← ST(0) – ST(i)	11011 d00 : 1110 R ST(i)	3/1	
FSUBP – Subtract and Pop			
ST(0) ← ST(0) – ST(i)	11011 110 : 1110 1 ST(i)	3/1	
FSUBR – Reverse Subtract			
ST(0) ← 32-bit memory – ST(0)	11011 000 : mod 101 r/m	3/1	
ST(0) ← 64-bit memory – ST(0)	11011 100 : mod 101 r/m	3/1	
ST(d) ← ST(i) – ST(0)	11011 d00 : 1110 R ST(i)	3/1	
FSUBRP – Reverse Subtract and Pop			
ST(i) ← ST(i) – ST(0)	11011 110 : 1110 0 ST(i)	3/1	
FTST – Test	11011 001 : 1110 0100	4/1	
FUCOM – Unordered Compare Real	11011 101 : 1110 0 ST(i)	4/1	
FUCOMP – Unordered Compare and Pop	11011 101 : 1110 1 ST(i)	4/1	
FUCOMPP – Unordered Compare and Pop Twice	11011 010 : 1110 1001	4/1	
FXAM – Examine	11011 001 : 1110 0101	21/21	
FXCH – Exchange ST(0) and ST(i)	11011 001 : 1100 1 ST(i)	1	3
FXTRACT – Extract Exponent and Significand	11011 001 : 1111 0100	13/13	
FYL2X – ST(1) × $\log_2$(ST(0))	11011 001 : 1111 0001	22–111	
FYL2XP1 – ST(1) × $\log_2$(ST(0) + 1.0)	11011 001 : 1111 1001	22–103	
FWAIT – Wait until FPU Ready	1001 1011	1/1	

intel ®

G

Report on Transcendental Functions

The Pentium microprocessor employs a new set of algorithms to implement its transcendental instructions. This chapter includes:

- A brief introduction to the algorithms

- A summary of their accuracy, monotonicity, and speed characteristics

- A description of the verification effort to validate the accuracy and monotonicity of the implemented algorithms

G.1. INTRODUCTION

There are two traditional classes of algorithm for implementing elementary transcendental functions.

The first class transforms an input argument to one with very small magnitude. An approximation to the function at that small argument is obtained by simple calculation, typically a couple of adds with a multiplication or division. Finally, the desired result is obtained by another transformation. This class of algorithm is referred to as *CORDIC* and has the characteristic that the underlying operations are very simple, typically involving only shifts and fixed-point additions. The bulk of the work in a CORDIC algorithm lies in the initial and final transformations, and the performance of the algorithm is limited by the sequential nature of the long series of shifts and adds. For descriptions of CORDIC algorithms, see [6, 7, 10]. There are several examples of microprocessors (including the Intel486 microprocessor) that implement these algorithms using on-chip hardware and firmware.

The second class of algorithm employs a rather simple transformation on an input argument, reducing it to one of moderate magnitude. To approximate the function value at the transformed argument, a polynomial or a rational function is evaluated at that point. To obtain roughly 64 bits of accuracy, a typical polynomial or rational function would require roughly 10 floating-point multiplications and additions, and one additional division if a rational function is used. Finally, a simple transformation is applied to create the value desired. These algorithms do not have a name analogous to CORDIC; they can simply be called polynomial-based algorithms. The bulk of the work here lies in the second step that involves a polynomial or rational function evaluation. For descriptions of this class of algorithm, see [2, 4].

In the past, hardware implementations of elementary functions mostly employed CORDIC algorithms because of their relatively simple hardware requirements. Recent hardware advancements resulting in the high speed of basic floating-point operations have made it possible and advantageous to implement polynomial-based algorithms.

The algorithms for the transcendental functions on the Pentium microprocessor can be thought of as a middle ground between the two approaches. By using tables of function values stored in ROM, one can significantly shorten the polynomial calculations that would normally be required in a polynomial-based algorithm. This class of algorithm is usually referred to as *table-driven.* Table-driven algorithms are by no means new, and recent uses for them can be found in [1, 3, 5, 8]. Such algorithms have been implemented in software libraries in the past, but never before on-chip. Although such algorithms require a moderate amount of ROM space and a small increase in argument reduction complexity, they offer a number of important advantages, especially if implemented on-chip. These are:

1. Accuracy. The combination of simple argument reduction and small reduced arguments leads to highly accurate final results. Also, access to internal data paths that are wider than the paths available to a software library further enhances the accuracy.

2. Monotonicity. The high accuracy also leads to monotonicity.

3. Proof of correctness. Rigorous error analyses become straightforward and also lead to tight error bounds.

4. Performance. The overall implementation algorithm leads to higher performance due to several reasons. The simple core calculations are marked by short polynomials. Access to microprogramming at the low level afforded within the Pentium CPU chip provides richer parallelism and control flow than that available to software libraries. The striking simplicity of the implementation adds no additional critical paths to the chip, allowing the clock rate to be taken to the limit imposed by other features.

G.2. SUMMARY OF ACCURACY, MONOTONICITY AND SPEED

G.2.1. Accuracy

Accuracy is measured in terms of units in the last place (ulp). For a given argument x, let $f(x)$ and $F(x)$ be the correct and computed function values respectively. The error in ulps is defined to be

$$\left| \frac{f(x) - F(x)}{2^{k-63}} \right|$$

where k is an integer such that $1 \leq 2^{-k}f(x) < 2$. Note that even if $F(x)$ is the same as $f(x)$ correctly rounded to 64 significant bits, the worst-case error is 1/2 ulp when rounding in nearest mode. An implementation $F(x)$ is considered extremely satisfactory if the worst-case error is under 1 ulp.

On the Pentium microprocessor, the worst case error on all transcendental functions is less than 1 ulp when rounding in nearest mode, and less than 1.5 ulps when rounding in other modes. This is summarized in Table G-1.

Table G-1. Summary of Accuracy

Function	Round to Nearest Mode	All Other Rounding Modes
All functions	Worst case error is less than 1 ulp.	Worst case error is less than 1.5 ulp.

G.2.2. Monotonicity

For a given argument x with x_- and x_+ as its lower and upper neighbors, the implemented function F is monotonic with respect to its input argument if...

$$F(x_-) \leq F(x) \leq F(x_+), \quad \text{if } f \text{ is increasing at } x,$$

or if...

$$F(x_-) \geq F(x) \geq F(x_+), \quad \text{if } f \text{ is decreasing at } x.$$

The functions are guaranteed to be monotonic with respect to the input operands throughout the domain supported by the instruction.

G.2.3. Speed

The speed is described by specifying the latency in terms of clock counts. The latency varies from function to function, with typical performance from 54 to 115 clocks. Table G-2 summarizes the latency of each of the functions. Three clock count numbers are provided. The first number is for special operands such as zero or infinity; the second and third numbers are the lower and upper bounds for non-special operands in the domain. For example, for FYL2X, when $x = 0$, the processor takes 22 clocks, and it takes 104 and 114 clocks when $|x - 1| \geq 1/8$ and when $|x - 1| < 1/8$ respectively.

G.3. VERIFICATION SUMMARY

A rigorous mathematical error analysis was performed for each function. Furthermore, a comprehensive verification program was undertaken to confirm the correctness of the error analysis (and consequently the accuracy and monotonicity characteristics) of the implemented algorithms.

Table G-2. Speed of Functions at Typical Arguments

Function	Latency* (clocks)	Function	Latency* (clocks)
F2XM1	13, 54, 60	FSIN	12, 59, 126
FCOS	14, 59, 126	FSINCOS	13, 83, 138
FPATAN	19, 98, 137	FPTAN	13, 115, 174
FYL2X	22, 104, 114	FYL2XP1	22, 103, 106

NOTE:

*The first number is for special operands, such as zero or infinity; the second and third numbers are the lower and upper bounds for nonspecial operands in the domain.

For each function, an average of 8500 specially chosen points were used to compare the results from the Pentium microprocessor against a set of results that are accurate to about 112 bits, derived from the VAX VMS H-functions Math Library. In addition, about 300 million points were randomly chosen for accuracy testing in a manner such that each binade of the input domain was covered; i.e. test points were chosen to cover intervals corresponding to each exponent value of the input domain.

For all cases tested, the actual error was found to lie below the bound obtained by the theoretical error analysis. Figure G-1 through Figure G-22 are ulp plots that illustrate this characterization information. For a given argument in the X-axis, a dot is printed to indicate the error in ulps of the function at that argument. Of particular interest are the peaks and the envelopes of these plots. The scatter plot characteristics observed track the error analyses closely. Table G-3 summarizes the number of arguments tested.

Table G-3. Number of Arguments Used in Accuracy Tests

Function	No. of Arguments (million)	Function	No. of Arguments (million)
FYL2X	35	FYL2XP1	28
FSIN	28	FCOS	37
FSINCOS	54	FPTAN	37
FPATAN	50	F2XM1	30

All the functions were tested for monotonicity. A total of about 145 million points were used for monotonicity characterization. No failures were found. Table G-4 summarizes the number of arguments tested.

Table G-4. Number of Arguments Used in Monotonicity Tests

Function	No. of Arguments (million)	Function	No. of Arguments (million)
FYL2X	30	FYL2XP1	18
FSIN	4	FCOS	8.5
FSINCOS	24.5	FPTAN	23.5
FPATAN	10	F2XM1	26

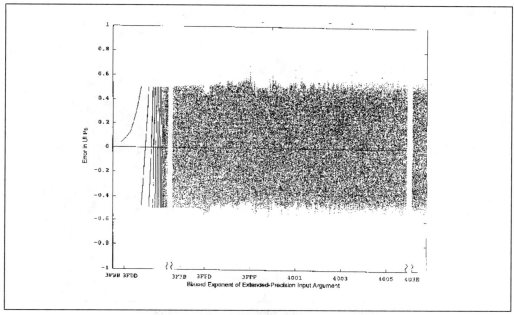

Figure G-5. Scatterplot for FCOS (3FBB-403E)

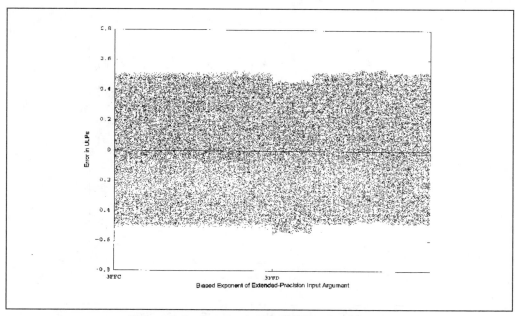

Figure G-6. Scatterplot for FCOS (3FFC-3FFD)

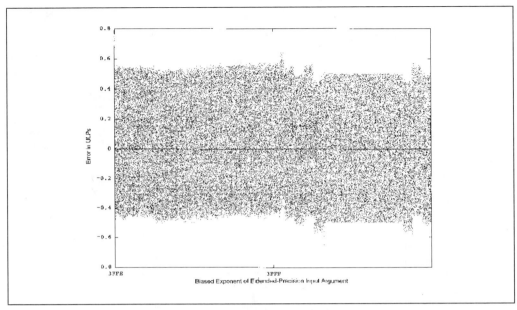

Figure G-7. Scatterplot for FCOS (3FFE-3FFF)

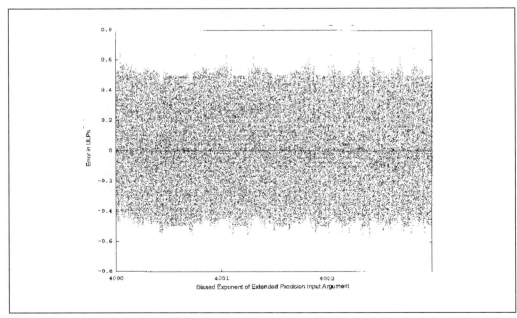

Figure G-8. Scatterplot for FCOS (4000-4002)

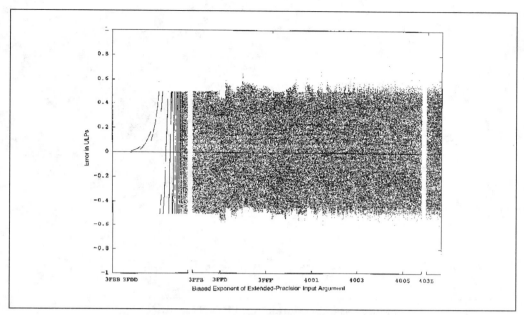

Figure G-9. Scatterplot for FSINCOS (SIN, 3FBB-403E)

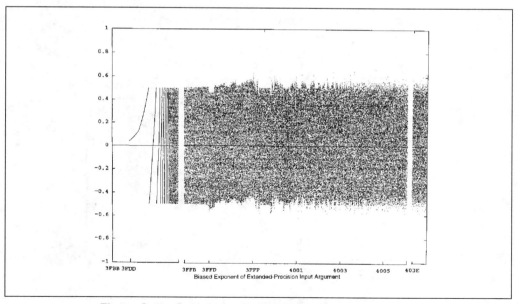

Figure G-10. Scatterplot for FSINCOS (COS, 3FBB-403E)

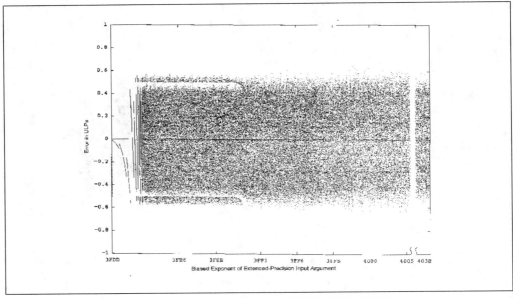

Figure G-11. Scatterplot for FPTAN (3FDD-403E)

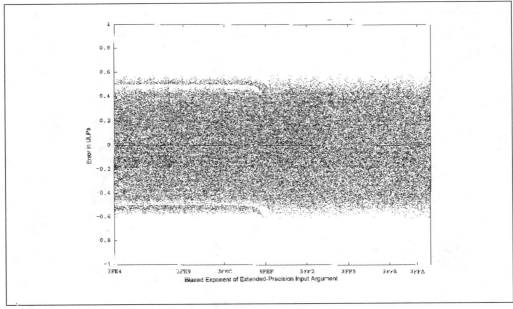

Figure G-12. Scatterplot for FPTAN (3FE4-3FFA)

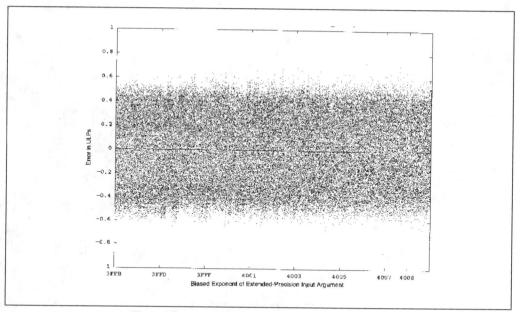

Figure G-13. Scatterplot for FPTAN (3FFB-4008)

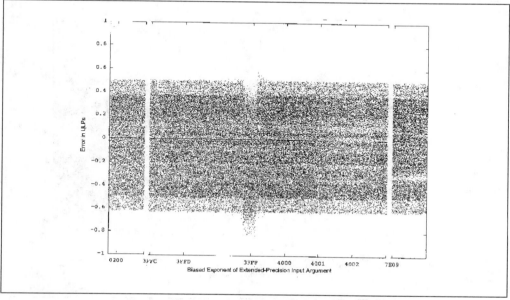

Figure G-14. Scatterplot for FYL2X (0001-7FFD)

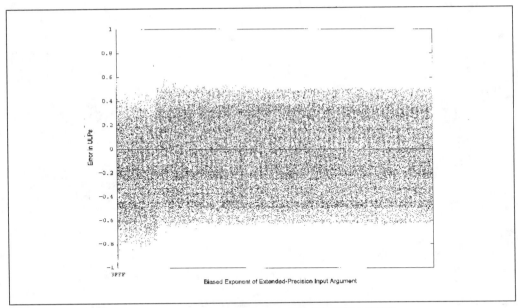

Figure G-15. Scatterplot for FYL2X (3FFF-3FFF)

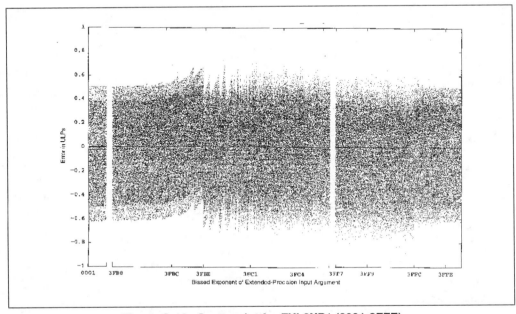

Figure G-16. Scatterplot for FYL2XP1 (0001-3FFE)

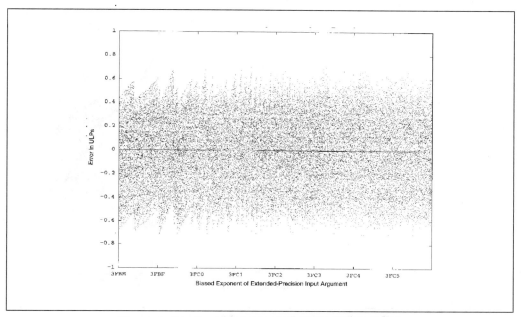

Figure G-17. Scatterplot for FYL2XP1 (3FBE-3FC5)

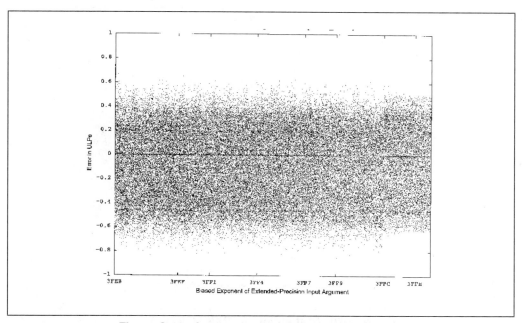

Figure G-18. Scatterplot for FYL2XP1 (3FEB-3FFE)

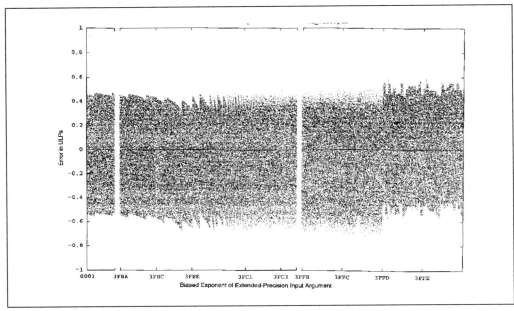

Figure G-19. Scatterplot for F2XM1 (0001-3FFE)

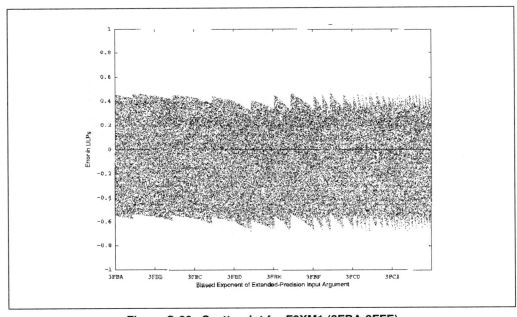

Figure G-20. Scatterplot for F2XM1 (3FBA-3FFE)

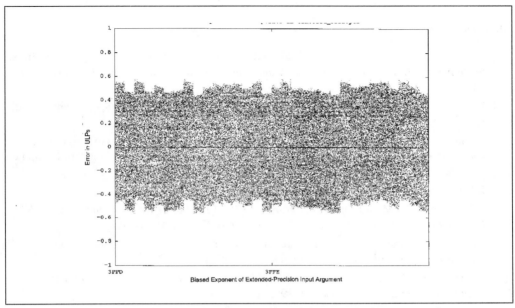

Figure G-21. Scatterplot for F2XM1 (3FFD-3FFE)

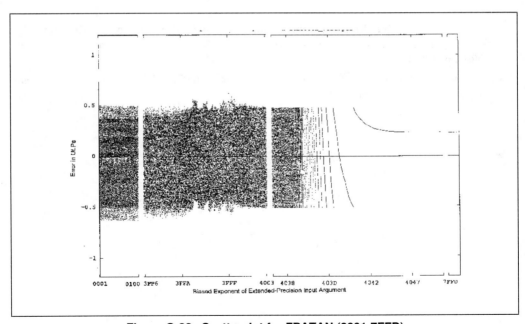

Figure G-22. Scatterplot for FPATAN (0001-7FFD)

References

[1] R. C. Agarwal et al., "New scalar and vector elementary functions for the IBM System/370," *IBM Journal of Research and Development,* 30, no. 2, March 1986, pp. 126-144.

[2] W. Cody and W. Waite, *Software Manual for the Elementary Functions,* Prentice-Hall, Englewood Cliffs, N.J., 1980.

[3] S. Gal, "Computing elementary functions: A new approach for achieving high accuracy and good performance," in *Accurate Scientific Computations,* Lecture Notes in Computer Science, Vol. 235, Springer, N.Y., 1985.

[4] J. Hart et al., *Computer Approximations,* John Wiley and Sons, N.Y., 1968.

[5] IBM Elementary Math Library, *Programming RPQ P81005, Program Number 5799-BTB, Program Reference and Operations Manual,* SH20-2230-1, August 1984.

[6] R. Nave, "Implementation of transcendental functions on a numeric processor," *Microprocessing and Microprogramming,* 11, 1983, pp. 221-225.

[7] W. H. Specker, "A class of algorithms for ln x, exp x, arctan x, and arcot x," *IEEE Transactions on Computers,* EC-14, 1965, pp. 85-86.

[8] P. T. P. Tang, "Table-driven implementation of the exponential function in IEEE floating-point arithmetic," *ACM Transactions on Mathematical Software,* 16, no. 2, June 1989, pp. 144-157.

[9] P. T. P. Tang, "Table-driven implementation of the logarithm function in IEEE floating-point arithmetic," *ACM Transactions on Mathematical Software,* 16, no. 2, December 1990, pp. 378-400.

[10] J. S. Walther, "A unified algorithm for elementary functions," *Proc. AFIPS, 1971 Joint Computer Conference,* pp. 379-385.

intel ®

H

Advanced Features

APPENDIX H
ADVANCED FEATURES

Some non-essential information regarding the Pentium processor are considered Intel confidential and proprietary and have not been documented in this publication. This information is provided in the *Supplement to the Pentium™ Processor User's Manual* and is available with the appropriate non-disclosure agreements in place. Please contact Intel Corporation for details.

intel ®

Glossary

GLOSSARY

Abort: An exception which is completely unrecoverable, such as stack exception during an attempt to invoke an exception handler.

Address: See *Logical Address, Linear Address,* and *Physical Address.*

Address Space: The range of memory locations which may be accessed by an address.

Address-Size Prefix: An instruction prefix which selects the size of address offsets. Offsets may be 16- or 32-bit. The default address size is specified by the D bit in the code segment for the instruction. Use of the address-size prefix selects the non-default size.

Address Translation: The process of mapping addresses from one address space to another. Segmentation and paging both perform address translation.

Alignment: The placement of code or data on a 2-, 4-, 8-, 16- or 32-byte boundary depending on the operand or cache-line size.

Base Address: The address of the beginning of a data structure, such as a segment, descriptor table, page, or page table.

Base Register: A register used for addressing an operand relative to an address held in the register.

Base: (1) A term used in logarithms and exponentials. In both contexts, it is a number that is being raised to a power. The two equations (y=log base b of x) and (by=x) are the same. (2) A number that defines the representation being used for a string of digits. Base 2 is the binary representation; base 10 is the decimal representation; base 16 is the hexadecimal representation. In each case, the base is the factor of increased significance for each succeeding digit (working up from the bottom). (3) See *Base Address.*

BCD: Binary Coded Decimal; a format for representing numbers in base 10. One byte is used for each digit of the number, with bit positions 0 to 3 specifying the value for the digit. The auxiliary carry flag isused to perform BCD arithmetic. The FPU supports a packed form of BCD, in which 18 digits and a sign bit are contained in an 80-bit operand.

Bias: A constant that is added to the true exponent of a real number to obtain the exponent field of that number's floating-point representation in the FPU. To obtain the true exponent, you must subtract the bias from the given exponent. For example, the single real format has a bias of 127 whenever the given exponent is nonzero. If the 8-bit exponent field contains 10000011 (binary), which is 131 (decimal), the true exponent is 131–127, or +4. Also known as an excess representation, in this case excess –127.

Biased Exponent: The exponent as it appears in a floating-point representation of a number. The biased exponent is interpreted as an unsigned, positive number. In the above example, 131 is the biased exponent.

Big-endien: A method used for storing data types that are larger than one byte where the low-order byte is stored at the highest address and the high-order byte at the lowest address. This is opposed to the little-endien method used by Intel's x86 architecture.

Binary Coded Decimal: A method of storing numbers that retains a base 10 representation.

Each decimal digit occupies 4 full bits (one hexdecimal digit). The hexadecimal values A through F (1010 to 1111) are not used. Intel's 32-bit x86 processors support a packed decimal format that consists of 9 bytes of binary coded decimal (18 decimal digits) and one sign byte.

Binary Point: An entity just like a decimal point, except that it exists in floating-point binary numbers. Each binary digit to the right of the binary point is multiplied by an increasing negative power of two.

Built-In Self Test (BIST): Consists of hardware and microcode self-test initiated by driving the INIT pin high when RESET transitions from high to low. Upon completion, the cumulative result of the tests are stored in the EAX register. If EAX is zero, all checks passed. Any non-zero result indicates a faulty processor unit. BIST also causes the FPU registers to be initialized following RESET.

Bit Field: A sequence of up to 32 bits which may start at any bit position of any byte address. Intel's 32-bit x86 processors have instructions for efficient operations on bit fields.

Bitmap: See I/O Permission Bitmap.

Bit String: A sequence of up to $2^{32}-1$ bits which may start at any bit position of any byte address. Intel's 32-bit x86 processors have instructions for efficient operations on bit strings.

Branch Prediction: See *Branch Target Buffer.*

Boundary Scan: IEEE Std. 1149.1 allows board manufacturers to test board interconnects and the Pentium processor through BIST.

Branch Target Buffer: A small cache used for the prediction of branch instructions. For more information, see Appendix H.

Breakpoint: An aid to program debugging in which the programmer specifies forms of memory access which generate exceptions. The exceptions invoke debugging software. Intel's 32-bit x86 processors support software and hardware breakpoints. A software breakpoint is an instruction inserted into the program being debugged. When the INT 3 instruction is executed, a breakpoint occurs. A hardware breakpoint is set up by programming the debugging registers. The contents of the debugging registers specify the address, size, and type of reference for as many as four breakpoints. Unlike software breakpoints, hardware breakpoints can be applied to data.

Byte: An 8-bit quantity of memory; the smallest unit of memory referenced by an address.

C3–C0: The four "condition code" bits of the FPU status word. These bits are set to certain values by the compare, test, examine, and remainder functions of the FPU.

Cache: A small, fast memory which holds the active parts of a larger, slower memory.

Cache Consistency: Maintaining cache consistency requires that when a processor accesses data cached in another processor, it must not receive incorrect data and when cached data is modified, all other processors which access that data receive the modified data.

Cache Flush: An operation which marks all cache lines as invalid. The Pentium and Intel486 processors have instructions for flushing internal and external caches.

Cache Line: The smallest unit of storage which can be allocated in a cache.

Cache Line Fill: An operation which loads an entire cache line using multiple read cycles to main memory.

Cache Miss: A request for access to memory which requires actually reading main memory.

Call Gate: A gate descriptor for invoking a procedure with a CALL or JUMP instruction.

Characteristic: A term used for some non-Intel computers, meaning the exponent field of a floating-point number.

Chop: In the FPU, to set one or more low-order bits of a real number to zero, yielding the nearest representable number in the direction of zero.

Code Segment: An address space which contains instructions; an executable segment. An instruction-fetch cycle must address a code segment. The type of information held in a segment is specified in its segment descriptor.

Condition Code: The four bits of the FPU status word that indicates the results of the compare, test, examine, and remainder functions of the FPU.

Conforming Segment: A code segment which executes with the RPL of the segment selector or the CPL of the calling program, whichever is less privileged.

Context Switch: See *Task Switch*.

Control Word: A 16-bit FPU register that the user can set, to determine the modes of computation the FPU will use and the exception interrupts that will be enabled.

Coprocessor: An extension to the base architecture and instruction set of a processor. The Intel387 numerics coprocessor is used to add floating-point arithmetic instructions and registers to the Intel386 processor. Coprocessors allow present-day systems to enjoy the architectural enhancements which will be available in future processor chips.

CPL: See *Current Privilege Level*.

CPU: Central Processor Unit. See *Processor*.

Current Privilege Level (CPL): The privilege level of the program which is executing. Normally, the privilege level is loaded from a code segment descriptor. It is loaded into the CS segment register, where it is visible to software as the two lowest bits of the register. When execution is transferred to a conforming code segment, the privilege level does not change. In this case, the CPL may be different from the privilege level specified in the descriptor (DPL).

Data Segment: An address space which contains data. As many as four data segments may be in use without reloading the segment registers. The type of information held in a segment is specified in its segment descriptor.

Data Structure: An area of memory defined for a particular use by hardware or software, such as a page table or task state segment (TSS).

Debug Registers: A set of registers used to specify as many as four hardware breakpoints. Unlike breakpoint instructions, which only can be used for code breakpoints, the debug registers can specify breakpoints in either code or data.

Denormal: A special form of floating-point number. On the FPU, a denormal is defined as a number that has a biased exponent of zero. By providing a significand with leading zeros, the range of possible negative exponents can be extended by the number of bits in the significand. Each leading zero is a bit of lost accuracy, so the extended exponent range is obtained by reducing significance.

Descriptor Privilege Level (DPL): The privilege level applied to a segment. The DPL is a field in the segment descriptor.

Descriptor Table: An array of segment descriptors. There are two kinds of descriptor tables: the Global Descriptor Table (GDT) and an arbitrary number of Local Descriptor Tables (LDTs).

Device Driver: A procedure or task used to manage a peripheral device, such as a disk drive.

Displacement: A constant used in calculating effective addresses. A displacement modifies the address independently of any scaled indexing. A displacement often is used to access operands which have a fixed relation to some other address, such as a field of a record in an array.

Double Extended: IEEE Std 754 term for the FPU's extended format, with more exponent and significand bits than the double format and an explicit integer bit in the significand.

Double Format: A floating-point format supported by the FPU that consists of a sign, an 11-bit biased exponent, an implicit integer bit, and a 52-bit significand, a total of 64 explicit bits.

Doubleword: A 32-bit quantity of memory.

DPL: See *Descriptor Privilege Level.*

Effective Address: The address produced from addressing-mode calculations. A base register, scaled index, and displacement may be used in the calculations.

Environment: The 14 or 28 (depending on addressing mode) bytes of FPU registers affected by the FSTENV and FLDENV instructions. It encompasses the entire state of the FPU, except for the 8 registers of the FPU stack. Included are the control word, status word, tag word, and the instruction, opcode, and operand information provided by interrupts.

ESC Instruction: An instruction encoding used for coprocessor instructions.

Exception: A forced call to a procedure or a task which is generated when the processor fails to interpret an instruction or when an INT *n* instruction is executed. Causes of exceptions include division by zero, stack overflow, undefined opcodes, and memory-protection violations. Exceptions are faults, traps, aborts, and software-initiated interrupts.

Exception Pointers: In the FPU, the indication used by exception handlers to identify the cause of an exception. This data consists of a pointer to the most recently executed ESC instruction and a pointer to the memory operand of this instruction, if it had a memory operand of this instruction, if it had a memory operand. An exception handler can use the FSTENV and FSAVE instructions to access these pointers.

Expand-Down Segment: A type of data segment in which the meaning of the segment limit is reversed. All other segments accept legal offsets from the base address to the base address plus the segment limit. An expand-down segment accepts legal addresses in two ranges: from 0 to one byte below the base address, and from one byte past the segment limit to the top of the address space.

Exponent: (1) Any number that indicates the power to which another number is raised. (2) The field of a floating-point number that indicates the magnitude of the number. This would fall under the above more general definition (I), except that a bias sometimes needs to be subtracted to obtain the correct power.

Extended Format: The FPU's implementation of the double extended format of IEEE Std

754. Extended format is the main floating-point format used by the FPU. It consists of a sign, a 15-bit biased exponent, and a significand with an explicit integer bit and 63 fractional-part bits.

External Cache: A cache memory provided outside of the processor chip. External caches can be added to any kind of processor which has external main memory. The Pentium and Intel486 processors have instructions and page-table entry bits which are used to control external caches from software.

Far Pointer: A reference to memory which includes both a segment selector and an offset. Used to access memory when the segment selector has not been loaded into the processor, for example when making a procedure call from one segment to another.

Fault: An exception which is reported at the instruction boundary immediately before the instruction which generated the exception. When a fault is generated, enough of the state of the processor is restored to permit another attempt to execute the instruction which generated the fault. The fault handler is called with a return address which points to the faulting instruction, rather than the instruction which follows the faulting instruction. After the handler fixes the source of the exception, such as a segment or page which is not present in memory, the program is restarted.

Flat Model: A memory organization in which all segments are mapped to the same range of linear addresses. This organization removes segmentation from the environment of application programs to the greatest degree possible.

Floating-Point Operand: A representation for a number expressed as a base, a sign, a significand, and a signed exponent. The value of the number is the signed product of its significand and the base raised to the power of the exponent. Floating-point representations are more versatile than integer representations in two ways. First, they include fractions. Second, their exponent parts allow a much wider range of magnitude than possible with fixed-length integer representations.

Floating-Point Unit (FPU): The part of the Intel486 processor which contains the floating-point registers and performs the operations required by floating-point instructions.

FPU: See *Floating-Point Unit.*

Flush: See *Cache Flush.*

Gate Descriptor: A segment descriptor which can be the destination of a call or jump. A gate descriptor can be used to invoke a procedure or task in another privilege level. There are four types of gate descriptors: call gates, trap gates, interrupt gates, and task gates.

GDT: See *Global Descriptor Table.*

Global Descriptor Table (GDT): An array of segment descriptors for all programs in a system. There is only one GDT in a system.

Gradual Underflow: A method of handling the floating-point underflow error condition that minimizes the loss of accuracy in the result. If there is a denormal number that represents the correct result, the denormal is returned. Thus, digits are lost only to the extent of denormalization. Most computers return zero when underflow occurs, losing all signficant digits.

Handler: A procedure or task which is called as a result of an exception or interrupt.

Hit: See *Cache Hit.*

IDT: See *Interrupt Descriptor Table.*

IEEE Standard 754: A set of formats and operations which apply to floating-point numbers. The formats cover 32-, 64-, and 80-bit operand sizes. The standard was developed by the Institute for Electrical and Electronics Engineeers (IEEE). The FPU supports all operand sizes covered by the standard.

Immediate Operand: Data encoded in an instruction.

Implicit Integer Bit: A part of the significand in the single real and double real floating-point formats that is not explicitly given. In these formats, the entire given significand is considered to be the right of the binary point. A single implicit integer bit to the left of the binary point is always one, except in one case. When the exponent is the minimum (biased exponent is zero), the implicit integer bit is zero.

Indefinite: A special value that is returned by floating-point functions when the inputs are such that no other sensible answer is possible. For each floating-point format these exits one quiet NaN that is designated as the indefinite value. For binary integer formats, the negative number furthest from zero is often considered the indefinite value. For the FPU packed decimal format, the indefinite value contains all 1's in the sign byte and the uppermost digits byte.

Index: A number used to access a table. An index is scaled (multiplied by shifting left) to account for the size of the operand. The scaled index is added to the base address of the table to get the address of the table entry.

Inexact: IEEE Std 754 term for the FPU's precision exception.

Infinity: A floating-point result that has greater magnitude than any integer or any real number. It is often useful to consider infinity as another number, subject to special rules of arithmetic. All three Intel floating-point formats provide representations for +infinity and − infinity.

Initialization: The process of setting up the programming environment following reset. The processor begins execution in real-address mode. A few processor registers have defined states following reset, which permit execution to begin. Initial states of the segment registers allow memory to be accessed, even though no segment selectors have been loaded. The DR7 register (debug control register) is clear, so no breakpoint will occur during initialization. The real mode program can set up data structures such as descriptor tables and page tables, then transfer execution to a program running in protected mode.

Inquire Cycle: Used to check whether the address being presented is contained within the cache of the Pentium processor. If the address hits a modified line in the data cache, the modified line is written back onto the bus.

Instruction Prefetch: Reading instructions into the processor from sequentially higher addresses in advance of execution; a technique for overlapping the execution of instructions.

Instruction Restart: An ability to make a second attempt to execute an instruction which generates an exception. Instruction restart is necessary for supporting virtual memory. When an application makes reference to a segment or page which is not present in memory, the application must be suspended in a way which allows restarting after the operating system has brought the segment or page into physical memory. Instruction restart restores enough of the processor state to allow the exception handler to be called with a return address pointing to the instruction which generated the exception, rather than the instruction following it.

Integer: A number (positive, negative, or zero) that is finite and has no fractional part. Integer can also mean the computer representation for such a number: a sequence of data bytes interpreted in a standard way. It is perfectly reasonable for integers to be represented in a floating-point format; this is what the FPU does whenever an integer is pushed onto the FPU stack.

Integer Bit: A part of the significand in floating-point formats. In these formats, the integer bit is the only part of the significand considered to be to the left of the binary point. The integer bit is always one, except in one case: when the exponent is the minimum (biased exponent is zero), the integer bit is zero. In the extended format the integer bit is explicit; in the single format and double format the integer bit is implicit; i.e., is not actually stored in memory.

Internal Cache: A cache memory on the processor chip. The Intel486 processor has 8K bytes of internal cache memory.

Interrupt: A forced transfer of program control caused by a hardware signal or execution of the INT *n* instruction. Interrupt handlers called by software are processed like exceptions.

Interrupt Descriptor Table (IDT): An array of gate descriptors for invoking the handlers associated with exceptions and interrupts. A handler may be invoked by a task gate, interrupt gate, or trap gate.

Interrupt Gate: A gate descriptor used to invoke an interrupt handler. An interrupt gate is different from a trap gate only in its effect on the IF flag. An interrupt gate clears the flag (disables interrupts) for the duration of the handler.

Invalid: Unallocated. Invalid cache lines do not cause cache hits. Valid cache lines have been loaded with data and may cause cache hits.

Invalid Operation: The exception condition for the FPU that covers all cases not covered by other exceptions. Included are FPU stack overflow and underflow, NaN inputs, illegal infinite inputs, out-of-range inputs, and inputs in unsupported formats.

I/O Permission Bitmap: Contained in the TSS, the I/O permission bitmap controls access for a task to specific I/O addresses if the CPL > IOPL or if the task is executing in virtual-8086 mode.

Label: An identifier used to name places in the source code of a program, so that statements can refer to those places. Places named by labels include procedure entry points, beginning of blocks of data, and base addresses for descriptor tables.

LDT: See *Local Descriptor Table.*

Linear Address: A 32-bit address into a large, unsegmented address space. If paging is enabled, it translates the linear address into a physical address. If paging is not enabled, the linear address is used as the physical address.

Little-Endien: A method used by the Intel x86 architecture for storing data types that are larger than one byte where the low-order byte is stored at the lowest address and the high-order byte at the high address.

Local Descriptor Table (LDT): An array of segment descriptors for one program. Each program may have its own LDT, a program may share its LDT with another program, or a program may have no LDT, in which case, it uses the global descriptor table (GDT).

Locked Instructions: Instructions which read and write a destination in memory without allowing other devices to become bus masters between the read cycle and the write cycle. This mechanism is necessary for supporting reliable communications among multiprocessors. The mechanism is invoked using the LOCK instruction prefix. Only certain instructions may be locked, and only when they have destination operands in memory (other uses of the LOCK prefix generate an invalid-opcode exception).

Logical Address: The number used by application programs to reference virtual memory. This number consists of two parts: a segment selector (16 bits) and an offset (32 bits). The segment selector is used to specify an independent, protected address space (segment). The offset is used as an address within that segment. Segmentation translates the logical address into a linear address.

Long Integer: An integer format supported by the FPU that consists of a 64-bit two's complement quantity.

Long Real: An older term for the FPU's 64-bit double format.

Main Memory: The large memory, external to the processor, used for holding most instruction code and data. Generally built from cost-effective DRAM memory chips. May be used with the internal cache of the processor and an optional external cache.

Mantissa: A term used with some non-Intel computers for the significand of a floating-point number.

Masked: A term that can apply to each of the six FPU exceptions I, D, A, O U, P. An exception is masked if a corresponding bit in the FPU control word is set to one. If an exception is masked, the FPU will not generate an interrupt when the exception condition occurs; it will instead provide its own exception recovery.

Memory Management: Support for simplified models of memory; a process consisting of address translation and protection checks. There are two forms of memory management, segmentation and paging. Segmentation provides protected, independent address spaces (segments). Paging provides access to data structures larger than the available memory space by keeping them partly in memory and partly on disk.

MESI Protocol: A cache consistency protocol with full support for multiprocessing. The MESI protocol consists of four states that define whether a line is modified (M), exclusive (E), shared (S), or invalid (I). Lines cached in the Pentium processor can change state due to processor generated activity or as a result of activity on the Pentium bus generated by other bus masters, such as snooping.

Microprocessor: See *Processor.*

Miss: See *Cache Miss.*

Mode: (1) One of the FPU status word fields "rounding control" and "precision control" which programs can set, sense, save, and restore to control the execution of subsequent arithmetic operations. (2) See *Real-Address Mode, Protected Mode, Virtual-8086 Mode, Supervisor Mode, User Mode.*

ModR/M Byte: A byte following an instruction opcode which is used to specify instruction operands.

MPU: Micro-Processor Unit. See *Processor.*

Multiprocessing: Using more than one processor in a system. The Intel486 processor supports two kinds of multiprocessing: coprocessors, which are special-purpose performance-enhancing extensions to the architecture and instruction set, and multiple general-purpose processors, such as additional Intel486 processors.

Multisegmented Model: A memory organization in which different segments are mapped to different ranges of linear addresses. This organization uses segmentation to protect data structures from damage caused by program errors. For example, the stack can be kept from growing into memory occupied by instruction code.

Multitasking: Timesharing a processor among several programs, executing some number of instructions from each. The Intel486 processor has instructions and data structures which support multitasking.

NaN: An abbreviation for "Not a Number"; a floating-point quantity that does not represent any numeric or infinite quantity. NaN's should be returned by functions that encounter serious errors. If created during a sequence of calculations, they are transmitted to the final answer and can contain information about where the error occurred.

Near Pointer: A reference to memory without a segment selector; an offset. Used to access memory when the segment selector has already been loaded into the processor, for example when one procedure calls another within the same segment.

Normal: The representation of a number in a floating-point format in which the significand has an integer bit one (either explicit or implicit).

Normalize: Convert a denormal floating-point representation of a number to a normal representation.

Offset: A 16- or 32-bit number which specifies a memory location relative to the base address of a segment. A program's code segment descriptor specifies whether 16- or 32-bit offsets are the default. An address-size prefix specifies use of the non-default size.

Operand: Data in a register or in memory which an instruction reads or writes (or both).

Operand-Size Prefix: An instruction prefix which selects the sizes of integer operands. Operands may be 8- and 16-bit, or they may be 8- and 32-bit. The default operand size is specified by the D bit in the descriptor for the code segment which contains the instruction. Use of the operand-size prefix selects the non-default size.

Overflow: A floating-point exception condition in which the correct answer is finite, but has magnitude too great to be represented in the destination format. This kind of overflow (also called numeric overflow) is not to be confused with stack overflow.

Packed BCD: Packed Binary Coded Decimal; a format for representing numbers in base 10. One byte is used for each two digits of the number, with bit positions 0 to 3 specifying the value for the less significant digit and bit positions 4 to 7 specifying the value for the more significant digit. Packed BCD is one of the data types supported by the FPU.

Packed Decimal: An integer format supported by the FPU. A packed decimal number is a 10-byte quantity, with nine bytes of 18 binary coded decimal digits and one byte for the sign.

Page Directory: The first-level page table. The paging hardware of the Intel486 processor uses two levels of page tables, where the physical address produced by the first-level page table is the base address of the second-level page table. The use of two levels allows the second-level tables to be paged to disk.

Page Directory Base Register (PDBR): A processor register which holds the base address of the page directory; same as the CR3 register. Because the contents of the PDBR register are loaded from the task state segment (TSS) during a task switch, each task can have its own page directory, so each can have a different mapping of virtual pages to physical pages.

Page Directory Pointer: An 8-byte entry in the Page Directory Pointer Table specifying the 36-bit physical address of the page directory, whether it's present in memory, and cache management (PCD and PWT) bits for the page directory.

Page Directory Pointer Table (PDPT): Contains four Page Directory Pointers used in page translation by the Pentium processor. The PDPT's physical address is specified by the CR3 register.

Page: A 4K-byte block of neighboring memory locations; the unit of memory used by paging hardware.

Page Table: A table which maps part of a linear address to a physical address. The paging hardware of the Intel486 processor uses two levels of page tables, where the physical address produced by the first-level page table is the base address of the second-level page table. The use of two levels allows the second-level tables to be paged to disk.

Page Table Entry: A 32-bit data structure in memory used for paging. It includes the physical address for a page and the page's protection information. It is set up by operating system software and accessed by paging hardware.

Paging: A form of memory management used to simulate a large, unsegmented address space using a small, fragmented address space and some disk storage. Paging provides access to data structures larger than the available memory space by keeping them partly in memory and partly on disk.

Pairing: The process of issuing two instructions in parallel to the dual execution units of a processor.

PDBR: See *Page Directory Base Register.*

Physical Address: The address which appears on the local bus. The Intel486 processor has a 32-bit physical address, which may be used to address as much as 4 gigabytes of memory.

Physical Memory: The address space on the local bus; the hardware implementation of memory. Memory is addressed as 8-bit bytes, but it is implemented as 32-bit doublewords which start at addresses which are multiples of four (addresses which are clear in their two least significant bits). The Intel486 processor may have up to 4 gigabytes of physical memory.

Precision: The effective number of bits in the significand of the floating-point representation of a number.

Precision Control: An option, programmed through the FPU control word, that allows all FPU arithmetic to be performed with reduced precision. Because no speed advantage results from this option, its only use is for strict compatibility with IEEE Std 754 and with other computer systems.

Precision Exception: An FPU exception condition that results when a calculation does not return an exact answer. This exception is usually masked and ignored; it is used only in extremely critical applications, when the user must know if the results are exact. The precision exceptions is called inexact in IEEE Std 754.

Privilege Level: A protection parameter applied to segments and segment selectors. There are four privilege levels, ranging from 0 (most privileged) to 3 (least privileged). Level 0 is used for critical system software, such as the operating system. Level 3 is used for application programs. Some system software, such as device drivers, may be put in intermediate levels 1 and 2.

Processor: The part of a computer system which executes instructions; also called microprocessor, CPU, or MPU.

Protected Mode: An execution mode in which the full 32-bit architecture of the processor is available.

Protection: A mechanism which can be used to protect the operating system and applications from programming errors in applications. Protection can be used to define the address spaces accessible to a program, the kind of memory references which may be made to those address spaces, and the privilege level required for access. Any violation of these protections generates a general-protection exception. Protection can be applied to segments or pages.

Pseudo-Descriptor: A 48-bit memory operand accessed when a descriptor table base register is loaded or stored.

Pseudozero: One of a set of special values of the extended real format. The set consists of numbers with a zero significand and an exponent that is neither all zeros nor all ones. Pseudozeros are not created by the FPU but are handled correctly when encountered as operands.

Quadword: A 64-bit operand. The CDQ instruction can be used to convert a doubleword to a quadword. A quadword held in the EDX and EAX registers may be the dividend used with a doubleword divisor.

Quiet NaN: A floating-point NaN in which the most significant bit of the fractional part of the significand is one. By convention, these NaN's can undergo certain operations without causing an exception.

Re-entrant: Allowing a program to call itself; recursive. For certain kinds of problems, such as operations performed on hierarchical data structures, procedures which call themselves are simple and efficient solutions. On the Intel486 processor, procedures may be re-entrant, however tasks are not. A task may not call itself because it has only one task state segment (TSS) for storing the processor state. Procedures store the processor state on the stack, so they may be re-entrant to an arbitrary number of levels.

Real-Address Mode: An execution mode which provides an emulation of the architecture of an 8086 processor; also called "real mode." In this mode the Intel486 processor appears as a fast 8086 processor. The architectural extensions for protection and multitasking are not available in this mode. Following reset initialization, the Intel486 processor begins execution in real mode.

Real: Any finite value (negative, positive, or zero) that can be represented by a (possibly infinite) decimal expansion. Reals can be represented as the points of a line marked off like a ruler. The term can also refer to a floating-point number that represents a real value.

Requested Privilege Level (RPL): The privilege level applied to a segment selector. If the RPL is less privileged than the current privilege level (CPL), access to a segment takes place at the RPL level. This keeps privileged software from being used by an application to interfere with the operating system or other applications. For example, a privileged program which loads memory from disk should not be permitted to overwrite the operating system as a result of a call from an application. With RPL, the attempt to access the memory space of the operating system takes place with the privleges of the application.

Reset: See *Initialization*.

RPL: See *Requested Privilege Level*.

Scheduling: The process of ordering instruction execution to obtain optimum performance.

Second Level Cache: See External Cache.

Segment: An independent, protected address space. A program may have as many as 16,383 segments, each of which can be up to 4 gigabytes in size.

Segmentation: A form of memory management used to provide multiple independent, protected address spaces. Segmentation aids program debugging by reporting programming errors when they first occur, rather than when their effects become apparent. Segmentation makes programs provided to the end-user more reliable by limiting the damage which can be caused by undetected errors. Segmentation increases the address space available to a program by providing up to 16,383 segments, each of which can be up to 4 gigabytes in size.

Segment Descriptor: A 64-bit data structure in memory used for segmentation. It includes the base address for a segment, its size (limit), its type, and protection information. It is set up by operating system software and accessed by segmentation hardware.

Segment-Override Prefix: An instruction prefix which overrides the default segment selection. There are six segment-override prefixes, one each for the CS, SS, DS, ES, FS, and GS segments.

Segment Selector: A 16-bit number used to specify an address space (segment). Bit position 3 to 15 are used as an index into a descriptor table. Bit position 2 specifies whether the global descriptor table (GDT) or local descriptor table (LDT) is used. Bit positions 0 and 1 are the requested privilege level (RPL), which may lower the priority of access, as an additional protection check.

Serializing Instructions: A class of instructions that serialize instruction execution in the U pipe only on the Pentium processor, that ensures modifications to flags, registers and memory from previous instructions are completed before the next instruction is fetched and executed.

Set-Associative: A form of cache organization in which the location of a data block in main memory constrains, but does not completely determine, its location in the cache. Set-associative organization is a compromise between direct-mapped organization, in which data from a given address in main memory has only one possible cache location, and fully-associative organization, in which data from anywhere in main memory can be put anywhere in the cache. An "n-way set-associative" cache allows data from a given address in main memory to be cached in any of n locations. Both the Translation Lookaside Buffer (TLB) and the integral cache of the Intel486 processor have a four-way set-associative organization.

Short Integer: An integer format supported by the FPU that consists of a 32-bit two's complement quantity. Short integer is not the shortest FPU integer format—the 16-bit word integer is.

Short Real: An older term for the FPU's 32-bit single format.

SIB Byte: A byte following an instruction opcode and modR/M bytes which is used to specify a scale factor, index, and base register.

Sign Extension: Conversion of data to a larger format, where empty bit positions are filled with the value of the sign. This form of conversion preserves the value of signed integers. See *Zero Extension.*

Signaling NaN: A floating-point NaN that causes an invalid-operation exception whenever it enters into a calculation or comparison, even an unordered comparison.

Significand: The part of a floating-point number that consists of the most significant nonzero bits of the number, if the number were written out in an unlimited binary format. The significand is composed of an integer bit and a fraction. The integer bit is implicit in the single format and double format. The significand is considered to have a binary point after the integer bit; the binary point is then moved according to the value of the exponent.

Single Extended: A floating-point format, required by the IEEE Std 754, that provides greater precision than single; it also provides an explicit integer bit in the significand. The FPU's extended format meets the single extended requirement as well as the double extended requirement.

Single Format: A floating-point format supported by the FPU, which consists of a sign, an 8-bit biased exponent, an implicit integer bit, and a 23-bit significand—a total of 32 explicit bits.

SMI: System Management Interrupt causing the processor to save its state to SMRAM and begin executing the SMM Handler.

SMM: See *System Management Mode.*

SMRAM: See *System Management RAM*

Snooping: See *Inquire Cycles.*

Stack Fault: A special case of the invalid-operation exception which is indicated by a one in the SF bit of the status word. This condition usually results from stack underflow or overflow in the FPU.

Stack Frame: The space used on the stack by a procedure. The stack frame includes parameters, return addresses, saved registers, temporary storage, and any other stack space the procedure uses.

Stack Segment: A data segment which is used to hold a stack. A stack segment may be expand-down, which allows the segment to be resized toward lower address. The type of information held in a segment is specified in its segment descriptor.

Status Word: A 16-bit FPU register that can be manually set, but which is usually controlled by side effects to FPU instructions. It contains condition codes, the FPU stack pointer, busy and interrupt bits, and exception flags.

String: A sequence of bytes, word, or doublewords which may start at any byte address in memory. The Intel486 processor has instructions for efficient operations on strings.

Superscalar: An architectural feature allowing the execution of multiple instructions in parallel.

Supervisor Mode: The privilege level applied to operating system pages. Paging only recognizes two privilege levels: supervisor mode and user mode. A program executing from a segment at privilege level 0, 1, 2 is in supervisor mode.

System Management Mode: An operating mode of the Pentium processor entered through an external interrupt through SMI# allowing system developers the ability to provide high-level systems functions such as power management and system security.

System Management RAM (SMRAM): An area of memory used by the Pentium processor which contains the processor state dump record prior to entering SMM.

Table: An array of records in memory having equal size.

Tag Word: A 16-bit FPU register that it automatically maintained by the FPU. For each space in the FPU stack, it tells if the space is occupied by a number; if so, it gives information about what kind of number.

Tag Word: A 16-bit FPU register that it automatically maintained by the FPU. For each space in the FPU stack, it tells if the space is occupied by a number; if so, it gives information about what kind of number.

Tag: The part of a cache line which holds the address information used to determine if a memory operation is a hit or a miss on that cache line.

Task Register: A register which holds a segment selector for the current task. The selector references a task state segment (TSS). Like the segment registers, the TR register has a visible part and an invisible part. The visible part holds the segment selector, and the invisible part holds information cached from the segment descriptor for the TSS.

Task State Segment (TSS): A segment used to store the processor state during a task switch. If a separate I/O address space is used, the TSS holds permission bits which control access to the I/O space. Operating systems may define additional structures which exist in the TSS.

Task Switch: A transfer of execution between tasks; a context switch. Unlike the procedure calls, which save only the contents of the general registers, a task switch saves most of the processor state. For example, the registers used for address translation are reloaded, so that each task can have a different logical-to-physical address mapping.

Task: A program running, or waiting to run, in a multitasking system.

Temporary Real: An older term for the FPU's 80-bit extended format.

Tiny: Of or pertaining to a floating-point number that is so close to zero that its exponent is smaller than smallest exponent that can be represented in the destination format.

TLB: See *Translation Lookaside Buffer*.

Top: The three-bit field of the status word that indicates which FPU register is the current top of stack.

Transcendental: One of a class of functions for which polynomial formulas are always appropriate, never exact for more than isolated values. The FPU supports trigonometric, exponential, and logarithmic functions; all are transcendental.

Translation Lookaside Buffer (TLB): The on-chip cache for page table entries. In typical systems, about 99% of the references to page table entries can be satisfied by information in the TLB.

Trap: An exception which is reported at the instruction boundary immediately following the instruction which generated the exception.

Trap Gate: A gate descriptor used to invoke an exception handler. A trap gate is different from an interrupt gate only in its effect on the IF flag. Unlike an interrupt gate, which clears the flag (disables interrupts) for the duration of the handler, a trap gate leaves the flag unchanged.

TSS: See *Task State Segment*.

Two's Complement: A method of representing integers. If the uppermost bit is zero, the number is considered positive, with the value given by the rest of the bits. If the uppermost bit is one, the number is negative, with the value obtained by subtracting $(2^{\text{bit count}})$ from all the given bits. For example, the 8-bit number 11111100 is -4, obtained by subtracting 2^8 from 252.

Ulps (Units in Last Place): A measurement of accuracy used for floating-point numbers.

Unbiased Exponent: The true value that tells how far and in which direction to move the binary point of the significand of a floating-point number. For example, if a single-format exponent is 131, we subtract the Bias 127 to obtain the unbiased exponent +4. Thus, the real number being represented is the significand with the binary point shifted 4 bits to the right.

Underflow: An exception condition in which the correct answer is nonzero, but has a magnitude too small to be represented as a normal number in the destination floating-point format. IEEE Std 754 specifies that an attempt be made to represent the number as a denormal. This denormalization may result in a loss of significant bits from the significand. This kind of underflow (also called numeric overflow) is not be confused with stack overflow.

Unmasked: A term that can apply to each of the six FPU exceptions: I, D, Z, O, U, P. An exception is unmasked if a corresponding bit in the FPU control word is set to zero. If an exception is unmasked, the FPU will generate an interrupt whent he exception condition occurs. You can provide an interrupt routine that customizes your exception recovery.

Unnormal: An extended real representation in which the explicit integer bit of the significand is zero and the exponent is nonzero. Unnormal values are not supported by the FPU. This includes several formats that are recognized by the 8087 and Intel287 coprocessors; they cause the invalid-operation exception when encountered as operands.

Unsupported Format: Any number representation that is not recognized by the FPU. This includes several formats that are recognized by the 8087 and Intel287 coprocessors; namely: pseudo-NaN, pseudoinfinity, and unnormal.

USE16: An assembly language directive for specifying 16-bit code and data segments.

USE32: An assembly language directive for specifying 32-bit code and data segments.

User Mode: The privilege level applied to application pages. Paging only recognizes two privilege levels: supervisor mode and user mode. A program executing from a segment at privilege level 3 is in user mode.

V86 Mode: See *Virtual-8086 Mode*.

Valid: Allocated. Valid cache lines have been loaded with data and may cause cache hits. Invalid cache lines do not cause cache hits.

Vector: A number used to identify the source of an exception or interrupt. A vector is used to index into the IDT table for a gate descriptor. The gate descriptor is used to call the handler for the exception or interrupt.

Virtual Memory: The memory model for application programs; a simplified organization for memory supported by memory management hardware and operating system software. On the Intel486 processor, virtual memory is supported by segmentation and paging. Segmentation is a mechanism for providing multiple independent, protected address spaces. Paging is a mechanism for providing access to data structures larger than physical memory by keeping them partly in memory and partly on disk.

Virtual-8086 Mode: An execution mode which provides an emulation of the architecture of an 8086 processor. Unlike real-address mode, virtual-8086 mode is compatible with multitasking; a protected mode operating system may be used to run a mix of protected mode and virtual-8086 mode tasks.

Word: A 16-bit quantity of memory. The Intel486 processor allows 16-bit words to begin at any byte address, but a performance penalty is taken when a word crosses the boundary between two doublewords in physical memory.

Word Integer: An integer format supported by the Intel486 processor that consists of a 16-bit two's complement quantity.

Write-Back: A form of caching in which memory writes load only the cache memory. Data propagates to main memory when a write-back operation is invoked.

Write-Through: A form of caching in which memory writes load both the cache memory and main memory.

Zero Divide: An exception condition in which floating-point inputs are finite, but the correct answer, even with an unlimited exponent, has infinite magnitude.

Zero Extension: Conversion of data to a larger format, where empty bit positions are filled with zero. This form of conversion preserves the value of unsigned integers. See *Sign Extension.*

NORTH AMERICAN SALES OFFICES

ALABAMA

Intel Corp.
600 Boulevard South
Suite 104-I
Huntsville 35802
Tel: (800) 628-8686
FAX: (205) 883-3511

ARIZONA

†Intel Corp.
410 North 44th Street
Suite 500
Phoenix 85008
Tel: (800) 628-8686
FAX: (602) 244-0446

CALIFORNIA

Intel Corp.
1 Sierra Gate Plaza
Suite 280C
Roseville 95678
Tel: (800) 628-8686
FAX: (916) 782-8153

†Intel Corp.
9665 Chesapeake Dr.
Suite 325
San Diego 92123
Tel: (800) 628-8686
FAX: (619) 292-0628

*†Intel Corp.
400 N. Tustin Avenue
Suite 450
Santa Ana 92705
Tel: (800) 628-8686
TWX: 910-595-1114
FAX: (714) 541-9157

*†Intel Corp.
1781 Fox Drive
San Jose 95131
Tel: (800) 628-8686
FAX: (408) 441-9540

†Intel Corp.
15260 Ventura Boulevard
Suite 360
Sherman Oaks 91403
Tel: (800) 628-8686
FAX: (818) 995-6624

COLORADO

*†Intel Corp.
600 S. Cherry St.
Suite 700
Denver 80222
Tel: (800) 628-8686
TWX: 910-931-2289
FAX: (303) 322-8670

CONNECTICUT

†Intel Corp.
103 Mill Plain Road
Danbury 06811
Tel: (800) 628-8686
FAX: (203) 794-0339

FLORIDA

†Intel Corp.
800 Fairway Drive
Suite 160
Deerfield Beach 33441
Tel: (800) 628-8686
FAX: (305) 421-2444

†Intel Corp.
5850 T.G. Lee Blvd.
Suite 340
Orlando 32822
Tel: (800) 628-8686
FAX: (407) 240-8097

GEORGIA

†Intel Corp.
20 Technology Parkway
Suite 150
Norcross 30092
Tel: (800) 628-8686
FAX: (404) 605-9762

ILLINOIS

*†Intel Corp.
Woodfield Corp. Center III
300 N. Martingale Road
Suite 400
Schaumburg 60173
Tel: (800) 628-8686
FAX: (708) 706-9762

INDIANA

†Intel Corp.
8910 Purdue Road
Suite 350
Indianapolis 46268
Tel: (800) 628-8686
FAX: (317) 875-8938

MARYLAND

*†Intel Corp.
10010 Junction Dr.
Suite 200
Annapolis Junction 20701
Tel: (800) 628-8686
FAX: (410) 206-3678

MASSACHUSETTS

*†Intel Corp.
Westford Corp. Center
5 Carlisle Road
2nd Floor
Westford 01886
Tel: (800) 628-8686
TWX: 710-343-6333
FAX: (508) 692-7867

MICHIGAN

†Intel Corp.
7071 Orchard Lake Road
Suite 100
West Bloomfield 48322
Tel: (800) 628-8686
FAX: (313) 851-8770

MINNESOTA

†Intel Corp.
3500 W. 80th St.
Suite 360
Bloomington 55431
Tel: (800) 628-8686
TWX: 910-576-2867
FAX: (612) 831-6497

NEW JERSEY

*†Intel Corp.
Lincroft Office Center
125 Half Mile Road
Red Bank 07701
Tel: (800) 628-8686
FAX: (908) 747-0983

NEW YORK

*Intel Corp.
850 Crosskeys Office Park
Fairport 14450
Tel: (800) 628-8686
TWX: 510-253-7391
FAX: (716) 223-2561

*†Intel Corp.
2950 Express Dr., South
Suite 130
Islandia 11722
Tel: (800) 628-8686
TWX: 510-227-6236
FAX: (516) 348-7939

†Intel Corp.
300 Westage Business Center
Suite 230
Fishkill 12524
Tel: (800) 628-8686
FAX: (914) 897-3125

OHIO

*†Intel Corp.
3401 Park Center Drive
Suite 220
Dayton 45414
Tel: (800) 628-8686
TWX: 810-450-2528
FAX: (513) 890-8658

*Intel Corp.
Four Commerce Park Square
23200 Chagrin Blvd., Suite 600
Beachwood 44122
Tel: (800) 628-8686
FAX: (216) 464-2270

OKLAHOMA

Intel Corp.
6801 N. Broadway
Suite 115
Oklahoma City 73162
Tel: (800) 628-8686
FAX: (405) 840-9819

OREGON

†Intel Corp.
15254 N.W. Greenbrier Pkwy.
Building B
Beaverton 97006
Tel: (800) 628-8686
TWX: 910-467-8741
FAX: (503) 645-8181

PENNSYLVANIA

*†Intel Corp.
925 Harvest Drive
Suite 200
Blue Bell 19422
Tel: (800) 628-8686
FAX: (215) 641-0785

*†Intel Corp.
400 Penn Center Blvd.
Suite 610
Pittsburgh 15235
Tel: (800) 628-8686
FAX: (412) 829-7578

SOUTH CAROLINA

Intel Corp.
100 Executive Center Drive
Suite 109, B183
Greenville 29615
Tel: (800) 628-8686
FAX: (803) 297-3401

TEXAS

†Intel Corp.
8911 N. Capital of Texas Hwy.
Suite 4230
Austin 78759
Tel: (800) 628-8686
FAX: (512) 338-9335

*†Intel Corp.
2950 Express Dr., South

*†Intel Corp.
5000 Quorum Drive
Suite 750
Dallas 75240
Tel: (800) 628-8686

*†Intel Corp.
20515 SH 249
Suite 401
Houston 77070
Tel: (800) 628-8686
TWX: 910-881-2490
FAX: (713) 988-3660

UTAH

†Intel Corp.
428 East 6400 South
Suite 135
Murray 84107
Tel: (800) 628-8686
FAX: (801) 268-1457

WASHINGTON

†Intel Corp.
2800 156th Avenue S.E.
Suite 105
Bellevue 98007
Tel: (800) 628-8686
FAX: (206) 746-4495

Intel Corp.
408 N. Mullan Road
Suite 105
Spokane 99206
Tel: (800) 628-8686
FAX: (509) 928-9467

WISCONSIN

Intel Corp.
400 N. Executive Dr.
Suite 401
Brookfield 53005
Tel: (800) 628-8686
FAX: (414) 789-2746

CANADA

BRITISH COLUMBIA

Intel Semiconductor of
Canada, Ltd.
999 Canada Place
Suite 404, #11
Vancouver V6C 3E2
Tel: (800) 628-8686
FAX: (604) 844-2813

ONTARIO

†Intel Semiconductor of
Canada, Ltd.
2650 Queensview Drive
Suite 250
Ottawa K2B 8H6
Tel: (800) 628-8686
FAX: (613) 820-5936

†Intel Semiconductor of
Canada, Ltd.
190 Attwell Drive
Suite 500
Rexdale M9W 6H8
Tel: (800) 628-8686
FAX: (416) 675-2438

QUEBEC

†Intel Semiconductor of
Canada, Ltd.
1 Rue Holiday
Suite 115
Tour East
Pt. Claire H9R 5N3
Tel: (800) 628-8686
FAX: 514-694-0064

†Sales and Service Office
*Field Application Location

NORTH AMERICAN DISTRIBUTORS

ALABAMA

Arrow/Schweber Electronics
1015 Henderson Road
Huntsville 35816
Tel: (205) 837-6955
FAX: (205) 895-0126

Hamilton/Avnet
4960 Corporate Drive, #135
Huntsville 35805
Tel: (205) 837-7210
FAX: (205) 830-8404

MTI Systems Sales
4950 Corporate Dr., #120
Huntsville 35805
Tel: (205) 830-9526
FAX: (205) 830-9557

Pioneer Technologies Group
4835 University Square, #5
Huntsville 35816
Tel: (205) 837-9300
FAX: (205) 837-9358

ARIZONA

Arrow/Schweber Electronics
2415 W. Erie Drive
Tempe 85282
Tel: (602) 431-0030
FAX: (602) 431-9555

Avnet Computer
1626 S. Edwards Drive
Tempe 85281
Tel: (602) 902-4642
FAX: (602) 902-4646

Hamilton/Avnet
1626 S. Edwards Drive
Tempe 85281
Tel: (602) 902-4700
FAX: (602) 902-4747

Wyle Laboratories
4141 E. Raymond
Phoenix 85040
Tel: (602) 437-2088
FAX: (602) 437-2124

CALIFORNIA

Arrow Commercial Systems Group
1502 Crocker Avenue
Hayward 94544
Tel: (510) 489-5371
FAX: (510) 391-1742

Arrow Commercial Systems Group
14242 Chambers Road
Tustin 92680
Tel: (714) 544-0200
FAX: (714) 454-4203

Arrow/Schweber Electronics
26707 W. Agoura Road
Calabasas 91302
Tel: (818) 880-9686
FAX: (818) 880-4687

Arrow/Schweber Electronics
9511 Ridgehaven Court
San Diego 92123
Tel: (619) 565-4800
FAX: (619) 279-0862

Arrow/Schweber Electronics
1180 Murphy Avenue
San Jose 95131
Tel: (408) 441-9700
FAX: (408) 453-4810

Arrow/Schweber Electronics
48834 Kato Rd., Suite 103
Fremont 94538
Tel: (510) 440-2681
FAX: (510) 490-1084

Arrow/Schweber Electronics
6 Cromwell, Suite 100
Irvine 92718
Tel: (714) 838-5422
FAX: (714) 454-4203

Avnet Computer
3170 Pullman Street
Costa Mesa 92626
Tel: (714) 641-4179
FAX: (714) 641-4170

Avnet Computer
1361 B West 190th Street
Gardena 90248
Tel: (310) 217-6830
FAX: (310) 327-5389

Avnet Computer
1175 Bordeaux Drive
Sunnyvale 94089
Tel: (408) 743-3454
FAX: (408) 743-3348

Hamilton/Avnet
3170 Pullman Street
Costa Mesa 92626
Tel: (714) 641-4182
FAX: (714) 641-4149

Hamilton/Avnet
1175 Bordeaux Drive
Sunnyvale 94089
Tel: (408) 743-3300
FAX: (408) 745-6679

Hamilton/Avnet
4545 Viewridge Avenue
San Diego 92123
Tel: (619) 571-7540
FAX: (619) 277-6136

Hamilton/Avnet
21150 Califa St.
Woodland Hills 91367
Tel: (818) 594-0404
FAX: (818) 594-8233

Hamilton/Avnet
755 Sunrise Avenue, #150
Roseville 95661
Tel: (916) 925-2216
FAX: (916) 925-3478

Pioneer Technologies Group
134 Rio Robles
San Jose 95134
Tel: (408) 954-9100
FAX: (408) 954-9113

Pioneer Standard
217 Technology Dr., #110
Irvine 92718
Tel: (714) 753-5090
FAX: (714) 753-5074

Pioneer Standard
5850 Canoga Ave., #400
Woodland Hills 91367
Tel: (818) 883-4640
FAX: (818) 883-9721

Wyle Laboratories
2951 Sunrise Blvd., #175
Rancho Cordova 95742
Tel: (916) 638-5282
FAX: (916) 638-1491

Wyle Laboratories
9525 Chesapeake Drive
San Diego 92123
Tel: (619) 565-9171
FAX: (619) 365-0512

Wyle Laboratories
3000 Bowers Avenue
Santa Clara 95051
Tel: (408) 727-2500
FAX: (408) 727-7359

Wyle Laboratories
17872 Cowan Avenue
Irvine 92714
Tel: (714) 863-9953
FAX: (714) 251-0365

Wyle Laboratories
26010 Mureau Road, #150
Calabasas 91302
Tel: (818) 880-9000
FAX: (818) 880-5510

COLORADO

Arrow/Schweber Electronics
61 Inverness Dr. East, #105
Englewood 80112
Tel: (303) 799-0258
FAX: (303) 799-4303

Hamilton/Avnet
9605 Maroon Circle, #200
Englewood 80112
Tel: (303) 799-7800
FAX: (303) 799-7801

Wyle Laboratories
451 E. 124th Avenue
Thornton 80241
Tel: (303) 457-9953
FAX: (303) 457-4831

CONNECTICUT

Arrow/Schweber Electronics
12 Beaumont Road
Wallingford 06492
Tel: (203) 265-7741
FAX: (203) 265-7988

Avnet Computer
55 Federal Road, #103
Danbury 06810
Tel: (203) 797-2880
FAX: (203) 791-2896

Hamilton/Avnet
55 Federal Road, #103
Danbury 06810
Tel: (203) 743-9799
FAX: (203) 797-0373

Pioneer-Standard
2 Trap Falls Rd., #101
Shelton 06484
Tel: (203) 929-5600
FAX: (203) 929-9791

FLORIDA

Arrow/Schweber Electronics
400 Fairway Drive, #102
Deerfield Beach 33441
Tel: (305) 429-8200
FAX: (305) 428-3991

Arrow/Schweber Electronics
37 Skyline Drive, #3101
Lake Mary 32746
Tel: (407) 333-9300
FAX: (407) 333-9320

Avnet Computer
541 S. Orlando Ave., #203
Maitlan 32751
Tel: (407) 539-2888
FAX: (407) 539-2085

Hamilton/Avnet
5371 N.W. 33rd Ave., #204
Ft. Lauderdale 33309
Tel: (305) 733-6300
FAX: (305) 484-8369

Hamilton/Avnet
3247 Tech Drive
St. Petersburg 35805
Tel: (813) 573-4346
FAX: (813) 572-0833

Hamilton/Avnet
7079 University Boulevard
Winter Park 32792
Tel: (407) 657-3300
FAX: (407) 678-4414

Pioneer Technologies Group
337 Northlake Blvd., #1000
Alta Monte Springs 32701
Tel: (407) 834-9090
FAX: (407) 834-0865

Pioneer Technologies Group
674 S. Military Trail
Deerfield Beach 33442
Tel: (305) 428-8877
FAX: (305) 481-2950

GEORGIA

Arrow Commercial Systems Group
3400 C. Corporate Way
Duluth 30136
Tel: (404) 623-8825
FAX: (404) 623-8802

Arrow/Schweber Electronics
4250 E. Rivergreen Pkwy., #E
Duluth 30136
Tel: (404) 497-1300
FAX: (404) 476-1493

Avnet Computer
3425 Corporate Way, #G
Duluth 30136
Tel: (404) 623-5400
FAX: (404) 476-0125

Hamilton/Avnet
3425 Corporate Way, #G
Duluth 30136
Tel: (404) 623-5475
FAX: (404) 623-5490

Pioneer Technologies Group
4250 C. Rivergreen Parkway
Duluth 30136
Tel: (404) 623-1003
FAX: (404) 623-0665

ILLINOIS

Arrow/Schweber Electronics
1140 W. Thorndale Rd.
Itasca 60143
Tel: (708) 250-0500
FAX: 708-250-0916

Avnet Computer
1124 Thorndale Avenue
Bensenville 60106
Tel: (708) 860-8573
FAX: (708) 773-7978

Hamilton/Avnet
1130 Thorndale Avenue
Bensenville 60106
Tel: (708) 860-7700
FAX: (708) 860-8532

MTI Systems
1140 W. Thorndale Avenue
Itasca 60143
Tel: (708) 250-8222
FAX: (708) 250-8275

Pioneer-Standard
2171 Executive Dr., #200
Addison 60101
Tel: (708) 495-9680
FAX: (708) 495-9831

INDIANA

Arrow/Schweber Electronics
7108 Lakeview Parkway West Dr.
Indianapolis 46268
Tel: (317) 299-2071
FAX: (317) 299-2379

Avnet Computer
655 W. Carmel Dr., #120
Carmel 46032
Tel: (317) 575-8029
FAX: (317) 844-4964

Hamilton/Avnet
485 Gradle Drive
Carmel 46032
Tel: (317) 844-9533
FAX: (317) 844-5921

Pioneer-Standard
9350 Priority Way West Dr.
Indianapolis 46250
Tel: (317) 573-0880
FAX: (317) 573-0979

IOWA

Hamilton/Avnet
2335A Blairsferry Rd., N.E.
Cedar Rapids52402
Tel: (319) 362-4757
FAX: (319) 393-7050

KANSAS

Arrow/Schweber Electronics
9801 Legler Road
Lenexa 66219
Tel: (913) 541-9542
FAX: (913) 752-2612

Avnet Computer
15313 W. 95th Street
Lenexa 61219
Tel: (913) 541-7989
FAX: (913) 541-7904

Hamilton/Avnet
15313 W. 95th Street
Overland Park 66215
Tel: (913) 888-1055
FAX: (913) 541-7951

NORTH AMERICAN DISTRIBUTORS (Contd.)

KENTUCKY

Hamilton/Avnet
1847 Mercer Rd., #G
Lexington 40511
Tel: (606) 288-4911
FAX: (606) 288-4936

MARYLAND

Arrow/Schweber Electronics
9800J Patuxent Woods Dr.
Columbia 21046
Tel: (301) 596-7800
FAX: (301) 596-7821

Arrow Commercial Systems Group
200 Perry Parkway
Gaithersburg 20877
Tel: (301) 670-1600
FAX: (301) 670-0188

Avnet Computer
7172 Columbia Gateway Dr.
Columbia 21046
Tel: (301) 995-3571
FAX: (301) 995-3515

Hamilton/Avnet
7172 Columbia Gateway Dr., #F
Columbia 21046
Tel: (301) 995-3554
FAX: (301) 995-3553

*North Atlantic Industries
Systems Division
7125 River Wood Dr.
Columbia 21046
Tel: (301) 312-5800
FAX: (301) 312-5850

Pioneer Technologies Group
9100 Gaither Road
Gaithersburg 20877
Tel: (301) 921-0660
FAX: (301) 921-4255

MASSACHUSETTS

Arrow Commercial Systems Group
250 Upton Drive
Wilmington 01887
Tel: (508) 658-7100
FAX: (508) 658-0977

Arrow/Schweber Electronics
25 Upton Dr.
Wilmington 01887
Tel: (508) 658-0900
FAX: (508) 694-1754

Avnet Computer
10 D Centennial Drive
Peabody 01960
Tel: (508) 532-9822
FAX: (508) 532-9887

Hamilton/Avnet
10 D Centennial Drive
Peabody 01960
Tel: (508) 531-7430
FAX: (508) 531-9802

Pioneer-Standard
44 Hartwell Avenue
Lexington 02173
Tel: (617) 861-9200
FAX: (617) 863-1547

Wyle Laboratories
15 Third Avenue
Burlington 01803
Tel: (617) 272-7300
FAX: (617) 272-6809

MICHIGAN

Arrow/Schweber Electronics
19880 Haggerty Road
Livonia 48152
Tel: (800) 231-7902
FAX: (313) 462-2686

Avnet Computer
41650 Garden Brook Rd. #120
Novi 48375
Tel: (313) 347-4067
FAX: (313) 347-1820

Hamilton/Avnet
2876 28th Street, S.W., #5
Grandville 49418
Tel: (616) 531-0345
FAX: (616) 531-0059

Hamilton/Avnet
41650 Garden Brook Rd., #100
Novi 48375
Tel: (313) 347-4270
FAX: (313) 347-4021

Pioneer-Standard
13485 Stamford Ct.
Livonia 48150
Tel: (313) 525-1800
FAX: (313) 427-3720

MINNESOTA

Arrow/Schweber Electronics
10100 Viking Drive, #100
Eden Prairie 55344
Tel: (612) 941-5280
FAX: (612) 829-8007

Avnet Computer
9800 Bren Road, East
Minnetonka 55343
Tel: (612) 829-0025
FAX: (612) 944-0638

Hamilton/Avnet
9800 Bren Road, East, #410
Minnetonka 55343
Tel: (612) 932-0600
FAX: (612) 932-0613

Pioneer-Standard
7625 Golden Triange Dr., #G
Eden Prairie 55344
Tel: (612) 944-3355
FAX: (612) 944-3794

MISSOURI

Arrow/Schweber Electronics
2380 Schuetz Road
St. Louis 63146
Tel: (314) 567-6888
FAX: (314) 567-1164

Avnet Computer
741 Goddard Avenue
Chesterfield 63005
Tel: (314) 537-2725
FAX: (314) 537-4248

Hamilton/Avnet
741 Goddard
Chesterfield 63005
Tel: (314) 537-4265
FAX: (314) 537-4248

NEW HAMPSHIRE

Avnet Computer
2 Executive Park Drive
Bedford 03102
Tel: (800) 442-8638
FAX: (603) 624-2402

NEW JERSEY

Arrow/Schweber Electronics
4 East Stow Rd., Unit 11
Marlton 08053
Tel: (609) 596-8000
FAX: (609) 596-9632

Arrow/Schweber Electronics
43 Route 46 East
Pine Brook 07058
Tel: (201) 227-7880
FAX: (201) 227-2064

Avnet Computer
1B Keystone Ave., Bldg. 36
Cherry Hill 08003
Tel: (609) 424-8962
FAX: (609) 751-2502

Hamilton/Avnet
1 Keystone Ave., Bldg. 36
Cherry Hill 08003
Tel: (609) 424-0110
FAX: (609) 751-2611

Hamilton/Avnet
10 Lanidex Plaza West
Parsippany 07054
Tel: (201) 515-5300
FAX: (201) 515-1600

MTI Systems Sales
43 US Rt. 46
Pinebrook 07058
Tel: (201) 882-8780
FAX: (201) 882-8901

Pioneer-Standard
14A Madison Rd.
Fairfield 07004
Tel: (201) 575-3510
FAX: (201) 575-3454

NEW MEXICO

Alliance Electronics, Inc.
10510 Research Ave., SE
Albuquerque 87123
Tel: (505) 292-3360
FAX: (505) 275-6392

Avnet Computer
7801 Academy Rd., SE
Bldg. 1, Suite 204
Albuquerque 87109
Tel: (505) 828-9722
FAX: (505) 828-0364

Hamilton/Avnet
7801 Academy Rd., NE
Bldg. 1, Suite 204
Albuquerque 87108
Tel: (505) 828-1058
FAX: (505) 828-0360

NEW YORK

Arrow/Schweber Electronics
3375 Brighton Henrietta Townline Rd.
Rochester 14623
Tel: (716) 427-0300
FAX: (716) 427-0735

Arrow/Schweber Electronics
20 Oser Avenue
Hauppauge 11788
Tel: (516) 231-1000
FAX: (516) 231-1072

Avnet Computer
933 Motor Parkway
Hauppauge 11788
Tel: (516) 434-7443
FAX: (516) 434-7459

Avnet Computer
2060 Townline Rd.
Rochester 14623
Tel: (716) 272-9110
FAX: (716) 272-9685

Hamilton/Avnet
933 Motor Parkway
Hauppauge 11788
Tel: (516) 231-9800
FAX: (516) 434-7426

Arrow Commercial Systems Group
120 Commerce
Hauppauge 11788
Tel: (516) 231-1175
FAX: (516) 435-2389

Hamilton/Avnet
2060 Townline Rd.
Rochester 14623
Tel: (716) 475-9130
FAX: (716) 475-9119

Hamilton/Avnet
103 Twin Oaks Drive
Syracuse 13120
Tel: (315) 453-4000
FAX: (315) 453-4010

MTI Systems
1 Penn Plaza
250 W. 34th Street
New York 10119
Tel: (212) 643-1280
FAX: (212) 643-1288

Pioneer-Standard
68 Corporate Drive
Binghamton 13904
Tel: (607) 722-9300
FAX: (607) 722-9562

Pioneer-Standard
60 Crossway Park West
Woodbury, Long Island 11797
Tel: (516) 921-8700
FAX: (516) 921-2143

Pioneer-Standard
840 Fairport Park
Fairport 14450
Tel: (716) 381-7070
FAX: (716) 381-8774

NORTH CAROLINA

Arrow/Schweber Electronics
5240 Greensdairy Road
Raleigh 27604
Tel: (919) 876-3132
FAX: (919) 878-9517

Avnet Computer
2725 Millbrook Rd., #123
Raleigh 27604
Tel: (919) 790-1735
FAX: (919) 872-4972

Hamilton/Avnet
5250-77 Center Dr. #350
Charlotte 28217
Tel: (704) 527-2485
FAX: (704) 527-8058

Hamilton/Avnet
3510 Spring Forest Drive
Raleigh 27604
Tel: (919) 878-0819
FAX: (919) 954-0940

Pioneer Technologies Group
9401 L-Southern Pine Blvd.
Charlotte 28273
Tel: (704) 527-8188
FAX: (704) 522-8564

Pioneer Technologies Group
2810 Meridian Parkway, #148
Durham 27713
Tel: (919) 544-5400
FAX: (919) 544-5885

OHIO

Arrow Commercial Systems Group
284 Cramer Creek Court
Dublin 43017
Tel: (614) 889-9347
FAX: (614) 889-9680

Arrow/Schweber Electronics
6573 Cochran Road, #E
Solon 44139
Tel: (216) 248-3990
FAX: (216) 248-1106

Arrow/Schweber Electronics
8200 Washington Village Dr.
Centerville 45458
Tel: (513) 435-5563
FAX: (513) 435-2049

Avnet Computer
7764 Washington Village Dr.
Dayton 45459
Tel: (513) 439-6756
FAX: (513) 439-6719

Avnet Computer
2 Summit Park Dr., #520
Independence 44131
Tel: (216) 573-7400
FAX: (216) 573-7404

Hamilton/Avnet
7760 Washington Village Dr.
Dayton 45459
Tel: (513) 439-6633
FAX: (513) 439-6711

Hamilton/Avnet
2 Summit Park Dr., #520
Independence 44131
Tel: (216) 573-7400
FAX: (216) 573-7404

MTI Systems Sales
23404 Commerce Park Rd.
Beachwood 44122
Tel: (216) 464-6688
FAX: (216) 464-3564

Pioneer-Standard
4433 Interpoint Boulevard
Dayton 45424
Tel: (513) 236-9900
FAX: (513) 236-8133

Pioneer-Standard
4800 E. 131st Street
Cleveland 44105
Tel: (216) 587-3600
FAX: (216) 663-3906

*Self Certified Small Business per Federal Acquisition Regulations

NORTH AMERICAN DISTRIBUTORS (Contd.)

OKLAHOMA

Arrow/Schweber Electronics
12111 East 51st Street, #101
Tulsa 74146
Tel: (918) 252-7537
FAX: (918) 254-0917

Hamilton/Avnet
12121 E. 51st St., #102A
Tulsa 74146
Tel: (918) 252-7297
FAX: (918) 250-8763

OREGON

Almac/Arrow Electronics
1885 N.W. 169th Place, #106
Beaverton 97006
Tel: (503) 629-8090
FAX: (503) 645-0611

Arrow Commercial Systems Group
1885 N.W. 169th Place
Beaverton 97006-7312
Tel: (503) 629-8090
FAX: (503) 645-0611

Avnet Computer
9150 Southwest Nimbus Ave.
Beaverton 97005
Tel: (503) 627-0900
FAX: (503) 526-6242

Hamilton/Avnet
9409 Southwest Nimbus Ave.
Beaverton 97005
Tel: (503) 627-0201
FAX: (503) 641-4012

Wyle Laboratories
9640 Sunshine Court
Bldg. G, Suite 200
Beaverton 97005
Tel: (503) 643-7900
FAX: (503) 646-5466

PENNSYLVANIA

Avnet Computer
213 Executive Drive, #320
Mars 16046
Tel: (412) 772-1888
FAX: (412) 772-1890

Hamilton/Avnet
213 Executive, #320
Mars 16046
Tel: (412) 772-1881
FAX: (412) 772-1890

Pioneer-Standard
259 Kappa Drive
Pittsburgh 15238
Tel: (412) 782-2300
FAX: (412) 963-8255

Pioneer Technologies Group
500 Enterprise Road
Keith Valley Business Center
Horsham 19044
Tel: (215) 674-4000
FAX: (215) 674-3107

TEXAS

Arrow/Schweber Electronics
3220 Commander Drive
Carrollton 75006
Tel: (214) 380-6464
FAX: (214) 248-7208

Arrow/Schweber Electronics
10899 Kinghurst Dr., #100
Houston 77099
Tel: (713) 530-4700
FAX: (713) 568-8518

Avnet Computer
4004 Beltline, Suite 200
Dallas 75244
Tel: (214) 308-8168
FAX: (214) 308-8129

Avnet Computer
1235 North Loop West, #525
Houston 77008
Tel: (713) 867-7580
FAX: (713) 861-6851

Hamilton/Avnet
1826-F Kramer Lane
Austin 78758
Tel: (512) 832-4306
FAX: (512) 832-4315

Hamilton/Avnet
4004 Beltline, Suite 200
Dallas 75244
Tel: (214) 308-8105
FAX: (214) 308-8141

Hamilton/Avnet
1235 North Loop West, #521
Houston 77008
Tel: (713) 861-8517
FAX: (713) 861-6541

Pioneer-Standard
1826D Kramer Lane
Austin 78758
Tel: (512) 835-4000
FAX: (512) 835-9829

Pioneer-Standard
13765 Beta Road
Dallas 75244
Tel: (214) 263-3168
FAX: (214) 490-6419

Pioneer-Standard
10530 Rockley Road, #100
Houston 77099
Tel: (713) 495-4700
FAX: (713) 495-5642

Wyle Laboratories
1810 Greenville Avenue
Richardson 75081
Tel: (214) 235-9953
FAX: (214) 644-5064

Wyle Laboratories
4030 West Braker Lane, #420
Austin 78759
Tel: (512) 345-8853
FAX: (512) 345-9330

Wyle Laboratories
11001 South Wilcrest, #100
Houston 77099
Tel: (713) 879-9953
FAX: (713) 879-4069

UTAH

Arrow/Schweber Electronics
1946 W. Parkway Blvd.
Salt Lake City 84119
Tel: (801) 973-6913
FAX: (801) 972-0200

Avnet Computer
1100 E. 6600 South, #150
Salt Lake City 84121
Tel: (801) 266-1115
FAX: (801) 266-0362

Hamilton/Avnet
1100 East 6600 South, #120
Salt Lake City 84121
Tel: (801) 972-2800
FAX: (801) 263-0104

Wyle Laboratories
1325 West 2200 South, #E
West Valley 84119
Tel: (801) 974-9953
FAX: (801) 972-2524

WASHINGTON

Almac/Arrow Electronics
14360 S.E. Eastgate Way
Bellevue 98007
Tel: (206) 643-9992
FAX: (206) 643-9709

Arrow Commercial Systems Group
14360 S.E. Eastgate Way
Bellevue 98007
Tel: (206) 643-9992
FAX: (206) 643-9709

Hamilton/Avnet
17761 N.E. 78th Place, #C
Redmond 98052
Tel: (206) 241-8555
FAX: (206) 241-5472

Avnet Computer
17761 N.E. 78th Place
Redmond 98052
Tel: (206) 867-0160
FAX: (206) 867-0161

Wyle Laboratories
15385 N.E. 90th Street
Redmond 98052
Tel: (206) 881-1150
FAX: (206) 881-1567

WISCONSIN

Arrow/Schweber Electronics
200 N. Patrick Blvd., #100
Brookfield 53045
Tel: (414) 792-0150
FAX: (414) 792-0156

Avnet Computer
20875 Crossroads Circle, #400
Waukesha 53186
Tel: (414) 784-8205
FAX: (414) 784-6006

Hamilton/Avnet
28875 Crossroads Circle, #400
Waukesha 53186
Tel: (414) 784-4511
FAX: (414) 784-9509

Pioneer-Standard
120 Bishop Way #163
Brookfield 53005
Tel: (414) 784-3480
FAX: (414) 784-8207

ALASKA

Avnet Computer
1400 West Benson Blvd., #400
Anchorage 99503
Tel: (907) 274-9899
FAX: (907) 277-2639

CANADA

ALBERTA

Avnet Computer
108 1144 29th Ave., NE
Calgary T2E 7P1
Tel: (403) 291-3284
FAX: (403) 250-1591

Zentronics
6815 8th Street N.E., #100
Calgary T2E 7H7
Tel: (403) 295-8838
FAX: (403) 295-8714

BRITISH COLUMBIA

Almac-Arrow Electronics
8544 Baxter Place
Burnaby V5A 4T8
Tel: (604) 421-2333
FAX: (604) 421-5030

Hamilton/Avnet
8610 Commerce Court
Burnaby V5A 4N6
Tel: (604) 420-4101
FAX: (604) 420-5376

Zentronics
11400 Bridgeport Rd., #108
Richmond V6X 1T2
Tel: (604) 273-5575
FAX: (604) 273-2413

ONTARIO

Arrow Commercial Systems Group
1093 Meyerside Dr., Unit 2
Mississauga, Ontario
L5T 1M4
Tel: (416) 670-7784
FAX: (416) 670-7781

Arrow/Schweber Electronics
36 Antares Dr., Unit 100
Nepean K2E 7W5
Tel: (613) 226-6903
FAX: (613) 723-2018

Arrow/Schweber Electronics
1093 Meyerside, Unit 2
Mississauga L5T 1M4
Tel: (416) 670-7769
FAX: (416) 670-7781

Avnet Computer
151 Superior Blvd.
Mississuaga L5T 2L1
Tel: (416) 795-3895
FAX: (416) 795-3855

Avnet Computer
190 Colonnade Road
Nepean K2E 7J5
Tel: (613) 727-2000
FAX: (613) 727-2020

Hamilton/Avnet
151 Superior Blvd.
Mississauga L5T 2L1
Tel: (416) 795-3835
FAX: (416) 564-6036

Hamilton/Avnet
190 Colonnade Road
Nepean K2E 7J5
Tel: (613) 226-1700
FAX: (613) 226-1184

Zentronics
1355 Meyerside Drive
Mississauga L5T 1C9
Tel: (416) 564-9600
FAX: (416) 564-8320

Zentronics
155 Colonnade Rd., South
Unit 17/18
Nepean K2E 7K1
Tel: (613) 226-8840
FAX: (613) 226-6352

QUEBEC

Arrow/Schweber Electronics
1100 St. Regis Blvd.
Dorval H9P 2T5
Tel: (514) 421-7411
FAX: (514) 421-7430

Arrow Commercial Systems Group
500 Ave Street Jean Baptiste
Quebec City 2GE 5R9
Tel: (418) 871-7500
FAX: (418) 871-6816

Avnet Computer
2795 Rue Halpern
St. Laurent H4S 1P8
Tel: (514) 335-2483
FAX: (514) 335-2490

Hamilton/Avnet
2795 Rue Halpern
St. Laurent H4S 1P8
Tel: (514) 335-1000
FAX: (514) 335-2481

Zentronics
520 McCaffrey Street
St. Laurent H4T 1N1
Tel: (514) 737-9700
FAX: (514) 737-5212

EUROPEAN SALES OFFICES

FINLAND

Intel Finland OY
Ruosilantie 2
00390 Helsinki
Tel: (358) 0 544 644
FAX: (358) 0 544 030

FRANCE

Intel Corporation S.A.R.L.
1, Rue Edison-BP 303
78054 St. Quentin-en-Yvelines
Cedex
Tel: (33) (1) 30 57 70 00
FAX: (33) (1) 30 64 60 32

GERMANY

Intel GmbH
Dornacher Strasse 1
8016 Feldkirchen bei Muenchen
Tel: (49) 089/90992-0
FAX: (49) 089/9043948

ISRAEL

Intel Semiconductor Ltd.
Atidim Industrial Park-Neve Sharet
P.O. Box 43202
Tel-Aviv 61430
Tel: (972) 03 498080
FAX: (972) 03\t491870

ITALY

Intel Corporation Italia S.p.A.
Milanofiori Palazzo E
20094 Assago
Milano
Tel: (39) (2) 575441
FAX: (39) (2) 3498464

NETHERLANDS

Intel Semiconductor B.V.
Postbus 84130
3009 CC Rotterdam
Tel: (31) 10 407 11 11
FAX: (31) 10 455 4688

RUSSIA

Intel Technologies, Inc.
Krementshugskaya 6/7
121357 Moscow
Tel: 007-095-4439785
FAX: 007-095-4459420
TLX: 612092 smail su.

SPAIN

Intel Iberia S.A.
Zubaran, 28
28010 Madrid
Tel: (34) (1) 308 2552
FAX: (34) (1) 410 7570

SWEDEN

Intel Sweden A.B.
Dalvagen 24
171 36 Solna
Tel: (46) 8 705 5600
FAX: (46) 8 278085

UNITED KINGDOM

Intel Corporation (U.K.) Ltd.
Pipers Way
Swindon, Wiltshire SN3 1RJ
Tel: (44) (0793) 696000
FAX: (44) (0793) 641440

EUROPEAN DISTRIBUTORS/REPRESENTATIVES

AUSTRIA

†*Bacher Electronics GmbH
Rotenmuehlgasse 26
A-1120 Wien
Tel: (43) 222 81356460
FAX: (43) 222 834276

BELGIUM

†*Inelco Distribution
Avenue des Croix de Guerre 94
1120 Bruxelles
Tel: (32) 2 244 2811
FAX: (32) 2 216 3304

*Diode Belgium
Keiberg II, Minervastraat, 14/B2
1930 Zaventem
Tel: (32) 2 725 46 60
FAX: (32) 2 725 45 11

DENMARK

*Nortec Electronics AS
Transformervej 17
DK-2730 Herlev
Tel: (45) 4284 2000
FAX: (45) 4492 1552

†*ITT Multikomponent AS
Naverland 29
DK-2600 Glostrup
Tel: (45) 4245 6645
FAX: (45) 4245 7624

†*OY Fintronic AB
Heikkilantie 2a
SF-00210 Helsinki
Tel: (358) 0 692 6022
FAX: (358) 0 682 1251

FRANCE

*Almex
48, Rue de l'Aubepine
B.P. 102
92164 Antony Cedex
Tel: (33) (1) 4096 5400
FAX: (33) (1) 4666 6028

*Arrow Electronique
73-79 Rue des Solets
Silic 585
94663 Rungis Cedex
Tel: (33) (1) 4978 4978
FAX: (33) (1) 4978 0596

†Metrologie
Tour d'Asnieres
4, Avenue Laurent Cely
92606 Asnieres Cedex
Tel: (33) (1) 40 80 90 00
FAX: (33) (1) 47 91 05 61

*Tekelec
Cite des Bruyeres
5, Rue Carle Vernet-BP 2
92310 Sevres
Tel: (33) (1) 4623 2425
FAX: (33) (1) 4507 2191

GERMANY

*Electronic 2000
Bauelemente GmbH
Stahlgruberring 12
8000 Muenchen 82
Tel: (49) 89 42110-01
FAX: (49) 89 42110209

*Jermyn GmbH
Im Dachsstueck 9
6250 Limburg
Tel: (49) 6431 5080
FAX: (49) 6431 508289

†Metrologie GmbH
Steinerstrasse 15
8000 Muenchen 70
Tel: (49) 89 724470
FAX: (49) 89 72447111

*Proelectron Vertriebs GmbH
Max-Planck-Strasse 1-3
6072 Dreieich
Tel: (49) 6103 304343
FAX: (49) 6103 304425

†Rein Elektronik GmbH
Loetscher Weg 66
4054 Nettetal 1
Tel: (49) 2153 7330
FAX: (49) 2153 733513

GREECE

†Ergodata
Aigiroupoleos 2A
176 76 Kalithea
Tel: (30) 1 95 10 922
FAX: (30) 1 95 93 160

*Pouliadis Associates Corp.
Koumbari Square
Kolonaki Square
106 74 Athens
Tel: (30) 1 36 03 741
FAX: (30) 1 36 07 501

IRELAND

†*Micro Marketing
Taney Hall
Eglinton Terrace
Dundrum
Dublin 14
Tel: (353) (1) 298 9400
FAX: (353) (1) 298 9828

ISRAEL

†*Eastronics Limited
Rozanis 11
P.O.B. 39300
Tel Baruch
Tel-Aviv 61392
Tel: (972) 3 6458 777
FAX: (972) 3 6458 666

ITALY

*Intesi Div. Della Deutsche
Divisione ITT Industries GmbH
P.I. 06550110156
Milanofiori Palazzo e5
20094 Assago (Milano)
Tel: (39) 2 824701
FAX: (39) 2 8242631

*Lasi Elettronica
P.I. 00839000155
Viale Fulvio Testi, N.280
20126 Milano
Tel: (39) 2 661431
FAX: (39) 2 66101385

†Telcom
Via Trombetta
20090 Segrate-Milano
Tel: (39) 2 216 061
FAX: (39) 2 213 8010

NETHERLANDS

†Datelcom
Computerweg 10-16
3600 BD Maarsen
Tel: (39) 3465 95222
FAX: (39) 3465 71245

*Diode Components
Coltbaan 17
3439 NG Nieuwegein
Tel: (31) 3402 9 12 34
FAX: (31) 3402 3 59 24

†*Koning en Hartman
Energieweg 1
2627 AP Delft
Tel: (31) 15 609 906
FAX: (31) 15 619 194

NORWAY

†Computer System Integration A/S
Postbox 198
N-2013 Skjetten
Tel: (47) 6 84 54 11
FAX: (47) 6 84 53 10

*Nortec Electronics A/S
Postboks 123
Smedsvingen 4
N-1364 Hvalstad
Tel: (47) 284 6210
FAX: (47) 284 6545

PORTUGAL

*ATD Electronica LDA
Rua dr. Faria de Vasconcelos, 3a
1900 Lisboa
Tel: (351) (1) 847 2200
FAX: (351) (1) 847 2197

†Metrologia Iberica Portugal
Rua Dr. Faria de Vasconcelos 3A
1900 Lisboa
Tel: (351) (1) 847 2202
FAX: (351) (1) 847 2197

SOUTH AFRICA

†*EBE
PO Box 912-1222
Silverton 0127
178 Erasmus Street
Meyerspark
Pretoria 0184
Tel: (27) 12 803 7680-93
FAX: (27) 12 803 8294

SPAIN

*ATD Electronica
Avenue de la Industria, 32, 2B
28100 Alcobendas
Madrid
Tel: (34) (1) 661 6551
FAX: (34) (1) 661 6300

†Metrologia Iberica
Avda. Industria, 32-2
28100 Alcobendas
Madrid
Tel: (34) (1) 661 1142
FAX: (34) (1) 661 5755

SWEDEN

*ITT Multikomponent AB
Ankdammsgatan 32
Box 1330
S-171 26 Solna
Tel: (46) 8 830020
FAX: (46) 8 27 13 03

*Nortec Elektronics AB
Box 1830
S-171 27 Solna
Tel: (46) 8705 1800
FAX: (46) 883 6918

†Nortelco AB
Box 184
S-123 23 Farsta
Tel: (46) 8 705 18 00
FAX: (46) 8 735 2373

SWITZERLAND

†IMIC Microcomputer
Zurichstrasse
CH-8185 Winkel-Ruti
Tel: (41) (1) 8620055
FAX: (41) (1) 8620266

†*Industrade A.G.
Hertistrasse 31
CH-8304 Wallisellen
Tel: (41) (1) 8328111
FAX: (41) (1) 8307550

TURKEY

*Empa Electronic
34630 Besyol Londra Asfalti
Florya Is Merkezi Sefakoy
Istanbul
Tel: (90) (1) 599 3050
FAX: (90) (1) 598 5353

UNITED KINGDOM

*Arrow Electronics
St. Martins Business Centre
Cambridge Road
Bedford - MK42 0LF
Tel: (44) 234 270272
FAX: (44) 234 211434

*Avnet EMG Ltd.
Jubilee House
Jubilee Road
Letchworth
Hertsfordshire - SG6 1QH
Tel: (44) 462 488 500
FAX: (44) 462 488 567

*Bytech Components
12a Cedarwood
Chineham Business Park
Crockford Lane
Basingstoke
Hants RG12 1RW
Tel: (44) 256 707 107
FAX: (44) 256 707 162

†Bytech Systems
5 The Sterling Centre
Eastern Road
Bracknell
Berks - RG12 2PW
Tel: (44) 344 55 333
FAX: (44) 344 867 270

*Jermyn Electronics
Vestry Estate
Otford Road
Sevenoaks
Kent TN14 5EU
Tel: (44) 732 743 743
FAX: (44) 732 451 251

†Metrologie VA
Rapid House
Oxford Road
High Wycombe
Bucks - HP11 2E
Tel: (44) 494 526 271
FAX: (44) 494 452 144

*MMD/Rapid Ltd.
Rapid Silicon
3 Bennet Court
Bennet Road
Reading
Berks - RG2 0QX
Tel: (44) 734 750 697
FAX: (44) 734 313 255

*Technical Distributor
†VAD

INTERNATIONAL SALES OFFICES

AUSTRALIA

Intel Australia Pty. Ltd.
Unit 13
Allambie Grove Business Park
25 Frenchs Forest Road East
Frenchs Forest, NSW, 2086
Sydney
Tel: 61-2-975-3300
FAX: 61-2-975-3375

Intel Australia Pty. Ltd.
711 High Street
1st Floor
East Kw. Vic., 3102
Melbourne
Tel: 61-3-810-2141
FAX: 61-3-819 7200

BRAZIL

Intel Semiconductores do Brazil LTDA
Avenida Paulista, 1159-CJS 404/405
CEP 01311 - Sao Paulo - S.P.
Tel: 55-11-287-5899
FAX: 55-11-287-5119

CHINA/HONG KONG

Intel PRC Corporation
15/F, Office 1, Citic Bldg.
Jian Guo Men Wai Street
Beijing, PRC
Tel: (1) 500-4850
TLX: 22947 INTEL CN
FAX: (1) 500-2953

Intel Semiconductor Ltd.*
10/F East Tower
Bond Center
Queensway, Central
Hong Kong
Tel: (852) 844-4555
FAX: (852) 868-1989

INDIA

Intel Asia Electronics, Inc.
4/2, Samrah Plaza
St. Mark's Road
Bangalore 560001
Tel: 91-812-215773
TLX: 953-845-2646 INTEL IN
FAX: 091-812-215067

JAPAN

Intel Japan K.K.
5-6 Tokodai, Tsukuba-shi
Ibaraki, 300-26
Tel: 0298-47-8511
FAX: 0298-47-8450

Intel Japan K.K.*
Hachioji ON Bldg.
4-7-14 Myojin-machi
Hachioji-shi, Tokyo 192
Tel: 0426-48-8770
FAX: 0426-48-8775

Intel Japan K.K.*
Kawa-asa Bldg.
2-11-5 Shin-Yokohama
Kohoku-ku, Yokohama-shi
Kanagawa, 222
Tel: 045-474-7660
FAX: 045-471-4394

Intel Japan K.K.*
Ryokuchi-Eki Bldg.
2-4-1 Terauchi
Toyonaka-shi, Osaka 560
Tel: 06-863-1091
FAX: 06-863-1084

Intel Japan K.K.
Shinmaru Bldg.
1-5-1 Marunouchi
Chiyoda-ku, Tokyo 100
Tel: 03-3201-3621
FAX: 03-3201-6850

Intel Japan K.K.*
TK Gotanda Bldg. 9F
8-3-6 Nishi Gotanda
Shinagawa, Tokyo 141
Tel: 03-3493-6081
FAX: 03-3493-5951

KOREA

Intel Korea, Ltd.
16th Floor, Life Bldg.
61 Yoido-dong, Youngdeungpo-Ku
Seoul 150-010
Tel: (2) 784-8186
FAX: (2) 784-8096

MEXICO

Intel Tecnologia de Mexico
S.A. de C.V.
Av. Mexico No. 2798-9B, S.H.
44620 Guadalajara, Jal.
Tel. & FAX: 523-640-1259

SINGAPORE

Intel Singapore Technology, Ltd.
101 Thomson Road #08-03/06
United Square
Singapore 1130
Tel: (65) 250-7811
FAX: (65) 250-9256

TAIWAN

Intel Technology Far East Ltd.
Taiwan Branch Office
8th Floor, No. 205
Bank Tower Bldg.
Tung Hua N. Road
Taipei
Tel: 886-2-5144202
FAX: 886-2-717-2455

INTERNATIONAL DISTRIBUTORS/REPRESENTATIVES

ARGENTINA

Dafsys S.R.L.
Chacabuco, 90-6 Piso
1069-Buenos Aires
Tel. & FAX: 54.1334.1871

AUSTRALIA

Email Electronics
15-17 Hume Street
Huntingdale, 3166
Tel: 011-61-3-544-8244
TLX: AA 30895
FAX: 011-61-3-543-8179

NSD-Australia
205 Middleborough Rd.
Box Hill, Victoria 3128
Tel: 03 8900970
FAX: 03 8990819

BRAZIL

Microlinear
Largo do Arouche, 24
01219 Sao Paulo, SP
Tel: 5511-220-2215
FAX: 5511-220-5750

CHILE

Sisteco
Vecinal 40—Las Condes
Santiago
Tel: 562-234-1644
FAX: 562-233-9895

CHINA/HONG KONG

Novel Precision Machinery Co., Ltd.
Room 728 Trade Square
681 Cheung Sha Wan Road
Kowloon, Hong Kong
Tel: (852) 360-8999
TWX: 32032 NVTNL HX
FAX: (852) 725-3695

GUATEMALA

Abinitio
11 Calle 2—Zona 9
Guatemala City
Tel: 5022-32-4104
FAX: 5022-32-4123

INDIA

Priya International Limited
D-6, II Floor
Devatha Plaza, 131/132 Residency Rd.
Bangalore 560 025
Tel: (91) 812-214027, 812-214395
FAX: (91) 812-214105

Priya International Limited
Podar Chambers, 4th Floor
109, S.A. Brelvi Road, Fort
Bombay 400 001
Tel: (91) 22-2863611, 22-2863676,
          22-2863900, 22-2864026
FAX: (91) 22-2619935

Priya International Limited
Flat No. 8, 10th Floor
Akashdeep Building, Barakhamba Rd.
New Delhi 110 001
Tel: (91) 11-3314512, 11-3310413
FAX: (91) 11-3719107

Priya International Limited
5-J, Century Plaza
560-562 Mount Road, Teynampet
Madras 600 018
Tel: (91) 44-451031, 44-451597

Priya International Limited
No. 10, I Floor
Minerva House, 94 Sarojini Devi Rd.
Secunderabad 500 003
Tel: (91) 842-70220, 842-77059

SES Computers and Technologies Pvt. Ltd.
14, SNS Chambers
239 Palace Upper Orchards
Sankey Road, Sadashivanagar
Bangalore 560 080

S&S Corporation
1587 Kooser Road
San Jose, CA 95118
Tel: (408) 978-6216
TLX: 820281
FAX: (408) 978-8635

JAMAICA

MC Systems
10-12 Grenada Crescent
Kingston 5
Tel: (809) 926-0104
FAX: (809) 929-5678

JAPAN

Asahi Electronics Co. Ltd.
KMM Bldg. 2-14-1 Asano
Kokurakita-ku
Kitakyushu-shi 802
Tel: 093-511-6471
FAX: 093-551-7861

CTC Components Systems Co., Ltd.
4-8-1 Dobashi, Miyamae-ku
Kawasaki-shi, Kanagawa 213
Tel: 044-852-5121
FAX: 044-877-4268

Dia Semicon Systems, Inc.
Flower Hill Shinmachi Higashi-kan
1-23 Shinmachi, Setagaya-ku
Tokyo 154
Tel: 03-3439-1600
FAX: 03-3439-1601

Okaya Koki
2-4-18 Sakae
Naka-ku, Nagoya-shi 460
Tel: 052-204-8315
FAX: 052-204-8380

Ryoyo Electro Corp.
Konwa Bldg.
1-12-22 Tsukiji
Chuo-ku, Tokyo 104
Tel: 03-3546-5011
FAX: 03-3546-5044

KOREA

J-Tek Corporation
Dong Sung Bldg. 9/F
158-24, Samsung-Dong, Kangnam-Ku
Seoul 135-090
Tel: (822) 557-8039
FAX: (822) 557-8304

Samsung Electronics
Samsung Main Bldg.
150 Taepyung-Ro-2KA, Chung-Ku
Seoul 100-102
C.P.O. Box 8780
Tel: (822) 751-3680
TWX: KORSST K 27970
FAX: (822) 753-9065

MEXICO

PSI S.A. de C.V.
Fco. Villa esq. Ajusco s/n
Cuernavaca, MOR 62130
Tel: 52-73-11-1994/5
FAX: 52-73-17-5333

NEW ZEALAND

Email Electronics
36 Olive Road
Penrose, Auckland
Tel: 011-64-9-591-155
FAX: 011-64-9-592-681

SAUDI ARABIA

AAE Systems, Inc.
642 N. Pastoria Ave.
Sunnyvale, CA 94086
U.S.A.
Tel: (408) 732-1710
FAX: (408) 732-3095
TLX: 494-3405 AAE SYS

SINGAPORE

Electronic Resources Pte, Ltd.
17 Harvey Road
#03-01 Singapore 1336
Tel: (65) 283-0888
TWX: RS 56541 ERS
FAX: (65) 289-5327

SOUTH AFRICA

Electronic Building Elements
178 Erasmus St. (off Watermeyet St.)
Meyerspark, Pretoria, 0184
Tel: 011-2712-803-7680
FAX: 011-2712-803-8294

TAIWAN

Micro Electronics Corporation
12th Floor, Section 3
285 Nanking East Road
Taipei, R.O.C.
Tel: (886) 2-7198419
FAX: (886) 2-7197916

Acer Sertek Inc.
15th Floor, Section 2
Chien Kuo North Rd.
Taipei 18479 R.O.C.
Tel: 886-2-501-0055
TWX: 23756 SERTEK
FAX: (886) 2-5012521

URUGUAY

Interfase
Blvr. Espana 2094
11200 Montevideo
Tel: 5982-49-4600
FAX: 5982-49-3040

VENEZUELA

Unixel C.A.
4 Transversal de Monte Cristo
Edf. AXXA, Piso 1, of. 1&2
Centro Empresarial Boleita
Caracas
Tel: 582-238-7749
FAX: 582-238-1816

*Field Application Location

NORTH AMERICAN SERVICE OFFICES

PrimeService

Intel Corporation's North American Preferred Service Provider
Central Dispatch: 1-800-800-PRIM (1-800-800-7746)

ALABAMA
Birmingham
Huntsville

ALASKA
Anchorage

ARIZONA
Phoenix*
Tucson

ARKANSAS
Little Rock

CALIFORNIA
Bakersfield
Brea
Carson*
Fresno
Livermore
Mar Del Rey
Ontario*
Orange
Sacramento*
San Diego*
San Francisco*
Santa Clara*
Ventura
Sunnyvale
Walnut Creek*
Woodland Hills*

COLORADO
Colorado Springs
Denver
Englewood*

CONNECTICUT
Glastonbury*

DELAWARE
New Castle

FLORIDA
Ft. Lauderdale
Heathrow
Jacksonville
Melbourne
Pensacola
Tampa
West Palm Beach

GEORGIA
Atlanta*
Savannah
West Robbins

HAWAII
Honolulu

ILLINOIS
Buffalo*
Calumer City
Chicago
Lansing
Oak Brook

INDIANA
Carmel*
Ft. Wayne

KANSAS
Overland Park*
Wichita

KENTUCKY
Lexington
Louisville
Madisonville

LOUISIANA
Baton Rouge
Metarie

MAINE
Brunswick

MARYLAND
Frederick
Linthicum*
Rockville*

MASSACHUSETTS
Boston*
Natick*
Norton*
Springfield

MICHIGAN
Ann Harbor
Benton Harbor
Flint
Grand Rapids*
Leslie
Livonia*
St. Joseph
Troy*

MINNESOTA
Bloomington*
Deluth

MISSOURI
Springfield
St. Louis*

NEVADA
Minden
Las Vegas
Reno

NEW HAMSHIRE
Manchester*

NEW JERSEY
Edison*
Hamton Town*
Parsippany*

NEW MEXICO
Albuquerque

NEW YORK
Albany*
Amherst*
Dewitt*
Fairport*
Farmingdale*
New York City*

NORTH CAROLINA
Brevard
Charlotte
Greensboro
Haveluch
Raleigh
Wilmington

NORTH DAKOTA
Bismark

OHIO
Cincinnati*
Columbus
Dayton
Independence*
Middle Heights*
Toledo*

OREGON
Beaverton*

PENNSYLVANIA
Bala Cynwyd*
Camp Hill*
East Erie
Pittsburgh*
Wayne*

SOUTH CAROLINA
Charleston
Cherry Point
Columbia
Fountain Inn

SOUTH DAKOTA
Sioux Falls

TENNESSEE
Bartlett
Chattanooga
Knoxville
Nashville

TEXAS
Austin
Bay City
Beaumont
Canyon
College Station
Houston*
Irving*
San Antonio
Tyler

UTAH
Salt Lake City*

VIRGINIA
Charlottesville
Glen Allen
Maclean*
Norfolk
Virginia Beach

WASHINGTON
Bellevue*
Olympia
Renton
Richland
Spokane
Verdale

WASHINGTON D.C.*

WEST VIRGINIA
St. Albans

WISCONSIN
Brookfield*
Green Bay
Madison
Wausau

CANADA
Calgary*
Edmonton
Halifax
London*
Montreal*
Ottawa
Toronto*
Vancouver, BC*
Winnipeg
Regina
St. John

CUSTOMER TRAINING CENTERS

ARIZONA
Computervision Customer
Education
2401 W. Behrend Dr., Suite 17
Phoenix 85027
Tel: 1-800-234-8806

ILLINOIS
Computervision Customer
Education
1 Oakbrook Terrace
Suite 600
Oakbrook 60181
Tel: 1-800-234-8806

MASSACHUSETTS
Computervision Customer
Education
11 Oak Park Drive
Bedford 01730
Tel: 1-800-234-8806

SYSTEMS ENGINEERING OFFICES

MINNESOTA
3500 W. 80th Street
Suite 360
Bloomington 55431
Tel: (612) 835-6722

NEW YORK
2950 Expressway Dr., South
Islandia 11722
Tel: (506) 231-3300

*Carry-in locations